# FLUID DYNAMICS

Consulting Editor

# FLUID DYNAMICS

RICHARD H. F. PAO

*Rose Polytechnic Institute*

CHARLES E. MERRILL BOOKS, INC., COLUMBUS, OHIO

*Library of Congress Catalog Card Number: 66–24956*

PRINTED IN THE UNITED STATES OF AMERICA

# Preface

Fluid dynamics is a basic subject of study for many branches of engineering and applied science. This book has been written to present the fundamental principles of fluid dynamics and their applications to problems in engineering and applied science.

The student is assumed to have mathematical background through the regular differential equations course. Therefore, in this book mathematics is used freely and familiarly with vector notations. The vector- and tensor-field operators are treated in detail. Equations of fluid motion are derived in vector or vector-tensor form; the vector equations are then presented in scalar forms in Cartesian, cylindrical, and spherical coordinates, and summarized in tables for convenience of cross reference.

In this book the fluid medium is regarded as a continuum (i.e., a continuous medium). However, molecular consideration of fluids is also mentioned in several places. The text contains the following six groups of topics:

1. Introductory ideas concerning fluid medium (Chapter 1).
2. Basic laws of fluid flow (Chapter 2).
3. Potential flow (Chapters 3, 4, and 5).
4. Viscous flow (Chapters 6 and 7).
5. Boundary layer (Chapter 8).
6. Compressible flow (Chapter 9).
7. Magnetofluidmechanics (Chapter 10).

Because of the increasing demand in higher education to place more emphasis on independent studies by the student, I have attempted to make a careful and detailed presentation of each topic that is included in this book. References are given for those who wish to pursue the subject more deeply. I have also included many worked-out illustrative examples to serve as a guide to the student for his thorough understanding of the subject and to stimulate his interest in developing analytical ability to tackle new and challenging problems in fluid flow. Each chapter is followed by a number of problems that are to be solved by the student as a part of his daily assignment. The solution of these problems will serve to supplement the text material in bringing out some salient features in the understanding of the fundamental concepts and principles.

The abundance of topics presented in this book will allow each instructor to select those groups of topics which are most appropriate for his class of students. The entire book can serve adequately as a text for a one-year intensive course that will prepare students for graduate-level courses in fluid mechanics and other related subjects.

I take great pleasure in recording my sincere appreciation to the administrative officers of Rose Polytechnic Institute—Dr. John A. Logan, President; and Dean Herman A. Moench, Dean of the Faculty—for their kind encouragement and enthusiastic support. I am indebted to Professor W. W. Bowden, my colleague, for his review of the preliminary manuscript and his helpful suggestions in improving the quality of the text. Mrs. M. Smith deserves my thanks for her assistance in typing the manuscript.

*Richard H. F. Pao*

Terre Haute, Indiana
June 1, 1966

# Table of Contents

*Chapter* 3

# PRINCIPLES OF IRROTATIONAL FLOW            124

*Chapter* 4

# INCOMPRESSIBLE POTENTIAL FLOWS            159

## Chapter 5

# APPLICATION OF COMPLEX VARIABLES AND CONFORMAL TRANSFORMATIONS TO TWO-DIMENSIONAL PLANAR POTENTIAL FLOWS   219

*Chapter* **6**

# FLUID VISCOSITY AND FLOW OF VISCOUS FLUIDS          267

*Chapter* 7

# FLUID TURBULENCE AND TURBULENT FLOW OF INCOMPRESSIBLE VISCOUS FLUIDS      313

*Chapter* 8

# BOUNDARY LAYER THEORY                                       355

To My Mother

# 1          Introduction

## 1-1   *Introductory Remarks*

Fluid mechanics is the study of the behavior of fluids at rest and in motion. A knowledge of basic principles and concepts of fluid mechanics is essential to the analysis, design, and synthesis of technological problems having fluid as a medium. Thus, the need for an understanding of fluid mechanics pervades almost every branch of engineering and applied sciences.

In the analysis of fluid flow problems, in addition to constitutive equations describing the behavior of physical properties of fluids under varying conditions and states, modern fluid mechanics makes use of the following principles:

1. Consistency of geometry of motion and deformation of matter.
2. Conservation of mass.
3. Conservation of momentum.
4. Conservation of moment of momentum.
5. Conservation of energy (i.e., the first law of thermodynamics).
6. Principle of entropy (i.e., the second law of thermodynamics).
7. Electromagnetic equations.

Equations expressing the above principles are used to obtain pertinent relationships among different variables in any specific problem in fluid mechanics. However, not all the principles listed above may be needed in many problems. In this book we shall study the application of these principles to different fluid flow problems.

## 1-2  Dimensions and Units

Scientific analysis in fluid mechanics is made possible by the introduction of such physical concepts as length, time, velocity, acceleration, force, stress, mass, density, momentum, energy, viscosity, and many other quantities. These quantities are defined arbitrarily, and they are related either by definition or by physical law. The relationships among these quantities can be best studied by the adoption of a consistent dimensional system composed of the smallest number of independent dimensions in terms of which all the quantities may be expressed.

In fluid mechanics all quantities are expressible in terms of five basic dimensions—mass $(M)$, force $(F)$, length $(L)$, time $(T)$, and temperature $(\theta)$. The temperature is an independent basic dimension. The other four dimensions are, however, related by Newton's second law of motion, $\mathbf{F} = M\mathbf{a}$, since the equation may be written dimensionally as

$$F \equiv M\frac{L}{T^2} \quad \text{or} \quad \frac{FT^2}{ML} \equiv 1 \tag{1-1}$$

This dimensional equation shows that the four dimensions are interrelated. When three of the dimensions are assigned, the fourth one may be expressed in terms of the other three. Hence three independent basic dimensions are sufficient for describing any physical quantity encountered in Newtonian mechanics. They are usually chosen as either $M$, $L$, $T$ (called *mass-length-time system*) or $F$, $L$, $T$ (called *force-length-time system*). The choice of either system is arbitrary. If $M$ is chosen as a principal basic dimension, $F$ becomes a derived quantity having the dimensions $ML/T^2$, and vice versa.

The dimensions of any quantity are derived either from its definition or from physical law. For example, the dimensions of volume are $L^3$, of velocity $L/T$, and of energy $FL$ or $ML^2/T^2$. Some of the quantities commonly used in fluid mechanics and their dimensions in both the $MLT$ and $FLT$ systems are given in Table 1–1.

In the mathematical analysis of any problem in physical sciences, it is essential to have the derived equation dimensionally homogeneous. This means that both sides of a correct physical equation must have the same dimensions.

Several systems of units for measuring the basic dimensions are used in different fields of engineering and scientific application. The choice of a particular system of units is arbitrary. However, the use of pound mass

**TABLE 1–1. Quantities Commonly Used in Fluid Mechanics
and Their Dimensions**

| Quantity | MLT System | FLT System |
|---|---|---|
| Length ($L$) | $L$ | $L$ |
| Area ($A$) | $L^2$ | $L^2$ |
| Volume ($V$) | $L^3$ | $L^3$ |
| Time ($t$) | $T$ | $T$ |
| Velocity ($V$) | $LT^{-1}$ | $LT^{-1}$ |
| Acceleration ($a$) | $LT^{-2}$ | $LT^{-2}$ |
| Force ($F$) | $MLT^{-2}$ | $F$ |
| Specific weight ($\gamma$) | $ML^{-2}T^{-2}$ | $FL^{-3}$ |
| Mass ($m$) | $M$ | $FL^{-1}T^2$ |
| Density ($\rho$) | $ML^{-3}$ | $FL^{-4}T^2$ |
| Pressure ($p$) and stress ($\tau$) | $ML^{-1}T^{-2}$ | $FL^{-2}$ |
| Energy ($E$) and work | $ML^2T^{-2}$ | $FL$ |
| Momentum ($P$) | $MLT^{-1}$ | $FT$ |
| Dynamic viscosity ($\mu$) | $ML^{-1}T^{-1}$ | $FL^{-2}T$ |
| Kinematic viscosity ($\nu$) | $L^2T^{-1}$ | $L^2T^{-1}$ |
| Surface tension ($\sigma$) | $MT^{-2}$ | $FL^{-1}$ |

(lbm) and pound force (lbf) in engineering work causes considerable confusion in the proper use of these two fundamentally different units. A clear understanding of the units of mass and force can be gained by examining Newton's second law of motion. With any system of units, a conversion factor $g_c$ must be introduced into the Newtonian dynamics equation so that both sides of the equation will have the same units. Thus,

$$F = \frac{Ma}{g_c} \qquad (1\text{–}2)$$

in which the numerical value and units of $g_c$ depend on the units chosen for mass, force, length, and time.

The units of pound mass and pound force are related by the standard gravitational acceleration which has a value of 32.174 ft/sec². When a one-pound mass (1 lbm) is held at such a location on the earth's surface where the gravitational acceleration is 32.174 ft/sec², the mass weighs one pound force (1 lbf). With this system of units, the value of $g_c$ is determined as follows:

$$F = \frac{Ma}{g_c}$$

$$1\ \text{lbf} = \frac{1\ \text{lbm} \times 32.174\ \text{ft/sec}^2}{g_c}$$

whence

$$g_c = 32.174 \text{ lbm-ft/lbf-sec}^2$$

Thus, $g_c$ is merely a conversion factor and it should not be confused with the gravitational acceleration $g$. The numerical value of $g_c$ is a constant depending only on the system of units involved, and not on the value of the gravitational acceleration at a particular location.

For example, if this one-pound mass is moved to a place where the local gravitational acceleration is 28.957 ft/sec², the force of gravity $W$ on the mass becomes

$$W = \frac{Ma}{g_c} = \frac{1 \text{ lbm} \times 28.957 \text{ ft/sec}^2}{32.174 \text{ lbm-ft/lbf-sec}^2} = 0.900 \text{ lbf}$$

Note that, with the inclusion of $g_c$, the answer has the correct unit. This practice is strongly recommended in all numerical calculations.

The other two systems of units commonly used in engineering writings in the English language are the English gravitational units (Egu) and the British mass units (Bmu). In the Egu system the unit of mass is the *slug*. When a mass of one slug is acted upon by a force of 1 lbf, the mass will be accelerated at the rate of 1 ft/sec². Therefore, substituting these values into $F = Ma/g_c$, we have

$$1 \text{ lbf} = \frac{1 \text{ slug} \times 1 \text{ ft/sec}^2}{g_c}$$

whence

$$g_c = 1 \text{ slug-ft/lbf-sec}^2$$

The weight of one slug of mass is then

$$W = \frac{Ma}{g_c} = \frac{1 \text{ slug} \times g \text{ ft/sec}^2}{1 \text{ slug-ft/lbf-sec}^2} = g \text{ lbf}$$

where $g$ is the magnitude of the local gravitational acceleration.

In the Bmu system the unit of force is the *poundal*. A poundal is defined as the force required to accelerate a mass of 1 lbm at the rate of 1 ft/sec². Thus,

$$F = \frac{Ma}{g_c}$$

$$1 \text{ poundal} = \frac{1 \text{ lbm} \times 1 \text{ ft/sec}^2}{g_c}$$

$$g_c = 1 \text{ lbm-ft/poundal-sec}^2$$

The weight of 1 lbm at the location where the local gravitational acceleration is $g$ ft/sec² is

$$W = \frac{1 \text{ lbm} \times g \text{ ft/sec}^2}{1 \text{ lbm-ft/poundal-sec}^2} = g \text{ poundal}$$

Let us consider the MKS mass system of units. The letters MKS stand for "meter," "kilogram," and "second," respectively. The kilogram (kg) is regarded as a unit of mass. The unit of force is called a *newton*. A newton of force will cause a kilogram mass an acceleration of 1 m/sec². Therefore,

$$F = \frac{Ma}{g_c}$$

$$1 \text{ newton} = \frac{1 \text{ kg} \times 1 \text{ m/sec}^2}{g_c}$$

$$g_c = 1 \text{ kg-m/newton-sec}^2$$

We may summarize the units of the conversion factor $g_c$ for different systems as follows:

| Mass | Length | Time | Force | $g_c$ |
|------|--------|------|-------|-------|
| lbm | ft | sec | lbf | 32.174 lbm-ft/lbf-sec² |
| slug | ft | sec | lbf | 1 slug-ft/lbf-sec² |
| lbm | ft | sec | poundal | 1 lbm-ft/poundal-sec² |
| kg | m | sec | newton | 1 kg-m/newton-sec² |

Since the conversion factor $g_c$ is useful in numerical calculations only, the symbol $g_c$ will not be included in derivations of physical equations in the book. However, it will be included in the solutions of illustrative examples involving numerical calculations in order to make numerical answers come out with correct units.

The following relationships are given for the purpose of conversion between different systems of units of measurement:

Mass: 1 slug $\equiv$ 32.174 lbm $\equiv$ 14.595 kg

Force: 1 lbf $\equiv$ 32.174 poundal $\equiv$ 4.448 newton

Length: 1 ft $\equiv$ 0.3048 m

## 1-3   Fluid State

According to the molecular concept, the three states of matter—solid, liquid, and gaseous—differ in their average spacings of molecules. Individual molecules of a solid are more closely packed than those of a liquid; there are more void spaces in a liquid than in a solid; and the average molecular spacing in a gas is many times the average gas molecular diameter.

The liquid and the gas are collectively referred to as *fluids*. The fluid state is characterized by the relative ease of the mobility of molecules.

In spite of the molecular structure of matter, in fluid mechanics we shall consider fluids to be totally continuous and without voids. In adopting this simplifying assumption of a continuous fluid, we disregard the molecular structure of fluids, and thus simplify the mathematical analysis of fluid motion. The assumption is justified by the fact that we are not primarily interested in the behavior of the individual molecules and that under ordinary conditions the results of analysis of a continuous fluid agree fairly well with the observed behaviors of fluid motion. The concept of continuous fluids will be discussed further in the following sections.

Liquids and gases, as continuous fluids, have similar mechanical behaviors and are, therefore, studied together in fluid mechanics. Their main difference, so far as fluid mechanics is concerned, is in their relative compressibility. Under varying pressure and temperature, gases are more readily compressible than liquids.

In a technical sense, the distinction between the solid and the fluid state is their relative abilities to resist external forces. A solid is capable of withstanding a certain amount of tensile, compressive, and shearing forces. When a force is applied to a solid, the solid undergoes a finite deformation which will remain unchanged as long as the applied force is maintained at a constant magnitude. A fluid has very little tensile strength, and it can support compressive forces only when it is properly confined. A fluid at rest cannot sustain a shear force. A shear force can be sustained in a fluid only when relative motions occur between fluid particles. Thus, a fluid, when subjected to a shear force, deforms continuously as long as this force is applied. In fluid mechanics, we define a fluid as a substance which deforms immediately and continuously under the action of shear forces.

## 1-4   The Concept of a Continuum

The concept of a continuous medium or continuum as applied to a fluid is merely an idealization. Matter in the fluid state, whether liquid or gaseous, is discrete on the microscopic (i.e., molecular) level. However, when we deal with engineering problems on the macroscopic level in which the dimensions are very large compared with molecular distances, we are concerned with volumes that are considerably larger than molecular dimensions, and, therefore, contain many molecules. We are interested in the statistical average properties and behaviors of such large numbers of molecules but not in the properties and behaviors of individual molecules. Since we disregard the action of individual molecules, we can consider the fluid as being a continuous substance and adopt a continuum model of fluid. The model possesses appropriate continuum properties which are so defined as to ensure that, on the macroscopic level, the behavior of the model duplicates that of the real fluid.

Under ordinary conditions, the assumption of a continuous fluid is easily satisfied. For example, under standard atmospheric conditions, one cubic millimeter of air contains $2.7 \times 10^{16}$ molecules. The assumption of a continuum model loses its validity whenever the mean free path of the molecules approaches the smallest significant dimension of the problem. Therefore, whenever we deal with the flow of highly rarefied gases, as in rocket flight at extreme altitudes, high-vacuum technology, or electronic tubes, we have to abandon the continuum approach of classical fluid mechanics and thermodynamics and to adopt instead the microscopic approach of kinetic theory and statistical mechanics.

In the idealized concept of a continuum, we assume that such macroscopic properties of the fluid as mean density, mean pressure, mean temperature, mean viscosity, mean velocity, etc., vary continuously with size of element, with position in the medium, and with time. Variation with the size of an element becomes imperceptible when the element is very small and yet contains sufficient molecules to make continuum descriptions statistically meaningful. Such an element is called a *fluid particle*. The mean properties of the fluid particle are in the limit assigned to a point so that we may ultimately adopt a field representation for the continuum properties. Thus, fluid properties, such as density, pressure, velocity, etc., are expressed as continuous functions of position and time only.

To illustrate the idea of a continuum and the nature of a continuum property "at a point," we shall attempt to define the density $\rho$ of a fluid at a given point. Figure 1–1(a) shows the fluid mass $\delta m$ in a small volume $\delta V$ surrounding the point $P(x, y, z)$ in a continuous fluid. The mean density of the fluid within the volume $\delta V$ is defined as the ratio $\delta m / \delta V$. As the volume $\delta V$ is allowed to shrink about the point $P$, a graphical representation of $\delta m / \delta V$ versus $\delta V$ is shown in Fig. 1–1(b). The mean density is seen first to approach a certain value asymptotically as the volume $\delta V$ shrinks to $\delta V'$. However, when the volume $\delta V$ is shrunk further, it becomes so small that it may contain only a few molecules. The mean density varies greatly for small changes of volume as these few molecules may be momentarily inside or outside of the volume. Thus, it becomes impossible to fix a definite mean value for $\delta m / \delta V$ when $\delta V$ is smaller than $\delta V'$. The volume $\delta V'$ is therefore regarded as the lowest limit for a continuous fluid. We then define the density at point $P$ as

$$\rho \equiv \lim_{\delta V \to \delta V'} \frac{\delta m}{\delta V} \qquad (1\text{–}3)$$

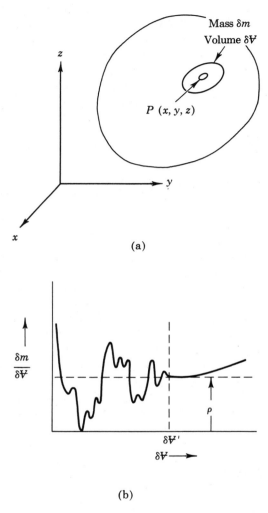

(a)

(b)

**Fig. 1-1.** Definition of fluid density at a point.

The field representation for $\rho$ is written as

$$\rho = \rho(x, y, z, t) \tag{1–4}$$

which states that fluid density is a function of position and time. Since the value of $\rho$ can be determined uniquely at each position and is independent of directional orientation, $\rho$ represents a scalar density field. In fluid dynamics, we shall also deal with vector fields (such as velocity) and with tensor fields (such as stress tensor).

## 1-5  Properties of the Continuum

In this section we shall discuss some other continuum properties which are useful concepts in the study of fluid mechanics.

**Fluid velocity at a point and fluid velocity vector field.** Consider again Fig. 1–1(a). The instantaneous velocity $\mathbf{V}$ of the fluid particle at point $P$ is defined as the average of instantaneous velocities of fluid molecules which occupy the volume $\delta \mathcal{V}'$ at this instant. Fluid velocity at a point is a vector quantity.

The field representation for $\mathbf{V}$ is

$$\mathbf{V} = \mathbf{V}(x, y, z, t) \tag{1-5}$$

Whenever the flow is steady, the velocity vector becomes a function of position only, i.e., $\mathbf{V} = \mathbf{V}(x, y, z)$, and is independent of time. A steady flow is thus characterized by the condition that all continuum properties at each position in the flow field remain invariant with time. In an unsteady flow, on the other hand, continuum properties are functions of both position and time. If the flow is uniform, the magnitude and direction of the velocity vector are constant throughout the entire flow field. The velocity vector for a steady uniform flow field is a constant. A uniform flow field can be unsteady, i.e., $\mathbf{V} = \mathbf{V}(t)$, just as a steady flow field is frequently nonuniform, i.e., $\mathbf{V} = \mathbf{V}(x, y, z)$.

**Streamlines, pathlines, and streaklines.** If at any particular instant of time a family of lines is traced through a moving fluid continuum in such a way as to be tangent to the velocity vector at every point in the flow field, these lines are called *instantaneous streamlines of the flow* (Fig. 1–2). This definition of streamlines implies that fluid always flows along a streamline and that no fluid crosses a streamline. In unsteady flows the

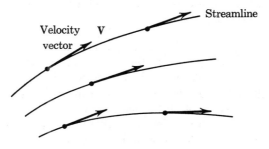

**Fig. 1-2.**  Streamlines.

pattern of streamlines will change from instant to instant. When the flow is steady, however, the streamlines remain unchanged at all times.

A *pathline* is the actual path, or trajectory, of a fluid particle of fixed identity. A *streakline* is a line joining the instantaneous positions of all fluid particles which passed through a given point in space at some previous time. In steady flows, streamlines, pathlines, and streaklines coincide. In unsteady flows they generally do not coincide.

**Stream tubes.** The circumferential surface of a stream tube is generated by a set of streamlines, each of which intersects a simple closed curve once in the flow field, as shown in Fig. 1–3. Since the walls of a

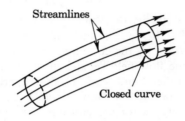

Streamlines

Closed curve

**Fig. 1-3.** Stream tube.

stream tube consist of streamlines, no flow crosses the walls of a stream tube. The concept of the stream tube has practical significance because such a tube behaves as if it were a solid tube. In complicated flow problems the whole field of flow can be divided up into a large number of stream tubes, thus yielding a clearer picture of the actual pattern of flow. Such a technique is usually referred to as the *flow net*, to be discussed in greater detail in Sec. 4–4. The boundaries of fluid motion, whether they be stationary or moving surfaces, are treated as peripheries of stream tubes, since it is a physical fact that no flow crosses the boundary surfaces.

A stream tube of infinitesimally small cross section is frequently referred to as a *stream filament*.

**Temperature at a point.** From the viewpoint of a continuum field, the fluid particle of mass $\rho \delta V'$ in the small volume $\delta V'$ of Fig. 1–1(a) is seen to move with a velocity $\mathbf{V}$. However, on the molecular level the actual velocity of each molecule is the sum of two velocity vectors, one of which is the average velocity $\mathbf{V}$ of all the molecules in $\delta V'$. The other vector is $\mathbf{V}_i'$, which is the vector difference between the actual velocity of the $i$th molecule and the vector $\mathbf{V}$ of the fluid particle. Although the velocity of the fluid mass $\rho\delta\mathcal{V}'$ on the macroscopic level is **V**, the total kinetic energy of the fluid mass depends on the actual velocities of individual molecules and will certainly involve the components $V_i'$. In order to account for this energy even when we are dealing with the fluid medium on the macroscopic level, we assign to the fluid mass $\rho\delta\mathcal{V}'$ a temperature $T$ which, according to the kinetic theory of perfect gases, is proportional to the average values of $V_i'^2$. The field representation for temperature is

$$T = T(x, y, z, t) \tag{1-6}$$

where $T$ is a scalar quantity.

**Stress at a point.** Let us imagine that a surface of area $\delta A$ is inserted in a given direction through point $P$ of the fluid medium as shown in Fig. 1–4(a). We assume that the fluid on one side of the surface exerts a force $\delta\mathbf{F}$ on the fluid on the other side. Likewise, the fluid on the latter side exerts an equal but opposite force on the fluid on the first side.

The stress **S** at point $P$ in the fluid medium is defined as

$$\mathbf{S} \equiv \lim_{\delta A \to \delta A'} \frac{\delta\mathbf{F}}{\delta\mathbf{A}} \tag{1-7}$$

The magnitude of the stress **S** depends on the force $\delta\mathbf{F}$ and the area element $\delta\mathbf{A}'$. Both $\delta\mathbf{F}$ and $\delta\mathbf{A}'$ are vector quantities. If a different plane had been passed through the same point $P$, the value of **S** would, in general, be different from that obtained by using the area as shown in Figure 1–4(a). From this we see that the stress **S** at a given point is not a vector but a tensor quantity, since it cannot be completely defined by its magnitude and direction alone. As will be discussed in Sec. 1–9, nine components are required to completely define a stress tensor at a point.

If, however, we specify a plane of reference about which stress is to be evaluated, the direction of the area element is thus fixed and the stress on a fixed plane of reference then becomes a vector stress. The common practice is to resolve the force $\delta\mathbf{F}$ into a set of orthogonal components as shown in Fig. 1–4(b). The component $\delta F_n$ is normal to the plane of $\delta A$, whereas the remaining two components $\delta F_{s1}$ and $\delta F_{s2}$ lie in the plane of $\delta A$. The limit of the ratio $\delta F_n/\delta A$ as $\delta A$ approaches $\delta A'$ is defined as the normal stress $\sigma$ at point $P$:

$$\sigma \equiv \lim_{\delta A \to \delta A'} \frac{\delta F_n}{\delta A} \tag{1-8}$$

Similarly, the limit of $\delta F_s/\delta A$ is defined as the shearing stress $\tau$ at point $P$:

$$\tau_{s1} \equiv \lim_{\delta A \to \delta A'} \frac{\delta F_{s1}}{\delta A} \tag{1-9}$$

and

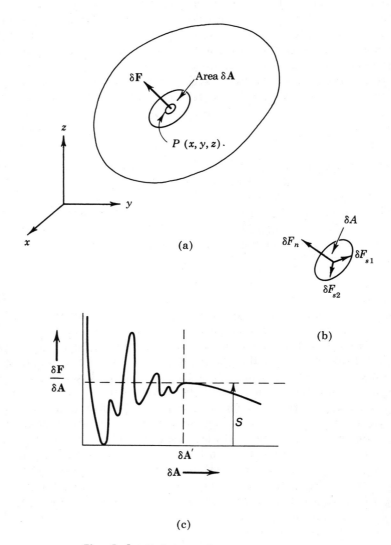

**Fig. 1-4.**  Definition of stress at a point.

$$\tau_{s2} \equiv \lim_{\delta A \to \delta A'} \frac{\delta F_{s2}}{\delta A} \tag{1–10}$$

The stress components $\sigma$, $\tau_{s1}$, $\tau_{s2}$ are scalar quantities. Their field representations are

$$\sigma = \sigma(x, y, z, t) \tag{1–11}$$

and
$$\tau = \tau(x, y, z, t) \tag{1-12}$$

It is important to note that the linear dimensions of $\delta A'$ are comparable to those of the fluid particle $\delta V'$. Figure 1–4(c) demonstrates again the significance of the continuum concept.

There are other continuum properties besides the ones that have been discussed above. They include mechanical continuum properties such as acceleration, vorticity, viscosity, etc., and thermodynamical continuum properties such as compressibility, internal energy, entropy, heat conductivity, etc., and electromagnetic continuum properties such as electrical conductivity, dielectric constant, magnetic permeability, etc. We shall discuss them in appropriate parts of the text.

All continuum properties are assumed to vary continuously throughout the fluid medium except at special points, lines, or surfaces of discontinuity, across which continuum properties change abruptly.

## 1-6  Mathematical Description of Continuum

The complexity of mathematically describing a fluid motion arises from the fact that the fluid continuum is composed of particles whose relative positions are not fixed from time to time. Each fluid particle has its own velocity and acceleration at any instant of time. The velocity and acceleration change both with respect to position and time. For a complete description of fluid motion it is necessary to observe the motion of fluid particles at various points in space and at successive instants of time.

Let us refer a fluid continuum to a rectangular Cartesian coordinate system for the purpose of mathematical description. At an arbitrarily chosen initial instant $t = t_0$, the coordinates of a particle of fluid are $x_0 = a$, $y_0 = b$, and $z_0 = c$. At a later instant when $t = t$, the coordinates of the same particle are $x$, $y$, and $z$. Then, $x$, $y$, and $z$ are functions of $t$, i.e., $x = x(t)$, $y = y(t)$, and $z = z(t)$. The scalar components of the velocity $V$ of the fluid particle at $(x, y, z)$ in the directions of the $x$-, $y$-, and $z$-axes are respectively

$$u = \frac{dx}{dt}, \qquad v = \frac{dy}{dt}, \qquad w = \frac{dz}{dt}$$

The two methods which are used in describing fluid motion for mathematical analysis are the Lagrangian method and the Eulerian method.

In the Lagrangian method of description, each fluid particle is identified by its initial position $(a, b, c)$ relative to the origin of the coordinate system at some arbitrarily chosen initial time $t_0$. We follow the paths of fluid particles of fixed identity. Then, at each instant of time $t$ the position $(x, y, z)$ and the continuum properties, such as density, temperature, state of stress, etc., associated with each fluid particle are functions of $a, b, c,$ and of $t$. The coordinates of a fluid particle may be written as

$$x = x(a, b, c, t)$$
$$y = y(a, b, c, t) \tag{1–13}$$
$$z = z(a, b, c, t)$$

and its velocity and acceleration components are then, respectively,

$$u = \frac{\partial x}{\partial t} \qquad a_x = \frac{\partial u}{\partial t} = \frac{\partial^2 x}{\partial t^2}$$
$$v = \frac{\partial y}{\partial t} \quad \text{and} \quad a_y = \frac{\partial v}{\partial t} = \frac{\partial^2 y}{\partial t^2}$$
$$w = \frac{\partial z}{\partial t} \qquad a_z = \frac{\partial w}{\partial t} = \frac{\partial^2 z}{\partial t^2}$$

in which $u, v,$ and $w,$ and $a_x, a_y,$ and $a_z$ are respectively the $x$-, $y$-, and $z$-components of velocity and acceleration of the fluid particle which occupies the position $(x, y, z)$ at the time $t$. In applying this method to a fluid flow problem, we attempt to seek a solution in the form of Eqs. 1–13 which are parametric equations of paths of fluid particles of fixed identity.

In the Eulerian method, we specify continuum properties of a fluid particle as functions of the position $(x, y, z)$ which the particle happens to occupy and of time $t$. Here we do not need to consider the history of each fluid particle. We simply describe what is happening at different positions in the entire flow field at any given time. In this method, the problem is to determine the velocity components of the fluid motion at various positions $(x, y, z)$ in the space at any given time $t$ in the form of the following three equations:

$$u = u(x, y, z, t)$$
$$v = v(x, y, z, t) \tag{1–14}$$
$$w = w(x, y, z, t)$$

The Eulerian equations (Eqs. 1–14) of fluid motion are related to the Lagrangian equations (Eqs. 1–13) by the following relationships:

$$u = \frac{dx}{dt}$$
$$v = \frac{dy}{dt} \tag{1–15}$$
$$w = \frac{dz}{dt}$$

Thus, the Lagrangian equations (Eqs. 1–13) can also be obtained by solving Eqs. 1–15 with the initial conditions $x = x_0 = a$, $y = y_0 = b$, and $z = z_0 = c$ at $t = t_0$. The solution of Eqs. 1–15, which is usually a difficult task, would give us the parametric equations of paths of fluid particles.

In general, the Eulerian method is mathematically more convenient than the Lagrangian method in the study of fluid mechanics. The Eulerian method is used exclusively in this book.

Let $B(x, y, z, t)$ represent any continuum property (e.g., density, velocity, temperature, state of stress, etc.) which, from the Eulerian point of view, is a function of position and time. According to the chain rule for partial differentiation, the increment $dB$ corresponding to arbitrary and independent increments $dx$, $dy$, $dz$, and $dt$ is written as

$$dB = \frac{\partial B}{\partial x}dx + \frac{\partial B}{\partial y}dy + \frac{\partial B}{\partial z}dz + \frac{\partial B}{\partial t}dt \tag{1-16}$$

From the Lagrangian point of view, $x$, $y$, and $z$ are functions of $t$. Hence, for a given fluid particle of fixed identity, $B$ is a function of $t$ only. The increment $dB$ in the Lagrangian method of representation is, therefore,

$$dB = \frac{dB}{dt}dt \tag{1-17}$$

If the increment $dB$ in Eq. 1–16 of the Eulerian description were obtained by following a fluid particle of fixed identity in its trajectory, the increments $dx$, $dy$, and $dz$ are no longer independent but are related to $dt$ by

$$dx = u\,dt, \qquad dy = v\,dt, \qquad dz = w\,dt$$

When these expressions are substituted into Eq. 1–16, we obtain

$$dB = \frac{\partial B}{\partial x}u\,dt + \frac{\partial B}{\partial y}v\,dt + \frac{\partial B}{\partial z}w\,dt + \frac{\partial B}{\partial t}dt \tag{1-18}$$

which is essentially an expression of Eulerian description but with the Lagrangian concept of following a fluid particle of fixed identity. Obviously, Eqs. 1–17 and 1–18 are identical, and the terms on their right-hand side can be equated to yield

$$\frac{dB}{dt} = u\frac{\partial B}{\partial x} + v\frac{\partial B}{\partial y} + w\frac{\partial B}{\partial z} + \frac{\partial B}{\partial t} \tag{1-19}$$

This equation then connects the Lagrangian and the Eulerian equations of fluid mechanics.

The special value of $dB/dt$ in Eq. 1–19 is obtained by following the motion of a particle of fixed identity and is assigned the symbol $DB/Dt$. The derivative $DB/Dt$ is called the *derivative following the fluid* or *substantive derivative*. The sum of the first three terms on the right-hand side of Eq. 1–19 is called the *convective derivative* because it represents the change in $B$ caused by the convection of a particle from one position to a second position having a different value of $B$. The last term $\partial B/\partial t$ denotes the rate of change of $B$ with respect to $t$ at a fixed position and is, therefore, called the *local derivative*.

As an example, let us use Eq. 1–19 to establish the acceleration field of a flow by taking velocity $\mathbf{V}$ as the continuum property $B$. The substantive derivative $D\mathbf{V}/Dt$ equals the acceleration $\mathbf{a}$. Hence

$$\mathbf{a} = \frac{D\mathbf{V}}{Dt} = u\frac{\partial \mathbf{V}}{\partial x} + v\frac{\partial \mathbf{V}}{\partial y} + w\frac{\partial \mathbf{V}}{\partial z} + \frac{\partial \mathbf{V}}{\partial t} \tag{1–20}$$

Since $\mathbf{V} = u\mathbf{i} + v\mathbf{j} + w\mathbf{k}$, the three scalar component equations of Eq. 1–20 are:

$$a_x = \frac{Du}{Dt} = u\frac{\partial u}{\partial x} + v\frac{\partial u}{\partial y} + w\frac{\partial u}{\partial z} + \frac{\partial u}{\partial t} \tag{1–21}$$

$$a_y = \frac{Dv}{Dt} = u\frac{\partial v}{\partial x} + v\frac{\partial v}{\partial y} + w\frac{\partial v}{\partial z} + \frac{\partial v}{\partial t} \tag{1–22}$$

$$a_z = \frac{Dw}{Dt} = u\frac{\partial w}{\partial x} + v\frac{\partial w}{\partial y} + w\frac{\partial w}{\partial z} + \frac{\partial w}{\partial t} \tag{1–23}$$

Equation 1–19 may also be expressed in vector form[1] as

$$\frac{DB}{Dt} = (\mathbf{V} \cdot \nabla)B + \frac{\partial B}{\partial t} \tag{1–24}$$

in which the symbol $\nabla$ (read "del") is the familiar gradient operator which is a vector quantity.

There is a definite advantage in using vector notations. Equation 1–24 is now no longer restricted to Cartesian coordinates since we know from vector analysis that vector operators may be expressed in terms of scalar components in any given coordinate system. For example, the gradient operator for the three most commonly used coordinate systems (shown in Fig. 1–5) can be written in the following manner:

Cartesian coordinates $(x, y, z)$:

$$\nabla \equiv \mathbf{grad} = \mathbf{i}\frac{\partial}{\partial x} + \mathbf{j}\frac{\partial}{\partial y} + \mathbf{k}\frac{\partial}{\partial z} \tag{1–25}$$

Cylindrical coordinates $(r, \theta, z)$:

$$\nabla \equiv \mathbf{grad} = \boldsymbol{\epsilon}_r\frac{\partial}{\partial r} + \boldsymbol{\epsilon}_\theta\frac{1}{r}\frac{\partial}{\partial \theta} + \boldsymbol{\epsilon}_z\frac{\partial}{\partial z} \tag{1–26}$$

where $\boldsymbol{\epsilon}_r$, $\boldsymbol{\epsilon}_\theta$, and $\boldsymbol{\epsilon}_z$ are respectively the unit vectors in the $r$-, $\theta$-, and $z$-direction.

Spherical coordinates $(R, \theta, \phi)$:

$$\nabla \equiv \mathbf{grad} = \boldsymbol{\epsilon}_R\frac{\partial}{\partial R} + \boldsymbol{\epsilon}_\theta\frac{1}{R}\frac{\partial}{\partial \theta} + \boldsymbol{\epsilon}_\phi\frac{1}{R \sin \theta}\frac{\partial}{\partial \phi} \tag{1–27}$$

---

[1] Vector notations and operations used in this book will be explained as they first appear in the book.

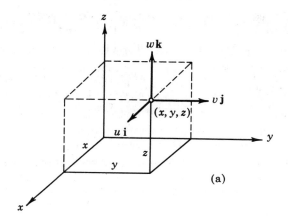

(a)

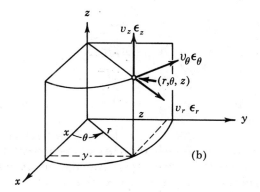

(b)

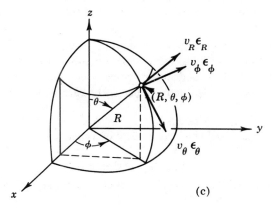

(c)

**Fig. 1-5.** Coordinate systems: (a) Cartesian, (b) cylindrical, and (c) spherical.

where $\epsilon_R$, $\epsilon_\theta$, and $\epsilon_\phi$ are respectively the unit vectors in the $R$-, $\theta$-, and $\phi$-direction.

If the flow is steady, $\partial B/\partial t = 0$. A steady flow is characterized by the condition that partial derivatives of continuum properties with respect to time are zero. Therefore, in steady motion, continuum properties are functions of position $(x, y, z)$ only and are independent of time. Continuum properties at each point of space may, however, change from instant to instant when unsteady motion prevails.

Truly steady motion is indeed very rarely observed in nature. When instantaneous values of any continuum property are measured at a fixed point in space, they are frequently found to fluctuate incessantly about a steady mean value as illustrated in Fig. 1–6. Therefore, the definition

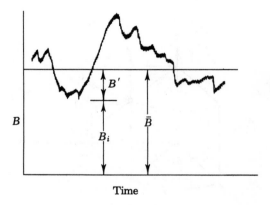

Time

**Fig. 1-6.** Fluctuations of instantaneous values of a continuum property $B$ at a fixed point of space in a steady flow.

of steady motion refers to a certain finite interval of time over which the mean of fluctuations $B'$ is zero. The phenomenon of fluctuations in instantaneous values of continuum properties at a fixed point of space is called *turbulence*. A detailed discussion of turbulence will be presented in Chapter 7.

*Illustrative Example 1-1.* The velocity field of a steady, two-dimensional flow is given by

$$\mathbf{V}(x, y) = Ax\mathbf{i} - Ay\mathbf{j}$$

where $A$ is a constant. Determine (a) the equation of the streamlines for this flow, and (b) the acceleration field of the flow.

*Solution:* (a) By definition, the streamlines must have the same slope as the velocity vector at all points in the flow field. Therefore,

$$\left(\frac{dy}{dx}\right)_{\text{streamline}} = \frac{v}{u} = \frac{-Ay}{Ax}$$

Separating the variables and integrating, we have

$$\ln x = -\ln y + \ln C$$

where $\ln C$ is the constant of integration. The above logarithmic equation can also be written as

$$xy = C$$

This is the desired equation of the streamlines for this flow. Clearly the streamlines form a family of rectangular hyperbolas. In the accompanying sketch, we have shown the streamlines in the first quadrant. These streamlines can be regarded as representing a steady, two-dimensional flow at a 90-degree corner.

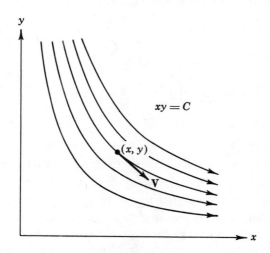

**Illustrative Example 1-1**

(b) The acceleration field of the flow can be determined by applying Eq. 1–20 to the given velocity field. Thus, for a steady, two-dimensional flow,

$$\mathbf{a}(x, y) = \frac{D\mathbf{V}}{Dt} = u\frac{\partial \mathbf{V}}{\partial x} + v\frac{\partial \mathbf{V}}{\partial y}$$

$$= (Ax)(A\mathbf{i}) + (-Ay)(-A\mathbf{j})$$

$$= A^2 x\mathbf{i} + A^2 y\mathbf{j}$$

## 1-7  Convective Motion of a Fluid Element

We shall now investigate the convective motion of a fluid element and examine what happens to the fluid element as it moves from one position to the next. Let us consider the steady motion of a fluid element. The center of this fluid element occupies position $(x, y, z)$ at time $t$. At time $t + dt$, it has moved to another position $(x + dx, y + dy, z + dz)$ an infinitesimal distance away. If the components of velocity at $(x, y, z)$ parallel to the x-, y-, and z-axes are respectively $u$, $v$, and $w$, then those at $(x + dx, y + dy, z + dz)$ become

$$u + du = u + \frac{\partial u}{\partial x}dx + \frac{\partial u}{\partial y}dy + \frac{\partial u}{\partial z}dz$$

$$v + dv = v + \frac{\partial v}{\partial x}dx + \frac{\partial v}{\partial y}dy + \frac{\partial v}{\partial z}dz \qquad (1\text{--}28)$$

$$w + dw = w + \frac{\partial w}{\partial x}dx + \frac{\partial w}{\partial y}dy + \frac{\partial w}{\partial z}dz$$

We shall now introduce the following notations:

$$\dot{\epsilon}_{xx} = \frac{\partial u}{\partial x}, \qquad \dot{\epsilon}_{yy} = \frac{\partial v}{\partial y}, \qquad \dot{\epsilon}_{zz} = \frac{\partial w}{\partial z}$$

$$\dot{\gamma}_{yz} = \frac{1}{2}\left(\frac{\partial w}{\partial y} + \frac{\partial v}{\partial z}\right), \qquad \dot{\gamma}_{xz} = \frac{1}{2}\left(\frac{\partial u}{\partial z} + \frac{\partial w}{\partial x}\right), \qquad \dot{\gamma}_{xy} = \frac{1}{2}\left(\frac{\partial v}{\partial x} + \frac{\partial u}{\partial y}\right)$$

$$\xi = \frac{1}{2}\left(\frac{\partial w}{\partial y} - \frac{\partial v}{\partial z}\right), \qquad \eta = \frac{1}{2}\left(\frac{\partial u}{\partial z} - \frac{\partial w}{\partial x}\right), \qquad \zeta = \frac{1}{2}\left(\frac{\partial v}{\partial x} - \frac{\partial u}{\partial y}\right) \quad (1\text{--}29)$$

so that Eqs. 1–28 can be written as

$$u + du = u + \dot{\epsilon}_{xx}\, dx + \dot{\gamma}_{xy}\, dy + \dot{\gamma}_{xz}\, dz + (\eta\, dz - \zeta\, dy)$$

$$v + dv = v + \dot{\gamma}_{xy}\, dx + \dot{\epsilon}_{yy}\, dy + \dot{\gamma}_{yz}\, dz + (\zeta\, dx - \xi\, dz) \quad (1\text{--}30)$$

$$w + dw = w + \dot{\gamma}_{xz}\, dx + \dot{\gamma}_{yz}\, dy + \dot{\epsilon}_{zz}\, dz + (\xi\, dy - \eta\, dx)$$

The purpose of transforming Eqs. 1–28 to Eqs. 1–30 is to show that as a fluid element moves about in a flow field, it undergoes a bodily displacement as well as a change in shape. The motion of the fluid element having originally the sides $dx$, $dy$, $dz$ with its center placed at $(x, y, z)$ may be regarded as made up of four parts—translation, linear deformation, angular deformation, and rotation. They are shown separately in Fig. 1–7 for a planar element.

The three velocity components $u$, $v$, and $w$ in Eqs. 1–30 correspond to rates of translation of the element as a whole [Fig. 1–7(a)]. The quantities $\dot{\epsilon}_{xx}\, dx$, $\dot{\epsilon}_{yy}\, dy$, and $\dot{\epsilon}_{zz}\, dz$ are the rates of linear deformations in the three coordinate directions [Fig. 1–7(b)]. Since the gradients of the velocity components in the transverse directions, such as $\partial u/\partial y$, $\partial v/\partial z$, $\partial w/\partial x$, $\partial u/\partial z$, etc., represent the rates of angular displacement of the surfaces of the fluid element, the quantities $2\dot{\gamma}_{yz}$, $2\dot{\gamma}_{xz}$, and $2\dot{\gamma}_{xy}$ which are the sums of these rates correspond to the rates of angular deformations, or shearing motion, about the three coordinate axes [Fig. 1–7(c)]. On the other hand, the average rates of angular displacement of the surfaces, i.e., $\xi$, $\eta$, and $\zeta$, are called *mean rates of rotation* [Fig. 1–7(d)].

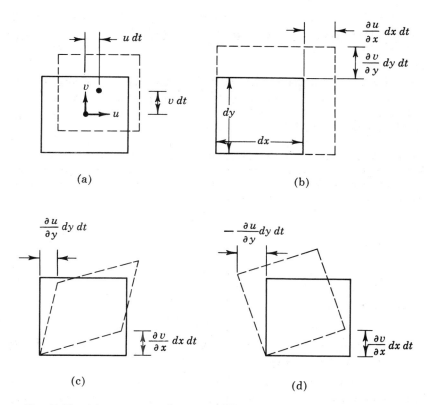

**Fig. 1-7.** (a) Translation, (b) linear deformation, (c) angular deformation, and (d) rotation of a planar fluid element.

The translation and rotation cause bodily displacement of a fluid element without changing its shape. Deformation of a fluid element is manifested by the three linear deformation terms ($\dot{\epsilon}_{xx}$, $\dot{\epsilon}_{yy}$, $\dot{\epsilon}_{zz}$) and the three angular deformation terms ($\dot{\gamma}_{yz}$, $\dot{\gamma}_{xz}$, $\dot{\gamma}_{xy}$). Deformation of fluid elements causes stresses in the flow. Relationships between stresses and rates-of-strain in viscous flows will be developed in Chapter 6.

The quantities $2\xi$, $2\eta$, and $2\zeta$ themselves form the components of the vorticity vector $\boldsymbol{\omega}$:

$$\boldsymbol{\omega} = 2(\xi\mathbf{i} + \eta\mathbf{j} + \zeta\mathbf{k})$$
$$= \left(\frac{\partial w}{\partial y} - \frac{\partial v}{\partial z}\right)\mathbf{i} + \left(\frac{\partial u}{\partial z} - \frac{\partial w}{\partial x}\right)\mathbf{j} + \left(\frac{\partial v}{\partial x} - \frac{\partial u}{\partial y}\right)\mathbf{k}$$

which, in vector analysis, is the **curl** of the velocity vector $\mathbf{V}$:

$$\boldsymbol{\omega} = \textbf{curl}\ \mathbf{V} = \boldsymbol{\nabla} \times \mathbf{V} = \begin{vmatrix} \mathbf{i} & \mathbf{j} & \mathbf{k} \\ \dfrac{\partial}{\partial x} & \dfrac{\partial}{\partial y} & \dfrac{\partial}{\partial z} \\ u & v & w \end{vmatrix} \tag{1-31}$$

Vorticity is an important phenomenon in fluid mechanics and its role in fluid motion will be discussed in appropriate parts of this book. Flows with zero vorticity, i.e., $\boldsymbol{\nabla} \times \mathbf{V} = 0$, are called *irrotational flows*, which will be discussed in detail in Chapter 3.

*Illustrative Example 1-2.* When a vertical cylinder of liquid is rotated about its vertical axis with a constant angular velocity $\Omega \boldsymbol{\epsilon}_z$, as shown in the accompanying figure, the liquid inside the cylinder is forced to rotate with the cylinder. The velocity field of the liquid is given by

$$\mathbf{V} = \Omega r \boldsymbol{\epsilon}_\theta$$

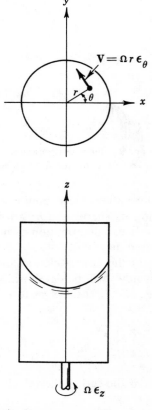

**Illustrative Example 1-2**

where $r$ is the radial distance from the cylinder axis and $\epsilon_\theta$ is the unit vector in the $\theta$-direction. Determine the vorticity at any point in the liquid.

*Solution:* Since the velocity field is expressed in cylindrical coordinates, we shall use the following cylindrical form of the **curl** of the velocity vector $\mathbf{V}$:

$$\boldsymbol{\omega} = \boldsymbol{\nabla} \times \mathbf{V}$$

$$= \left(\frac{1}{r}\frac{\partial v_z}{\partial \theta} - \frac{\partial v_\theta}{\partial z}\right)\epsilon_r + \left(\frac{\partial v_r}{\partial z} - \frac{\partial v_z}{\partial r}\right)\epsilon_\theta + \frac{1}{r}\left(\frac{\partial r v_\theta}{\partial r} - \frac{\partial v_r}{\partial \theta}\right)\epsilon_z$$

Substituting the given velocity field into this equation, we obtain

$$\boldsymbol{\omega} = 2\Omega\epsilon_z$$

which is the vorticity for this flow. The vorticity is constant at any point in the flow field, and it is equal to twice the value of the rate of rotation.

## 1-8 Fluid Properties and Their Influences on Fluid Motion

In fluid mechanics we study the motion of fluids under the action of forces. The system of forces acting on a fluid particle includes those forces which are inherent in the fluid properties. Therefore, the study requires a thorough knowledge of various properties of fluids and their effect on the resulting fluid motion.

The first step in solving a given fluid mechanics problem is to set up differential equations which will describe the flow processes. The degree of complexity of these equations depends very largely on the mathematical description of fluid properties and flow processes. These differential equations are usually difficult to solve if we insist on the exact mathematical description of the fluid properties and the flow processes involved in the problem. As in all problems in engineering and applied sciences, it is necessary to introduce certain simplifying assumptions concerning the mathematical description of fluid properties and flow processes in order to make the problem amenable to mathematical analysis. We have already introduced such a simplifying assumption by adopting the concept of a continuous fluid. The assumptions must be realistic; and yet they must yield results which are compatible with the actual flow process.

In this section we shall examine several fluid properties and their relative effect on fluid motion.

**Density, specific volume, and specific gravity.** *Density* is defined as the amount of mass per unit volume. The dimensions of density are $M/L^3$. In fluid mechanics equations, fluid density $\rho$ appears in the form of fluid inertia whenever there is a change of fluid velocity.

The ratio $V/m$ is the volume occupied by a unit mass of substance and is called the *specific volume* $v$, i.e.,

$$v = \frac{V}{m} = \frac{1}{\rho} \tag{1–32}$$

since $m/V$ is the density $\rho$ of the substance. The dimensions of $v$ are $L^3/M$.

The density of a liquid is slightly affected by changes in temperature and pressure, whereas the density of a gas varies greatly with temperature and pressure. The constitutive equation describing the functional relationship between the density of gases and the temperature and pressure is called the *equation of state*. For example, the equation of state of a system of $m$ lbm of a perfect gas whose molecular weight is $\mathscr{M}$ and which occupies a volume $V$ at an absolute temperature $T$ and absolute pressure $p$ is given approximately by

$$pV = \frac{m}{\mathscr{M}}\bar{R}T \tag{1-33}$$

where $\bar{R}$ is a universal gas constant. The numerical value of this universal gas constant depends on the units used and it has the same numerical value in any chosen system of units for all gases which behave in accordance with Eq. 1-33. For the most frequently used systems of units, the values of $\bar{R}$ are as follows:

$$\bar{R} = 1545 \text{ ft-lbf/lbm-mole-}°\text{Rankine}$$
$$\bar{R} = 1.986 \text{ Btu/lbm-mole-}°\text{Rankine}$$
$$\bar{R} = 1.986 \text{ cal/gm-mole-}°\text{Kelvin}$$

The gas constant is, however, frequently listed in terms of $R = \bar{R}/\mathscr{M}$ for each substance. We call $R$ the *individual gas constant*, because it is a constant having a particular numerical value for each substance. Values of $R$ for different gases can be found in Table 1-2. Therefore, the equation of state for a perfect gas can also be written as

$$pv = RT \quad \text{or} \quad \rho = \frac{p}{RT} \tag{1-33a}$$

The term *specific gravity* of a substance refers to the ratio of the density of the substance to that of water. Since the density of fluids varies with temperature and pressure, to be precise, the temperature and pressure

### TABLE 1-2. Properties of Common Gases

| Gas | $k = c_p/c_v$ | $R$, ft-lbf/lbm-°R |
|---|---|---|
| Air | 1.40 | 53.3 |
| Helium, He | 1.66 | 386 |
| Carbon monoxide, CO | 1.40 | 55.1 |
| Hydrogen, $H_2$ | 1.41 | 767 |
| Nitrogen, $N_2$ | 1.40 | 55.1 |
| Oxygen, $O_2$ | 1.40 | 48.2 |
| Carbon dioxide, $CO_2$ | 1.30 | 34.9 |
| Water vapor, $H_2O$ | 1.33 | 85.6 |
| Methane, $CH_4$ | 1.32 | 96.1 |

of the fluid in question and of the water as a reference should be specified in connection with values of specific gravity. Specific gravity is a dimensionless quantity.

Values of density and specific gravity for some common fluids are given in tables in the Appendix.

**Specific weight.** The specific weight $\gamma$ of a substance is the force of gravity on the mass in a unit volume. The specific weight is thus equal to the product of density and the local gravitational acceleration, i.e.,

$$\gamma = \rho g \tag{1-34}$$

and has the dimensions $F/L^3$. Strictly speaking, specific weight is not a true fluid property because its value depends on the magnitude of the local gravitational acceleration. Specific weight becomes important in fluid mechanics whenever there is a change in elevation in the fluid motion.

**Fluid viscosity.** Fluid viscosity is an important quantity in the study of fluid friction and fluid turbulence whenever relative motions occur between adjacent fluid particles. The viscosity of a fluid is a measure of its frictional resistance to the sliding motion of one layer of fluid over another. The idealized model, shown in Fig. 1–8, has often been used to derive a quantitative definition for fluid viscosity. The spacing between the two parallel plates of surface area $A$ is filled with a fluid. A tangential force $F$ is applied to the top plate to move it at a constant velocity $U$ parallel to the stationary bottom plate. In the absence of gravity and

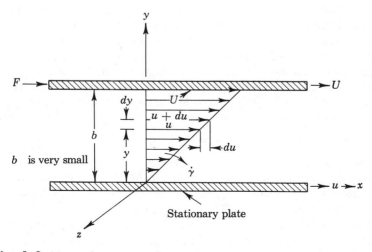

**Fig. 1-8.** Newton's conceptual model for defining the viscosity of a real fluid.

pressure gradient, the ratio $U/b$ is proportional to the tangential force per unit area $F/A$. That is,

$$\frac{F}{A} = \mu \frac{U}{b}$$

where the constant of proportionality $\mu$ is defined as the coefficient of viscosity or dynamic viscosity.

The linear velocity profile in the fluid motion of Fig. 1–8 results from another unique behavior of viscous fluids. It is an experimental fact that ordinary viscous fluid particles immediately in contact with a solid surface adhere to the surface and do not slip relative to it. This phenomenon is often referred to as the condition of *no slip of viscous fluid at solid boundary*. The condition of no slip serves as an important boundary condition for solving viscous flow problems.

For the one-dimensional flow of Fig. 1–8, $F/A = \tau_{yx}$, where $\tau_{yx}$ is the shear stress at any point in this flow field, and $U/b = du/dy$, where $du/dy$ is the slope of the linear velocity profile. We can then write

$$\tau_{yx} = \mu \frac{du}{dy} \qquad (1\text{–}35)$$

This equation is the well-known Newton's law of viscosity. Fluids which behave in accordance with this law and have a constant viscosity at a given temperature and pressure are called *Newtonian fluids*. The viscosity of a non-Newtonian fluid at a given temperature and pressure is not a constant and is frequently a function of the velocity gradient. Ordinary fluids, like water, air, etc., are Newtonian in behavior. In this book we deal exclusively with Newtonian fluids.

To extend the physical implication of Eq. 1–35 to multidimensional viscous flow, we need to recognize that the velocity gradient $du/dy$ in the one-dimensional flow of Fig. 1–8 is the rate of shear strain of any fluid element in this flow. Hence we may define the dynamic viscosity $\mu$ as the ratio of shear stress to rate-of-shear-strain of a fluid element. Multidimensional viscous flow will be discussed in Chapter 6.

By definition the dimensions of $\mu$ are either $FT/L^2$ or $M/TL$. The ratio of the dynamic viscosity to the density of the fluid is defined as the kinematic viscosity $\nu$; that is,

$$\nu = \frac{\mu}{\rho} \qquad (1\text{–}36)$$

The dimensions of $\nu$ are $L^2/T$.

When fluid viscosities are expressed in MKS units of measurement, the basic unit of $\mu$ is called a *poise*, which is 1 gram mass per centimeter-second and the unit for $\nu$ is a *stoke*, which is 1 cm²/sec.

Fluid viscosity varies substantially with change in temperature, but is practically independent of variation in pressure. Dynamic and kinematic viscosities of some common fluids are plotted as a function of temperature in Figs. 1–9 and 1–10, respectively. These curves show that

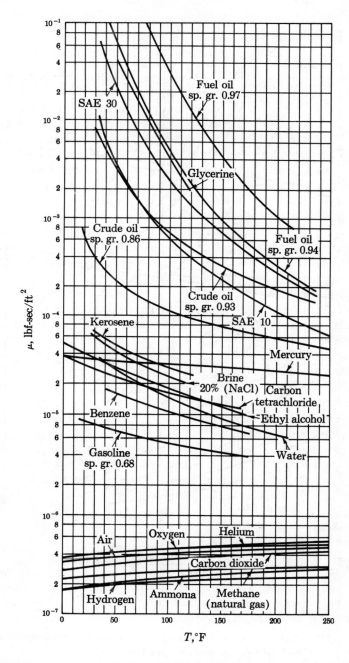

**Fig. 1-9.** Curves showing the variation of dynamic viscosities with temperature (at constant pressure).

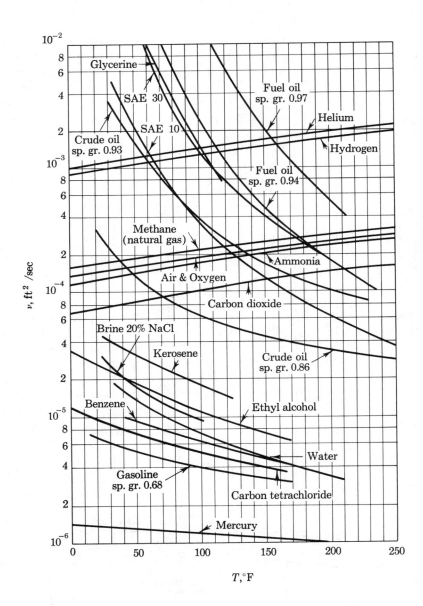

**Fig. 1-10.** Curves showing the variation of kinematic viscosities with temperature (at constant pressure).

the variation of temperature has an opposite effect on the viscosities of gases and liquids. The viscosity of a gas increases with temperature, but the viscosity of a liquid decreases with an increase in temperature. This difference can be explained by the different molecular behaviors which cause viscosities in gases and liquids. The viscosity of a fluid depends on both the intermolecular cohesive forces and the rate of momentum transfer by molecules moving at random. In a gas the molecules are widely spaced, the intermolecular cohesive forces are small, and viscosity is caused primarily by momentum transfer due to random molecular motions. An increase in temperature causes a rapid increase in molecular activities in a gas, thus causing the viscosity of a gas to increase with temperature. On the other hand, in a liquid the molecules are close together; intermolecular cohesive forces are the main source of viscosity. An increase in temperature in a liquid reduces cohesive forces among molecules and, therefore, causes a decrease in viscosity.

Compare Figs. 1–9 and 1–10. The $\mu$ and $\nu$ of liquids have the same rate of change with temperature, because the density of liquids changes only slightly with temperature. However, in the case of gases, their density decreases considerably with increasing temperature, and so $\nu$ increases more rapidly with temperature than $\mu$.

***Inviscid fluids.*** An inviscid (or nonviscous) fluid is another idealization in that the fluid is assumed to have zero coefficient of viscosity. This assumption means physically that there is no shear stress in the flow of an inviscid fluid. No real fluids are inviscid although some fluids, like water and air, have extremely small coefficients of viscosity. The concept of an inviscid fluid is nevertheless immensely useful inasmuch as it provides a mathematically simple model, and yet at the same time its motion approximates those of real fluids in many situations in which the velocity gradients and, consequently, the shear stresses are negligibly small. The assumption of an inviscid fluid also implies that it does not adhere to solid boundaries. Therefore, an inviscid fluid is assumed to slip past solid boundaries with complete freedom.

***Boundary layers.*** Many fluids frequently encountered in engineering problems have a small coefficient of viscosity. Their motion often agrees very well with that of an inviscid fluid in regions remote from solid boundaries because of the small velocity gradient in the flow in these regions. However, the frictional effect of the fluid near a solid boundary cannot be neglected. Consider a fluid flowing past a stationary plane surface, as illustrated in Fig. 1–11. Since the fluid adheres to the solid boundary, the frictional forces retard the motion of the fluid in a thin

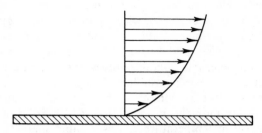

**Fig. 1-11.** Velocity profile in the boundary layer in the vicinity of a solid boundary.

"boundary layer" near the solid surface. Within the boundary layer the fluid velocity increases from zero at the solid surface to that of the main stream of the fluid flow as shown in Fig. 1–11, and hence the velocity gradient is high.

In the solution of many fluid mechanics problems, a flow field may be divided into (a) a viscous boundary layer flow and (b) an inviscid flow outside the boundary layer. This division of the flow field into two distinctive parts has the great practical advantage of reducing a complicated problem to simple components, each of which can be treated by analytical methods. The solutions of the two components are then joined by matching their boundary conditions to yield a complete solution for the entire flow field. Much of the recent advance in fluid mechanics has been made by this technique. The theory of boundary layer will be discussed in Chapter 8.

**Fluid compressibility.** All fluids are to a certain extent compressible under the application of pressure. The compressibility of a fluid is described quantitatively by its bulk modulus $E$. When a unit volume $v$ of fluid at pressure $p$ is subjected to an increase in pressure $\Delta p$, this volume is decreased by an amount $\Delta v$. The bulk modulus of this fluid is defined as

$$E = \lim_{\Delta v \to 0} \frac{-\Delta p}{\Delta v/v} = \frac{-dp}{dv/v} \qquad (1\text{-}37)$$

The negative sign in this equation is necessary because a positive $\Delta p$ is always accompanied by a negative $\Delta v$, and vice versa. Equation 1–37 indicates that the more compressible the fluid is, the lower its value of $E$.

The bulk modulus can also be expressed in terms of $\rho$ and $d\rho$. By definition (Eq. 1–32), $v = 1/\rho$ and its differential form is

$$v \, d\rho + \rho \, dv = 0 \quad \text{or} \quad -\frac{dv}{v} = \frac{d\rho}{\rho}$$

Therefore, Eq. 1–37 may also be written as

$$E = \frac{dp}{d\rho/\rho} \tag{1-37a}$$

The ratio $d\rho/\rho$ in the denominator represents the relative change in density caused by a pressure change $dp$.

The magnitude of $d\rho/\rho$ is an indication of the significance of the effect of compressibility of a fluid. The effect of fluid compressibility can be neglected whenever the relative change in density becomes very small, i.e., $d\rho/\rho \ll 1$. For example, water under normal pressure has a value of bulk modulus of 300,000 lbf/in². A pressure increase of 1 standard atmosphere (i.e., 14.7 lbf/in²) will cause a relative change in density of about 1/20,400, or less than 0.005 per cent. Other liquids also have small values of $d\rho/\rho$ comparable to that of water. Hence flows of liquids are regarded incompressible except when the the liquid flow is subjected to extremely high acceleration, as in the phenomenon of waterhammer in which the effect of compressibility of water is taken into consideration in analytical treatment.

The bulk modulus of a gas depends on the thermodynamic relationship between changes in pressure and density of the gas as it goes through the compression and expansion processes. For example, if the state of a perfect gas changes isothermally,

$$p = C\rho$$

By taking the natural logarithm of this equation,

$$\ln p = \ln C + \ln \rho$$

and then differentiating,

$$\frac{dp}{p} = \frac{d\rho}{\rho}$$

Therefore,

$$E_{\text{isothermal}} = \frac{dp}{d\rho/\rho} = p \tag{1-38}$$

If a perfect gas follows an isentropic (i.e., adiabatic and reversible) process during a pressure change,

$$pv^k = C \quad \text{or} \quad p = C\rho^k$$

where $k$ is the ratio of specific heat capacities. Values of $k$ for some common gases are given in Table 1–2. Logarithmic differentiation of the above isentropic equation yields

$$\frac{dp}{p} = k\frac{d\rho}{\rho}$$

Thus,

$$E_{\text{isentropic}} = \frac{dp}{d\rho/\rho} = kp \qquad (1\text{--}39)$$

Air at standard atmospheric conditions has a value of bulk modulus $E_{\text{isentropic}} = 1.4 \times 14.7\ \text{lbf/in}^2 = 20.58\ \text{lbf/in}^2$, which means that the standard air is about 14,580 times more compressible than water.

In spite of the fact that gases are very readily compressed, we nevertheless frequently neglect the compressibility effect of gases in some gas flow problems and assume the gas flows to be incompressible. This assumption is permissible whenever the value of $d\rho/\rho$ remains very small. To investigate the conditions under which a gas flow may be reasonably assumed to be incompressible, we have to make use of the following two familiar facts which are discussed in elementary physics textbooks and which will also be discussed in detail in subsequent parts of this book.

(a) Whenever a small pressure disturbance occurs in a flow field, the velocity $a$ at which small pressure waves are propagated throughout the fluid medium is: (see Sec. 9–2)

$$a = \sqrt{\frac{dp}{d\rho}} = \sqrt{\left(\frac{\partial p}{\partial \rho}\right)_s} = \sqrt{\frac{E_{\text{isentropic}}}{\rho}}$$

or

$$E_{\text{isentropic}} = a^2 \rho \qquad (1\text{--}40)$$

The velocity $a$ is also called the *sonic velocity* or *acoustic velocity*. The subscript $s$ means that the ratio $dp/d\rho$ is evaluated at constant entropy. We do this for the following reasons. The changes in density, pressure, and temperature in the pressure wave propagation are all infinitesimally small and so the process is nearly reversible. Furthermore, the rapidity of the pressure wave propagation and the accompanying infinitesimal changes in temperature make the process almost adiabatic. As a result, the process involved in an infinitesimal pressure wave is very close to being isentropic.

(b) The pressure change $dp$ in a flow field can be determined from Bernoulli's theorem to be of the order of magnitude of $\rho V^2/2$ (see Sec. 2–13), i.e.,

$$dp \approx \frac{\rho V^2}{2} \qquad (1\text{--}41)$$

where $V$ is the magnitude of the velocity at the point where the pressure change takes place.

Using Eqs. 1–37a, 1–40, and 1–41, we obtain for $d\rho/\rho$:

$$\frac{d\rho}{\rho} = \frac{dp}{E_{\text{isentropic}}} \approx \frac{\rho V^2/2}{a^2 \rho} \approx \frac{1}{2}\left(\frac{V}{a}\right)^2$$

The ratio $V/a$ is defined as the Mach number $M$. The velocity is subsonic when $M < 1$ and supersonic when $M > 1$. Sonic velocity occurs at $M = 1$. Thus,

$$\frac{d\rho}{\rho} \approx \frac{1}{2}M^2 \tag{1-42}$$

and the magnitude of $M$ is seen to be a criterion for deciding whether or not a gas flow may be reasonably assumed incompressible for engineering calculation. If $M \approx 0$, the flow can be assumed incompressible. For most engineering calculations, $M = 0.3$ has been accepted as the limit below which a gas flow can be safely regarded to be incompressible. The sonic velocity of air at standard atmospheric conditions is approximately $a = 1100$ ft/sec, which means that air flows at a velocity of 330 ft/sec or less are usually treated as incompressible flows.

*Ideal fluid.* An ideal fluid is both incompressible and inviscid. No such fluid actually exists. An ideal fluid is still another conceptual model which is adopted to simplify the mathematical treatment of fluid flow.

It is important to recognize that although the magnitudes of different physical properties for various fluids may be different, the effects of a particular property for different fluids on fluid motion are essentially similar. Thus, the viscosity of water is many times greater than that of air, yet the principle of modern fluid mechanics will show that models of airships may be tested in water tunnels and, likewise, models of submarines are frequently tested in wind tunnels to determine their respective resistance characteristics, simply because the principle of resistance due to fluid viscosity is the same for all viscous fluids.

## 1-9  State of Stress at a Point in a Flow Field

In setting up the equations of motion of fluids, we will need to know the relationships among internal stresses in a flow field. The stress at a given point, which was defined by Eq. 1-7, depends on the force $\delta \mathbf{F}$ and the surface area $\delta \mathbf{A}'$ on which $\delta \mathbf{F}$ acts. Since both $\delta \mathbf{F}$ and $\delta \mathbf{A}'$ are vector quantities, nine scalar components are required to completely specify the state of stress at a given point. Hence the stress at a point is a tensor quantity of second order.

The three-dimensional element in Fig. 1-12(a) represents a fluid particle isolated as free body. The vector stress (i.e., surface force per unit area) on each surface is resolved into a normal component and two tangential (or shear) components along the three rectangular Cartesian coordinates. The surface stress components shown are average values on each surface that passes through the fluid particle. Here a double subscript notation has been adopted to identify the various component stresses. The first subscript denotes the direction of the normal to the surface on which the component stress acts and the second subscript denotes the direction of the component stress itself. Thus, $\tau_{xy}$ denotes a shear stress acting on the face that is perpendicular to the $x$-axis, the shear stress acting in the direction of the $y$-axis. The normal stress has repeated subscripts since both the normal to the surface and the normal stress are in the same direction.

We shall adopt a sign convention for the stress components by agreeing, first, that a positive area vector $\delta\mathbf{A}$ points outward from the enclosed volume. Then a stress component is positive if the stress itself and the area vector of the surface on which the stress acts both have the same sense in either the positive or the negative direction of the reference axes. The stress component is negative whenever these two quantities are of opposite sense. Thus, tensile normal stresses are positive. Shear stresses on faces farthest from the reference planes are positive if they point in the positive direction of the reference axes, whereas shear stresses on faces nearest the reference planes are positive if they point in the negative direction of the reference axes. All the stress components shown in Fig. 1–12(a) are positive.

The nine scalar components of a stress tensor on the fluid particle of Fig. 1–12(a) can be arranged in a stress matrix as follows:

$$\begin{pmatrix} \sigma_{xx} & \tau_{xy} & \tau_{xz} \\ \tau_{yx} & \sigma_{yy} & \tau_{yz} \\ \tau_{zx} & \tau_{zy} & \sigma_{zz} \end{pmatrix} \tag{1-43}$$

Actually, however, not all nine Cartesian components of the above stress tensor are independent, as can be shown by considering the moments of the fluid element. Thus, in Fig. 1–12, by taking the moment about the $x$-, $y$-, and $z$-axes, respectively, we can write the moment equations as

$$(\tau_{yz}\,\delta z'\,\delta x')\,\delta y' = (\tau_{zy}\,\delta y'\,\delta x')\,\delta z'$$
$$(\tau_{xz}\,\delta z'\,\delta y')\,\delta x' = (\tau_{zx}\,\delta x'\,\delta y')\,\delta z'$$
$$(\tau_{xy}\,\delta y'\,\delta z')\,\delta x' = (\tau_{yx}\,\delta x'\,\delta z')\,\delta y'$$

These moment equations reduce to

$$\tau_{yz} = \tau_{zy}, \qquad \tau_{xz} = \tau_{zx}, \qquad \tau_{xy} = \tau_{yx} \tag{1-44}$$

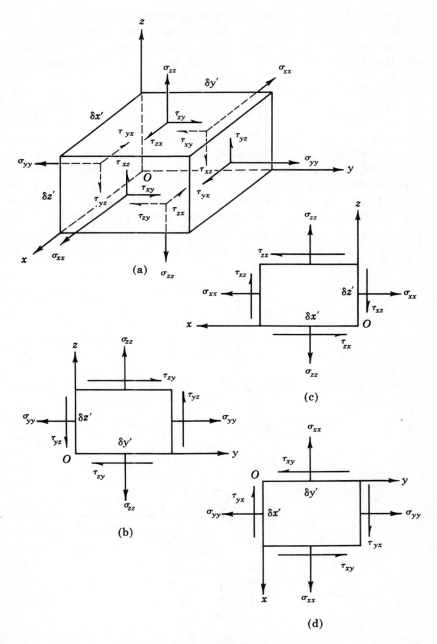

**Fig. 1-12.** Three-dimensional stress field.

indicating that there are only three independent shear stresses instead of six, as previously written. Thus, six, rather than nine, scalar components are sufficient to determine the state of stress at a given point, and the stress tensor of Eq. 1–43 then becomes a symmetrical stress matrix:

$$\begin{pmatrix} \sigma_{xx} & \tau_{xy} & \tau_{xz} \\ \tau_{xy} & \sigma_{yy} & \tau_{yz} \\ \tau_{xz} & \tau_{yz} & \sigma_{zz} \end{pmatrix} \qquad (1\text{–}45)$$

since the off-diagonal stress components are equal in pairs.

In order to show that six scalar stress components are sufficient to determine the state of stress at a given point, let us pass an oblique plane $\overline{ABC}$ of arbitrary orientation through the three-dimensional element of Fig. 1–12(a). The result is a tetrahedron of fluid particle in Fig. 1–13. Let the area of the oblique face $\overline{ABC}$ be $\delta A_o$. The direction of the surface $\overline{ABC}$ is defined by the angles that its outward normal makes with the

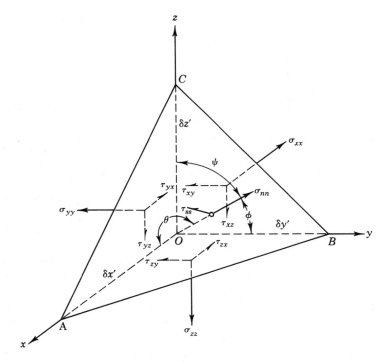

**Fig. 1-13.** Normal and shear stress components on faces of a tetrahedron.

$x$-, $y$-, and $z$-axes. These angles are designated as $\theta$, $\phi$, and $\psi$, repectively, and the direction cosines of the surface $\overline{ABC}$ are

$$\cos \theta = l, \qquad \cos \phi = m, \qquad \cos \psi = n$$

Therefore, the areas of the three orthogonal faces of the tetrahedron of Fig. 1–13 are related in the following manner:

$$\overline{OBC} = \frac{\delta y' \, \delta z'}{2} = l \, \delta A_o$$

$$\overline{OAC} = \frac{\delta x' \, \delta z'}{2} = m \, \delta A_o \qquad \text{(1–46)}$$

$$\overline{OAB} = \frac{\delta x' \, \delta y'}{2} = n \, \delta A_o$$

The normal stress $\sigma_{nn}$ is perpendicular to $\delta A_o$, and the shear stress $\tau_{ss}$ is in the plane of $\delta A_o$. The direction cosines of $\sigma_{nn}$ are also $l$, $m$, and $n$.

Expressing Newton's second law of motion in the direction of $\sigma_{nn}$, we obtain

$$\sigma_{nn} \delta A_0 - \sigma_{xx}\overline{OBC}\, l - \tau_{xy}\overline{OBC}\, m - \tau_{xy}\overline{OBC}\, n$$
$$- \tau_{yx}\overline{OAC}\, l - \sigma_{yy}\overline{OAC}\, m - \tau_{yz}\overline{OAC}\, n$$
$$- \tau_{zx}\overline{OAB}\, l - \tau_{zy}\overline{OAB}\, m - \sigma_{zz}\overline{OAB}\, n$$
$$+ \rho \frac{\delta x' \, \delta y' \, \delta z'}{6} g_n = \rho \frac{\delta x' \, \delta y' \, \delta z'}{6} a_n$$

where $g_n$ is the gravitational acceleration component and $a_n$ is the acceleration component in the direction of $\sigma_{nn}$. As the volume is of a higher order of differentials than the surface areas, the two acceleration terms in the above equation are negligible in comparison with stress terms. The above equation, after the acceleration terms are dropped, becomes

$$\sigma_{nn} = \sigma_{xx} l^2 + \sigma_{yy} m^2 + \sigma_{zz} n^2 + 2\tau_{xy} lm + 2\tau_{yz} mn + 2\tau_{zx} nl \qquad \text{(1–47)}$$

In a similar manner we may express the two orthogonal components of the shear stress $\tau_{ss}$ on the inclined surface $\overline{ABC}$ in terms of the same six scalar stress components.

Since the inclination of the surface $\overline{ABC}$ is arbitrary, the direction cosines $l$, $m$, $n$ in Eq. 1–47 can take on any numerical values. Hence, if the normal and shear stress components are known for three mutually perpendicular planes passing through a given point, stresses on all other planes (i.e., for any set of direction cosines) passing through the same point may be determined in terms of the known scalar stress components.

The stress tensor is connected with the rate-of-strain tensor through the coefficient of viscosity. The stress and rate-of-strain relationships in a viscous flow field will be developed in Chapter 6.

When a fluid is at rest or in uniform motion, all the shear stress components are everywhere equal to zero. For this simple case, we may write Newton's second law of motion for the tetrahedron of Fig. 1–13 (with zero shear stresses) in the directions of the $x$-, $y$-, and $z$-axes. Dropping the acceleration terms as in the previous case and simplifying the resulting equations, we then have

$$\sigma_{xx} = \sigma_{nn}, \qquad \sigma_{yy} = \sigma_{nn}, \qquad \sigma_{zz} = \sigma_{nn}$$

Hence, in the absence of viscous shear stresses, the normal stress at a point is the same in all directions; that is,

$$\sigma_{xx} = \sigma_{yy} = \sigma_{zz} = \sigma_{nn} = -p \qquad (1\text{–}48)$$

We have indicated in the above equation that, for the flow under consideration, the normal stress is simply the negative of pressure. Therefore, in the absence of shear stresses, the stress tensor field degenerates into a scalar pressure field.

In practice, a fluid pressure is measured with respect to an arbitrarily chosen datum. When a fluid pressure is measured with respect to the absolute zero pressure as the datum, it is referred to as an *absolute pressure*. Another frequently used datum is the *local atmospheric pressure;* the difference between the fluid pressure and the local atmospheric pressure is called the *gage pressure*. For example, a pressure of 10.0 lbf/in² higher than a local atmospheric pressure of 14.7 lbf/in² absolute may be said to be 24.7 lbf/in² absolute or 10.0 lbf/in² gage. A pressure of 5.0 lbf/in² below the same local atmospheric pressure is recorded as 9.7 lbf/in² absolute or 5.0 lbf/in² vacuum.

## 1-10  Fluid Statics

Fluid statics is chiefly concerned with the manner in which pressure varies in a fluid at rest and the forces of pressure which act on different interfaces.

Since we are now interested in the variation of pressure in a fluid medium, we shall adopt a three-dimensional fluid element [as shown in Fig. 1–14(a)] which contains many fluid particles as a free body. Pressure is assumed to vary continuously within such a fluid element. The center of this element is located at $(x, y, z)$, and the pressure at this point is $p$, which is a function of the position of this point, i.e., $p = p(x, y, z)$.

Figure 1–14(b) is used to illustrate the concept of pressure variation within a continuous medium. The curve shows graphically the magnitude of pressure along a line parallel to the $x$-axis and passing through the point $(x, y, z)$. The slope of the tangent to the curve at $(x, y, z)$ is $\partial p / \partial x$.

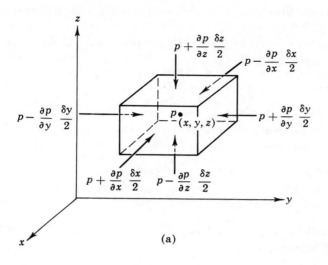

(a)

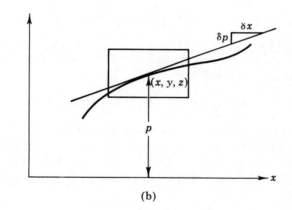

(b)

**Fig. 1-14.** (a) Pressure acting on different faces of a fluid element; (b) pressure variation along the x-direction.

The approximate average pressure at the left face is

$$p - \frac{\partial p}{\partial x} \frac{\delta x}{2}$$

and at the right face is

$$p + \frac{\partial p}{\partial x} \frac{\delta x}{2}$$

These values become exact as the element is allowed to shrink toward its center as a limit.

The resultant pressure force, $\delta F_{px}$, in the positive $x$-direction is

$$\delta F_{px} = \left( p - \frac{\partial p}{\partial x}\frac{\delta x}{2} \right) \delta y \, \delta z - \left( p + \frac{\partial p}{\partial x}\frac{\delta x}{2} \right) \delta y \, \delta z$$

$$= -\frac{\partial p}{\partial x} \delta x \, \delta y \, \delta z \qquad (1\text{--}49\text{a})$$

In a similar manner we can write the pressure forces, $\delta F_{py}$ and $\delta F_{pz}$, in the $y$- and $z$-directions as

$$\delta F_{py} = -\frac{\partial p}{\partial y} \delta x \, \delta y \, \delta z \qquad (1\text{--}49\text{b})$$

$$\delta F_{pz} = -\frac{\partial p}{\partial z} \delta x \, \delta y \, \delta z \qquad (1\text{--}49\text{c})$$

Therefore, the total pressure force $\delta \mathbf{F}_p$ on the element can be written in the vector form as

$$\delta \mathbf{F}_p = \delta F_{px}\mathbf{i} + \delta F_{py}\mathbf{j} + \delta F_{pz}\mathbf{k}$$

$$= -\left( \frac{\partial p}{\partial x}\mathbf{i} + \frac{\partial p}{\partial y}\mathbf{j} + \frac{\partial p}{\partial z}\mathbf{k} \right) \delta x \, \delta y \, \delta z$$

where $\mathbf{i}, \mathbf{j}$, and $\mathbf{k}$ are unit vectors in the $x$-, $y$-, and $z$-directions, respectively. Dividing the above equation by the volume $\delta x \, \delta y \, \delta z$, we get the following force equation per unit volume:

$$\frac{\delta \mathbf{F}_p}{\delta x \, \delta y \, \delta z} = \mathbf{f}_p = -\left( \frac{\partial p}{\partial x}\mathbf{i} + \frac{\partial p}{\partial y}\mathbf{j} + \frac{\partial p}{\partial z}\mathbf{k} \right) \qquad (1\text{--}50)$$

which is an important physical equation in the mechanics of continuum relating a vector force (per unit volume) field and a scalar pressure field. The expression on the right-hand side of Eq. 1–50 is a familiar vector operator, called the *gradient operator*. Consequently, Eq. 1–50 can also be written as

$$\mathbf{f}_p = -\mathbf{grad}\, p = -\nabla p \qquad (1\text{--}51)$$

In a fluid at rest the forces acting on the fluid element of Fig. 1–14(a) are the pressure forces from the fluid surrounding the element and the force of gravity on the element. In Fig. 1–14(a), by assuming the $z$-axis parallel to the direction of gravity, we may write the equilibrium equation for the element as

$$-\gamma(\delta x \, \delta y \, \delta z)\, \mathbf{k} + (-\mathbf{grad}\, p)\, \delta x \, \delta y \, \delta z = 0 \qquad (1\text{--}52)$$

from which the scalar equations may be written as

$$\frac{\partial p}{\partial x} = 0 \qquad (1\text{--}53\text{a})$$

$$\frac{\partial p}{\partial y} = 0 \tag{1-53b}$$

$$\frac{\partial p}{\partial z} = -\gamma \tag{1-53c}$$

The pressure is thus seen to vary only in the direction of gravity, and to remain constant over any horizontal plane in a fluid at rest. Since $p$ is not a function of $x$ and $y$, the partial differentiation of Eq. 1–53(c) becomes total differentiation:

$$\frac{dp}{dz} = -\gamma \tag{1-54}$$

This equation indicates that within a fluid at rest the pressure increases in the downward direction at the rate equivalent to the specific weight $\gamma$ of the fluid because, in the above derivations, the upward direction of $z$ is considered positive.

If the fluid is incompressible, $\gamma$ becomes a constant quantity and the integration of Eq. 1–54 can be carried out directly, yielding the following hydrostatic equation:

$$p = -\gamma z + \text{constant} \tag{1-55}$$

If the fluid is compressible, we must know something about the behavior of $p$ or $\gamma$ with respect to $z$ before Eq. 1–54 can be integrated.

The following examples will illustrate the engineering applications of the theory of fluid statics.

***Illustrative Example 1-3.*** Determine the pressure difference $p_B - p_A$ from the indicated manometer readings.

*Solution:* In solving this type of problem, we shall make use of the hydrostatic equation (Eq. 1–55). The pressure equation for this manometer system, by starting from $A$, is

$$p_A - \gamma_A(-a) - \gamma_g(-b) - \gamma_g(+c\sin 30°) - \gamma_B(+d\sin 30°) = p_B$$

Hence

$$p_B - p_A = \gamma_A a + \gamma_g(b - c\sin 30°) - \gamma_B(d\sin 30°)$$

The numerical result can be easily calculated by substituting the given data in the accompanying figure into the above equation. Thus,

$$p_B - p_A = 62.4\frac{\text{lbf}}{\text{ft}^3}\left(\frac{10}{12}\text{ft}\right) + 150\frac{\text{lbf}}{\text{ft}^3}\left(\frac{24}{12}\text{ft} - \frac{18}{12}\text{ft}\sin 30°\right)$$
$$- 75\frac{\text{lbf}}{\text{ft}^3}\left(\frac{12}{12}\text{ft}\sin 30°\right)$$

or

$$p_B - p_A = 202.0\frac{\text{lbf}}{\text{ft}^2}$$

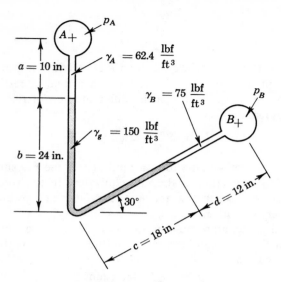

**Illustrative Example 1-3**

***Illustrative Example 1-4.*** The pressure $p_z$ and density $\rho_z$ of the earth's atmosphere at any altitude $z$ are found to vary polytropically in accordance with the following formula:

$$\frac{p_z}{\rho_z^n} = \frac{p_0}{\rho_0^n} = \text{constant} \tag{A}$$

The subscript 0 refers to the altitude at the sea level and $n$ is the polytropic expansion exponent having a numerical value of $n = 1.235$.

The gravitational acceleration $g_z$ at any altitude $z$ varies inversely as the square of the distance from the center of the earth:

$$g_z = \left(\frac{r_e}{r_e + z}\right)^2 g_0 = \frac{g_0}{\left(1 + \dfrac{z}{r_e}\right)^2} \tag{B}$$

where $g_0$ is the standard gravitational acceleration at the sea level, and $r_e$ is the mean radius of the earth having a numerical value of approximately 3960 miles.

Derive an expression relating the pressure $p_z$ and the altitude $z$.

*Solution:* From Eq. (A),

$$\rho_z = \rho_0 \left(\frac{p_z}{p_0}\right)^{1/n} \tag{C}$$

This value is substituted into Eq. 1–54 to obtain the following differential equation:

$$\frac{dp_z}{dz} = -\rho_z g_z = -g_z \rho_0 \left(\frac{p_z}{p_0}\right)^{1/n} \tag{D}$$

If the full expression for $g_z$ is substituted into Eq. (D), the resulting differential equation is difficult to solve. Therefore, we shall restrict ourselves to the condition that $z/r_e$ is small. Then the right-hand side of Eq. (B) can be expanded in a binomial form:

$$g_z = g_0\left(1 + \frac{z}{r_e}\right)^{-2} = g_0\left(1 - \frac{2z}{r_e} + \cdots\right) \tag{E}$$

By introducing this value of $g_z$ into Eq. (D) and then transforming the resulting equation, we have

$$p_z^{-1/n}\,dp_z = -\rho_0 g_0 p_0^{-1/n}\left(1 - \frac{2z}{r_e}\right)dz$$

This equation is to be integrated between the conditions at the sea level and the altitude $z$. The result is

$$\frac{n}{n-1}[p_z^{(n-1)/n} - p_0^{(n-1)/n}] = -\rho_0 g_0 p_0^{-(1/n)}\left[(z - z_0) - \frac{(z - z_0)^2}{r_e}\right]$$

The last term $(z - z_0)^2/r_e$ is the correction factor for the variation of gravitational acceleration.

*Illustrative Example 1-5.* Determine the magnitude, location, and direction of the total force of water pressure on the plane surface area shown in the accompanying figure.

*Solution:* The force $d\mathbf{F}$ on the differential area shown is

$$d\mathbf{F} = \mathbf{k}\gamma_w(8 + y)\cos 30°(10 - y)\,dy \quad \text{lbf}$$

and the total force is then

$$\mathbf{F} = \mathbf{k}\gamma_w \cos 30° \int_0^6 (8 + y)(10 - y)\,dy \quad \text{lbf}$$
$$= \mathbf{k}\,24{,}000 \text{ lbf}$$

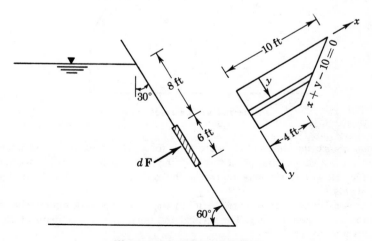

**Illustrative Example 1-5**

with $\gamma_w = 62.4\,\text{lbf/ft}^3$. The direction of **F** is normal to the plane surface as shown.

To find the location of **F**, we need to take moments of forces about the $x$- and $y$-axes. Thus, the moment equation about the $x$-axis yields

$$\bar{y} = \frac{\gamma_w \cos 30° \int_0^6 (8+y)(10-y)\,y\,dy \quad \text{ft-lbf}}{\gamma_w \cos 30° \int_0^6 (8+y)(10-y)\,dy \quad \text{lbf}} = 2.84 \text{ ft}$$

and the moment equation about the $y$-axis yields

$$\bar{x} = \frac{\gamma_w \cos 30° \int_0^6 [8+y][(10-y)^2/2]\,dy \quad \text{ft-lbf}}{\gamma_w \cos 30° \int_0^6 (8+y)(10-y)\,dy \quad \text{lbf}} = 3.58 \text{ ft}$$

***Illustrative Example 1-6.*** Determine the total force of water pressure on the curved surface shown in the accompanying illustration.

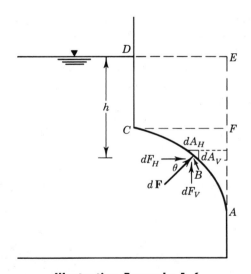

**Illustrative Example 1-6**

*Solution:* Since the differential hydrostatic force $d\mathbf{F}$ acting on the submerged curved surface varies from point to point, the resultant is a system of force and a couple. However, we may represent the resultant by its three orthogonal components.

Let us assume that the curve $\widehat{ABC}$ in the accompanying figure represents the trace of a curved surface. The vertical and horizontal components of $d\mathbf{F}$ are respectively

$$dF_H = dF \sin \theta = p\,dA \sin \theta$$

and
$$dF_V = dF \cos \theta = p \, dA \cos \theta$$
But $p = \gamma h$, where $h$ is the vertical distance of $dA$ below the free water surface, $dA \sin \theta = dA_V$, the vertical projection of $dA$, and $dA \cos \theta = dA_H$, the horizontal projection of $dA$. Therefore,
$$F_H = \int dF_H = \gamma \iint h \, dA_V$$
and
$$F_V = \int dF_V = \gamma \iint h \, dA_H \, .$$
Clearly $F_H$ is the total horizontal force of water pressure on the vertical projection $\overline{AF}$ of the curved surface, and $F_V$ is equivalent to the weight of water in the volume $ABCDEFA$ above the curved surface. The force $F_V$ must act through the center of gravity of the water in the volume $ABCDEFA$.

## PROBLEMS

**1–1.** Verify the dimensions of dynamic viscosity $\mu$ that are given in Table 1–1 by considering Newton's definition of viscosity:
$$\tau = \mu \frac{du}{dy}$$

where $\tau$ is the shear stress;
  $u$ is the velocity of flow in the $x$-direction;
  $y$ is a linear measurement perpendicular to $u$.

**1–2.** We define the Reynolds number $\boldsymbol{R}$ of flow in a pipe as
$$\boldsymbol{R} = \frac{VD\rho}{\mu}$$

where $V$ is the average velocity of flow in the pipe;
  $D$ is the diameter of the pipe;
  $\rho$ is the density of the fluid;
  $\mu$ is the dynamic viscosity of the fluid.
What are the dimensions of $\boldsymbol{R}$?

**1–3.** The partial differential equation for the torsion of a prismatical bar takes the following form:
$$\frac{\partial^2 \phi}{\partial x^2} + \frac{\partial^2 \phi}{\partial y^2} = -2$$

where $\phi$ is the stress function whose gradient is defined as shear stress. What must be the dimensions of the constant $-2$?

**1–4.** The partial differential equation for a vibrating string, shown in Fig. 1–15, is written as
$$a^2 \frac{\partial^2 y}{\partial x^2} = \frac{\partial^2 y}{\partial t^2}$$

where $t$ denotes time. Determine the dimensions for $a$.

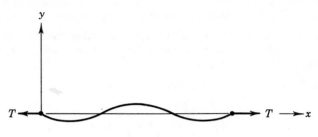

**Fig. 1-15.**

**1-5.** If a 30-newton force is applied to accelerate a mass of 0.8 slug, what is the acceleration of the mass in meters/sec² and ft/sec²?

**1-6.** Air at standard atmospheric pressure and 70°F has a dynamic viscosity $\mu$ of $3.82 \times 10^{-7}$ lbf-sec/ft². Convert this value to poises. 1 poise $\equiv$ 1 dyne-sec/cm². How many stokes of kinematic viscosity does the air have? Kinematic viscosity $\nu$ is defined as $\nu = \mu/\rho$. 1 stoke $\equiv$ 1 cm²/sec.

**1-7.** The temperature $T$ in a flowing fluid at the point $(x, y, z)$ and time $t$ is denoted by $T(x, y, z, t)$. (a) Define the total differential $dT$. (b) What is the physical meaning of $dT/dt$? Of $\partial T/\partial t$? (c) Derive the expression for $dT/dt$ in terms of the velocity components $u$, $v$, $w$, and the partial derivatives of $T$.

**1-8.** The velocity field of a flow is given by the equation:

$$\mathbf{V} = (6xy + 5xt)\mathbf{i} - 3y^2\mathbf{j} + (7xy^2 - 5zt)\mathbf{k}$$

Determine the velocity and acceleration of a fluid particle at position $(2, 1, 4)$ and time $t = 3$.

**1-9.** The $x$-component of velocity of a two-dimensional flow is given by the following equation:

$$u = \ln(x + y^2)$$

Calculate the difference of values of $u$ at the points $(2, 3)$ and $(2.1, 2.9)$ by means of the total differential. Compare the result with the value obtained by subtracting $u$ at $(2, 3)$ from $u$ at $(2.1, 2.9)$.

**1-10.** Given the velocity field of a flow:

$$\mathbf{V} = 3y\mathbf{i} + 2x\mathbf{j} - 5t\mathbf{k}$$

(a) Determine the velocity at position $(3, 1, 2)$ and time $t = 6$. (b) Sketch a set of streamlines for this flow at $t = 0$. (c) Determine the acceleration at position $(3, 1, 2)$ and $t = 6$.

**1-11.** The velocity field of a two-dimensional flow is given as

$$\mathbf{V} = \frac{5\cos\theta}{r^2}\boldsymbol{\epsilon}_r + \frac{5\sin\theta}{r^2}\boldsymbol{\epsilon}_\theta$$

Determine the velocity and acceleration of a fluid particle at position $(x = 3, y = 4)$.

**1–12.** A steady two-dimensional flow about a cylinder of radius $r_0$ is shown in Fig. 1–16. The velocity field of this flow can be written, in cylindrical

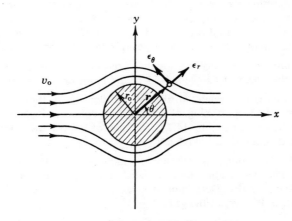

**Fig.   1-16.**

notations, in the following form:

$$\mathbf{V} = V_0\left(1 - \frac{r_0^2}{r^2}\right)\cos\theta\,\boldsymbol{\epsilon}_r - V_0\left(1 + \frac{r_0^2}{r^2}\right)\sin\theta\,\boldsymbol{\epsilon}_\theta$$

where $V_0$ is the uniform velocity of flow which approaches the cylinder. Determine the velocity and acceleration of a fluid particle at ($r = r_0$ and $\theta = \pi/2$).

**1–13.** The equation of the streamlines for a two-dimensional flow is given by

$$\frac{x^2}{2} + xy = C$$

where $C$ is a constant. Determine the velocity and acceleration of a fluid particle at point (2, 3).

**1–14.** Given a two-dimensional velocity field:

$$\mathbf{V} = x^2 y\mathbf{i} - xy^2\mathbf{j}$$

(a) Determine the equation of the streamline passing through the point (3, 2). (b) Determine the velocity and acceleration of a fluid particle at point (3, 2).

**1–15.** Calculate the vorticity and the mean rates of rotation of a fluid element in the flow field of Problem 1–14 at point (3, 2).

**1–16.** Given a velocity field:

$$\mathbf{V} = (3x^2 - 2xy)\mathbf{i} + (y^2 - 6xy + 3yz^2)\mathbf{j} - (z^3 + xy^2)\mathbf{k}$$

(a) Determine the vorticity and the mean rates of rotation of a fluid element at position (2, 3, 1). (b) Determine the velocity and acceleration of a fluid particle at position (2, 3, 1).

**1-17.** For a flow with the following velocity field:

$$\mathbf{V} = (5t^2 + 3t)\mathbf{i} + (y^2 - z^2 + 1)\mathbf{j} - (2yz + y)\mathbf{k}$$

(a) Determine the vorticity and the mean rates of rotation of a fluid element at position (4, 2, 5) and time $t = 3$. (b) Identify the surface on which this flow is always irrotational. (c) Determine the velocity and acceleration of a fluid particle at position (4, 2, 5) and time $t = 3$.

**1-18.** Determine the vorticity and the mean rates of rotation of a fluid element in the flow field of Problem 1-11 at the point ($x = 3, y = 4$).

**1-19.** Calculate (a) the weight, in lbf, (b) the density, in lbm/ft³, and (c) the specific volume, in ft³/slug, of one cubic foot of air at 70°F and a standard atmospheric pressure of 14.7 lbf/in². abs. at a position where $g$ has its standard value of 32.174 ft/sec².

**1-20.** A tank has a volume of 8 ft³ and contains a gas with a molecular weight of 24. The temperature and pressure of the gas are, respectively, 80°F and 20 lbf/in². abs. Determine the density, in slugs/ft³, and the specific volume, in ft³/lbm, of the gas.

**1-21.** Calculate the temperature, on a Fahrenheit scale, of 15 lbm of air in a 11.5 ft³ container under a pressure of 250 lbf/in² abs.

**1-22.** If the pressure $p$ is expressed in dynes/cm² and the density $\rho$ in gm/cm³, the experimental value of $\rho$ for air at 273°K is found to be

$$\rho = 1.276\,p \times 10^{-9}$$

Calculate the value of $R$ for air in the ft-lbm-sec-°R system of units.

**1-23.** In Fig. 1-17, a 3 ft × 3 ft square plate is allowed to slide down a long inclined surface on which there is a film of oil, 0.005 in. thick. The plate weighs 40 lbf. Estimate the dynamic viscosity of the oil if the terminal speed of the sliding plate is 2 ft/sec.

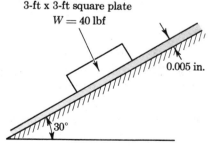

3-ft x 3-ft square plate
$W = 40\ \text{lbf}$

0.005 in.

30°

**Fig.  1-17.**

**1-24.** The diameters of a shaft and its sleeve are respectively 3.00 and 3.02 in., and the length of the sleeve is 12 in. If the space between the shaft and its sleeve is filled with a lubricating oil having a dynamic viscosity $\mu =$ 0.0002 lbf-sec/ft², what power is required to overcome viscous resistance when the shaft is rotated at a constant angular speed of 600 rpm?

1–25. The rotating cone shown in Fig. 1–18 has a 6-in. diameter at the base and is 8 in. high. A film of oil fills the 0.005 in. clearance between the

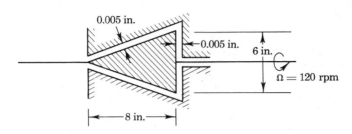

**Fig.  1-18.**

cone and its container. The oil has a dynamic viscosity $\mu = 3.7 \times 10^{-5}$ lbf-sec/ft². Calculate the torque required to rotate this cone at a constant angular speed of 120 rpm relative to its container.

1–26. The velocity profile of an oil flow in a round pipe is given by the following formula:

$$v_z = \frac{A}{4\mu}\left(\frac{D^2}{4} - r^2\right)$$

where $A$ is a constant;
    $r$ is the radial distance from the pipe axis;
    $v_z$ is the velocity at position $r$;
    $D$ is the diameter of the pipe.
For the given numerical values in Fig. 1–19, calculate (a) the shear stress at the pipe wall, and (b) the shear stress at $r = D/8$.

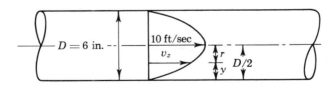

**Fig.  1-19.**

1–27. Estimate the increase of pressure required to reduce a given volume of water by 0.5 per cent.

1–28. A gas obeys the van der Waal's equation of state:

$$\left(p + \frac{a}{v^2}\right)(v - b) = RT$$

Calculate its value of $E_{\text{isothermal}}$ in terms of $a$, $b$, $p$ and $v$.

**1-29.** Write the vector which represents the triangular area $ABC$ shown in Fig. 1-20. What are the direction cosines of the area $ABC$?

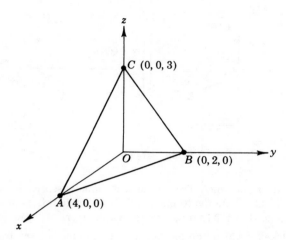

**Fig. 1-20.**

**1-30.** In the special case of a two-dimensional flow, the normal and shear stresses $\sigma_{zz}$, $\tau_{xz}$, $\tau_{yz}$, $\tau_{zx}$, and $\tau_{zy}$ in the $z$-direction are all zero. The data given at the point shown in Fig. 1-21 are:

$$\sigma_{xx} = -200 \text{ lbf/in}^2$$
$$\sigma_{yy} = 500 \text{ lbf/in}^2$$
$$\tau_{xy} = \tau_{yx} = 80 \text{ lbf/in}^2$$

Determine the normal stress $\sigma_{nn}$.

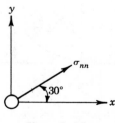

**Fig. 1-21.**

**1-31.** The stress field of a fluid flow is given as

$$\begin{pmatrix} 5x + 7y^2 & -6x^2 & 0 \\ -6x^2 & 9xy - 4y^2 & 0 \\ 0 & 0 & 0 \end{pmatrix}$$

Determine the scalar average normal stress field and the average normal stress at position (3, 2, 1) in this flow field.

**1–32.** If $\mathbf{\Phi}$ is a dyad and $\mathbf{V}$ is a vector, show that

$$\nabla(\mathbf{V\Phi}) = \mathbf{V}\nabla\mathbf{\Phi} + (\mathbf{\Phi}\nabla)\mathbf{V}$$

**1–33.** What is the pressure at $A$ shown in Fig. 1–22?

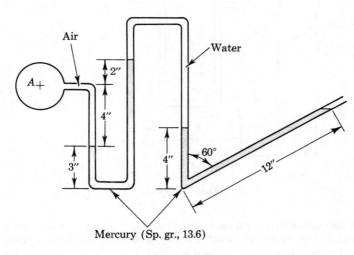

**Fig. 1-22.**

**1–34.** The two air tanks shown in Fig. 1–23 are air-tight. The pressure gage at

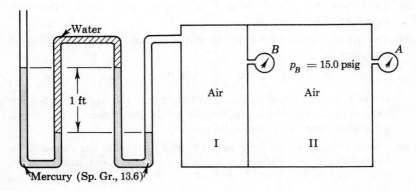

**Fig. 1-23.**

*B* reads 15.0 lbf/in². The local barometric pressure is 30.0 in. of mercury. Determine (a) the absolute pressures of air in tanks I and II, and (b) the gage reading at *A*.

**1–35.** What are the respective gage pressures in the containers *A* and *B* in Fig. 1–24?

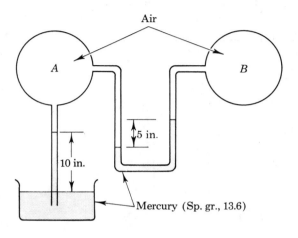

**Fig. 1-24.**

**1–36.** A cubical tank, 3 ft on each side, contains 1.5 ft of mercury and 1 ft of water. If the tank is open to the atmosphere at the top, find the total force and the position of the resultant force on each side. The specific gravity of mercury is 13.6.

**1–37.** Determine the total force and the position of the resultant force on the triangular surface shown in Fig. 1–25.

**1–38.** Solve Problem 1–37 if the base of the triangle is at the top and the vertex at the bottom.

**1–39.** The specific weight $\gamma$ of the liquid, shown in Fig. 1–26, varies with depth according to

$$\gamma = 60 + \frac{h}{4} \quad (\text{lbf/ft}^3)$$

where $h$ is the vertical distance, in feet, below the free liquid surface. Determine the magnitude and location of the total force on the vertical rectangular gate due to the liquid pressure.

**1–40.** Derive an equation for the pressure $p_z$ as a function of the altitude $z$ for an isothermal atmosphere in a uniform gravitational field. Assume $p_z = p_0$ at $z = 0$.

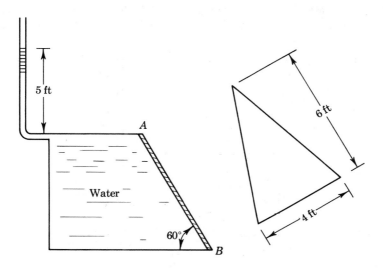

**Fig.   1-25.**

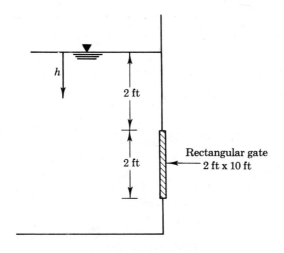

**Fig.   1-26.**

**1–41.** Verify Archimedes' principle of buoyancy of a submerged object by considering the pressure forces on the surfaces of the object.

**1–42.** A 500-lbf circular lid covers a 3-ft diameter hole on the top of a closed tank, as shown in Fig. 1–27. An open manometer tube is tapped into the

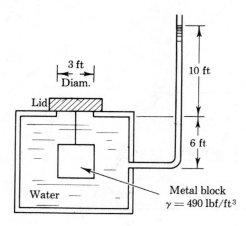

**Fig.   1-27.**

side of the tank, and water rises to a height of 16 ft. A metal block is suspended from the lid to hold it in place. Determine the minimum volume of the block if the specific weight of the metal is 490 lbf/ft³.

**1–43.** Find the total force of water pressure on the curved surface $AB$ shown in Fig. 1–28.

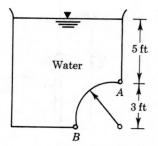

The tank is 4 feet wide
perpendicular to the paper.

**Fig.   1-28.**

**1–44.** A solid cylinder of circular cross section is used as an automatic gate as shown in Fig. 1–29. The cylindrical gate opens by turning about its hinge

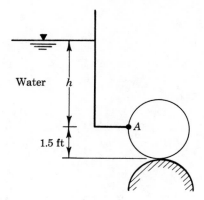

**Fig.   1-29.**

at $A$. If the homogeneous cylindrical gate weighs 800 lbf per foot of its length, what is the maximum depth $h$ of water in the reservoir without causing the gate to open?

# 2 Basic Laws of Fluid Flow

## 2-1 System, Control Volume, and Control Surface

Whenever basic laws are used in the analysis of physical problems, it is necessary that these laws be stated in terms of a "system" or a "control volume."

A *system* is defined as a quantity of matter of fixed mass and identity. This definition of system corresponds to the so-called "closed system" in thermodynamics. The quantity of matter in a system must be confined within a prescibed boundary which may be rigid, deformable, or even imaginary. Everything external to the system is referred to as the *surroundings*. In solving physical problems we frequently focus our attention on the system and then observe interactions between the system and the surroundings, because such interactions will affect the behavior of the system.

A system may change its shape, position, and thermodynamic properties, but it must always contain the same matter. Figure 2–1 illustrates a system, for the gas contained in the closed cylinder has a fixed quantity and identity. If a heater is placed near the cylinder, the temperature of the gas inside the cylinder will increase and the piston will move outward.

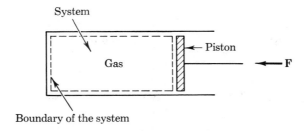

**Fig. 2-1.** Example of a system.

The shape of the system changes and the internal energy of the system increases, but the matter contained in the system is fixed.

The most important first step in the successful solution of a physical problem is the careful selection and identification of the system to be considered. For example, let us consider the application of Newton's second law of motion: $\mathbf{F} = D(m\mathbf{V})/Dt$. This law must be applied to a distinct system in a given inertial reference, because $\mathbf{F}$ is the resultant force exerted by all the surroundings on the system; $m$ is the mass of the system, and $D(m\mathbf{V})/Dt$ is the time rate of momentum change experienced by the mass of the system as a result of the interaction between the system and its surroundings. Without the clear-cut identification of a distinct system to which the motion equation is applied, the equation itself becomes meaningless.

Now, in fluid flow problems, because fluids are extremely mobile, we experience difficulties in identifying the boundaries of a fluid system for any appreciable length of time. For example, in the case of flow through a turbojet engine, the fluid particles passing through the engine follow rather different and complicated paths. We soon lose track of the fluid particles that were originally in the chosen system. In dealing with fluid mechanics problems it is, therefore, more convenient to consider a control volume which has a fixed volume in space and through which fluid flows. The amount and identity of the fluid occupying the control volume may change from instant to instant, but the size and shape of the control volume remain invariant with time.

The boundary of a control volume is called the *control surface*. Hence the size and shape of the control surface must also remain invariant with time. A control surface is always a closed surface. For example, in order to study the flow of fluid through a divergent duct in which there is a fan, as shown in Fig. 2-2, we could choose as a control volume the interior of the duct (excluding the fan).

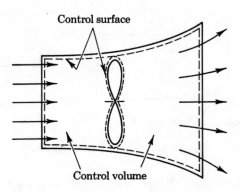

**Fig. 2-2.** Example of a control volume.

## 2-2　Connection Between the System Approach and the Control Volume Approach

In Fig. 2–3 the streamlines represent a flow field with $\mathbf{V} = \mathbf{V}(x, y, z, t)$ at time $t$, the solid closed curve represents a control surface, and the two dotted closed curves represent the boundaries of a system of fluid of mass $m$ at time $t$ and $t + \delta t$, respectively. At time $t$ the system under consideration is the fluid inside the control volume. Let $B$ denote the total quantity of some arbitrary property of fluid flow, such as mass, momentum, energy, etc., in the fluid of the system, and let $b$ denote its magnitude per unit mass, such that $B = \iiint\limits_{\text{system}} b\rho \, d\mathcal{V}$, where $d\mathcal{V}$ is an element of volume of the system. In thermodynamics $B$, whose measure depends on the amount of substance present in the system, is called an *extensive property*, and $b$, whose measure is independent of the amount of substance present in the system, is called an *intensive property*. Examples of extensive properties are the total weight, momentum, energy, etc., of the system. A change in the amount of mass in the system will directly change the quantities of these extensive properties. For each of these extensive properties we assign an intensive property in terms of a distributive measure, such as weight per unit mass, momentum per unit mass, energy per unit mass, etc. We call these distributive quantities specific quantities, such as specific weight, specific momentum, specific energy, etc. In addition, such properties as temperature and pressure are by their mass-independent nature also intensive properties.

We now relate the rate of change of $B$ for the system and the rate of

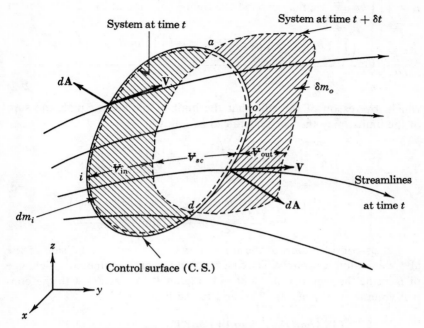

**Fig. 2-3.** Flow of fluid through a control volume.

change of $B$ associated with the control volume of Fig. 2–3 by first denoting $B_t$ and $B_{t+\delta t}$ as the total quantities of $B$ in the system at times $t$ and $t + \delta t$, respectively. Then

$$\left(\frac{dB}{dt}\right)_{\text{system}} = \frac{DB}{Dt} = \lim_{\delta t \to 0} \frac{B_{t+\delta t} - B_t}{\delta t} \tag{2–1}$$

Let us consider the flow through the control volume. Part of fluid mass $\delta m_o$ has moved out of the control volume through the part of the control surface which is shown as $\widehat{aod}$ in Fig. 2–3 during the time interval $\delta t$. Since the fluid medium is continuous, the control volume must be completely filled with fluid at all times. Hence fluid mass $\delta m_i$ has immediately moved into the control volume through the remaining portion of the control surface $\widehat{aid}$ during $\delta t$ to fill the vacated part of the control volume. We have divided the volume which is occupied by the system at both times $t$ and $t + \delta t$ into three regions which are labeled as $V_{\text{in}}$, $V_{SC}$, and $V_{\text{out}}$. The volume $V_{SC}$ inside the control volume is occupied by the system at both times $t$ and $t + \delta t$.

Referring to the three regions in Fig. 2–3 and recalling that

$B = \iiint\limits_{\text{system}} b\rho \, d\mathcal{V}$, we may expand the right-hand side of Eq. 2–1 to obtain

$$\frac{DB}{Dt} = \lim_{\delta t \to 0} \frac{\left( \iiint\limits_{\mathcal{V}_{out}} b\rho \, d\mathcal{V} + \iiint\limits_{\mathcal{V}_{SC}} b\rho \, d\mathcal{V} \right)_{t+\delta t} - \left( \iiint\limits_{\mathcal{V}_{in}} b\rho \, d\mathcal{V} + \iiint\limits_{\mathcal{V}_{SC}} b\rho \, d\mathcal{V} \right)_t}{\delta t}$$

(2–2)

which, by reason of the rule that the limit of the sums equals the sum of the limits, may then be rearranged as follows:

$$\frac{DB}{Dt} = \lim_{\delta t \to 0} \frac{\left( \iiint\limits_{\mathcal{V}_{SC}} b\rho \, d\mathcal{V} \right)_{t+\delta t} - \left( \iiint\limits_{\mathcal{V}_{SC}} b\rho \, d\mathcal{V} \right)_t}{\delta t}$$

(2–3)

$$+ \lim_{\delta t \to 0} \frac{\left( \iiint\limits_{\mathcal{V}_{out}} b\rho \, d\mathcal{V} \right)_{t+\delta t}}{\delta t} - \lim_{\delta t \to 0} \frac{\left( \iiint\limits_{\mathcal{V}_{in}} b\rho \, d\mathcal{V} \right)_t}{\delta t}$$

Let us consider each of the three terms on the right-hand side of the above equation separately. The first term represents the time rate of change of $B$ inside the region $\mathcal{V}_{SC}$. As $\delta t \to 0$, region $\mathcal{V}_{SC}$ coincides with the control volume (C.V.) of Fig. 2–3, and in the limit we have

$$\lim_{\delta t \to 0} \frac{\left( \iiint\limits_{\mathcal{V}_{SC}} b\rho \, d\mathcal{V} \right)_{t+\delta t} - \left( \iiint\limits_{\mathcal{V}_{SC}} b\rho \, d\mathcal{V} \right)_t}{\delta t} = \frac{\partial}{\partial t} \iiint\limits_{\text{C.V.}} b\rho \, d\mathcal{V}$$

(2–4)

where the integral $\iiint\limits_{\text{C.V.}} b\rho \, d\mathcal{V}$ is the instantaneous amount of $B$ inside the control volume at time $t$. In the second term the integral

$$\left( \iiint\limits_{\mathcal{V}_{out}} b\rho \, d\mathcal{V} \right)_{t+\delta t}$$

represents the amount of $B$ that has moved out of the control volume through $\overset{\frown}{aod}$ during $\delta t$, and the ratio

$$\frac{\left( \iiint\limits_{\mathcal{V}_{out}} b\rho \, d\mathcal{V} \right)_{t+\delta t}}{\delta t}$$

is then the average rate of efflux of $B$ across $\overset{\frown}{aod}$ during $\delta t$. In the limit as $\delta t \to 0$, this ratio becomes the instantaneous rate of efflux of $B$ through $\overset{\frown}{aod}$ at time $t$. Similarly, the last term of Eq. 2–3, in the limit as $\delta t \to 0$, becomes the instantaneous rate of influx of $B$ into the control volume through $\overset{\frown}{aid}$ at time $t$. Thus, the last two terms of Eq. 2–3 account for the flow of $B$ across the entire control surface at time $t$. For detailed calculations, these two flux terms can be written in a working form in the following manner. Let $dA$ denote an area element of the control surface. The vector representing $dA$ points outward from the enclosed control volume. Then $\rho V \cdot dA$ is the mass efflux through $dA$ per unit time, and $b\rho V \cdot dA$ becomes the efflux of $B$ through $dA$ per unit time. Integrating for the entire control surface (C.S.) of Fig. 2–3, we have

$$
\begin{array}{l}
\text{Efflux of } B \text{ from the} \\
\text{control volume through} \\
\text{the control surface}
\end{array}
= \lim_{\delta t \to 0} \frac{\left( \iiint_{\Psi_{\text{out}}} b\rho \, d\Psi \right)_{t+\delta t}}{\delta t} - \lim_{\delta t \to 0} \frac{\left( \iiint_{\Psi_{\text{in}}} b\rho \, d\Psi \right)_{t}}{\delta t}
$$

$$
= \oiint_{\text{C.S.}} b\rho \, V \cdot dA \qquad (2\text{-}5)
$$

where the symbol $\oiint_{\text{C.S.}}$ denotes surface integration over the entire control surface. In evaluating the surface integral in Eq. 2–5, we must observe the directions of the $V$ and $dA$ vectors. Over the portion of a control surface, such as $\widehat{aod}$ of Fig. 2–3, where fluid flows out of the control volume, the velocity vector points outward from the control surface and the dot product $V \cdot dA$ is positive, thus giving a positive contribution to the surface integration. On the other hand, over the portion of a control surface, such as $\widehat{aid}$ of Fig. 2–3, where fluid flows into the control volume, the velocity vector points inward to the control volume, the dot product $V \cdot dA$ is negative, and this part of surface integration gives a negative contribution.

Substituting Eqs. 2–4 and 2–5 into Eq. 2–3, we finally obtain the following mathematical expression which relates the system approach and the control volume approach for any property $B$ of fluid flow:

$$
\frac{DB}{Dt} = \oiint_{\text{C.S.}} b(\rho V \cdot dA) + \frac{\partial}{\partial t} \iiint_{\text{C.V.}} b\rho \, d\Psi \qquad (2\text{-}6)
$$

| Rate of change of $B$ for a system at time $t$ | Rate of efflux of $B$ across the control surface at time $t$ | Rate of change of $B$ inside a control volume which coincides with the system at time $t$ |

Equation 2–6 is frequently called the *transformation law* between the system approach and the control volume approach. We shall make use of this law in deriving fundamental equations of fluid flow in the following sections of this chapter. These equations form the basis of the analytical work in fluid mechanics.

## 2-3  Conservation of Mass Flow—Equation of Continuity

When the law of conservation of mass flow is applied to the flow through a control volume, experimental observations indicate that, in the absence of relativity and nuclear effects, the net rate of mass efflux from the control volume through its entire control surface equals the rate of decrease of mass inside the control volume.

We shall derive a mathematical expression for this statement by first considering conservation of mass of the system which occupies the control volume at time $t$, as shown in Fig. 2–3. Then we employ the transformation law (Eq. 2–6) to change the system approach to the control volume approach in exactly the same way as we did previously.

By definition the total mass $m$ of the system in Fig. 2–3 must remain invariant with respect to time, i.e.,

$$\left(\frac{dm}{dt}\right)_{\text{system}} = \frac{Dm}{Dt} = 0 \tag{2–7}$$

Since $m = \iiint\limits_{\text{system}} \rho \, d\mathcal{V}$, the intensive property $b$ is unity for this case. By using Eq. 2–6, the mathematical equation for conservation of mass flow through the control volume of Fig. 2–3 at time $t$ becomes

$$\frac{Dm}{Dt} = \oiint\limits_{\text{C.S.}} \rho \mathbf{V} \cdot d\mathbf{A} + \frac{\partial}{\partial t} \iiint\limits_{\text{C.V.}} \rho \, d\mathcal{V} = 0 \tag{2–8}$$

which can then be rearranged in a more meaningful form as:

$$\underbrace{\oiint\limits_{\text{C.S.}} \rho \mathbf{V} \cdot d\mathbf{A}}_{\substack{\text{Net rate of mass} \\ \text{efflux through the} \\ \text{control surface at} \\ \text{time } t}} = \underbrace{-\frac{\partial}{\partial t} \iiint\limits_{\text{C.V.}} \rho \, d\mathcal{V}}_{\substack{\text{Rate of decrease of} \\ \text{mass inside the con-} \\ \text{trol volume at time } t}} \tag{2–8a}$$

The above equation and its many alternate forms are called the *equation of continuity*, which states that in a fluid flow matter is neither created nor annihilated within any volume of fixed size at any time.

The integration operations in Eq. 2–8a are indeed complicated and are, therefore, seldom carried out in their original forms. In actual calculations we divide the control surface into two parts, $A_i$ and $A_o$, which correspond to $\widehat{aid}$ and $\widehat{aod}$, respectively, of the the control surface in Fig. 2–3. By using subscripts $i$ and $o$ for conditions at inlet and outlet areas respectively, Eq. 2–8a becomes

$$\oiint\limits_{\text{C.S.}} \rho \mathbf{V} \cdot dA = \iint\limits_{A_i} \rho_i \mathbf{V}_i \cdot d\mathbf{A}_i + \iint\limits_{A_o} \rho_o \mathbf{V}_o \cdot d\mathbf{A}_o = -\frac{\partial}{\partial t} \iiint\limits_{\text{C.V.}} \rho \, d\mathcal{V}$$

$$\tag{2–8b}$$

Denoting $V_{\text{in}}$ and $V_{\text{on}}$ as velocity components normal to $dA_i$ and $dA_o$, respectively, and employing the previously discussed sign convention of using an outward vector to represent an area, we may rewrite Eq. 2–8b in the following scalar form:

$$-\iint\limits_{A_i} \rho_i V_{\text{in}}\, dA_i + \iint\limits_{A_o} \rho_o V_{\text{on}}\, dA_o = -\frac{\partial}{\partial t} \iiint\limits_{\text{C.V.}} \rho\, d\mathcal{V} \qquad \text{(2–8c)}$$

A simplified form of the equation of continuity can be obtained when the fluid flow satisfies either one of the following restrictions:

1. When the flow field is steady with respect to a reference fixed to the control volume, all fluid properties at any fixed position in the reference must remain unchanged at all times. Clearly the total mass inside the control volume remains invariant with time, and the right-hand side of Eq. 2–8a vanishes. The equation of continuity then takes the following simplified form:

$$\oiint\limits_{\text{C.S.}} \rho \mathbf{V} \cdot d\mathbf{A} = 0 \qquad \text{(2–9)}$$

This equation simply states that, for a control volume in a steady flow field, the incoming and outgoing rates of mass flow are identical at all times, i.e.,

$$\iint\limits_{A_i} \rho_i V_{\text{in}}\, dA_i = \iint\limits_{A_o} \rho_o V_{\text{on}}\, dA_o \qquad \text{(2–9a)}$$

2. If the fluid is incompressible and homogeneous, $\rho$ is constant at all positions in the flow field and at all times even though the velocity field may be unsteady. The right-hand term in Eq. 2–8a again becomes zero, and in the remaining surface integration term we can extract the constant $\rho$ from under the surface integral sign to obtain

$$\oiint\limits_{\text{C.S.}} \mathbf{V} \cdot d\mathbf{A} = 0 \qquad \text{(2–10)}$$

This equation indicates that, for an incompressible flow of a homogeneous fluid, conservation of mass flow is degenerated to conservation of volume flow. The scalar form of Eq. 2–10 is

$$\iint\limits_{A_i} V_{\text{in}}\, dA_i = \iint\limits_{A_o} V_{\text{on}}\, dA_o \qquad \text{(2–10a)}$$

**One-dimensional steady flow.** The essential assumption of one-dimensional steady flow is that all fluid properties and flow characteristics are expressible as functions of position along some flow passage. For example, in the steady flow through a device shown in Fig. 2–4, fluid enters the device through a pipe of area $A_i$ and leaves the device through a second pipe of area $A_o$. If the velocities are normal to the control surfaces at these areas, and both $\rho$ and $V$ are constant over each cross section, integration of Eq. 2–9a yields the following equation of continuity for one-dimensional steady flow:

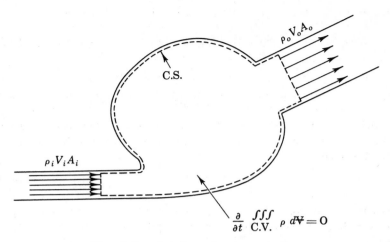

**Fig. 2-4.** One-dimensional steady flow.

$$\rho_i V_i A_i = \rho_o V_o A_o \qquad (2\text{–}11)$$

If the fluid is incompressible and homogeneous, $\rho_i = \rho_o$ and the above equation is further reduced to

$$V_i A_i = V_o A_o \qquad (2\text{–}12)$$

Both Eqs. 2–11 and 2–12 are of great practical utility for the calculation of steady flow problems which are of one-dimensional type.

## 2-4  Equation of Continuity in Differential Form

We use Gauss' theorem to transform the surface integration term of Eq. 2–8 to a volume integration:

$$\oiint_{\text{C.S.}} \rho \mathbf{V} \cdot d\mathbf{A} = \iiint_{\text{C.V.}} (\mathbf{\nabla} \cdot \rho \mathbf{V}) \, d\mathcal{V} \qquad (2\text{–}13)$$

in which, $(\mathbf{\nabla} \cdot \rho \mathbf{V})$ represents the rate of efflux of mass per unit volume. Therefore, Eq. 2–8 becomes

$$\iiint_{\text{C.V.}} \left[ (\mathbf{\nabla} \cdot \rho \mathbf{V}) + \frac{\partial \rho}{\partial t} \right] d\mathcal{V} = 0 \qquad (2\text{–}14)$$

since the control volume does not vary with time. Equation 2–14 holds for any volume; hence the integrand must vanish; i.e.,

$$\mathbf{\nabla} \cdot \rho \mathbf{V} + \frac{\partial \rho}{\partial t} = 0 \qquad (2\text{–}15)$$

This is the differential equation of continuity describing the conservation

[§ 2-4]      BASIC LAWS OF FLUID FLOW      65

of mass flow at any point in a flow field. We may expand the divergence term to rewrite the above equation in an alternate form as

$$\rho \mathbf{\nabla} \cdot \mathbf{V} + \mathbf{V} \cdot (\mathbf{\nabla} \rho) + \frac{\partial \rho}{\partial t} = \rho \mathbf{\nabla} \cdot \mathbf{V} + \frac{D\rho}{Dt} = 0 \qquad \textbf{(2–15a)}$$

For steady flow the term $\partial \rho / \partial t$ vanishes so that the divergence of $\rho \mathbf{V}$ vector must everywhere be equal to zero; i.e.,

$$\mathbf{\nabla} \cdot \rho \mathbf{V} = \rho \mathbf{\nabla} \cdot \mathbf{V} + \mathbf{V} \cdot (\mathbf{\nabla} \rho) = 0 \qquad \textbf{(2–16)}$$

In an incompressible flow of a homogeneous fluid, $\rho$ is constant with respect to both position and time and the continuity equation can be further simplified to the following form:

$$\mathbf{\nabla} \cdot \mathbf{V} = 0 \qquad \textbf{(2–17)}$$

As will be shown in later chapters, any mathematical function which represents a possible case of flow must satisfy Eq. 2–15 everywhere in the flow field except at a point of discontinuity where the derivatives are not defined. However, in analyzing flow conditions in the neighborhood of a point of discontinuity, one may apply Eq. 2–8a, which is essentially an integral equation of continuity, to a control volume containing the point of discontinuity.

Equation 2–15 is a vector equation. For convenience of reference, we shall express it in scalar forms in the three most commonly used coordinate systems as shown in Fig. 1–5.

In Cartesian coordinates $(x, y, z)$, $\mathbf{V} = u\mathbf{i} + v\mathbf{j} + w\mathbf{k}$, and Eq. 2–15 can be written as

$$\frac{\partial}{\partial x}(\rho u) + \frac{\partial}{\partial y}(\rho v) + \frac{\partial}{\partial z}(\rho w) + \frac{\partial \rho}{\partial t} = 0 \qquad \textbf{(2–18)}$$

In cylindrical coordinates $(r, \theta, z)$, $\mathbf{V} = v_r \boldsymbol{\epsilon}_r + v_\theta \boldsymbol{\epsilon}_\theta + v_z \boldsymbol{\epsilon}_z$, and Eq. 2–15 becomes

$$\frac{1}{r}\frac{\partial}{\partial r}(r\rho v_r) + \frac{1}{r}\frac{\partial}{\partial \theta}(\rho v_\theta) + \frac{\partial}{\partial z}(\rho v_z) + \frac{\partial \rho}{\partial t} = 0 \qquad \textbf{(2–19)}$$

Finally in the spherical coordinate system $(R, \theta, \phi)$ of Fig. 1–5(c), the scalar form of Eq. 2–15 is

$$\frac{1}{R^2}\frac{\partial}{\partial R}(R^2 \rho v_R) + \frac{1}{R \sin \theta}\frac{\partial}{\partial \theta}(\rho v_\theta \sin \theta) + \frac{1}{R \sin \theta}\frac{\partial}{\partial \phi}(\rho v_\phi) + \frac{\partial \rho}{\partial t} = 0$$

$$\textbf{(2–20)}$$

*Illustrative Example 2–1.* In a steady two-dimensional flow of an incompressible fluid, the radial component of velocity is

$$v_r = -\frac{A \cos \theta}{r^2}$$

where $A$ is a constant. Determine $v_\theta$, the tangential component of velocity.

*Solution:* Since the velocity components are expressed in cylindrical polar coordinates, the proper form of the continuity equation for this two-dimensional flow can be obtained from Eq. 2–19 as

$$\frac{\partial (rv_r)}{\partial r} + \frac{\partial v_\theta}{\partial \theta} = 0$$

from which

$$\frac{\partial v_\theta}{\partial \theta} = -\frac{\partial (rv_r)}{\partial r} = -\frac{\partial}{\partial r}\left(-\frac{A \cos\theta}{r}\right) = -\frac{A \cos\theta}{r^2}$$

Hence

$$v_\theta = \int -\frac{A \cos\theta}{r^2}\,\partial\theta = -\frac{A \sin\theta}{r^2} + f(r)$$

The constant of integration could be a function of $r$, that is, $f(r)$.

## 2-5   Conservation of Momentum—Momentum Equations

Newton's second law of motion:

$$\mathbf{F} = \frac{D(m\mathbf{V})}{Dt} \tag{2–21}$$

is a vector equation relating the total force $\mathbf{F}$ which acts on a body of mass $m$ and the resulting rate of change of momentum $D(m\mathbf{V})/Dt$ of the same body in a given inertial reference. Equation 2–21 may be expanded as follows:

$$\mathbf{F} = \frac{D(m\mathbf{V})}{Dt} = m\frac{D\mathbf{V}}{Dt} + \mathbf{V}\frac{Dm}{Dt} = m\,\mathbf{a}_{\text{abs}} + \mathbf{V}\frac{Dm}{Dt} \tag{2–21a}$$

We use the notation $\mathbf{a}_{\text{abs}}$ to denote "absolute acceleration" in order to emphasize that, in using Newton's law, the motion must be measured relative to an inertial reference as specified in Galilean-Newtonian mechanics. If the acceleration of the body being studied is measured relative to a noninertial reference, as, for example, when it is expressed with respect to a coordinate system which is attached to an accelerating and rolling space vehicle streaming around the globe, it must first be referred to an inertial reference before we can use it in Eq. 2–21a. Kinematic relations between motions in different references can be found in any mechanics textbook. First we shall study momentum equations of fluid flow in an inertial reference.

## 2-6   Momentum Equation for a Control Volume in an Inertial Reference

Let us consider a finite fluid system, such as the one shown in Fig. 2–5, moving in a flow field relative to an inertial reference. Since momentum of an element of fluid mass $\rho\,d\mathcal{V}$ inside the system is defined as $\mathbf{V}\rho\,d\mathcal{V}$, the total momentum $\mathbf{P}$ of the system at time $t$ is

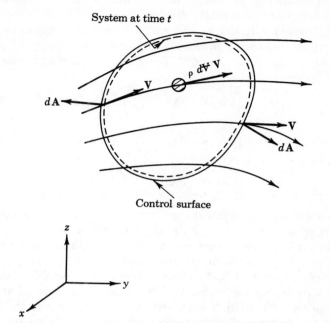

**Fig. 2-5.** Flow of fluid through a control volume which is either fixed in, or translating at a constant velocity relative to, the inertial system (x, y, z).

$$\mathbf{P} = \iiint_{\text{system}} \mathbf{V}\rho \, d\mathcal{V} \qquad (2\text{--}22)$$

and the momentum equation for the system then becomes

$$\mathbf{F} = \frac{D\mathbf{P}}{Dt} = \frac{D}{Dt} \iiint_{\text{system}} \mathbf{V}\rho \, d\mathcal{V} \qquad (2\text{--}23)$$

where $\mathbf{F}$ is the resultant of all body forces and surface forces exerted by the surroundings on the system.

Applying the transformation law (Eq. 2–6) to the extensive property $\mathbf{P}$ in the above equation and recognizing that in this case the intensive property is $\mathbf{V}$, we have

$$\mathbf{F} = \frac{D\mathbf{P}}{Dt} = \oiint_{\text{c.s.}} \mathbf{V}(\rho \mathbf{V} \cdot d\mathbf{A}) + \frac{\partial}{\partial t} \iiint_{\text{c.v.}} \mathbf{V}\rho \, d\mathcal{V} \qquad (2\text{--}24)$$

Net rate of efflux of momentum through the control surface at time $t$    Rate of change of momentum inside the control volume at time $t$

which is the desired momentum equation for fluid flow through a control volume in an inertial reference. Both **F** and **V** in this equation are measured relative to an inertial reference.

In engineering calculations the scalar momentum equations in the orthogonal $x$-, $y$-, and $z$-directions are formed by simply taking the components of the vectors **F** and **V**. Therefore, the Cartesian components of Eq. 2–24 are:

$$F_x = \oiint_{\text{C.S.}} u(\rho \mathbf{V} \cdot d\mathbf{A}) + \frac{\partial}{\partial t} \iiint_{\text{C.V.}} u\rho \, d\mathcal{V} \qquad (2\text{–}25\text{a})$$

$$F_y = \oiint_{\text{C.S.}} v(\rho \mathbf{V} \cdot d\mathbf{A}) + \frac{\partial}{\partial t} \iiint_{\text{C.V.}} v\rho \, d\mathcal{V} \qquad (2\text{–}25\text{b})$$

$$F_z = \oiint_{\text{C.S.}} w(\rho \mathbf{V} \cdot d\mathbf{A}) + \frac{\partial}{\partial t} \iiint_{\text{C.V.}} w\rho \, d\mathcal{V} \qquad (2\text{–}25\text{c})$$

in which there are two different sign conventions for the different terms. The signs of $u$, $v$, $w$, and $F_x$, $F_y$, $F_z$ depend on the positive directions chosen for the $x$-, $y$-, and $z$-axes, respectively. The sign for the dot product **V** · $d\mathbf{A}$ depends on the local orientation of the control surface relative to the velocity vector at that surface element. To exemplify this, let us consider a rocket engine bolted to a test stand (Fig. 2–6) so as to fire in the negative $z$-direction. The control surface extends over the exhaust area. The rate of mass efflux for the control surface at the rocket exhaust is simply $+ \rho_e V_e A_e$, because at the exhaust both **V** and **A** vectors are in the same direction. On the other hand, the velocity component $w$ in the integration over the control surface is given by $- V_e$, since it is directed in the negative $z$-direction of the chosen coordinate system shown. Thus the surface integration over the exhaust area yields $(- V_e)(+ \rho_e V_e A_e)$. All the forces shown in Fig. 2–6 have negative signs.

Finally, let us examine the external forces which make up the **F** term in Eq. 2–24. The external forces may be divided into two categories: (1) surface forces and (2) body forces. Surface forces are identified in terms of surface stresses, both normal and shear, discussed in Sec. 1–9. Body forces result from external fields, such as gravitational and electromagnetic fields. They are proportional either to the mass or to the volume of the fluid inside a control volume. The gravity force per unit mass is **g** and the total gravity force on the fluid mass inside a control volume is $\iiint_{\text{C.V.}} \mathbf{g}\rho \, d\mathcal{V}$, where **g** is the local gravitational acceleration. The electromagnetic force per unit volume is $\mathbf{J} \times \mathbf{B}$, where **J** is the current-flux density and **B** the magnetic induction. The total electromagnetic force on the fluid inside a control volume is, therefore, $\iiint_{\text{C.V.}} \mathbf{J} \times \mathbf{B} \, d\mathcal{V}$.

In this section, we have derived the momentum equation for a general control volume. The selection of a control volume most suitable for a

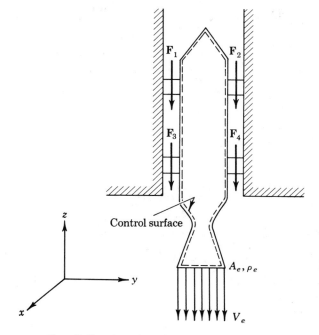

**Fig. 2-6.** A rocket engine in a test stand.

given problem depends very largely on experience. Often the most difficult part in the solution of a problem in fluid mechanics is in the process of assessing a physical situation so that we may idealize it sufficiently to be represented by a mathematically tractable formulation. The following examples have been worked out in detail to illustrate the application of momentum equations to solving fluid mechanics problems and to help clarify the meaning of different terms in momentum equations.

*Illustrative Example 2–2.* Calculate the thrust exerted by the flowing fluid on the reducing pipe bend as shown in the accompanying illustration. The fluid flows steadily from section 1 to section 2. The geometry of the reducing pipe bend and the average values of flow characteristics at the two sections are known.

*Solution:* The interior of the reducing pipe bend is shown as a control volume. Forces $R_x$ and $R_y$ are components of the total surface force **R** exerted by the pipe bend on the flowing fluid inside the chosen control volume, **R** being the resultant of fluid pressure forces and shear forces distributed nonuniformly over the curved portion of the control surface. The force components of the thrust exerted by the fluid on the pipe bend must be equal and opposite to $R_x$ and $R_y$. The gage pressures $p_1$ and $p_2$ of the fluid at sections 1 and 2 can be assumed to distribute uniformly over the cross-sectional areas at 1 and 2, respectively. The

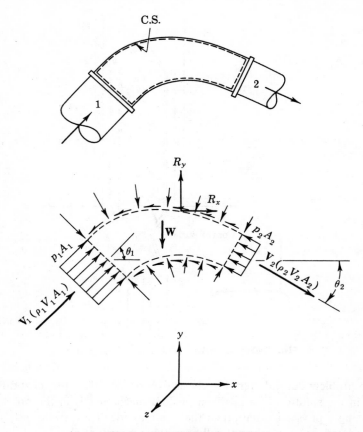

**Illustrative Example 2-2**

body force is shown as $W$, which is the weight of the fluid inside the control volume. Hence the $x$- and $y$-components of the total force acting on the fluid inside the control volume may be written as

$$F_x = p_1 A_1 \cos \theta_1 - p_2 A_2 \cos \theta_2 + R_x$$
$$F_y = p_1 A_1 \sin \theta_1 + p_2 A_2 \sin \theta_2 - W + R_y$$

The next step is to evaluate the momentum flux through the chosen control surface. Since fluid flows steadily from section 1 to section 2, the time derivative of the volume integral is zero, and it is only necessary to carry out surface integrations at the inlet and outlet surfaces of the control volume. With the normal velocities $V_1$ and $V_2$ uniform over the two flow sections, the momentum efflux from the control surface simply becomes

$$\oiint_{C.S.} \mathbf{V}(\rho \mathbf{V} \cdot d\mathbf{A}) = \mathbf{V}_2(\rho_2 V_2 A_2) - \mathbf{V}_1(\rho_1 V_1 A_1)$$

The scalar components of the above vector equation in the x- and y-directions can be written as

$$\oint_{C.S.} u(\rho \mathbf{V} \cdot d\mathbf{A}) = (V_2 \cos \theta_2)(\rho_2 V_2 A_2) - (V_1 \cos \theta_1)(\rho_1 V_1 A_1)$$

$$\oint_{C.S.} v(\rho \mathbf{V} \cdot d\mathbf{A}) = (-V_2 \sin \theta_2)(\rho_2 V_2 A_2) - (V_1 \sin \theta_1)(\rho_1 V_1 A_1)$$

In these equations, the continuity equation for the steady flow through this control volume specifies that $\rho_1 V_1 A_1 = \rho_2 V_2 A_2$.

Finally, we substitute the preceding results into the x- and y-components of the momentum equation to get

$$p_1 A_1 \cos \theta_1 - p_2 A_2 \cos \theta_2 + R_x = (V_2 \cos \theta_2)(\rho_2 V_2 A_2) - (V_1 \cos \theta_1)(\rho_1 V_1 A_1)$$

$$p_1 A_1 \sin \theta_1 + p_2 A_2 \sin \theta_2 - W + R_y$$
$$= (-V_2 \sin \theta_2)(\rho_2 V_2 A_2) - (V_1 \sin \theta_1)(\rho_1 V_1 A_1)$$

from which $R_x$ and $R_y$ can be determined, since the geometry of the reducing pipe bend and the flow characteristics are known.

***Illustrative Example 2–3.*** The curved vane shown in the accompanying figure is moving with a constant speed $U$ in the same direction as the approaching jet of an incompressible fluid. The free jet of area $A_j$ and velocity $\mathbf{V}_j$ hits the moving vane tangentially. Determine (a) the horizontal force exerted by the jet on the vane and (b) the value of the ratio $U/V_j$ such that the power developed by the restraining force of the vane is a maximum.

*Solution:* (a) We choose a control volume which includes the fluid stream attached to the moving vane. The control volume is translating at a constant speed $U$ relative to the inertial reference $xyz$ which is fixed to the ground. Therefore, the reference $x_u y_u z_u$ which is attached to the moving control volume is also an inertial reference for which the momentum equations derived in Sec. 2–6 are valid. We shall demonstrate the application of these equations to the chosen control volume as viewed in both references.

Forces $R_x$ and $R_y$ are components of the total surface force exerted by the vane on the fluid stream inside the control volume.

To evaluate the mass rate of flow through a moving control volume, we have to use velocities relative to the control volume. The inlet velocity $\mathbf{V}_i$ of the jet relative to the control volume is $\mathbf{V}_i = \mathbf{V}_j - \mathbf{U}$, and the mass rate of inflow is $\iint_{A_i} \rho \mathbf{V}_i \cdot d\mathbf{A}_i = \rho(V_j - U)A_j$. The magnitude of the relative velocity remains the same along the curved surface of the vane if friction loss is assumed zero. Therefore, the mass rate of outflow from the control volume is

$$\iint_{A_o} \rho \mathbf{V}_o \cdot d\mathbf{A}_o = \rho(V_j - U)A_2$$

By the continuity equation,

$$\rho(V_j - U)A_j = \rho(V_j - U)A_2$$

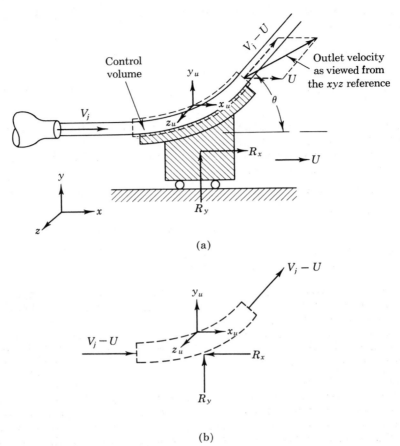

(a)

(b)

**Illustrative Example 2-3**

We now write the momentum equation for this control volume as viewed in both references. If we attach ourselves to the $xyz$ reference and look at the flow conditions of the moving control volume, we observe that the inlet velocity to the control volume is $V_j\mathbf{i}$ and the outlet velocity is $[(V_j - U)\cos\theta + U]\mathbf{i} + (V_j - U)\sin\theta\mathbf{j}$ as shown in part (a) of the figure. The $x$-component of the momentum equation can be written as

$$R_x = [(V_j - U)\cos\theta + U]\rho(V_j - U)A_2 - V_j\rho(V_j - U)A_j$$
$$= \rho(V_j - U)^2(\cos\theta - 1)A_j$$

On the other hand, if we view the control volume by attaching ourselves to the $x_uy_uz_u$ reference, the control volume would appear to be stationary. Then the inlet and outlet velocities would appear to be $(V_j - U)\mathbf{i}$ and $(V_j - U)\cos\theta\mathbf{i} +$

$(V_j - U) \sin \theta \mathbf{j}$, respectively, as shown in part (b) of the figure, and the $x$-component of the momentum equation becomes

$$R_x = [(V_j - U) \cos \theta][\rho(V_j - U)A_2] - (V_j - U)[\rho(V_j - U)A_j]$$
$$= \rho(V_j - U)^2 (\cos \theta - 1)A_j$$

It is not surprising to find that the results are identical in both references, inasmuch as both are inertial references.

(b) In mechanics the power developed by a working agent is defined as the rate at which work is done by that agent. Therefore, the power $P$ developed by the restraining force of the vane is equal to $R_x U$, or

$$P = R_x U = \rho(V_j - U)^2 (\cos \theta - 1)A_j U$$

Mathematically, the value of $U$ to produce maximum power for a given jet velocity $V_j$ may be determined by taking the partial derivative $\partial P/\partial U$ and then equating it to zero. Thus

$$\frac{\partial P}{\partial U} = \rho A_j(\cos \theta - 1)[(V_j - U)^2 + U2(V_j - U)(-1)] = 0$$

By setting the quantity inside the brackets equal to zero, and factoring out $(V_j - U)$, we finally have

$$(V_j - U)(V_j - U - 2U) = 0$$

One of the roots is $U/V_j = 1$, which is obviously a trivial solution. The other root, $U/V_j = \frac{1}{3}$, is the desired answer.

***Illustrative Example 2–4.*** In the accompanying figure, a test rocket of an initial mass $m_0$ ($m_0$ being the total mass of the rocket casing and the fuel) is fired vertically upward near the surface of the earth so that $g$ remains constant during the flight. The mass efflux rate $\dot{m}$ of exhaust gases and the relative velocity $v_e$ of the exhaust gases with respect to the rocket are constant. The discharge pressure of the exhaust gases is $p_e$ which is different from the ambient pressure $p_a$. Assuming that if the aerodynamic resistance $R$ can be approximated as proportional to the time $t$ after firing, i.e., $R = Kt$, where $K$ is a constant, derive an expression for the velocity $V$ of the upward flight of the rocket during the burnout.

*Solution:* The interior of the rocket is chosen as a control volume. Since the rocket is being accelerated vertically upward during its burnout, the chosen control volume is obviously a noninertial control volume. The momentum equations derived in Sec. 2–6 cannot be applied to the noninertial reference $x_r y_r z_r$ which is attached to the accelerating control volume. Momentum equations for a noninertial reference will be derived in Sec. 2–8. In this solution, we shall restrict ourselves to the inertial reference $xyz$ which is fixed to the ground, and apply Eq. 2–25b to the control volume at time $t$ when the rocket has attained a velocity $V$.

Let us evaluate the three terms in Eq. 2–25b. The total vertical force acting on the control volume is

$$F_y = -mg + (p_e - p_a)A_e - Kt$$

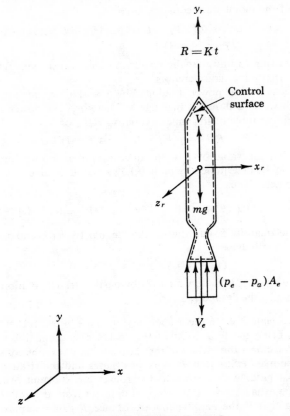

**Illustrative Example 2-4**

where $m$ is the mass of the rocket casing and its fuel at time $t$, and $A_e$ is the nozzle area at the exhaust. Clearly $m = m_0 - \dot{m}t$. The two momentum terms can be written in the following manner:

$$\oiint_{\text{C.S.}} \mathbf{V}\rho\mathbf{V} \cdot d\mathbf{A} = \iint_{A_o} \mathbf{V}_o\rho\mathbf{V}_o \cdot d\mathbf{A}_o = (V - v_e)\dot{m}\mathbf{j}$$

where $(V - v_e)\mathbf{j}$ is the velocity of the exhaust gases, as viewed from the ground.

$$\frac{\partial}{\partial t} \iiint_{\text{C.V.}} \mathbf{V}\rho\, d\mathcal{V} = \mathbf{j}\frac{\partial}{\partial t}(Vm) = \left(V\frac{\partial m}{\partial t} + m\frac{\partial V}{\partial t}\right)\mathbf{j}$$

$$= \left[V(-\dot{m}) + (m_o - \dot{m}t)\frac{\partial V}{\partial t}\right]\mathbf{j}$$

Substituting the foregoing results into Eq. 2–25b, we obtain for the component of the momentum equation in the direction of flight

$$-(m_0 - \dot{m}t)g + (p_e - p_a)A_e - Kt = (V - v_e)\dot{m} + V(-\dot{m}) + (m_0 - \dot{m}t)\frac{\partial V}{\partial t}$$

This equation can be simplified and rearranged into the following form:

$$\frac{\partial V}{\partial t} = \frac{\dot{m}v_e}{m_0 - \dot{m}t} + \frac{(p_e - p_a)A_e}{m_0 - \dot{m}t} - \frac{Kt}{m_0 - \dot{m}t} - g$$

Integration of this equation, with the initial condition that $V = 0$ at $t = 0$, yields the following desired expression for $V$ during the burnout:

$$V = v_e \ln \frac{m_0}{m_0 - \dot{m}t} + \frac{(p_e - p_a)A_e}{\dot{m}} \ln \frac{m_0}{m_0 - \dot{m}t}$$

$$- \left( -\frac{Kt}{\dot{m}} + \frac{Km_0}{\dot{m}^2} \ln \frac{m_0}{m_0 - \dot{m}t} \right) - gt$$

$$= \left[ v_e + \frac{(p_e - p_a)A_e}{\dot{m}} - \frac{Km_0}{\dot{m}^2} \right] \ln \frac{m_0}{m_0 - \dot{m}t} + \left( \frac{K}{\dot{m}} - g \right)t$$

In rocketry the propulsive force developed by a rocket engine is called the *thrust*. It is seen from the above calculation that the thrust of a rocket is equal to the sum of the momentum efflux $V\dot{m}$ and the pressure force $(p_e - p_a)A_e$ at the exhaust. The momentum efflux $V\dot{m}$ is frequently written as $v_e\rho v_e A_e$ and has the dimensions of force $(= ML/T^2)$.

***Illustrative Example 2–5.*** The accompanying figure shows the longitudinal profile of a steady flow of water over a small control weir which is built across a 10-ft-wide rectangular flume. Calculate the total force on the weir.

*Solution:* The required force can be determined by writing the $x$-component momentum equation for the chosen control volume. Since the force $F_x$ shown is the total force acting on the flowing water by the weir, the required force on the weir is opposite to $F_x$.

For simplicity, we shall assume the velocity to be uniform at every section of the channel, and neglect the friction forces at the wetted surface of the channel between the two end sections of the control volume. Because the flow is in the $x$-direction, hydrostatic pressure distribution exists at both end sections of the control volume.

Under these conditions, the $x$-component momentum equation for the control volume may be written in the following manner:

$$\gamma y_{1c}A_1 - \gamma y_{2c}A_2 + F_x = \rho V_2^2 A_2 - \rho V_1^2 A_1$$

where subscripts 1 and 2 refer to the two end sections of the control surface through which water is entering and leaving, respectively, as shown in the figure.

The continuity equation for the flow of water through the control volume is

$$A_1 V_1 = A_2 V_2$$

from which,

$$V_2 = \frac{A_1}{A_2} V_1 = \frac{3 \text{ ft} \times 10 \text{ ft}}{0.5 \text{ ft} \times 10 \text{ ft}} \times 2 \frac{\text{ft}}{\text{sec}} = 12 \text{ ft/sec}$$

By substituting numerical values into the momentum equation, we have

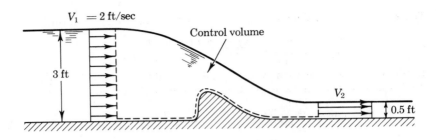

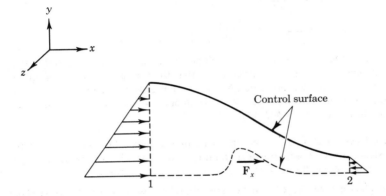

**Illustrative Example 2-5**

$$\left(62.4\,\frac{\text{lbf}}{\text{ft}^3}\right)(1.5\text{ ft})(3\text{ ft}\times10\text{ ft})$$

$$-\left(62.4\,\frac{\text{lbf}}{\text{ft}^3}\right)(0.25\text{ ft})(0.5\text{ ft}\times10\text{ ft})+F_x$$

$$=\frac{62.4\text{ lbf/ft}^3}{32.2\text{ ft/sec}^2}\times(12\text{ ft/sec})^2\times(0.5\text{ ft}\times10\text{ ft})$$

$$-\frac{62.4\text{ lbf/ft}^3}{32.2\text{ ft/sec}^2}\times(2\text{ ft/sec})^2\times(3\text{ ft}\times10\text{ ft})$$

Hence

$$F_x=-1566\text{ lbf}$$

Thus the total force on the weir is $+1566$ lbf **i**.

*Illustrative Example 2-6.* The accompanying figure shows the velocity distributions at the inlet section 1 and a downstream section 2 of a pipe of diameter $D$ in which there is a steady flow of an incompressible fluid of density $\rho$. At section 1 the velocity $V_1$ is constant; at section 2 the velocity distribution is a

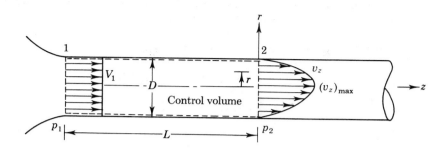

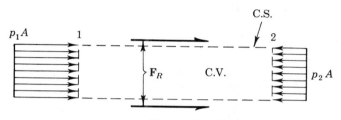

**Illustrative Example 2-6**

paraboloid of revolution. The pressure at sections 1 and 2 are, respectively, $p_1$ and $p_2$. Calculate the total frictional force of the fluid on the wall of the pipe between sections 1 and 2 in terms of the given quantities, $p_1$, $p_2$, $L$, $D$, and $V_1$.

*Solution:* We choose the interior of the pipe between sections 1 and 2 as a control volume. The force $\mathbf{F}_R$ shown is applied on the fluid from the wall; therefore, the required frictional force on the wall is opposite to $\mathbf{F}_R$. Clearly $\mathbf{F}_R$ can be determined by writing the $z$-component momentum equation for the flow through the chosen control volume. Since the velocity of efflux from section 2 of the control surface is nonuniform, we must evaluate the momentum efflux by integration. Therefore, the $z$-component momentum equation becomes

$$p_1 A - p_2 A + F_R = \iint_{A_o} \rho v_z^2 \, dA - \rho V_1^2 A$$

To solve for $F_R$, we must first express $v_z$ in terms of the given quantities.

By applying the method of analytical geometry to the parabolic velocity profile at section 2, we obtain for $v_z$:

$$v_z = (v_z)_{\max}\left(1 - \frac{4r^2}{D^2}\right)$$

where $(v_z)_{\max}$ is the maximum velocity at the axis of the pipe. We may express

$(v_z)_{max}$ in terms of $V_1$ by writing the continuity equation for the flow between sections 1 and 2 of the control volume. Thus

$$V_1 \times \frac{\pi D^2}{4} = \int_0^{D/2} v_z 2\pi r \, dr$$

$$= \int_0^{D/2} (v_z)_{max} \left(1 - \frac{4r^2}{D^2}\right) 2\pi r \, dr$$

$$= (v_z)_{max} \pi \frac{D^2}{8}$$

Hence

$$(v_z)_{max} = 2V_1$$

and

$$v_z = 2V_1 \left(1 - \frac{4r^2}{D^2}\right)$$

Substituting the given quantities into the momentum equation, we have

$$p_1 \frac{\pi D^2}{4} - p_2 \frac{\pi D^2}{4} + F_R = \int_0^{D/2} \rho \left[2V_1 \left(1 - \frac{4r^2}{D^2}\right)\right]^2 2\pi r \, dr - \rho V_1^2 \frac{\pi D^2}{4}$$

Therefore

$$F_R = -(p_1 - p_2)\frac{\pi D^2}{4} + \frac{1}{12}\pi D^2 \rho V_1^2$$

## 2-7 Momentum Equation in Differential Form

The differential momentum equation can be derived by first employing Gauss' theorem to transform the surface integral term in Eq. 2–24 to a volume integral as

$$\oiint_{\text{C.S.}} \mathbf{V}(\rho \mathbf{V} \cdot d\mathbf{A}) = \iiint_{\text{C.V.}} [\nabla \cdot \rho \mathbf{V}\mathbf{V}] \, d\mathcal{V} \qquad (2\text{–}26)$$

The quantity $[\nabla \cdot \rho \mathbf{V}\mathbf{V}]$ is not the ordinary divergence in vector calculus because of the tensorial nature of $\rho \mathbf{V}\mathbf{V}$. Whereas the divergence of a vector is a scalar quantity, the result of $[\nabla \cdot \rho \mathbf{V}\mathbf{V}]$ is a vector quantity. We have used [ ] to enclose this special quantity in order to differentiate it from the divergence of $\rho \mathbf{V}$. The physical interpretation of $[\nabla \cdot \rho \mathbf{V}\mathbf{V}]$ is, however, analogous to that of $(\nabla \cdot \rho \mathbf{V})$. Thus $(\nabla \cdot \rho \mathbf{V})$ represents the rate of efflux of mass (a scalar quantity) per unit volume, whereas $[\nabla \cdot \rho \mathbf{V}\mathbf{V}]$ represents the rate of efflux of momentum (a vector quantity) per unit volume.

At this point it seems appropriate to explain the mathematical operation of this special quantity $[\nabla \cdot \rho \mathbf{V}\mathbf{V}]$. The product of two vectors, such as $\mathbf{V}\mathbf{V}$, is called a *dyadic*. Dyadics are usually denoted by capital Greek letters. For example,

$$\mathbf{\Phi} = \mathbf{V}\mathbf{V} \qquad (2\text{–}27)$$

We may carry out the multiplication of the components of two vectors to get for the dyadic

$$\begin{aligned}
\mathbf{\Phi} = \mathbf{VV} &= (u\mathbf{i} + v\mathbf{j} + w\mathbf{k})(u\mathbf{i} + v\mathbf{j} + w\mathbf{k}) \\
&= uu\mathbf{ii} + uv\mathbf{ij} + uw\mathbf{ik} \\
&\quad + vu\mathbf{ji} + vv\mathbf{jj} + vw\mathbf{jk} \\
&\quad + wu\mathbf{ki} + wv\mathbf{kj} + ww\mathbf{kk}
\end{aligned} \qquad (2\text{--}28)$$

Each term in this equation is called a *dyad*. Note that the sequence of the components of the two vectors is maintained in all dyads in the above multiplication, since **ij**, for example, is not the same as **ji**. The quantities **ii**, **ij**, etc., are called *unit dyads* and the coefficients *uu*, *uv*, etc., are the *components* of the dyadic **Φ**.

Equation 2–28 may also be written in a matrix form as

$$\mathbf{\Phi} = \mathbf{VV} = $$

|   | i | j | k |
|---|---|---|---|
| **i** | *uu* | *uv* | *uw* |
| **j** | *vu* | *vv* | *vw* |
| **k** | *wu* | *wv* | *ww* |

$$(2\text{--}29)$$

The significance of this matrix is evident by comparison with Eq. 2–28. Each unit vector in the first vertical column is multiplied with each unit vector of the top row to form a unit dyad. The coefficient of each dyad is in turn found in the matrix at the intersection of the horizontal row pertaining to the first unit vector of the unit dyad and the vertical column headed by the second unit vector of the same unit dyad. Therefore, a dyadic is merely a mathematical generalization[1] of a vector and it has no physical meaning as such.

Carrying out the operation $[\nabla \cdot \rho\mathbf{VV}]$, we have

$$\begin{aligned}
[\nabla \cdot \rho\mathbf{VV}] &= [\nabla \cdot \rho\mathbf{\Phi}] \\
&= \left(\frac{\partial}{\partial x}\mathbf{i} + \frac{\partial}{\partial y}\mathbf{j} + \frac{\partial}{\partial z}\mathbf{k}\right) \cdot \rho\mathbf{\Phi} \\
&= \frac{\partial}{\partial x}\mathbf{i} \cdot \rho\mathbf{\Phi} + \frac{\partial}{\partial y}\mathbf{j} \cdot \rho\mathbf{\Phi} + \frac{\partial}{\partial z}\mathbf{k} \cdot \rho\mathbf{\Phi}
\end{aligned} \qquad (2\text{--}30)$$

This dot product is obtained by taking the dot product of each component of $\nabla$ with each dyad of **Φ** by maintaining the same sequence. With the

---

[1] Still further generalization leads to *triadics* which are formed by the product of three vectors. A triadic consists of 27 terms. A study of how the components of a dyadic or triadic transform from one system of coordinates to another leads to the subject of tensor analysis.

value of $\boldsymbol{\Phi}$ from Eq. 2–28, we can form the dot product $\mathbf{i} \cdot \boldsymbol{\Phi}$ of Eq. 2–30 as follows:

$$\begin{aligned}
\mathbf{i} \cdot \boldsymbol{\Phi} = {} & \mathbf{i} \cdot uu\mathbf{ii} + \mathbf{i} \cdot uv\mathbf{ij} + \mathbf{i} \cdot uw\mathbf{ik} \\
& + \mathbf{i} \cdot vu\mathbf{ji} + \mathbf{i} \cdot vv\mathbf{jj} + \mathbf{i} \cdot vw\mathbf{jk} \\
& + \mathbf{i} \cdot wu\mathbf{ki} + \mathbf{i} \cdot wv\mathbf{kj} + \mathbf{i} \cdot ww\mathbf{kk}
\end{aligned} \qquad (2\text{–}31)$$

in which, for example, $\mathbf{i} \cdot vw\mathbf{jk}$ (the sixth term on the right-hand side) may also be rearranged as $vw(\mathbf{i} \cdot \mathbf{j})\mathbf{k}$ by maintaining the same sequence of the unit vectors. Thus, after rearranging each term in Eq. 2–31 in the aforestated manner, and by recognizing that $\mathbf{i} \cdot \mathbf{j} = \mathbf{i} \cdot \mathbf{k} = 0$ and $\mathbf{i} \cdot \mathbf{i} = 1$, we may reduce Eq. 2–31 to

$$\mathbf{i} \cdot \boldsymbol{\Phi} = uu\mathbf{i} + uv\mathbf{j} + uw\mathbf{k} \qquad (2\text{–}32)$$

Similarly,

$$\mathbf{j} \cdot \boldsymbol{\Phi} = vu\mathbf{i} + vv\mathbf{j} + vw\mathbf{k} \qquad (2\text{–}33)$$

$$\mathbf{k} \cdot \boldsymbol{\Phi} = wu\mathbf{i} + wv\mathbf{j} + ww\mathbf{k} \qquad (2\text{–}34)$$

Finally, we substitute these values into Eq. 2–30 and group terms having the same unit vector to get

$$\begin{aligned}
[\boldsymbol{\nabla} \cdot \rho \mathbf{VV}] = {} & \left[ \frac{\partial}{\partial x}(\rho uu) + \frac{\partial}{\partial y}(\rho vu) + \frac{\partial}{\partial z}(\rho wu) \right] \mathbf{i} \\
& + \left[ \frac{\partial}{\partial x}(\rho uv) + \frac{\partial}{\partial y}(\rho vv) + \frac{\partial}{\partial z}(\rho wv) \right] \mathbf{j} \\
& + \left[ \frac{\partial}{\partial x}(\rho uw) + \frac{\partial}{\partial y}(\rho vw) + \frac{\partial}{\partial z}(\rho ww) \right] \mathbf{k}
\end{aligned} \qquad (2\text{–}35)$$

which is a vector quantity.

Returning to the derivation of momentum equation in differential form, we then substitute Eq. 2–26 into Eq. 2–24 and set $\mathbf{F} = \iiint_{\text{c.v.}} \mathbf{f}\, d\mathscr{V}$, where $\mathbf{f}$ is the average of $\mathbf{F}$ per unit volume so that Eq. 2–24 becomes

$$\iiint_{\text{c.v.}} \mathbf{f}\, d\mathscr{V} = \iiint_{\text{c.v.}} [\boldsymbol{\nabla} \cdot \rho \mathbf{VV}]\, d\mathscr{V} + \frac{\partial}{\partial t} \iiint_{\text{c.v.}} \mathbf{V}\rho\, d\mathscr{V} \qquad (2\text{–}36)$$

With a fixed control volume, the order of differentiation and integration for the last term of the above equation can be interchanged. Thus,

$$\iiint_{\text{c.v.}} \mathbf{f}\, d\mathscr{V} = \iiint_{\text{c.v.}} \left( [\boldsymbol{\nabla} \cdot \rho \mathbf{VV}] + \frac{\partial}{\partial t}\rho \mathbf{V} \right) d\mathscr{V} \qquad (2\text{–}36\text{a})$$

Since this equation holds for all control volumes, the integrands on both sides must necessarily be equal to each other, i.e.,

$$\mathbf{f} = [\boldsymbol{\nabla} \cdot \rho \mathbf{VV}] + \frac{\partial}{\partial t}\rho \mathbf{V} \qquad (2\text{–}37)$$

This is the desired momentum equation in differential form. We may further expand its right-hand side as

$$\mathbf{f} = \rho(\mathbf{V} \cdot \nabla)\mathbf{V} + \mathbf{V}(\nabla \cdot \rho\mathbf{V}) + \mathbf{V}\frac{\partial \rho}{\partial t} + \rho\frac{\partial \mathbf{V}}{\partial t} \qquad (2\text{--}37\text{a})$$

in which the sum of the second and third terms on the right-hand side vanishes by reason of the equation of continuity (Eq. 2–15). Hence the above equation is reduced to

$$\mathbf{f} = \rho(\mathbf{V} \cdot \nabla)\mathbf{V} + \rho\frac{\partial \mathbf{V}}{\partial t} = \rho\frac{D\mathbf{V}}{Dt} \qquad (2\text{--}37\text{b})$$

In this form the momentum equation is indeed the equation of motion of a mass of unit volume subject to an external resultant force $\mathbf{f}$.

The differential momentum equations developed in this section are indeed very general and are of great importance in fluid mechanics. Classical equations of fluid motion can be deduced from the differential momentum equation. For example, when Eq. 2–37b is applied to the motion of a fluid element in a frictionless flow field, the result is the so-called "Euler's equation." For a frictionless flow the surface force on a fluid element is then due only to fluid pressure $p$, and, in accordance with the discussion in Secs. 1–9 and 1–10, this force can be expressed as $-\nabla p$ per unit volume. In the absence of an electromagnetic field, gravity is the only body force encountered in fluid flow. The gravity force per unit volume is $\rho\mathbf{g}$, where $\mathbf{g}$ is the local gravitational acceleration. Substitution of these forces for $\mathbf{f}$ in Eq. 2–37b yields the following form of Euler's equation:

$$\underset{\substack{\text{pressure}\\\text{force}}}{-\nabla p} + \underset{\substack{\text{gravity}\\\text{force}}}{\rho\mathbf{g}} = \underset{\text{inertia}}{\rho\frac{D\mathbf{V}}{Dt}} = \rho\left[(\mathbf{V} \cdot \nabla)\mathbf{V} + \frac{\partial \mathbf{V}}{\partial t}\right] \qquad (2\text{--}38)$$

which is actually an equation of motion of a fluid element in a frictionless flow field in which the only body force is that of gravity. The significance of Euler's equation will be shown in Sec. 2–13 when we integrate it to obtain Bernoulli's equation which is another well-known classical equation in fluid mechanics.

Furthermore, if we write the equation of motion for a fluid element in a viscous flow field, we shall obtain the Navier-Stokes equation. In a viscous flow, the surface forces on a fluid element also include, in addition to the pressure forces, viscous forces. The Navier-Stokes equation will be derived in Chapter 6.

For convenience of reference, the scalar components of Euler's equation (Eq. 2–38) in different coordinate systems are given in Table 2–1.

### TABLE 2–1.    Euler's Equation in Different Coordinate Systems

#### 1. Cartesian coordinates $(x, y, z)$

$x$-component:
$$-\frac{\partial p}{\partial x} + \rho g_x = \rho\left(u\frac{\partial u}{\partial x} + v\frac{\partial u}{\partial y} + w\frac{\partial u}{\partial z} + \frac{\partial u}{\partial t}\right) \tag{A}$$

$y$-component:
$$-\frac{\partial p}{\partial y} + \rho g_y = \rho\left(u\frac{\partial v}{\partial x} + v\frac{\partial v}{\partial y} + w\frac{\partial v}{\partial z} + \frac{\partial v}{\partial t}\right) \tag{B}$$

$z$-component:
$$-\frac{\partial p}{\partial z} + \rho g_z = \rho\left(u\frac{\partial w}{\partial x} + v\frac{\partial w}{\partial y} + w\frac{\partial w}{\partial z} + \frac{\partial w}{\partial t}\right) \tag{C}$$

#### 2. Cylindrical coordinates $(r, \theta, z)$

$r$-component:
$$-\frac{\partial p}{\partial r} + \rho g_r = \rho\left(v_r\frac{\partial v_r}{\partial r} + \frac{v_\theta}{r}\frac{\partial v_r}{\partial \theta} - \frac{v_\theta^2}{r} + v_z\frac{\partial v_r}{\partial z} + \frac{\partial v_r}{\partial t}\right) \tag{D}$$

$\theta$-component:
$$-\frac{1}{r}\frac{\partial p}{\partial \theta} + \rho g_\theta = \rho\left(v_r\frac{\partial v_\theta}{\partial r} + \frac{v_\theta}{r}\frac{\partial v_\theta}{\partial \theta} + \frac{v_r v_\theta}{r} + v_z\frac{\partial v_\theta}{\partial z} + \frac{\partial v_\theta}{\partial t}\right) \tag{E}$$

$z$-component:
$$-\frac{\partial p}{\partial z} + \rho g_z = \rho\left(v_r\frac{\partial v_z}{\partial r} + \frac{v_\theta}{r}\frac{\partial v_z}{\partial \theta} + v_z\frac{\partial v_z}{\partial z} + \frac{\partial v_z}{\partial t}\right) \tag{F}$$

#### 3. Spherical coordinates $(R, \theta, \phi)$

$R$-component:
$$-\frac{\partial p}{\partial R} + \rho g_R = \rho\left(v_R\frac{\partial v_R}{\partial R} + \frac{v_\theta}{R}\frac{\partial v_R}{\partial \theta} + \frac{v_\phi}{R\sin\theta}\frac{\partial v_R}{\partial \phi} - \frac{v_\theta^2 + v_\phi^2}{R} + \frac{\partial v_R}{\partial t}\right) \tag{G}$$

$\theta$-component:
$$-\frac{1}{R}\frac{\partial p}{\partial \theta} + \rho g_\theta = \rho\left(v_R\frac{\partial v_\theta}{\partial R} + \frac{v_\theta}{R}\frac{\partial v_\theta}{\partial \theta} + \frac{v_\phi}{R\sin\theta}\frac{\partial v_\theta}{\partial \phi} + \frac{v_R v_\theta}{R} - \frac{v_\phi^2\cot\theta}{R} + \frac{\partial v_\theta}{\partial t}\right) \tag{H}$$

$\phi$-component:
$$-\frac{1}{R\sin\phi}\frac{\partial p}{\partial \phi} + \rho g_\phi = \rho\left(v_R\frac{\partial v_\phi}{\partial R} + \frac{v_\theta}{R}\frac{\partial v_\phi}{\partial \theta} + \frac{v_\phi}{R\sin\theta}\frac{\partial v_\phi}{\partial \phi} + \frac{v_\phi v_R}{R} + \frac{v_\theta v_\phi}{R}\cot\theta + \frac{\partial v_\phi}{\partial t}\right) \tag{I}$$

#### 4. Streamline coordinates $(s, n, m)$†

$s$-component:
$$-\frac{\partial p}{\partial s} + \rho g_s = \rho\left(V\frac{\partial V}{\partial s} + \frac{\partial V}{\partial t}\right) \tag{J}$$

$n$-component:
$$-\frac{\partial p}{\partial n} + \rho g_n = \rho\left(\frac{V^2}{R} + \frac{\partial V_n}{\partial t}\right) \tag{K}$$

$m$-component:
$$-\frac{\partial p}{\partial m} + \rho g_m = 0 \tag{L}$$

---

†The *snm* axes form an orthogonal coordinate system at any point on a curved streamline. The *s*-axis is along the velocity vector at this point, and the *n*-axis is along the radius of curvature of the streamline at the same point. Both the *s*- and *n*-axes are in the plane of curvature of the streamline. The symbol $R$ denotes the radius of curvature of the streamline at the given point.

*Illustrative Example 2-7.* At point $A$ on a curved streamline in a steady frictionless flow, the velocity of flow is 20 ft/sec and is decreasing at a rate of 3 ft/sec/ft along the streamline. The radius of curvature of the streamline at point $A$ is 5 ft. If the curvature of the streamline at point $A$ lies on a horizontal plane, calculate the pressure gradient on a unit volume of fluid of density $\rho \equiv 1.94$ slugs/ft³ as it passes point $A$.

*Solution:* We introduce a coordinate system at point $A$ as shown in the accompanying figure. The curvature of the streamline at point $A$ lies in the $xy$ plane so

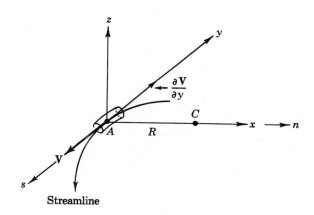

**Illustrative Example 2-7**

that the $z$-axis is parallel to the direction of gravity. Point $C$ on the $x$-axis is the center of curvature of the streamline at point $A$. Since the flow is steady and frictionless, the equation of motion for a unit volume of fluid at point $A$ is the following simplified Euler's equation:

$$-\nabla p + \rho \mathbf{g} = \rho(\mathbf{V} \cdot \nabla)\mathbf{V}$$

By following the notations in the figure, this equation becomes

$$-\nabla p - \rho g \mathbf{k} = \rho \left( V \frac{\partial V}{\partial y} \mathbf{j} + \frac{V^2}{R} \mathbf{i} \right)$$

in which we have used Eqs. J and K in Table 2–1 to evaluate the acceleration terms on the right-hand side. Substituting numerical values with proper signs into the above equation and employing the conversion factor $g_c \equiv 1$ slug-ft/lbf-sec², we have

$$-\nabla p - \left( \frac{1.94 \text{ slugs/ft}^3}{1 \text{ slug-ft/lbf-sec}^2} \times 32.2 \frac{\text{ft}}{\text{sec}^2} \right) \mathbf{k}$$

$$= \frac{1.94 \text{ slug/ft}^3}{1 \text{ slug-ft/lbf-sec}^2} \left[ \left( -20 \frac{\text{ft}}{\text{sec}} \right) \left( 3 \frac{\text{ft/sec}}{\text{ft}} \right) \mathbf{j} + \frac{(20 \text{ ft/sec})^2}{5 \text{ ft}} \mathbf{i} \right]$$

Therefore

$$\nabla p = -155.2\mathbf{i} + 116.4\mathbf{j} - 62.4\mathbf{k} \quad \frac{\text{lbf/ft}^2}{\text{ft}}$$

## 2-8 Momentum Equation for a Noninertial Control Volume

Figure 2–7 shows a control volume which is moving and rotating in an arbitrary manner relative to an inertial reference $x_i y_i z_i$. A noninertial

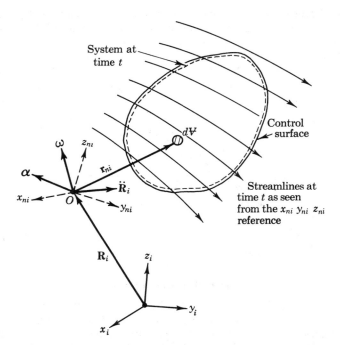

**Fig. 2-7.** Flow of fluid through a noninertial control volume.

reference $x_{ni} y_{ni} z_{ni}$ is introduced in such a way that the control volume is either fixed in, or translating at a constant velocity relative to it. Therefore, both the control volume and the reference $x_{ni} y_{ni} z_{ni}$ have the same accelerating and rotational motions relative to the inertial reference $x_i y_i z_i$. Subscripts $i$ and $ni$ denote respectively quantities measured relative to an inertial and a noninertial reference. For example, the origin $O$ of the $x_{ni} y_{ni} z_{ni}$ reference is located in the $x_i y_i z_i$ reference by the position vector $\mathbf{R}_i$ and a fluid element $d\mathcal{V}$ in the control volume is located in the $x_{ni} y_{ni} z_{ni}$ reference by the position vector $\mathbf{r}_{ni}$. From our previous study of mechanics[2], we know that the acceleration $\mathbf{a}_i$ of the fluid element $d V$ relative to the inertial reference $x_i y_i z_i$ is related to the acceleration $\mathbf{a}_{ni}$ of the same fluid element relative to the noninertial reference $x_{ni} y_{ni} z_{ni}$ in the following manner:

$$\mathbf{a}_i = \mathbf{a}_{ni} + \ddot{\mathbf{R}}_i + \boldsymbol{\alpha} \times \mathbf{r}_{ni} + 2\boldsymbol{\omega} \times \mathbf{V}_{ni} + \boldsymbol{\omega} \times (\boldsymbol{\omega} \times \mathbf{r}_{ni}) \qquad (2\text{-}39)$$

in which, besides those terms which have been defined previously,

$\ddot{\mathbf{R}}_i \equiv$ acceleration of the origin $O$ relative to the $x_i y_i z_i$ reference,

$\boldsymbol{\alpha} \equiv$ angular acceleration of the $x_{ni} y_{ni} z_{ni}$ reference and the control volume about an axis of rotation through the origin $O$,

$\boldsymbol{\omega} \equiv$ angular velocity of the $x_{ni} y_{ni} z_{ni}$ reference and the control volume about an axis of rotation through the origin $O$, and

$\mathbf{V}_{ni} \equiv$ velocity of the fluid element $d V$ relative to the $x_{ni} y_{ni} z_{ni}$ reference.

Hence, with $\mathbf{a}_{abs} = \mathbf{a}_i$, Newton's law for the system of fluid in Fig. 2-7 becomes

$$\mathbf{F} = \iiint_{\text{system}} \mathbf{a}_i \rho \, d V$$

$$= \iiint_{\text{system}} [\mathbf{a}_{ni} + \ddot{\mathbf{R}}_i + \boldsymbol{\alpha} \times \mathbf{r}_{ni} + 2\boldsymbol{\omega} \times \mathbf{V}_{ni} + \boldsymbol{\omega} \times (\boldsymbol{\omega} \times \mathbf{r}_{ni})] \rho \, d V \qquad (2\text{-}40)$$

which may be rearranged as

$$\mathbf{F} - \iiint_{\text{system}} [\ddot{\mathbf{R}}_i + \boldsymbol{\alpha} \times \mathbf{r}_{ni} + 2\boldsymbol{\omega} \times \mathbf{V}_{ni} + \boldsymbol{\omega} \times (\boldsymbol{\omega} \times \mathbf{r}_{ni})] \rho \, d V$$

$$= \iiint_{\text{system}} \mathbf{a}_{ni} \rho \, d V = \frac{D}{Dt_{ni}} \iiint_{\text{system}} \mathbf{V}_{ni} \rho \, d V = \frac{D\mathbf{P}_{ni}}{Dt_{ni}} \qquad (2\text{-}41)$$

Here $D/Dt_{ni}$ denotes a time derivative performed as one follows the system in the noninertial $x_{ni} y_{ni} z_{ni}$ reference, and $\mathbf{P}_{ni}$ is the momentum of the system as measured relative to the $x_{ni} y_{ni} z_{ni}$ reference. If we recall D'Alembert's principle in mechanics, we will immediately recognize that the group of terms inside the volume integral sign on the left-hand side of the above equation actually represents the so-called imaginary "forces," which an observer riding on the $x_{ni} y_{ni} z_{ni}$ reference would vis-

---

[2]See Robert L. Halfman, *Dynamics: Particles, rigid bodies, and systems.* (Reading, Mass.: Addison-Wesley Publishing Company, Inc., 1962), Vol. I, Chap. 2.

ualize, acting on the fluid in the system.[3] The terms

$$-\iiint_{\text{system}} (2\boldsymbol{\omega} \times \mathbf{V}_{ni})\rho \, d\mathcal{V} \quad \text{and} \quad -\iiint_{\text{system}} \boldsymbol{\omega} \times (\boldsymbol{\omega} \times \mathbf{r}_{ni})\rho \, d\mathcal{V}$$

are, respectively, Coriolis and centrifugal forces.

Again we employ the transformation law (Eq. 2–6) to get for $DP_{ni}/Dt_{ni}$ in Eq. 2–41:

$$\frac{D\mathbf{P}_{ni}}{Dt_{ni}} = \oiint_{\text{C.S.}} \mathbf{V}_{ni}(\rho \mathbf{V}_{ni} \cdot d\mathbf{A}) + \frac{\partial}{\partial t_{ni}} \iiint_{\text{C.V.}} \mathbf{V}_{ni} \rho \, d\mathcal{V} \qquad (2\text{–}42)$$

which may now be substituted into Eq. 2–41 to yield the following desired momentum equation for a noninertial control volume:

$$\mathbf{F} - \iiint_{\text{C.V.}} [\ddot{\mathbf{R}}_i + \boldsymbol{\alpha} \times \mathbf{r}_{ni} + 2\boldsymbol{\omega} \times \mathbf{V}_{ni} + \boldsymbol{\omega} \times (\boldsymbol{\omega} \times \mathbf{r}_{ni})]\rho \, d\mathcal{V}$$

$$= \oiint_{\text{C.S.}} \mathbf{V}_{ni}(\rho \mathbf{V}_{ni} \cdot d\mathbf{A}) + \frac{\partial}{\partial t_{ni}} \iiint_{\text{C.V.}} \mathbf{V}_{ni} \rho \, d\mathcal{V} \qquad (2\text{–}43)$$

Note that we have changed the limit for the integral over imaginary forces from system to C.V., since the system has the same volume at time $t$ as the control volume.

*Illustrative Example 2–8.* Work Ex. 2–4 by using the momentum equation for the accelerating control volume which is attached to the noninertial reference $x_r y_r z_r$, as shown in the figure for Ex. 2–4.

*Solution:* The $y$-component of Eq. 2–43 is to be applied to the accelerating control volume. The total force acting on the control volume is still

$$F_y = -mg + (p_e - p_a)A_e - Kt$$

where $m$ is the mass of the rocket casing and its fuel at time $t$. Therefore, $m = m_0 - \dot{m}t$. Since the rocket is moving vertically upward, we need only consider the linear acceleration term $\ddot{\mathbf{R}}_i$ which is then $(\partial V/\partial t)\mathbf{j}$, the upward acceleration of the rocket relative to the inertial reference $xyz$. The $y$-component

---

[3]This description simply reflects a difference in viewpoint. To illustrate this point, consider a mass $m$ which is accelerated linearly by an external force $\mathbf{F}$. Newton's law $\mathbf{F} = m\mathbf{a}_{\text{abs}}$ is written from the viewpoint of an inertial observer. The inertial observer sees the acceleration $\mathbf{a}_{\text{abs}}$ of $m$ as a result of the applied force $\mathbf{F}$. On the other hand, we can also employ D'Alembert's principle to write the above equation as $\mathbf{F} + (-m\mathbf{a}_{\text{abs}}) = 0$. Here we can regard $-m\mathbf{a}_{\text{abs}}$ as representing an inertia force. D'Alembert's principle says that a noninertial observer riding on the mass which accelerates relative to an inertial reference sees no motion for the mass, and, from his viewpoint, he must instead visualize the inertia force $(-m\mathbf{a}_{\text{abs}})$ to keep the mass in equilibrium. Note that an inertia force is never seen by an inertial observer, and for this reason it is frequently classified as an imaginary force. Likewise, a noninertial observer riding on a rotating body may find it convenient to use Coriolis and centrifugal forces, which are also classified as imaginary forces.

of the volume integral on the left-hand side of Eq. 2–43 is simply

$$\iiint_{\text{C.V.}} \ddot{\mathbf{R}}_i \rho \, d\mathcal{V} = m \frac{\partial V}{\partial t} \mathbf{j} = (m_0 - \dot{m}t) \frac{\partial V}{\partial t} \mathbf{j}$$

The remaining two integral terms on the right-hand side of Eq. 2–43 are to be formulated as we view the control volume from the noninertial reference. The surface integral can be written as

$$\oiint_{\text{C.S.}} \mathbf{V}_{ni}(\rho \mathbf{V}_{ni} \cdot d\mathbf{A}) = -\dot{m}v_e \mathbf{j}$$

since tψe mass efflux rate of the exhaust gases from the control volume is $\dot{m}$, and the velocity of the exhaust gases relative to the noninertial reference is $-v_e\mathbf{j}$. The last volume integral is zero for the following reasons: (1) The control volume has zero velocity relative to the noninertial reference at all times, and so there can be no change in momentum for the control volume even though the mass of the control volume is being reduced by the exhaust gases. (2) Because the velocity $v_e$ of the exhaust gases remains constant relative to the noninertial reference, there can be no change in momentum for the exhaust gases as viewed from the noninertial reference.

When the above results are substituted into Eq. 2–43, the $y$-component momentum equation for the accelerating control volume becomes

$$-(m_0 - \dot{m}t)g + (p_e - p_a)A_e - Kt - (m_0 - \dot{m}t)\frac{\partial V}{\partial t} = -\dot{m}v_e$$

Dividing this equation by $(m_0 - \dot{m}t)$ and rearranging terms, we finally obtain the following differential equation:

$$\frac{\partial V}{\partial t} = \frac{\dot{m}v_e}{m_0 - \dot{m}t} + \frac{(p_e - p_a)A_e}{m_0 - \dot{m}t} - \frac{Kt}{m_0 - \dot{m}t} - g$$

which is exactly the same differential equation that we obtained in Ex. 2–4.

## 2-9  Conservation of Moment of Momentum

The equation of moment of momentum is obtained when we take the moment of each side of Newton's dynamical equation about a fixed point $A$ in space. Thus, for a free body of mass $m$ moving relative to an inertial reference, we have

$$\mathbf{r} \times \mathbf{F} = \mathbf{r} \times \frac{D}{Dt}(m\mathbf{V}) \qquad (2\text{–}44)$$

where $\mathbf{r}$ is the position vector from point $A$ which is fixed in the inertial reference. The cross product $\mathbf{r} \times \mathbf{F}$ is obviously the moment about point $A$ of the resultant force $\mathbf{F}$ on the free body, and we shall denote this moment as $\mathbf{M}$. The cross product on the right-hand side can also be written in a more familiar form as the time derivative of $\mathbf{r} \times m\mathbf{V}$, because

$$\frac{D}{Dt}(\mathbf{r} \times m\mathbf{V}) = \frac{D\mathbf{r}}{Dt} \times m\mathbf{V} + \mathbf{r} \times \frac{D}{Dt}(m\mathbf{V})$$

in which $D\mathbf{r}/Dt = \mathbf{V}$, thus making the first term on the right-hand side vanish and leaving the remaining two terms equal to each other. Therefore, we can also write Eq. 2–44 as

$$\mathbf{M} = \mathbf{r} \times \mathbf{F} = \frac{D}{Dt}(\mathbf{r} \times m\mathbf{V}) \qquad (2\text{–}45)$$

This is the desired equation of moment of momentum.

We shall now consider a finite fluid system moving in a flow field relative to an inertial reference $xyz$, as shown in Fig. 2–8. Point $A$ is fixed

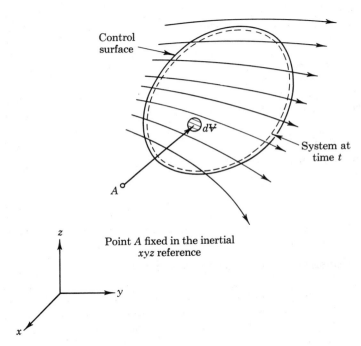

**Fig. 2-8.** Flow of fluid through an inertial control volume to illustrate the conservation of moment of momentum.

in the $xyz$ reference. Denoting the moment of momentum of the system at time $t$ by the symbol $\mathbf{H}$ and defining it as

$$\mathbf{H} = \iiint\limits_{\text{system}} \mathbf{r} \times \mathbf{V}\rho \, dV \qquad (2\text{–}46)$$

we can express the moment of momentum equation for the system in the following form:

$$\mathbf{M} = \mathbf{r} \times \mathbf{F} = \frac{D\mathbf{H}}{Dt} = \frac{D}{Dt} \iiint_{\text{system}} \mathbf{r} \times \mathbf{V}\rho \, d\mathcal{V} \qquad (2\text{--}47)$$

where $\mathbf{M}$ is the resultant moment about point $A$ due to all surface forces and body forces exerted on the system by the surroundings.

In using the transformation law (Eq. 2–6) for this case, the extensive property is $\mathbf{H}$ and the intensive property is $\mathbf{r} \times \mathbf{V}$. Thus,

$$\frac{D\mathbf{H}}{Dt} = \oiint_{\text{c.s.}} (\mathbf{r} \times \mathbf{V})(\rho \mathbf{V} \cdot d\mathbf{A}) + \frac{\partial}{\partial t} \iiint_{\text{c.v.}} \mathbf{r} \times \mathbf{V}\rho \, d\mathcal{V} \qquad (2\text{--}48)$$

which can be substituted into Eq. 2–47 to yield the following desired moment of momentum equation for the control volume of Fig. 2–8:

$$\mathbf{M} = \oiint_{\text{c.s.}} (\mathbf{r} \times \mathbf{V})(\rho \mathbf{V} \cdot d\mathbf{A}) + \frac{\partial}{\partial t} \iiint_{\text{c.v.}} \mathbf{r} \times \mathbf{V}\rho \, d\mathcal{V} \qquad (2\text{--}49)$$

Net rate of efflux of moment of momentum through the control surface at time $t$ ⎯ Rate of change of moment of momentum inside the control volume at time $t$

In most engineering problems we will use a single scalar equation by taking moment about a fixed axis in the inertial reference. By taking moments about, say, the $z$-axis, the scalar moment of momentum equation for the control volume becomes

$$M_z = \oiint_{\text{c.s.}} rV_\theta(\rho \mathbf{V} \cdot d\mathbf{A}) + \frac{\partial}{\partial t} \iiint_{\text{c.v.}} rV_\theta\rho \, d\mathcal{V} \qquad (2\text{--}50)$$

where the subscript $\theta$ for velocities denotes the tangential component which is normal to the radial distance $r$ measured from the $z$-axis. Note that $r$ is in a plane normal to the $z$-axis.

The moment of momentum equation is especially valuable for the analysis of turbomachines, such as water, steam, and gas turbines, centrifugal pumps, and many types of rotating fluid couplings, in which we have to deal with moments of forces (or torques) rather than with forces themselves.

*Illustrative Example 2–9.* The horizontal impeller shown in the accompanying illustration is held in a stationary position by an externally applied torque $\mathbf{M}_t$ while air flows through its four blade passages. Each passage is 1 inch wide at the inner periphery of the impeller and 0.75 in. wide at the outer periphery, and has a uniform depth of 3 in. At the intake end on the inner periphery the direction of the passage makes an angle $\theta_i = 45°$ with the tangent to the circle of radius $r_i = 6$ in. At the discharge end on the outer periphery the direction of the passage makes an angle $\theta_o = 60°$ with the tangent to the circle of radius

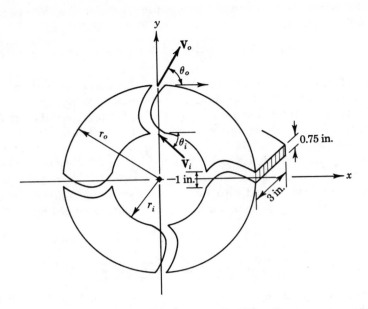

**Illustrative Example 2-9**

$r_0 = 12$ in. Air is drawn from a vertical center pipe and discharges through each passage at a steady rate $\hat{Q} = 2.5$ ft³/sec per passage. Assuming air to be incompressible and to have a specific weight of 0.0785 lbf/ft³, determine the torque $\mathbf{M}_t$ required to hold the impeller in the stationary position.

*Solution:* The impeller blade passages are taken as a control volume. The torque on the impeller can be determined by applying Eq. 2–50 to the air flow through the chosen control volume, with the axis of rotation chosen as the moment axis. Since the air flow through the impeller blade passages is steady, the volume integral in Eq. 2–50 drops out and the moment of momentum equation about the axis of rotation for the chosen control volume becomes

$$M_t = \oiint_{C.S.} rV_\theta(\rho \mathbf{V} \cdot d\mathbf{A})$$

$$= \iint_{A_o} r_o V_{o\theta}(\rho \mathbf{V}_o \cdot d\mathbf{A}_o) - \iint_{A_i} r_i V_{i\theta}(\rho \mathbf{V}_i \cdot d\mathbf{A}_i)$$

$$= 4\{[-r_o(V_o \cos \theta_o)\rho V_o A_o] - [r_i(V_i \cos \theta_i)\rho V_i A_i]\}$$

The velocities $V_o$ and $V_i$ can be determined from the continuity equation:

$$V_o = \frac{\hat{Q}}{A_o} = \frac{2.5 \text{ ft}^3/\text{sec}}{(0.75/12 \text{ ft})(3/12 \text{ ft})} = 160 \text{ ft/sec}$$

$$V_i = \frac{\hat{Q}}{A_i} = \frac{2.5 \text{ ft}^3/\text{sec}}{(1/12 \text{ ft})(3/12 \text{ ft})} = 120 \text{ ft/sec}$$

Substitution of the numerical values into the moment of momentum equation yields

$$M_t = 4\left\{\left[-\frac{12}{12}\,\text{ft}\left(160\,\frac{\text{ft}}{\text{sec}}\right)(0.5) \times \frac{0.0785\,\text{lbf/ft}^3}{32.2\,\text{ft/sec}^2} \times 160\,\frac{\text{ft}}{\text{sec}} \times \frac{0.75\,\text{in.} \times 3\,\text{in.}}{144\,\text{in}^2/\text{ft}^2}\right]\right.$$
$$\left. -\left[\frac{6}{12}\,\text{ft}\left(120\,\frac{\text{ft}}{\text{sec}}\right)(0.707) \times \frac{0.0785\,\text{lbf/ft}^3}{32.2\,\text{ft/sec}^2} \times 120\,\frac{\text{ft}}{\text{sec}} \times \frac{1\,\text{in.} \times 3\,\text{in.}}{144\,\text{in}^2/\text{ft}^2}\right]\right\}$$
$$= -2.98\,\text{ft-lbf}$$

Therefore, $\mathbf{M}_t = -2.98\,\mathbf{k}$ ft-lbf

**Illustrative Example 2-10.** The sprinkler shown in the diagram for this example discharges a steady rate of $\hat{Q}$ ft³/sec of water through its nozzle of area $A_o$. If the arm is rotating at a constant angular velocity $\Omega\mathbf{k}$ radians per second, determine the torque on the rotating arm about the axis of rotation from the flow of water.

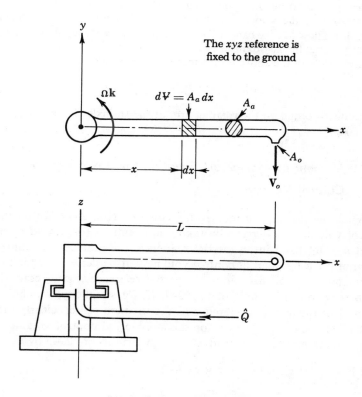

**Illustrative Example 2-10**

*Solution:* The interior of the rotating arm is chosen as a control volume. The reference *xyz* is fixed to the ground and is, therefore, an inertial reference.

Viewing the rotating control volume from the inertial reference, we can use Eq. 2–49 to formulate the moment of momentum equation for the control volume.

We use the vector $\mathbf{M}_t$ to denote the torque about the axis of rotation of the surface forces from the rotating arm on the control volume. The required torque on the rotating arm is then opposite to $\mathbf{M}_t$. The body force is gravity which cannot exert a torque about the $z$-axis, leaving $\mathbf{M}_t$ as the only torque on the control volume.

To evaluate the surface integral in Eq. 2–49, we must calculate the velocity of the water jet relative to the inertial reference $xyz$. The velocity of the water jet relative to the nozzle is $\mathbf{V}_o = -(\hat{Q}/A_o)\mathbf{j}$, and the nozzle is moving at a velocity of $\Omega L \mathbf{j}$ relative to the $xyz$ reference; so the velocity of the water jet relative to the $xyz$ reference must be $[-(\hat{Q}/A_o) + \Omega L]\mathbf{j}$. Hence

$$\iint\limits_{\text{C.S.}} \mathbf{r} \times \mathbf{V}(\rho\mathbf{V} \cdot d\mathbf{A}) = L\mathbf{i} \times \left(-\frac{\hat{Q}}{A_o} + \Omega L\right)\mathbf{j}(\rho\hat{Q}) = -L\rho\frac{\hat{Q}^2}{A_o}\mathbf{k} + \Omega L^2\rho\hat{Q}\mathbf{k}$$

Finally, by choosing the volume element $d\mathcal{V} = A_a\,dx$ as shown in the diagram, and noting that the velocity of this element relative to the $xyz$ reference is $[(\hat{Q}/A_a)\mathbf{i} + \Omega\mathbf{k} \times x\mathbf{i}]$, we can easily ascertain that, for steady flow through the control volume, the last term in Eq. 2–49 is zero.

Substitution of the above results into Eq. 2–49 yields

$$\mathbf{M}_t = -L\rho\frac{\hat{Q}^2}{A_o}\mathbf{k} + \Omega L^2\rho\hat{Q}\mathbf{k}$$

The required torque on the rotating arm of the sprinkler is then $(L\rho\hat{Q}^2/A_o - \Omega L^2\rho\hat{Q})\mathbf{k}$.

## 2-10  Moment of Momentum Equation for a Noninertial Control Volume

While the moment of momentum equation (Eq. 2–49) for an inertial control volume was derived by taking moments of forces and momenta about a point fixed in an inertial reference, the moment of momentum equation for a noninertial control volume will be derived by taking moments about a point fixed in a noninertial reference. Let us consider the noninertial control volume of Fig. 2–7. If, for simplicity, we choose the origin $O$ of the $x_{ni}y_{ni}z_{ni}$ reference as the moment center, clearly the moment of momentum equation for this noninertial control volume is obtained by taking the cross product of each term in Eq. 2–43 by $r_{ni}$. Thus,

$$\mathbf{r}_{ni} \times \mathbf{F} - \iiint\limits_{\text{C.V.}} \mathbf{r}_{ni} \times [\ddot{\mathbf{R}}_i + \boldsymbol{\alpha} \times \mathbf{r}_{ni} + 2\boldsymbol{\omega} \times \mathbf{V}_{ni} + \boldsymbol{\omega} \times (\boldsymbol{\omega} \times \mathbf{r}_{ni})]\rho\,d\mathcal{V}$$

$$= \iint\limits_{\text{C.S.}} (\mathbf{r}_{ni} \times \mathbf{V}_{ni})(\rho\mathbf{V}_{ni} \cdot d\mathbf{A}_{ni}) + \frac{\partial}{\partial t_{ni}}\iiint\limits_{\text{C.V.}} (\mathbf{r}_{ni} \times \mathbf{V}_{ni})\rho\,d\mathcal{V} \tag{2-51}$$

where $\mathbf{r}_{ni} \times \mathbf{F}$ represents the moment about $O$ of the resultant of all surface forces and body forces exerted on the control volume by the surroundings.

All other terms in this equation were defined in Sec. 2–8. Note that, in this equation, except for the vectors $\mathbf{R}_i$, $\boldsymbol{\alpha}$, and $\boldsymbol{\omega}$ all quantities and time derivatives are measured relative to the noninertial $x_{ni}y_{ni}z_{ni}$ reference and the noninertial control volume.

***Illustrative Example 2–11.*** If the $xyz$ reference in Ex. 2–10 is attached to the rotating arm of the sprinkler, it then becomes a noninertial reference. Work this example by using the moment of momentum equation for a control volume in a noninertial reference.

*Solution:* The interior of the rotating arm shown in the accompanying diagram is chosen as a control volume which is now fixed in the noninertial $xyz$ reference. In this solution we must use Eq. 2–51.

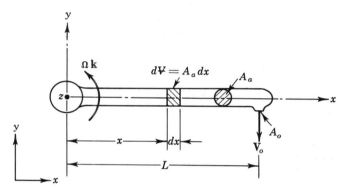

**Illustrative Example 2-11**

We use the vector $\mathbf{M}_t$ to denote the torque about the $z$-axis of the surface forces from the rotating arm on the control volume. The last term in Eq. 2–51 is zero due to the steady flow through the control volume. Furthermore, vectors $\ddot{\mathbf{R}}$ and $\boldsymbol{\alpha}$ are both zero. By neglecting the small amount of water in the nozzle and noting that $d\mathcal{V} = A_a\,dx$ as shown in the diagram, we may evaluate the volume integral on the left-hand side of Eq. 2–51 in the following manner:

$$\iiint\limits_{\text{C.V.}} \mathbf{r}_{ni} \times [2\boldsymbol{\omega} \times \mathbf{V}_{ni} + \boldsymbol{\omega} \times (\boldsymbol{\omega} \times \mathbf{r}_{ni})]\rho\,d\mathcal{V}$$

$$= \int_0^L x\mathbf{i} \times \left[2\Omega\mathbf{k} \times \frac{\hat{Q}}{A_a}\mathbf{i} + \Omega\mathbf{k} \times (\Omega\mathbf{k} \times x\mathbf{i})\right]\rho A_a\,dx$$

$$= \int_0^L \left[2\Omega\frac{\hat{Q}}{A_a}x\mathbf{k}\right]\rho A_a\,dx = \Omega L^2\rho\hat{Q}\mathbf{k}$$

To calculate the surface integral on the right-hand side of Eq. 2–51, we note that the velocity of the water jet relative to the noninertial reference is $-(\hat{Q}/A_o)\mathbf{j}$. Hence

$$\oiint\limits_{\text{C.S.}} \mathbf{r}_{ni} \times \mathbf{V}_{ni}(\rho\mathbf{V}_{ni} \cdot d\mathbf{A}_{ni}) = L\mathbf{i} \times \left(-\frac{\hat{Q}}{A_o}\right)\mathbf{j}(\rho\hat{Q}) = -L\rho\frac{\hat{Q}^2}{A_o}\mathbf{k}$$

Substituting the foregoing results into Eq. 2–51, and transposing the volume integral term, we have

$$\mathbf{M}_t = -L\rho \frac{\hat{Q}^2}{A_o}\mathbf{k} + \Omega L^2 \rho \hat{Q}\mathbf{k}$$

which is identical to the result obtained in Ex. 2–10.

## 2-11  Conservation of Energy—First Law of Thermodynamics

The general principle of conservation of energy is embodied in the first law of thermodynamics. As a generalization based on many macroscopic experiments, the first law stipulates that the variation in energy of a system during any transformation is equal to the amount of energy that the system receives from, or imparts to, its surroundings. In thermodynamics we classify, for convenience, energy under two categories, stored energy and energy in transition. Stored energy includes all the energy associated with the mass of a system in a given state. This energy might be present in a variety of forms:

(a) Kinetic energy (KE) which is associated with the motion of the mass of the system;

(b) Potential energy (PE) which is associated with the position of the mass of the system in external fields;

(c) Internal energy ($\hat{U}$) which includes molecular and atomic energy associated with the internal fields of the mass of the system.

On the other hand, energy in transition accounts for the energy which is transferred from a system to its surroundings, or vice versa, as a result of interactions between the system and its surroundings. There are two types of energy in transition, heat and work. *Heat* is energy in transition between a system and its surroundings as a result of a temperature difference between the two. *Work* is energy in transition between a system and its surroundings when forces, acting at the boundary of the system, move through a distance.

Consider Fig. 2–9 in which fluid flows through a control volume. We define the fluid mass which occupies the control volume at time $t$ as a *system*. During a time interval $dt$ this system undergoes a change of state if energy crosses the boundary of the system as either heat or work. Both heat and work may be transferred into or out of the system. Conservation of energy requires that the net energy which crosses the boundary of the system be exactly equal to the net change in the stored energy of the system. Thus, if we denote $\delta Q$ as heat transferred into the system, $\delta W$ as work done by the system on the surroundings, and $dE$ as the net change in the stored energy of the system during the time interval $dt$, the

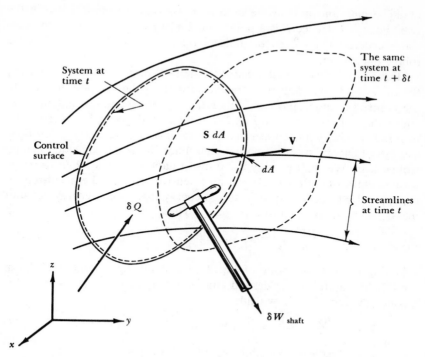

**Fig. 2-9.** Flow of fluid through a control volume showing the conservation of energy.

first law of thermodynamics for the system can be written in differential form as:

$$\delta Q - \delta W = dE = d(\text{KE} + \text{PE} + \hat{U}) \qquad (2\text{--}52)$$

After we divide through by $dt$ and set the limit $dt \to 0$, this differential equation becomes a rate equation:

$$\frac{dQ}{dt} - \frac{dW}{dt} = \frac{DE}{Dt} \qquad (2\text{--}53)$$

In Eq. 2–52 we use $\delta Q$ and $\delta W$ instead of $dQ$ and $dW$ in order to emphasize that both $Q$ and $W$ are not perfect differentials. We learn in thermodynamics that both $Q$ and $W$ are path functions; i.e., changes in $Q$ and $W$ depend on the actual path that the system follows. Therefore, when we express these two quantities in rate form in Eq. 2–53, we simply use the usual time derivative notations $dQ/dt$ and $dW/dt$. On the other hand, $dE$ is a perfect differential. Thermodynamic studies reveal that for any process the quantity $dE$ depends only on the initial and final states of the system and not on the path that the system follows between the two end states. Hence $E$ is a point function. In Eq. 2–53 we use the substantive derivative $DE/Dt$ to indicate that this rate is evaluated as we follow the system.

Equation 2–53 is a mathematical statement of conservation of energy for the system. We shall now transform it from the system approach to the control volume approach. Since the system under investigation occupies the control volume of Fig. 2–9 at time $t$ and since all the derivatives in Eq. 2–53 are evaluated at time $t$, we can also regard $dQ/dt$ and $dW/dt$ as rates of energy in transition between fluids inside and outside the control surface. We shall employ the transformation law (Eq. 2–6) to transform the term $DE/Dt$. Clearly $E$ is an extensive property. Let us introduce the symbol $e$ to denote specific stored energy (i.e., stored energy per unit mass) which is an intensive property. Thus,

$$\frac{DE}{Dt} = \oiint_{\text{C.S.}} e\rho \mathbf{V} \cdot d\mathbf{A} + \frac{\partial}{\partial t} \iiint_{\text{C.V.}} e\rho \, dV \qquad (2\text{–}54)$$

Equating the left-hand side of Eq. 2–53 and the right-hand side of Eq. 2–54 yields the following desired equation of conservation of energy for a control volume in a flow field:

$$\frac{dQ}{dt} - \frac{dW}{dt} = \oiint_{\text{C.S.}} e\rho \mathbf{V} \cdot d\mathbf{A} + \frac{\partial}{\partial t} \iiint_{\text{C.V.}} e\rho \, dV \qquad (2\text{–}55)$$

| Net rate of energy transferred into the control volume by heat and work at time $t$ | Net rate of efflux of stored energy from the control volume at time $t$ | Rate of increase of stored energy inside the control volume at time $t$ |

To be of value in solving fluid mechanics problems, this equation must be further transformed to a working form which will be readily applicable to fluid flow problems. The transformation is worked out in the following paragraphs.

**Rate of change of stored energy.** Since the specific stored energy $e$ in a given mass is a thermodynamic property, its value at any state can be evaluated, for any chosen process, from the known value of $e$ at another state. We may therefore define $e$ as the net energy that must be expended on a unit mass to bring it from rest to the designated values of specific kinetic, potential, and internal energies. The kinetic energy of a differential mass $\rho \, dV$ is $\rho \, dV \, V^2/2$ and the specific kinetic energy is then $V^2/2$. If we assume that the only external field is the earth's gravitational field, the potential energy of the differential mass $\rho \, dV$ at an elevation $z$ above an arbitrarily chosen elevation datum is $\rho \, dV \, gz$ and its specific potential energy then has the quantity $gz$, where $g$ is the local gravitational acceleration at the elevation $z$. We use the lower case $\hat{u}$ to denote the specific internal energy. Hence in the absence of electricity, magnetism, and capillarity, $e$ is given by

$$e = \frac{V^2}{2} + gz + \hat{u} \qquad (2\text{-}56)$$

in which each term has the dimensions of energy per unit mass.

### Rate of work $(dW/dt)$ done by the fluid inside the control volume on the surroundings.

In general the work performed by the fluid mass inside the control volume at time $t$ on the surroundings consists of two basic types:

(a) Shaft work due to torque transmitted by the part of a shaft located inside the control surface to the other part of the shaft located outside of the control surface. This torque arises from resisting forces which act on the portion of the rotating shaft and blades in contact with the fluid inside the control surface. We shall denote the rate of shaft work by $dW_{\text{shaft}}/dt$.

(b) Flow work done on the surroundings due to forces at those positions of the control surface across which fluid flows. To evaluate flow work, let us consider an area element $dA$ of the control surface through which fluid flows out of the control volume as shown in Fig. 2–10. The force acting at this area element from the fluid inside the control volume on the surroundings is shown as $\mathbf{S}\,dA$, where $\mathbf{S}$ is the vector stress at this point. Note that here the positive direction of the vector $\mathbf{S}\,dA$ is directed

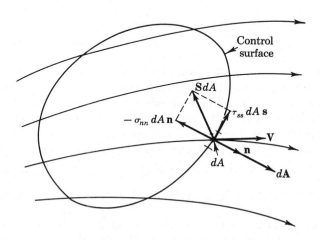

**Fig. 2-10.** Evaluation of flow work.

toward the interior of the control volume because the flow work is performed on the surroundings. The components of this vector stress are normal stress $\sigma_{nn}$ and shear stress $\tau_{ss}$. If $\mathbf{V}$ is the velocity of efflux of the fluid passing through the area element, the rate of work being transferred out of the control volume through $d\mathbf{A}$ is then the dot product $\mathbf{S}\, d A \cdot \mathbf{V}$. Hence the net rate of flow work $(dW_{\text{flow}}/dt)$ transferred out of the control volume through the entire control surface is $\oiint_{\text{C.S.}} \mathbf{S}\, dA \cdot \mathbf{V}$. Since

$$\mathbf{S} = -\sigma_{nn}\mathbf{n} + \tau_{ss}\mathbf{s}$$

where $\mathbf{n}$ is the outward unit vector normal to the area element $dA$ and $\mathbf{s}$ is the unit vector in the direction of $\tau_{ss}$, we may also write

$$
\begin{aligned}
\frac{dW_{\text{flow}}}{dt} &= \oiint_{\text{C.S.}} \mathbf{S}\, dA \cdot \mathbf{V} \\
&= \oiint_{\text{C.S.}} -\sigma_{nn}\mathbf{n}\, dA \cdot \mathbf{V} + \oiint_{\text{C.S.}} \tau_{ss}\mathbf{s}\, dA \cdot \mathbf{V} \qquad (2\text{–}57) \\
&= \oiint_{\text{C.S.}} -\sigma_{nn}\mathbf{V} \cdot d\mathbf{A} + \oiint_{\text{C.S.}} \tau_{ss}\mathbf{s} \cdot \mathbf{V}\, dA
\end{aligned}
$$

By substituting these results into Eq. 2–55, we see that the energy equation for a control volume assumes the following very general form:

$$
\begin{aligned}
\frac{dQ}{dt} - \frac{dW_{\text{shaft}}}{dt} - \oiint_{\text{C.S.}} &-\sigma_{nn}\mathbf{V} \cdot d\mathbf{A} - \oiint_{\text{C.S.}} \tau_{ss}\mathbf{s} \cdot \mathbf{V}\, dA \\
&= \oiint_{\text{C.S.}} \left(\frac{V^2}{2} + gz + \hat{u}\right)\rho \mathbf{V} \cdot d\mathbf{A} + \frac{\partial}{\partial t}\iiint_{\text{C.V.}} e\rho\, d V
\end{aligned} \qquad (2\text{–}58)
$$

This equation in its present form is, however, seldom used in engineering calculations because of the difficulty in evaluating shear work due to shear stress $\tau_{ss}$. We can, however, make the surface integration involving $\tau_{ss}$ vanish since shear work is transferred only at that portion of the control surface through which the fluid velocity has a component tangent to the control surface.[4] If the flow entering and leaving a control volume is everywhere normal to the control surface, this type of shear work is zero. Therefore, in engineering calculations, one always chooses the control surface at the inflow and outflow sections normal to the local velocity so as to make the integral $\oiint_{\text{C.S.}} \tau_{ss}\mathbf{s} \cdot \mathbf{V}\, dA$ equal to zero. Furthermore, if the streamlines are straight and parallel as they cross the

---

[4] It should be emphasized here that at a solid boundary in the flow field the velocity of flow relative to the solid boundary is zero. Therefore, shear forces do not perform any work on solid boundaries.

control surface, $\sigma_{nn} = -p$. Hence for these conditions we get for the rate of flow work transferred through the entire control surface

$$\frac{dW_{\text{flow}}}{dt} = \oiint_{\text{C.S.}} p\mathbf{V} \cdot d\mathbf{A} \tag{2-59}$$

By definition the product of the density $\rho$ and the specific volume $v$ is unity. We may insert $\rho v$ into the integrand of the above equation without changing its value to get

$$\frac{dW_{\text{flow}}}{dt} = \oiint_{\text{C.S.}} p v \rho \mathbf{V} \cdot d\mathbf{A} \tag{2-59a}$$

Then the energy equation for a control volume takes on this more familiar form:

$$\frac{dQ}{dt} - \frac{dW_{\text{shaft}}}{dt} = \oiint_{\text{C.S.}} \left(\frac{V^2}{2} + gz + \hat{u} + pv\right) \rho \mathbf{V} \cdot d\mathbf{A} + \frac{\partial}{\partial t} \iiint_{\text{C.V.}} e\rho \, dV$$

$$\tag{2-60}$$

in which the sum $\hat{u} + pv$ forms another intensive property called *specific enthalpy h*. In the above equation although the $pv$ term is added to other specific energy terms, it is not a form of specific energy. We must always regard the product $pv$ as flow work per unit mass which is transferred through the control surface. For steady flows the term $\partial\left(\iiint_{\text{C.V.}} e\rho \, dV\right)\Big/\partial t$ vanishes.

Since these equations are derived from the first law of thermodynamics, their only restrictions are those associated with the first law. Note also that, in the above derivation, the stored energy consists of kinetic energy, gravitational potential energy, and internal energy. In the event that energies in other forms should be present in a given problem, we must add them to the above equation.

## 2-12 Energy Equation for One-dimensional Steady Flow

Consider Fig. 2–11. This sketch may represent a steady flow through a machine such as a pump, turbine, or compressor. The interior of the machine is chosen as a control volume. Sections *ii* and *oo* of the control surface have been established in the inlet and outlet pipes of the machine. Flows through these two sections are one-dimensional and the velocities at these two sections are normal to the control surface.

When Eq. 2–60 is applied to this problem, the last term becomes zero since for steady flow the stored energy inside the control volume remains constant with time, and the surface integration is taken over the inlet and outlet areas. Hence the energy equation for the one-dimensional

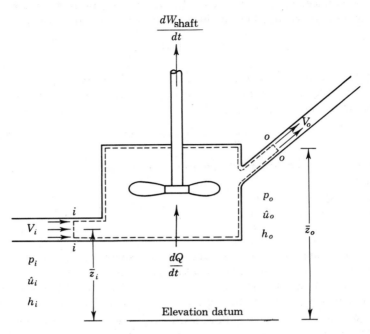

**Fig. 2-11.** One-dimensional steady flow through a machine.

steady flow of Fig. 2–11 takes the following form:

$$\frac{dQ}{dt} - \frac{dW_{\text{shaft}}}{dt} = \iint\limits_{A_i} \left(\frac{V_i^2}{2} + gz_i + h_i\right)\rho_i \mathbf{V}_i \cdot d\mathbf{A}_i$$
$$+ \iint\limits_{A_o} \left(\frac{V_o^2}{2} + gz_o + h_o\right)\rho_o \mathbf{V}_o \cdot d\mathbf{A}_o$$

(2–61)

in which $h = \hat{u} + pv$ as previously defined. If all properties are constant over cross sections $ii$ and $oo$, the surface integrations of Eq. 2–61 can be further simplified. For example, at the inlet area, the kinetic energy term can be simplified in the following manner:

$$\iint\limits_{A_i} \frac{V_i^2}{2}\rho_i \mathbf{V}_i \cdot d\mathbf{A}_i = \iint\limits_{A_i} \frac{V_i^2}{2}\rho_i(-V_i\,dA_i) = -\frac{V_i^2}{2}\rho_i V_i A_i$$

since the cosine of the angle between the $\mathbf{V}_i$ and $d\mathbf{A}_i$ vectors equals minus one, and both $\rho_i$ and $V_i$ are constant over the inlet area $A_i$. Likewise, the gravitational potential energy term becomes

$$\iint\limits_{A_i} gz_i\rho_i \mathbf{V}_i \cdot d\mathbf{A}_i = \iint\limits_{A_i} gz_i\rho_i(-V_i\,dA_i) = -g\bar{z}_i\rho_i V_i A_i$$

where $\bar{z}_i$ is the $z$-coordinate of the centroid of the inlet area. Similar calculation can be carried out for the outlet area. Thus, integration of Eq. 2–61 yields

$$\frac{dQ}{dt} - \frac{dW_{\text{shaft}}}{dt} = -\left(\frac{V_i^2}{2} + g\bar{z}_i + h_i\right)\rho_i V_i A_i + \left(\frac{V_o^2}{2} + g\bar{z}_o + h_o\right)\rho_o V_o A_o$$

$$(2\text{–}62)$$

The equation of continuity for this one-dimensional steady flow is

$$\rho_i V_i A_i = \rho_o V_o A_o = \frac{dm}{dt} \qquad (2\text{–}63)$$

where $dm/dt$ is the rate of mass flow through this machine. Dividing Eq. 2–62 by $dm/dt$ and rearranging terms, we obtain the following familiar energy equation for a one-dimensional steady flow through a control volume:

$$\left(\frac{V_i^2}{2} + g\bar{z}_i + h_i\right) + \frac{dQ/dt}{dm/dt} = \left(\frac{V_o^2}{2} + g\bar{z}_o + h_o\right) + \frac{dW_{\text{shaft}}/dt}{dm/dt} \qquad (2\text{–}64)$$

| stored energy and flow work | heat | stored energy and flow work | shaft work |

per unit mass of flow transferred into the control volume at time $t$      per unit mass of flow transferred out of the control volume at time $t$

Many thermodynamics textbooks refer to this equation as the *first law of thermodynamics for steady-state open systems.* Each term in this equation has the dimensions of energy per unit mass. This equation also shows that any unit mass of fluid carries with it during its motion an amount of energy $V^2/2 + gz$ plus an amount of enthalpy $h$.

*Illustrative Example 2–12.* During a steady flow process, 5 lbm/sec of fluid passes through a machine in which the discharge pipe is 25 ft below the level of the inlet connection. Pertinent data regarding the working fluid are

|  | At the inlet | At the discharge |
|---|---|---|
| Fluid density | 1 lbm/ft³ | 0.16 lbm/ft³ |
| Fluid pressure | 150 lbf/in.² (abs) | 15 lbf/in.² (abs) |
| Velocity of flow | 100 ft/sec | 1000 ft/sec |
| Internal energy | 8 Btu/lbm | 6 Btu/lbm |

If the rate at which heat is transferred out of the machine is 50 Btu/sec, calculate the power transferred by machine work.

*Solution:* We choose the control volume to include the interior of the machine and to terminate at the inlet and discharge pipe sections where the above data were measured. The steady flow in this problem is one-dimensional, and so we may apply Eq. 2–64 to the inlet $i$ and the discharge $d$ sections to obtain

$$\left(\frac{V_i^2}{2} + g\bar{z}_i + h_i\right) + \frac{dQ/dt}{dm/dt} = \left(\frac{V_d^2}{2} + g\bar{z}_d + h_d\right) + \frac{dW_{\text{shaft}}/dt}{dm/dt}$$

in which the shaft work is assumed to be transferred out of the control volume. To solve for $(dW_{shaft}/dt)/(dm/dt)$

$$\frac{dW_{shaft}/dt}{dm/dt} = \frac{V_i^2 - V_d^2}{2} + g(\bar{z}_i - \bar{z}_d) + (h_i - h_d) + \frac{dQ/dt}{dm/dt}$$

and by calculating each term in this equation in the units of ft-lbf/lbm of the working fluid, using $g_c \equiv 32.174$ lbm-ft/lbf-sec$^2$ and $J \equiv 778.16$ ft-lbf/Btu as conversion factors to obtain correct units,

$$\frac{V_i^2 - V_d^2}{2 g_c} = \frac{(\overline{100^2} - \overline{1000^2})(\text{ft/sec})^2}{2 \times 32.174 \text{ lbm-ft/lbf-sec}^2} = -15{,}385 \frac{\text{ft-lbf}}{\text{lbm}}$$

$$\frac{g(\bar{z}_i - \bar{z}_d)}{g_c} = \frac{(32.174 \text{ ft/sec}^2)(25 \text{ ft})}{32.174 \text{ lbm-ft/lbf-sec}^2} = 25 \frac{\text{ft-lbf}}{\text{lbm}}$$

$$h_i - h_d = \left(J\hat{u}_i + \frac{p_i}{\rho_i}\right) + \left(J\hat{u}_d + \frac{p_d}{\rho_d}\right)$$

$$= \left[778.16 \frac{\text{ft-lbf}}{\text{Btu}} \times 8 \frac{\text{Btu}}{\text{lbm}} + \frac{(150 \text{ lbf/in}^2)(144 \text{ in}^2/\text{ft}^2)}{1 \text{ lbm/ft}^3}\right]$$

$$- \left[778.16 \frac{\text{ft-lbf}}{\text{Btu}} \times 6 \frac{\text{Btu}}{\text{lbm}} + \frac{(15 \text{ lbf/in}^2)(144 \text{ in}^2/\text{ft}^2)}{0.16 \text{ lbm/ft}^3}\right]$$

$$= 9656 \text{ ft-lbf/lbm}$$

$$J\frac{dQ/dt}{dm/dt} = 778.16 \frac{\text{ft-lbf}}{\text{Btu}} \times \frac{-50 \text{ Btu/sec}}{5 \text{ lbm/sec}}$$

$$= -7782 \frac{\text{ft-lbf}}{\text{lbm}}$$

Therefore,

$$\frac{dW_{shaft}/dt}{dm/dt} = -15{,}385 + 25 + 9656 + (-7782)$$

$$= -13{,}486 \frac{\text{ft-lbf}}{\text{lbm}}$$

The negative sign indicates that the shaft work is actually being transferred into the control volume. Thus the power transferred into the control volume is

$$13{,}486 \frac{\text{ft-lbf}}{\text{lbm}} \times 5 \frac{\text{lbm}}{\text{sec}} = 67{,}430 \frac{\text{ft-lbf}}{\text{sec}}$$

which, upon dividing by 550 ft-lbf/sec/hp, is equivalent to 122.6 hp.

## 2-13 Bernoulli's Equation along a Streamline

Bernoulli's equation along a streamline may be obtained by the integration of Euler's equation (Eq. 2-38) for frictionless flow. Let us rewrite Eq. 2-38 here for convenience of reference:

$$-\nabla p + \rho\mathbf{g} = \rho \frac{D\mathbf{V}}{Dt}$$

For our present purpose we shall modify this equation by first assuming that the $z$-axis is in a vertical position with its positive direction pointed upward so that the second term $\rho g$ can be written as $-\rho g \, \nabla z$. Next, to integrate this equation along a streamline, the streamline coordinates (Fig. 2–12) are adopted. If the symbol $s$ denotes the position of a fluid

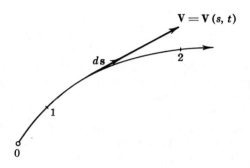

**Fig. 2-12.**   Streamline coordinates.

particle along a particular streamline, we may write $\mathbf{V} = \mathbf{V}(s, t)$. Thus, on the right-hand side, the acceleration term $D\mathbf{V}/Dt = V(\partial \mathbf{V}/\partial s) + \partial \mathbf{V}/\partial t$. After making substitutions and then dividing the equation through by $\rho$, we see that Euler's equation takes the following form:

$$-\frac{\nabla p}{\rho} - g\nabla z = V\frac{\partial \mathbf{V}}{\partial s} + \frac{\partial \mathbf{V}}{\partial t}$$

We now form the dot product of each term in the above equation with the displacement vector $d\mathbf{s}$ along a streamline to obtain

$$-\frac{\nabla p}{\rho} \cdot d\mathbf{s} - g\,\nabla z \cdot d\mathbf{s} = V\frac{\partial \mathbf{V}}{\partial s} \cdot d\mathbf{s} + \frac{\partial \mathbf{V}}{\partial t} \cdot d\mathbf{s}$$

As we learn from vector analysis, the projection of the gradient on any direction is the derivative in that direction. Thus, in the first term $\nabla p \cdot d\mathbf{s}$ becomes $dp$, the differential change in pressure along a streamline, and in the second term $\nabla z \cdot d\mathbf{s} = dz$, the differential change in elevation along a streamline. On the right-hand side, the first term $V(\partial \mathbf{V}/\partial s) \cdot d\mathbf{s}$ $= V(\partial V/\partial s)\, ds = V\, dV = d(V^2/2)$, and the second term $(\partial V/\partial t) \cdot d\mathbf{s}$ simply becomes $(\partial V/\partial t)\, ds$, since $\mathbf{V}$ and $d\mathbf{s}$ are collinear. Hence we may make substitutions and transpose terms to obtain the following Euler's equation along a streamline:

$$\frac{dp}{\rho} + g\, dz + d\frac{V^2}{2} + \frac{\partial V}{\partial t}\, ds = 0$$

Taking $g$ as a constant and integrating between any two points 1 and 2 along a streamline yields

$$\int_1^2 \frac{dp}{\rho} + g(z_2 - z_1) + \frac{V_2^2 - V_1^2}{2} + \int_1^2 \frac{\partial V}{\partial t} ds = B(t)$$

where $B(t)$, an arbitrary function of time, is called the *Bernoulli function*. Since points 1 and 2 are arbitrary, we may also write the above equation for every point along a streamline as

$$\int_0^p \frac{dp}{\rho} + gz + \frac{V^2}{2} + \int_0^s \frac{\partial V}{\partial t} ds = B(t) \qquad (2\text{-}65)$$

This equation is applicable for frictionless compressible unsteady flows. We may interpret the equation as follows: At any instant, the sum of four terms on the left-hand side has the same value of Bernoulli function at all points of a streamline in an unsteady flow field. However, this Bernoulli function will vary from streamline to streamline. Likewise, on a particular streamline, its Bernoulli function varies with time. If the flow is steady, the time-varying factors drop out and Eq. 2-65 is simplified to

$$\int_0^p \frac{dp}{\rho} + gz + \frac{V^2}{2} = B \qquad (2\text{-}66)$$

The Bernoulli constant $B$ will remain the same only on a particular stream-line, and, in general, will vary from streamline to streamline. Equation 2-66 is commonly referred to as *Bernoulli's equation for compressible flows*. Integration of the first term can be carried out once the functional relationship between $p$ and $\rho$ is known. For example, the density of a barotropic fluid is a single-valued function of $p$, i.e., $\rho = \rho(p)$, and the first term can be readily integrated.

If the flow is incompressible, Bernoulli's equation takes the following simple form:

$$\frac{p}{\rho} + gz + \frac{V^2}{2} = B \qquad (2\text{-}67)$$

In words, Eq. 2-67 states that for each unit mass the sum of flow work, potential energy, and kinetic energy is conserved along a streamline in a frictionless incompressible steady flow field. Hence we may write Bernoulli's equation for any two positions 1 and 2 along a streamline as

$$\frac{p_1}{\rho} + gz_1 + \frac{V_1^2}{2} = \frac{p_2}{\rho} + gz_2 + \frac{V_2^2}{2} \qquad (2\text{-}68)$$

The more familiar form of Bernoulli's equation is obtained when each term in Eq. 2-67 is divided by $g$. Thus, with $\gamma = \rho g$,

$$\frac{p}{\gamma} + z + \frac{V^2}{2g} = H \qquad (2\text{-}69)$$

in which each term has the dimensions of energy per unit weight. In the foot-pound-second system, a pound force has approximately the same magnitude as a pound mass, and each term is frequently expressed (though wrongly) in the unit of ft. As a result the terms $p/\gamma$, $z$, and $V^2/2g$ are respectively called *pressure head*, *elevation head*, and *velocity head*. The sum of $(p/\gamma) + z$ is usually called *potential head*, $h_{pz}$ (or piezometric head). The sum of all three terms in Eq. 2–69 is called the *total head H*.

The physical significance of Eq. 2–69 and the interpretation of representing each term as head can be most easily understood by examining Fig. 2–13 in which Bernoulli's equation is represented graphically by the

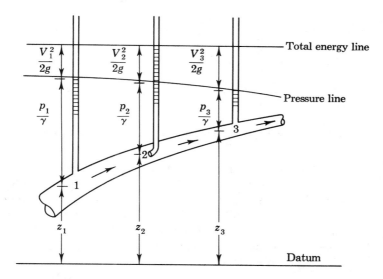

**Fig. 2-13.** Graphical representation of Bernoulli's equation.

total energy line and pressure line (sometimes called *piezometric line*) of fluid flow along a streamline. The horizontal line at the top is the total energy line. This is also the elevation to which the liquid will rise in a *stagnation tube*. The pressure line is everywhere at a distance of $V^2/2g$ below the total energy line. The liquid in a *piezometric tube* rises to an elevation indicated by the pressure line.

**Bernoulli's equation as a special form of the first law of thermodynamics.** Comparison of Eqs. 2–68 and 2–64 reveals the close similarity between the terms in Bernoulli's equation and those in the energy equation for one-dimensional steady flow. We shall now explore the relationship between these two equations.

Let us apply the first law of thermodynamics to a control volume
which consists of a portion of a stream tube in a steady flow as shown
in Fig. 2–14. The flow in the stream tube is one-dimensional so that we

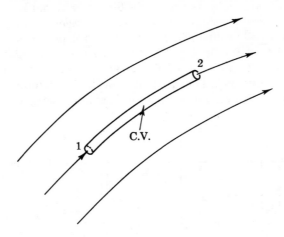

**Fig. 2-14.**  Steady flow through a portion of a stream tube.

may use Eq. 2–64 to relate the energy transformation of flow through
this control volume. With no machine located inside the control volume,
the shaft work term vanishes. Furthermore, since the cross sections of
the control volume are infinitesimally small, we may replace $\bar{z}$ by $z$.
Applying Eq. 2–64 to the control volume of Fig. 2–14, using the subscripts
for the two sections of the stream tube, and rearranging terms, we then
have the following energy equation:

$$\frac{p_1}{\rho_1} + gz_1 + \frac{V_1^2}{2} = \frac{p_2}{\rho_2} + gz_2 + \frac{V_2^2}{2} + \left[ (\hat{u}_2 - \hat{u}_1) - \frac{dQ/dt}{dm/dt} \right] \quad (2\text{–}70)$$

Equation 2–70 is valid for the steady flow of both compressible and
incompressible fluids. When the flow is incompressible, $\rho_1 = \rho_2 = \rho$.
In incompressible flows, an increase in internal energy merely produces
an increase in temperature and is generally nonrecoverable as useful
energy for the flow system. This increased internal energy is eventually
transferred out of the flow system just as the heat transfer term. Hence
the terms inside the square brackets are associated with friction loss from
the flow system. Thus,

$$(\hat{u}_2 - \hat{u}_1) - \frac{dQ/dt}{dm/dt} = gh_L \quad (2\text{–}71)$$

in which $h_L$ is the friction loss per unit weight of the fluid flowing through
a control volume.

The energy equation for a steady flow of an incompressible viscous fluid in a stream tube may also be written as

$$\frac{p_1}{\rho} + gz_1 + \frac{V_1^2}{2} = \frac{p_2}{\rho} + gz_2 + \frac{V_2^2}{2} + gh_L \qquad (2\text{–}72)$$

The direction of flow is always from section 1 to section 2. If the flow is assumed frictionless, the last term vanishes and Eq. 2–72 is simplified to

$$\frac{p_1}{\rho} + gz_1 + \frac{V_1^2}{2} = \frac{p_2}{\rho} + gz_2 + \frac{V_2^2}{2} \qquad (2\text{–}73)$$

Since both sections 1 and 2 are chosen arbitrarily, it follows that

$$\left(\frac{p}{\rho} + gz + \frac{V^2}{2}\right)_{\text{any section}} = \text{constant} \qquad (2\text{–}74)$$

which is Bernoulli's equation for the steady frictionless flow of an incompressible fluid in a stream tube.

**Applications of Bernoulli's equations.** Although there is always some friction loss in the flow of real fluids, in many engineering problems the assumption of frictionless flow may yield satisfactory results, and so Bernoulli's equation can be used to determine the essential characteristics of flow. However, in applying Bernoulli's equation to any fluid flow problem, one must observe the restrictions of Bernoulli's equation which have been outlined carefully in the above derivations.

The following examples illustrate the applications of Bernoulli's equations.

*Illustrative Example 2–13.* In the inclined pipeline shown in the accompanying diagram, the 8-in. (diameter) pipe is connected to a 4-in. (diameter) pipe by a short well-streamlined pipe reducer. Water flows in the upward direction. For a manometer reading of 10 in. of mercury, what is the discharge in cubic feet per second? The specific gravity of mercury is 13.6.

*Solution:* Denote $h$ as the vertical distance between section $c$ and the water-mercury interface in the manometer tube and $y$ as the vertical distance between the centers of the two sections in which manometer tappings are located. If the flow constriction in the pipe, as shown in the figure, is well-streamlined, the loss of energy is practically equal to zero, and so Bernoulli's equation can be applied to sections $a$ and $c$:

$$\frac{p_a}{\gamma_w} + z_a + \frac{V_a^2}{2g} = \frac{p_c}{\gamma_w} + z_c + \frac{V_c^2}{2g}$$

By taking section $a$ as the elevation datum,

$$\frac{p_a}{\gamma_w} + 0 + \frac{V_a^2}{2g} = \frac{p_c}{\gamma_w} + y + \frac{V_c^2}{2g}$$

This equation can be rearranged as

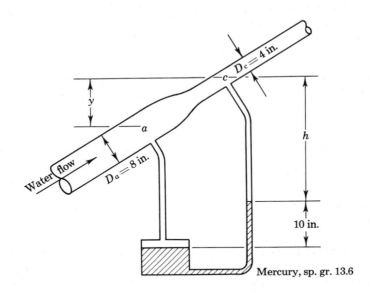

**Illustrative Example 2-13**

$$\frac{V_c^2}{2g} - \frac{V_a^2}{2g} = \frac{p_a}{\gamma_w} - \frac{p_c}{\gamma_w} - y \qquad \text{(A)}$$

The difference in pressure head $(p_a/\gamma_w - p_c/\gamma_w)$ is determined by writing the pressure equation for the differential manometer starting at section $a$:

$$\frac{p_a}{\gamma_w} + \left(h - y + \frac{10}{12}\right) - \frac{10}{12}(13.6) - h = \frac{p_c}{\gamma_w}$$

in which the unit for each term is ft (of water). Hence

$$\frac{p_a}{\gamma_w} - \frac{p_c}{\gamma_w} = y + \frac{10}{12}(13.6) - \frac{10}{12}$$

which may now be substituted into Eq. (A) to obtain

$$\frac{V_c^2}{2g} - \frac{V_a^2}{2g} = y + \frac{10}{12}(13.6) - \frac{10}{12} - y = \frac{10}{12}(12.6)\,\text{ft} \qquad \text{(B)}$$

The continuity equation of flow is

$$A_a V_a = A_c V_c$$

or

$$\frac{\pi}{4}\left(\frac{8}{12}\right)^2 V_a = \frac{\pi}{4}\left(\frac{4}{12}\right)^2 V_c$$

$$V_a = \frac{1}{4} V_c$$

Then, by substituting $V_c/4$ for $V_a$ in Eq. (B),

$$\frac{V_c^2}{2g}\left(1 - \frac{1}{16}\right) = \frac{10}{12}(12.6)\,\text{ft}$$

Hence the velocity at section $c$ is

$$V_c = \sqrt{2g\,\frac{\text{ft}}{\text{sec}^2} \times 12.6 \times \frac{10}{12}\text{ft} \times \frac{16}{15}} = 26.8 \text{ ft/sec}$$

The discharge is

$$\hat{Q} = A_c V_c = \frac{\pi}{4}\left(\frac{4\text{ in.}}{12\text{ in/ft}}\right)^2 \times 26.8\,\frac{\text{ft}}{\text{sec}} = 2.34 \text{ ft}^3/\text{sec}$$

*Illustrative Example 2–14.* A large tank of liquid has a horizontal tapered pipe of length $L$ connected to it, as shown in the accompanying figure. The tank is

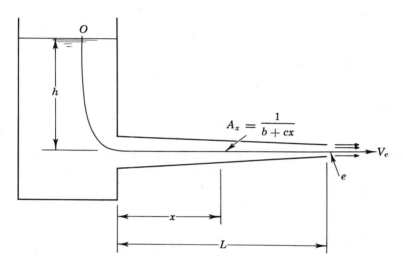

$$A_x = \frac{1}{b + cx}$$

**Illustrative Example 2-14**

open to the atmosphere, and the surface of liquid in the tank is at a height $h$ above the axis of the pipe. At any position $x$ from the pipe entrance, the cross-sectional area $A_x$ of the tapered pipe can be expressed by the following equation:

$$A_x = \frac{1}{b + cx}$$

where $b$ and $c$ are constants. The open end $e$ of the pipe is originally plugged. At time $t = 0$, the plug is pulled out of the open end, and liquid begins to flow under the action of gravity. Derive an expression relating the velocity $V_e$ and time $t$ after the plug is pulled out of the open end of the pipe.

*Solution:* Points $O$ and $e$ are designated as shown in the figure. It is evident that the flow through the pipe is unsteady; that is, $V_x = V_x(x, t)$ and $V_e = V_e(t)$.

Therefore, for the streamline joining points $O$ and $e$, Eq. 2–65 yields

$$\frac{p_O}{\rho} + gz_O + \frac{V_O^2}{2} = \frac{p_e}{\rho} + gz_e + \frac{V_e^2}{2} + \int_0^L \frac{\partial V}{\partial t}\, dx \qquad (A)$$

in which we have assumed a quasi-steady condition in the tank because the tank area is large compared to the cross-sectional area of the pipe. Hence $V_O^2/2 \approx 0$. Since $p_O = p_e = p_{\text{atm.}}$, the pressure terms cancel. The difference of elevations is $z_O - z_e = h$. The continuity equation for the flow through the pipe is

$$V_x A_x = \frac{V_x}{b + cx} = V_e A_e = \frac{V_e}{b + cL}$$

Whence

$$V_x = \frac{b + cx}{b + cL}\, V_e$$

and

$$\frac{\partial V_x}{\partial t} = \frac{b + cx}{b + cL}\, \frac{\partial V_e}{\partial t}$$

Consequently, Eq. (A) becomes

$$gh = \frac{V_e^2}{2} + \int_0^L \frac{b + cx}{b + cL}\, \frac{\partial V_e}{\partial t}\, dx$$

or, after integration,

$$gh = \frac{V_e^2}{2} + \frac{bL + cL^2/2}{b + cL}\, \frac{\partial V_e}{\partial t}$$

This is a differential equation for $V_e$. We separate the variables to obtain

$$dt = \frac{2bL + cL^2}{b + cL}\, \frac{dV_e}{2gh - V_e^2}$$

which may be readily integrated with the initial condition $V_e = 0$ at $t = 0$, to yield

$$t = \frac{2bL + cL^2}{(b + cL)\sqrt{2gh}}\, \text{arctanh}\, \frac{V_e}{\sqrt{2gh}}$$

or

$$V_e = \sqrt{2gh}\, \tanh \frac{(b + cL)\sqrt{2gh}}{2bL + cL^2}\, t$$

**Illustrative Example 2–15.** The accompanying figure shows a closed conduit which is rectangular in cross section. The centroidal axis of the conduit contains a circular bend with radius $R$ as shown. Assume that the incompressible flow in the conduit is steady and frictionless, and that the streamlines of the flow in the bend are also circular arcs with centers on the axis of the bend. Derive an expression for the pressure difference $p_o - p_i$ between points $o$ and $i$ which are respectively on the outside and inside of the bend, as shown, in terms of $z_o$, $z_i$, $R$, $H$, $b$, $\hat{Q}$, and $\rho$; $\hat{Q}$ is the rate of flow in the conduit.

*Solution:* Let us consider a streamline with radius $r$. Since the flow is incompressible and frictionless, the equation of motion for any fluid particle on this streamline is then Euler's equation. Using the streamline coordinates in Table 2–1,

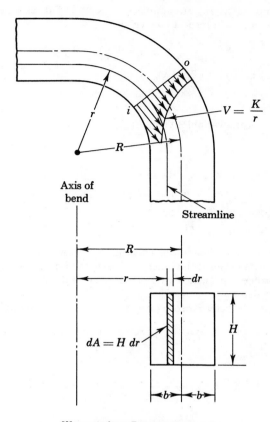

$$V = \frac{K}{r}$$

Axis of bend

Streamline

$$dA = H\,dr$$

**Illustrative Example 2-15**

we may write the $n$-component Euler's equation for a steady incompressible flow as

$$-\frac{1}{\rho}\frac{\partial p}{\partial n} - g\frac{\partial z}{\partial n} = \frac{V^2}{r}$$

where $-\partial z/\partial n$ represents the cosine of the angle between the $n$-axis and the negative $z$-axis, which has been chosen as the direction of gravity. We will recall that the $n$-axis is taken in a direction toward the center of the curvature of a curved streamline. Hence $dn = -dr$, and the above equation then becomes

$$\frac{\partial}{\partial r}\left(\frac{p}{\rho} + gz\right) = \frac{V^2}{r} \tag{A}$$

Furthermore, Bernoulli's equation

$$\frac{p}{\rho} + gz + \frac{V^2}{2} = \text{constant}$$

may also be applied to any streamline in this flow. Partial differentiation of Bernoulli's equation with respect to $r$ yields

$$\frac{\partial}{\partial r}\left(\frac{p}{\rho} + gz\right) + V\frac{\partial V}{\partial r} = 0 \tag{B}$$

By substituting Eq. (B) into Eq. (A), we obtain

$$\frac{V^2}{r} + V\frac{\partial V}{\partial r} = 0$$

Then separation of the variables yields

$$\frac{\partial r}{r} + \frac{\partial V}{V} = 0$$

This differential equation is readily integrated to give

$$\ln r + \ln V = \ln (rV) = \text{constant}$$

Therefore,

$$rV = K \quad \text{or} \quad V = \frac{K}{r} \tag{C}$$

where $K$ is a constant of integration. This equation shows that the maximum and minimum velocities occur at the inner and outer radii of the bend, respectively. The velocity profile represented by Eq. (C) is evidently an arc of a hyperbola, as shown in the figure.

The constant $K$ is determined by using the continuity equation:

$$\hat{Q} = \iint_A V \, dA = K \iint_A \frac{dA}{r}$$

Hence

$$K = \frac{\hat{Q}}{\iint_A (dA/r)} = \frac{\hat{Q}}{H \int_{R-b}^{R+b} (dr/r)} \tag{D}$$

$$= \frac{\hat{Q}}{H \ln [(R + b)/(R - b)]}$$

To determine the pressure difference $p_0 - p_i$, we return to Eq. (A) and rewrite it in the following form after $V$ is replaced by $K/r$:

$$\partial\left(\frac{p}{\rho} + gz\right) = \frac{K^2}{r^3}\partial r$$

Integrating this equation between points $i$ and $o$ and then substituting Eq. (D) for $K$, we have

$$\left(\frac{p}{\rho} + gz\right)_o - \left(\frac{p}{\rho} + gz\right)_i = -\frac{K^2}{2r^2}\Big|_{R-b}^{R+b}$$

$$= \frac{1}{2}\left\{\frac{\hat{Q}}{H \ln [(R + b)/(R - b)]}\right\}^2\left[\frac{1}{(R - b)^2} - \frac{1}{(R + b)^2}\right]$$

Therefore,

$$p_0 - p_i = \rho g(z_i - z_o) + 2\rho Rb\left\{\frac{\hat{Q}}{(R^2 - b^2)H \ln [(R + b)/(R - b)]}\right\}^2$$

## PROBLEMS

**2-1.** A square duct, 4 in. on each side, is connected to a 3-in.-diameter pipe. A steady flow of air of 15 lbm/min occurs in this pipe system. At section $A$ in the duct the pressure is 50 lbf/in² gage and the temperature 100°F. At section $B$ in the pipe the following conditions are recorded: $p_B = 25$ lbf/in² gage and $T_B = 60$°F. Calculate the average velocities of air flow at sections $A$ and $B$, respectively. The barometer reads 29.0 inches of mercury.

**2-2.** A steady flow of a compressible fluid occurs through a stream tube in Fig. 2-15. By using the indicated notations and the idea of conservation

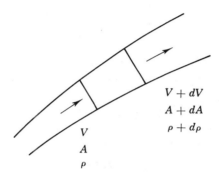

$$V + dV$$
$$A + dA$$
$$\rho + d\rho$$

$$V$$
$$A$$
$$\rho$$

**Fig. 2-15.**

of mass flow, show that the equation of continuity for this flow is

$$\frac{d\rho}{\rho} + \frac{dA}{A} + \frac{dV}{A} = 0$$

What is the integrated form of this equation?

**2-3.** A steady flow of an incompressible fluid of density $\rho$ occurs in a round tube of diameter $D$. The velocity distributions at the inlet section 1 and a downstream section 2 are shown in Fig. 2-16. At section 1 the velocity

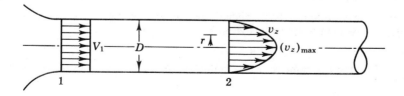

**Fig. 2-16.**

$V_1$ is constant; at section 2 the velocity distribution is a paraboloid of revolution with a maximum point velocity $(v_z)_{\max}$ at the axis of the tube. Show that $(v_z)_{\max} = 2V_1$.

**2–4.** By using the infinitesimal control volume in Fig. 2–17 and the concept of conservation of mass flow, determine the divergence operator for the vector $\rho V$ in the cylindrical coordinates.

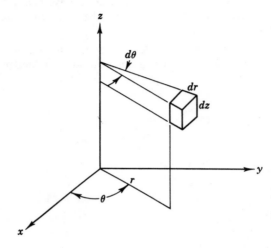

**Fig. 2-17.**

**2–5.** Determine which of the following pairs of velocity components $u$ and $v$ satisfy the equation of continuity for a two-dimensional planar flow of an incompressible fluid.

(a) $u = Ax$  
     $v = -Ay$

(b) $u = Ax/(x^2 + y^2)$  
     $v = Ay/(x^2 + y^2)$

(c) $u = A \sin xy$  
     $v = -A \sin xy$

(d) $u = -Ax/y$  
     $v = A \ln xy$

**2–6.** Do the velocity fields given in Problems 1–8, 1–10, 1–11, 1–12, 1–13, 1–14, 1–16, and 1–17 satisfy the law of conservation of mass flow for an incompressible flow?

**2–7.** In a two-dimensional, planar flow of an incompressible fluid, the $x$-component of velocity is given by

$$u = \tfrac{1}{2}x^2 + x - 2y$$

Use the two-dimensional equation of continuity to derive an expression for $v$.

**2–8.** A two-dimensional vortex flow can be represented by the equations: $v_\theta = kr = k\sqrt{x^2 + y^2}$ and $v_r = 0$. Show in both Cartesian and polar notations that the equation of continuity for an incompressible flow is satisfied.

**2–9.** In a two-dimensional, planar flow of an incompressible fluid, the radial component of velocity is given by

$$v_r = \frac{A \cos \theta}{r^2}$$

where $A$ is a constant. Use the equation of continuity to determine an expression for $v_\theta$.

**2–10.** The $x$-component of the velocity field for a steady, two-dimensional, incompressible flow is defined by $u = 3x^2 - y$. On the $x$-axis, the $y$-component of velocity is given by $v = 2/x$. Determine the velocity field of the flow completely.

**2–11.** Determine the unknown velocity component so that the resulting flow fields satisfy the equation of continuity:

(a) $u = x^2 + 2y^2$        (b) $u = 2xyz + y^2 + 5$
    $v = yz + zx$               $v = ?$
    $w = ?$                 $w = y^2 - yz^2 + 10$

Can you obtain unique answers?

**2–12.** Water enters a 60° horizontal reducing bend with a velocity $V_1 = 20$ ft/sec as shown in Fig. 2–18. The diameters of the entrance and exit sections are 12 in. and 8 in., respectively. The static pressure is 15 lbf/in? gage at

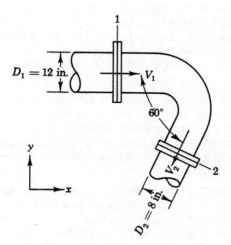

**Fig. 2-18.**

section 1 and 6 lbf/in² gage at section 2. Calculate the $x$ and $y$ components of the reaction force on the bend.

**2–13.** In the schematic diagram of a water jet pump shown in Fig. 2–19, at section 1 a primary water jet of cross-sectional area $A_j = 0.08$ ft² and

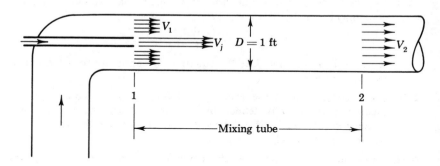

**Fig. 2-19.**

velocity $V_j = 75$ ft/sec entrains a secondary stream of water having a velocity $V_1 = 10$ ft/sec. The water is thoroughly mixed in the 1-ft-diameter tube before it passes through section 2 with a uniform velocity $V_2$. Assuming that the pressure of the jet and the secondary stream is the same at section 1 and that the wall shear stresses are negligible in the mixing tube, determine (a) the velocity $V_2$ and (b) the pressure difference $p_2 - p_1$.

**2–14.** A jet airplane is cruising horizontally through still air with a constant speed of 550 miles per hour. The jet engine is consuming fuel at a rate of 4800 lbm/hour. The air-fuel ratio is 120. The velocity of exhaust gases at the tailpipe is 2000 ft/sec relative to the airplane. Assuming atmospheric pressure at the exhaust, calculate the thrust developed by this jet engine. Use $g = 32.174$ ft/sec².

**2–15.** A rocket, which weighs 50,000 lbf including 40,000 lbf of fuel, is fired vertically upward. It burns fuel at a constant rate of 800 lbf/sec and the exit velocity of exhaust gases is 10,000 ft/sec relative to the rocket. Considering $g$ constant at 32.2 ft/sec² and neglecting drag resistance, calculate the speed of the rocket at the instant of burnout and the maximum height reached by the rocket.

**2–16.** The total weight of a test rocket sled is 10,000 lbf which includes 3000 lbf of fuel. When the sled is set in motion on a track, the total motion resistance on the rocket is estimated to be $F_R = -KV$, where $K$ is a constant having a numerical value of 120 lbf per ft/sec, and $V$ is the speed of the rocket sled, in ft/sec. On a particular test run, the rocket burns fuel at a constant rate of 250 lbf/sec and the exit velocity of exhaust gases is

8000 ft/sec relative to the rocket. Calculate the maximum speed which is attained by the rocket sled. Use $g = 32.2$ ft/sec².

**2–17.** A lunar landing craft is designed for soft landing to descend vertically onto the surface of the moon at a constant velocity of 10ft/sec by means of a retro-rocket (see Fig. 2–20). The total weight of the craft is 1200 lbf on the surface of the earth. The moon's gravitational acceleration is approximately 1/6 the earth's gravitational acceleration. The lunar atmosphere is so thin that we can neglect the drag resistance on the descending craft. The fluid jet coming out of the retro-rocket has a density $\rho = 0.5$ slug/ft³, and the nozzle outlet has an area of 2 ft². Calculate the mass rate of flow of the retro-rocket jet in slugs/sec. The jet efflux pressure is the same as the ambient pressure.

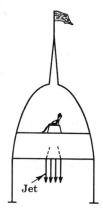

**Fig. 2-20.**

**2–18.** Figure 2–21 shows the horizontal profile of water flow under an obstruction in a 10 ft wide rectangular channel. If the flow rate is 480 ft³/sec, what is the horizontal force on the obstruction?

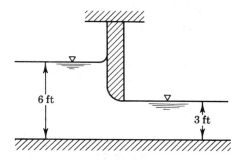

**Fig. 2-21.**

**2–19.** The velocity field of a steady, incompressible flow is given as

$$\mathbf{V} = (3x^2 - 2xy)\mathbf{i} + (y^2 - 6xy + 3yz^2)\mathbf{j} - (z^3 + xy^2)\mathbf{k} \quad \text{ft/sec}$$

Determine the pressure gradient on a fluid particle which occupies the position

$$\mathbf{r} = 2\mathbf{i} + 3\mathbf{j} + \mathbf{k} \quad \text{ft}$$

Use $\rho = 1.94$ slugs/ft³ and $\mathbf{g} = -32.2\,\mathbf{k}$ ft/sec².

**2–20.** The velocity field of an incompressible flow is given by the equation:

$$\mathbf{V} = (6xy + 5xt)\mathbf{i} - 3y^2\mathbf{j} + (7xy^2 - 5zt)\mathbf{k} \quad \text{ft/sec}$$

Determine the pressure gradient on a fluid particle which occupies the position

$$\mathbf{r} = 2\mathbf{i} - \mathbf{j} + 4\mathbf{k} \quad \text{ft}$$

at time $t = 3$ sec. Use $\rho = 1.94$ slugs/ft³ and $\mathbf{g} = -32.2\,\mathbf{k}$ ft/sec².

**2–21.** The pressure field of a steady incompressible flow is given as

$$p = 4x^3 - 2y^2 - yz^2 + 5z \quad \text{lbf/ft}^2$$

If the density of the fluid is $\rho = 1.94$ slugs/ft³, what is the acceleration of a fluid particle which occupies the position

$$\mathbf{r} = 3\mathbf{i} + \mathbf{j} - 5\mathbf{k} \quad \text{ft}$$

Use $\mathbf{g} = -32.2\,\mathbf{k}$ ft/sec².

**2–22.** Figure 2–22 shows a streamline in a two-dimensional water flow on a horizontal plane. The velocities at A and C are respectively 5**j** ft/sec and

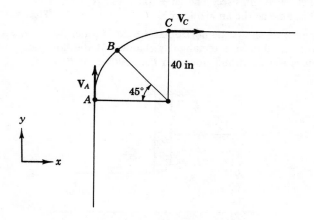

**Fig. 2-22.**

25**i** ft/sec. The magnitude of the velocity increases linearly along the circular path $\overset{\frown}{ABC}$. Determine the pressure gradient at points $A$, $B$, and $C$.

**2–23.** Figure 2–23 shows a nozzle which is 16 in. long and has diameters of 6 in.

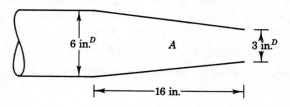

**Fig. 2-23.**

and 3 in. respectively at the base and the tip. If water flows steadily at a rate of 2.5 ft³/sec, calculate the acceleration at point $A$ which is at the midpoint between the base and the tip of the nozzle.

**2–24.** An open cubical tank is 3 ft on each side and is filled with water to a depth of 2 ft. Calculate the force of water pressure acting on the side of the tank (a) when it is accelerated at 8.05 ft/sec² vertically upward and (b) when it is accelerated at 8.05 ft/sec² vertically downward. Use $g = 32.2$ ft/sec².

**2–25.** An open cylindrical tank, 2 ft in diameter and 4 ft deep, is filled to the brim with water. If the tank is rotated about its axis at 60 revolutions per minute, how much water is spilled and what is the depth of water at the axis?

**2–26.** Work Problem 2–15 by using the momentum equation for the accelerating control volume which coincides with the rocket casing.

**2–27.** Work Problem 2–16 by using the momentum equation for the accelerating control volume which coincides with the rocket casing.

**2–28.** Figure 2–24 shows a jet-driven helicopter rotor which is rotating at a

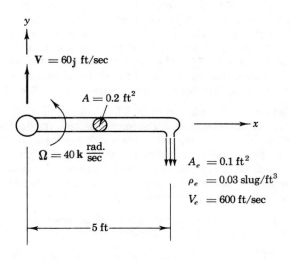

**Fig. 2-24.**

constant angular velocity $\Omega = 40\,\mathbf{k}$ rad/sec in the horizontal $xy$ plane. At the instant shown, the helicopter is moving at a velocity $\mathbf{V} = 60\mathbf{j}$ ft/sec. A steady flow of gases occurs through the rotor arm and discharges at its tip with a speed $V_e = 600$ ft/sec relative to the rotor tip. Calculate the torque on the rotating arm about the axis of rotation from the flow of gases.

**2–29.** Work the preceding problem if the helicopter is also accelerating with an acceleration $\mathbf{a} = 10\mathbf{j}$ ft/sec².

**2–30.** The sprinkler shown in Fig. 2–25 is discharging 5 gallons per minute of water through each nozzle. Neglecting mechanical friction, calculate the speed of rotation of the arms.

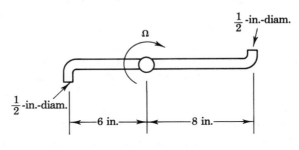

**Fig. 2-25.**

**2–31.** Calculate the horsepower required by a compressor if air flowing at a steady rate of 4.0 lbm/sec enters at 15.0 lbf/in.² abs. and 70°F, with a velocity of 250 ft/sec, and leaves at 60.0 lbf/in.² abs. and 200°F, with a velocity of 500 ft/sec. The internal energy of the air may be assumed to be $\hat{u} = c_v T$, where $c_v$ is the specific heat of air at constant volume and has a numerical value of 0.171 ft-lbf/lbm-°R, and $T$ is the temperature in degrees Rankine. Heat transfer from the air to the cooling water circulating through the compressor casing amounts to 12 Btu/lbm of air.

**2–32.** Water is pumped along a horizontal 6-in. diameter pipeline which terminates at a 3-in. diameter nozzle. The gage pressure at the base of the nozzle is 50 lbf/in.². The jet coming out of the nozzle impinges tangentially on a stationary horizontal vane which deflects it through an angle of 150 degrees. Because of friction, the water jet leaves the vane at 90 per cent of its approach speed. Determine (a) the velocity of the jet as it leaves the vane, and (b) the force of water jet on the vane.

**2–33.** Assuming no friction loss, calculate the rate of water flow in the pipeline shown in Fig. 2–26.

**2–34.** Figure 2–27 shows a laboratory experiment of air flow at 14.7 lbf/in.² abs. and 70°F. Calculate the horsepower input of the fan when the scale reads 7.50 lbf. Assume the system to be frictionless.

**2–35.** In Fig. 2–28 the pump is delivering 5 horsepower to the flowing water. Determine the scale reading by assuming the system to be frictionless.

**2–36.** An open cylindrical tank, 6 ft in diameter and 9 ft high, is filled with water. Find the time required to empty the tank through a 2-in. diameter, well-rounded hole at the bottom of the tank. Assume frictionless flow.

**2–37.** A rectangular tank, 12 ft long, 10 ft wide, and 16 ft high, is divided into two compartments as shown in Fig. 2–29. The depths of water are initially

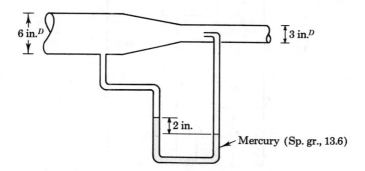

**Fig. 2-26.**

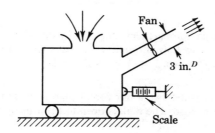

**Fig. 2-27.**

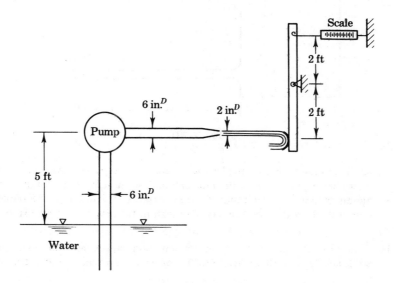

**Fig. 2-28.**

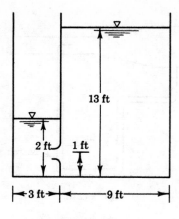

**Fig. 2-29.**

13 ft in the large compartment and 2 ft in the smaller compartment. If water is allowed to flow through a 2-in. diameter, well-rounded hole in the partition as shown, how long will it take for the levels of water to become equal?

2–38. A large tank of water has a horizontal pipe of length $L$ connected to it as shown in Fig. 2–30. The tank is open to the atmosphere, and the water

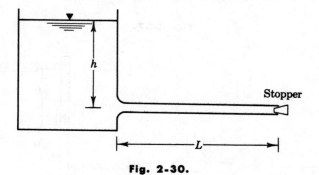

**Fig. 2-30.**

surface in the tank is at an elevation $h$ above the pipe axis. At time $t = 0$, a stopper is pulled out of the pipe exit and water starts to flow under the action of gravity. Neglecting friction losses and assuming $h$ to remain constant, show that the velocity $V$ of flow in the pipe at any time is

$$V = \sqrt{2gh} \tanh (\sqrt{2gh}\, t/2L)$$

2–39. A horizontal pipe, 5000 ft long, has one end capped and the other end subjected to a constant head of 20 ft of water. The cap is removed, and water starts to flow. Neglecting friction, calculate the time in which 50 per cent of the final velocity in the pipe is attained. How long will it take for 99 per cent of the final velocity in the pipe to be attained? (Hint: Use the result in Problem 2–38.)

# 3    Principles of
     Irrotational Flow

## 3-1  Introductory Remarks

One of the primary aims in studying fluid mechanics is to enable us to predict characteristics of flow for a given set of physical conditions by means of analytical methods. The control volume approach, developed in the preceding chapter, can be used very effectively to predict certain overall characteristics of flow that are often of interest for engineering purposes. However, in order to analyze flow patterns in detail, it is necessary to set up differential equations of motion which will describe accurately fluid motion at every point in a flow field. In addition, these differential equations must satisfy certain boundary conditions for any given problem. Indeed differential equations can be formed for the most general case of three-dimensional motion including all realistic effects which might be conceived to be involved in a flow. But the solution of such equations involves mathematical difficulties so great that the task is beyond the reach of available methods of analysis. For example, as will be shown in Chapter 6, the differential equations of motion for a viscous fluid were formulated in the form of Navier-Stokes equations in the mid-nineteenth century. Unfortunately, these differential equations were nonlinear and their general solutions are yet not available. Hence, as in most engineering problems, it is necessary for us to adopt simple idealized models of flow which are amenable to mathematical analysis, but which at the same time will yield results of value concerning the real and more complicated flow patterns.

The concept of an irrotational flow leads to important simplifications in the analytical studies of fluid flows. A flow is characterized as irrotational if all fluid elements do not rotate during motion. In Sec. 3-2 we shall establish the mathematical criterion for an irrotational flow.

From the physical viewpoint, the development of rotation in a fluid element which is initially irrotational can be attributed to various physical phenomena, such as viscous shear stresses, nonuniform heating, and nonuniform dissipative effects. These phenomena are present to some degree in all flows of real fluids.

Let us consider the effect of viscous shear stresses on the rotation of a fluid element. By definition, the viscous shear stress of a Newtonian fluid is equal to the product of viscosity and velocity gradient. Thus, the shear stress in a flow depends on both the fluid viscosity and the spatial variation of flow velocity. In regions where the velocity gradient is zero, the shear stress will be zero no matter how large the viscosity is, and an initially irrotational flow will remain irrotational. In many flows of fluids of small viscosities, such as water and air, regions of irrotational flow may constitute a large portion of the flow field. For example, consider an air flow moving uniformly over a streamlined object as shown in Fig. 3-1(a). If the flow originates from a region of zero rotation, it will remain irrotational over most of the flow field except in the immediate vicinity of the object. Near a solid surface the frictional effect of the air flow cannot be ignored even though air has an extremely small coefficient of viscosity. The air sticks to the solid surface; thus the air velocity at the solid surface must be zero relative to the solid surface, and at a comparatively small distance away it is almost equal to the free-stream velocity, as shown in Fig. 3-1(a). The region adjacent to the solid surface in which the air velocity changes from zero to that of the free-stream flow is called the *boundary layer*. Within the boundary layer sizable velocity gradient is present to cause shear stresses of consequential magnitude, despite the low coefficient of viscosity of the air, and the flow therein is rotational. The rotational flow in the boundary layer will leave the solid object at the trailing edge in the form of a narrow wake, shown in Fig. 3-1(a). Thus, except for flows in the boundary layer and in the wake, the remaining flow field can be considered irrotational. Hence, in the analytical treatment, we may divide the flow field into two regions: (1) the boundary layer flow and the wake in which the effect of fluid viscosity must be

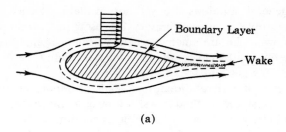

(a)

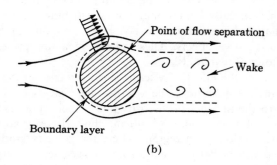

(b)

**Fig. 3-1.** Motion of fluid relative to (a) a streamlined object, and (b) a nonstreamlined object.

taken into consideration, and (2) the main flow in which the flow is irrotational. This division of the flow field into two distinct regions has the great practical value of reducing complicated problems to simple components, each of which can be handled by analytical methods. Then the solutions of the two components are matched together to yield a complete solution for the problem.

In case the submerged object is not streamlined [Fig. 3–1(b)], a phenomenon called *flow separation* from the boundary surface will occur. The flow inside the separated regions is again rotational. As a result the flow pattern in the vicinity of the object becomes very much different from that of an irrotational flow. In such cases experimental methods are frequently required. Boundary layer, wakes, and flow separation will be discussed in Chapter 8.

## 3-2 Rotational and Irrotational Flows

The rotation of a fluid element is represented by a vorticity vector $\boldsymbol{\omega}$ which is the **curl** of the velocity vector $\mathbf{V}$ at the center of the element. Thus, in Cartesian coordinates $(x, y, z)$, with $\mathbf{V} = u\mathbf{i} + v\mathbf{j} + w\mathbf{k}$,

$$\omega = \text{curl } \mathbf{V} = \nabla \times \mathbf{V}$$

$$= \left(\frac{\partial w}{\partial y} - \frac{\partial v}{\partial z}\right)\mathbf{i} + \left(\frac{\partial u}{\partial z} - \frac{\partial w}{\partial x}\right)\mathbf{j} + \left(\frac{\partial v}{\partial x} - \frac{\partial u}{\partial y}\right)\mathbf{k} \tag{3-1}$$

In cylindrical coordinates $(r, \theta, z)$, $\mathbf{V} = v_r\epsilon_r + v_\theta\epsilon_\theta + v_z\epsilon_z$, and we may write

$$\omega = \nabla \times \mathbf{V} = \left[\frac{1}{r}\frac{\partial v_z}{\partial \theta} - \frac{\partial v_\theta}{\partial z}\right]\epsilon_r + \left[\frac{\partial v_r}{\partial z} - \frac{\partial v_z}{\partial r}\right]\epsilon_\theta$$

$$+ \left[\frac{1}{r}\frac{\partial(rv_\theta)}{\partial r} - \frac{1}{r}\frac{\partial v_r}{\partial \theta}\right]\epsilon_z \tag{3-2}$$

In spherical coordinates $(R, \theta, \phi)$, $\mathbf{V} = v_R\epsilon_R + v_\theta\epsilon_\theta + v_\phi\epsilon_\phi$, and the vorticity vector then becomes

$$\omega = \nabla \times \mathbf{V} = \left[\frac{1}{R\sin\theta}\frac{\partial v_\theta}{\partial \phi} - \frac{1}{R}\frac{\partial v_\phi}{\partial \theta} - \frac{\cot\theta}{R}v_\phi\right]\epsilon_R$$

$$+ \left[\frac{1}{R}\frac{\partial(Rv_\phi)}{\partial R} - \frac{1}{R\sin\theta}\frac{\partial v_R}{\partial \phi}\right]\epsilon_\theta + \left[\frac{1}{R}\frac{\partial v_R}{\partial \theta} - \frac{1}{R}\frac{\partial(Rv_\theta)}{\partial R}\right]\epsilon_\phi \tag{3-3}$$

As long as the vorticity vector $\omega$ has a finite value, the flow is characterized as *rotational*.

Flows with zero vorticity are therefore called *irrotational* flows. Hence, in an irrotational flow, the condition

$$\nabla \times \mathbf{V} = 0 \tag{3-4}$$

or, in Cartesian coordinates,

$$\frac{\partial w}{\partial y} = \frac{\partial v}{\partial z}, \qquad \frac{\partial u}{\partial z} = \frac{\partial w}{\partial x}, \qquad \frac{\partial v}{\partial x} = \frac{\partial u}{\partial y} \tag{3-5}$$

must be satisfied throughout the flow field.

Although the difference between rotational and irrotational flows is strictly based on the above mathematical criterion, we may illustrate it graphically as shown in Fig. 3–2. In an irrotational flow the median lines of a fluid element must always be oriented in the same directions parallel to their original directions no matter how excessively the element itself may deform; that is, these lines have pure rectilinear motion and do not rotate.

The vorticity of a fluid element cannot be changed except through the action of viscosity, nonuniform heating, and nonuniform dissipative effects. Thus, if a flow originates from an irrotational region, it will remain irrotational as long as viscosity, nonuniform heating, and other nonuniform dissipative effects are absent. Even in the region where viscous effect cannot be neglected, flow is frequently irrotational for a short time after motion starts from rest.

A theorem of vector analysis states that if the **curl** of a vector is everywhere zero, i.e., for example,

$$\nabla \times \mathbf{V} = 0$$

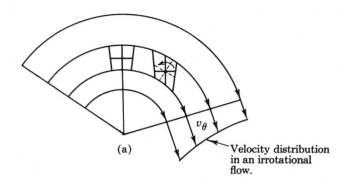

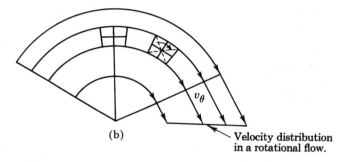

**Fig. 3-2.** A two-dimensional flow around a curved path; deformation of a fluid element in a two-dimensional, (a) irrotational, and (b) rotational flow.

then that vector can be expressed as the gradient of some scalar potential $\phi$ (e.g., $\mathbf{V} = \nabla\phi$ in our case). This potential is called *velocity potential*. The velocity potential $\phi$ is a scalar function of space and time. Using Cartesian coordinates, we have

$$\phi = \phi(x, y, z, t) \qquad (3\text{-}6)$$

The main advantage of introducing the concept of velocity potential is that the problem is reduced to a scalar field problem rather than a (velocity) vector field problem.

To explore the connection between the vorticity of a flow and the existence of a velocity potential, it is necessary to introduce a new concept, called *circulation*, which will be discussed in the following two sections.

*Illustrative Example 3–1.* A two-dimensional flow of an incompressible fluid has the following velocity field:

$$\mathbf{V} = \left(\frac{y^3}{3} + 2x - x^2y\right)\mathbf{i} + \left(xy^2 - 2y - \frac{x^3}{3}\right)\mathbf{j}$$

Show that this velocity field represents a possible case of an irrotational flow.

*Solution:* The function given above satisfies the continuity equation, for the divergence of **V** is equal to zero:

$$\nabla \cdot \mathbf{V} = \frac{\partial}{\partial x}\left(\frac{y^3}{3} + 2x - x^2y\right) + \frac{\partial}{\partial y}\left(xy^2 - 2y - \frac{x^3}{3}\right)$$

$$= (2 - 2xy) + (2xy - 2) = 0$$

Therefore the given velocity field represents a possible case of fluid flow.
    The vorticity vector **ω** of any fluid element in the flow field is

$$\boldsymbol{\omega} = \nabla \times \mathbf{V} = \left(\frac{\partial w}{\partial y} - \frac{\partial v}{\partial z}\right)\mathbf{i} + \left(\frac{\partial u}{\partial z} - \frac{\partial w}{\partial x}\right)\mathbf{j} + \left(\frac{\partial v}{\partial x} - \frac{\partial u}{\partial y}\right)\mathbf{k}$$

$$= \left[\frac{\partial}{\partial x}\left(xy^2 - 2y - \frac{x^3}{3}\right) - \frac{\partial}{\partial y}\left(\frac{y^3}{3} + 2x - x^2y\right)\right]\mathbf{k}$$

$$= [(y^2 - x^2) - (y^2 - x^2)]\mathbf{k} = 0$$

which shows that the given velocity field could represent an irrotational flow.

## 3-3  Circulation

*Circulation* is a mathematical concept defined as the line integral of the tangential component velocity around a closed path. Consider a closed curve $C$ drawn in a flow field which is represented by the pattern of streamlines at time $t$ as shown in Fig. 3–3. Using the notations in Fig. 3–3 and denoting the circulation by the symbol $\Gamma$, we may write

$$\Gamma = \oint_C \mathbf{V} \cdot d\mathbf{L} \tag{3–7}$$

where the symbol $\oint_C$ denotes the line integral around the closed curve $C$. In Cartesian coordinates $\mathbf{V} = u\mathbf{i} + v\mathbf{j} + w\mathbf{k}$ and $d\mathbf{L} = \mathbf{i}\,dx + \mathbf{j}\,dy + \mathbf{k}\,dz$, Eq. 3–7 becomes

$$\Gamma = \oint_C \mathbf{V} \cdot d\mathbf{L} = \oint_C (u\mathbf{i} + v\mathbf{j} + w\mathbf{k}) \cdot (\mathbf{i}\,dx + \mathbf{j}\,dy + \mathbf{k}\,dz)$$

$$= \oint_C (u\,dx + v\,dy + w\,dz) \tag{3–8}$$

The closed curve $C$ may be regarded as the periphery of a curved surface of any shape.

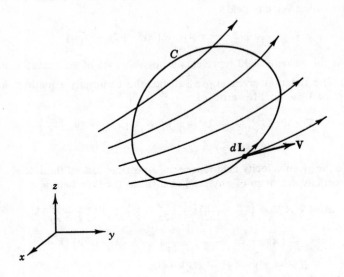

**Fig. 3-3.** A closed curve in a flow field to illustrate the concept of circulation.

*Relationship between circulation and vorticity.* In order to establish the relationship between circulation and vorticity, let us compute the circulation around an infinitesimal rectangular path in the $xy$ plane as shown in Fig. 3–4. Proceeding in a counterclockwise direction from point

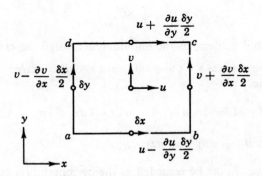

**4.** Velocities around an infinitesimal rectangular path in the $xy$ plane.

*a* with the velocity components as shown in Fig. 3–4, we have

$$\delta\Gamma = \oint_{abcda} \mathbf{V} \cdot d\mathbf{L}$$

$$= \left(u - \frac{\partial u}{\partial y}\frac{\delta y}{2}\right)\delta x + \left(v + \frac{\partial v}{\partial x}\frac{\delta x}{2}\right)\delta y$$

$$- \left(u + \frac{\partial u}{\partial y}\frac{\delta y}{2}\right)\delta x - \left(v - \frac{\partial v}{\partial x}\frac{\delta x}{2}\right)\delta y$$

or, after simplifying,

$$\delta\Gamma = \oint_{abcda} \mathbf{V} \cdot d\mathbf{L} = \left(\frac{\partial v}{\partial x} - \frac{\partial u}{\partial y}\right)\delta x\,\delta y \qquad (3\text{–}9)$$

The quantity in the parenthesis is the *z*-component of the vorticity vector **ω** in Eq. 3–1. Therefore, we may also write Eq. 3–9 as

$$\delta\Gamma = \oint_{abcda} \mathbf{V} \cdot d\mathbf{L} = (\nabla \times \mathbf{V})_z\,\delta A_z \qquad (3\text{–}10)$$

where $(\nabla \times \mathbf{V})_z$ is the *z*-component of the **curl** of V and $\delta A_z$ is the area of the rectangular element $\delta x\,\delta y$. Clearly this relationship between circulation and vorticity holds for elementary areas of any shape. We have used a planar rectangular element in the above development merely for convenience.

Now consider a closed curve *C* enclosing a finite area in the *xy* plane as shown in Fig. 3–5. This area has been divided into infinitesimal area elements. Applying Eq. 3–10 to each of the area elements and summing them up, we have

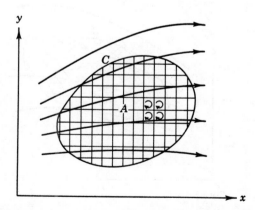

**Fig. 3-5.** A finite planar area enclosed by a closed curve C in a flow field.

$$\sum_{m=1}^{\infty} \oint_m \mathbf{V} \cdot d\mathbf{L} = \sum_{m=1}^{\infty} (\nabla \times \mathbf{V})_z \, \delta A_z \qquad (3\text{–}11)$$

It is easily seen that if we proceed in the same direction around the periphery of each element, the contributions to the line integrals of adjoining elements will cancel each other because they are traversed in opposite directions, and the only contributions are those of the boundary curve $C$. Hence the total line integral is that of the boundary curve:

$$\sum_{m=1}^{\infty} \oint_m \mathbf{V} \cdot d\mathbf{L} = \oint_C \mathbf{V} \cdot d\mathbf{L} \qquad (3\text{–}12)$$

where the line integral on the right-hand side is taken around the closed boundary curve $C$. The summation on the right-hand side of Eq. 3–11 reduces to a surface integration as

$$\sum_{m=1}^{\infty} (\nabla \times \mathbf{V})_z \, \delta A_z = \iint_A (\nabla \times \mathbf{V})_z \, dA_z \qquad (3\text{–}13)$$

Therefore, substitution of Eqs. 3–12 and 3–13 into Eq. 3–11 yields

$$\oint_C \mathbf{V} \cdot d\mathbf{L} = \iint_A (\nabla \times \mathbf{V})_z \, dA_z \qquad (3\text{–}14)$$

This equation relates the circulation of a velocity field around a closed path and the vorticity component of the field normal to the plane area enclosed by the path.

For a curved open surface, we may also divide the surface area into infinitesimal area elements by a network of lines drawn on the surface as shown in Fig. 3–6. We shall use a modified form of Eq. 3–10 to account

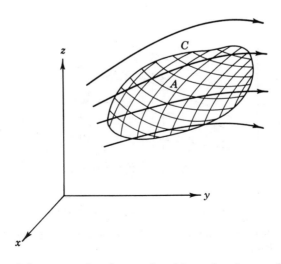

**Fig. 3-6.**  A finite curved surface enclosed by a closed curve C in a flow field.

for the circulation of any one of these area elements:

$$\delta\Gamma = \oint \mathbf{V} \cdot d\mathbf{L} = (\nabla \times \mathbf{V})_n \, \delta A = (\nabla \times \mathbf{V}) \cdot \delta\mathbf{A} \qquad (3\text{--}15)$$

where $(\nabla \times \mathbf{V})_n$ is the component of the $(\nabla \times \mathbf{V})$-vector normal to the area element. When we integrate the above equation for all area elements on the finite curved surface, line integration over interior boundaries will again vanish. The result is then

$$\oint_c \mathbf{V} \cdot d\mathbf{L} = \iint_A (\nabla \times \mathbf{V}) \cdot d\mathbf{A} \qquad (3\text{--}16)$$

This equation is the famous Stokes theorem. It states that the surface integral of the normal component of the **curl** of the velocity field taken over any surface is equal to the line integral of the velocity field around the periphery of the surface.

**Thomson's theorem of invariance of circulation.** Let us again consider Fig. 3–3. Since the closed curve $C$ is drawn in the flow field at time $t$, the curve itself may be considered as composed of particles of fluid. As the fluid flows, the curve $C$ moves and deforms with the fluid and the velocity $\mathbf{V}$ at any point of the curve $C$ changes with time. But the circulation $\Gamma$ around the curve which is composed of the same fluid particles remains invariant with time, provided that the fluid is homogeneous and frictionless. This principle was derived by William Thomson (Lord Kelvin). Accordingly the circulation on a closed fluid line in a frictionless flow is characterized as an *integral invariant*.

Mathematically, Thomson's theorem may be written as

$$\frac{D\Gamma}{Dt} = \frac{D}{Dt} \oint_c \mathbf{V} \cdot d\mathbf{L} = 0 \qquad (3\text{--}17)$$

Here we have used the substantive derivative in order to emphasize the fact that we are following the motion of the closed curve which is composed of the same fluid particles at all times.

We shall now prove Thomson's theorem. The first step is to carry out the differentiation of Eq. 3–17. Thus,

$$\frac{D}{Dt} \oint_c \mathbf{V} \cdot d\mathbf{L} = \oint_c \frac{D\mathbf{V}}{Dt} \cdot d\mathbf{L} + \oint_c \mathbf{V} \cdot \frac{D(d\mathbf{L})}{Dt} \qquad (3\text{--}18)$$

since the order of integration and differentiation is insignificant. The first term on the right-hand side denotes the rate of change of velocities of fluid particles on the curve, and the second term accounts for the rate of change in the shape of the curve. From Euler's equation for frictionless flow, we have

$$\frac{D\mathbf{V}}{Dt} = -\frac{1}{\rho} \nabla p - g \nabla z \qquad (3\text{--}19)$$

which may be substituted into the first integral on the right-hand side of Eq. 3–18 to yield

$$\oint_c \frac{D\mathbf{V}}{Dt} \cdot d\mathbf{L} = -\oint_c \left( \frac{1}{\rho} \nabla p \cdot d\mathbf{L} + g\nabla z \cdot d\mathbf{L} \right)$$

$$= -\oint_c \left( \frac{1}{\rho} dp + g\,dz \right) \tag{3–20}$$

where $dp$ and $dz$ represent the differential changes in pressure and elevation, respectively, along the infinitesimal displacement $d\mathbf{L}$ of the closed curve $C$. Next, let us consider the last integral of Eq. 3–18. Since we are following fluid particles on the closed curve $C$,

$$\frac{D\mathbf{L}}{Dt} = \mathbf{V} \quad \text{and} \quad \frac{D(d\mathbf{L})}{Dt} = d\mathbf{V}$$

Hence

$$\oint_c \mathbf{V} \cdot \frac{D(d\mathbf{L})}{Dt} = \oint_c \mathbf{V} \cdot d\mathbf{V} = \oint_c d\frac{V^2}{2} \tag{3–21}$$

We then substitute Eqs. 3–20 and 3–21 into Eq. 3–18 to obtain

$$\frac{D}{Dt} \oint_c \mathbf{V} \cdot d\mathbf{L} = \oint_c \left( -\frac{1}{\rho} dp - g\,dz + d\frac{V^2}{2} \right) \tag{3–22}$$

Clearly if $\rho$ is a single-valued function of $p$, and the gravitational acceleration $g$ is constant, the integrands on the right-hand side all become exact differentials. Then the line integral on the right-hand side vanishes because the integration is taken over a closed path. Thus,

$$\frac{D}{Dt} \oint_c \mathbf{V} \cdot d\mathbf{L} = 0$$

which, after integration with respect to $t$, becomes

$$\oint_c \mathbf{V} \cdot d\mathbf{L} = \Gamma = \text{constant} \tag{3–23}$$

This equation is a mathematical statement of Thomson's theorem.

In the foregoing proof, although we have included gravity as the only body force, it is easily verified that Thomson's theorem remains valid for frictionless flows with other conservative body forces. Note also that Thomson's theorem is valid for both compressible and incompressible fluids because we only specified the fluid density to be a single-valued function of pressure.

Thomson's theorem shows that if a frictionless flow starts from rest, or if in some region the flow is found to be uniform and parallel, then the circulation in these regions is zero and the entire flow is irrotational provided that all body forces are conservative and fluid density is a single-valued function of pressure.

*Illustrative Example 3-2.* Calculate the circulation of a two-dimensional flow which has velocity components in cylindrical coordinates as follows:

$$v_\theta = r\Omega \qquad v_r = 0$$

where $\Omega$ is a constant.

*Solution:* The streamlines for this flow are concentric circles and the velocity component $v_\theta$ increases linearly with respect to the radius $r$, as shown in the figure. This flow is sometimes called a *forced vortex motion* as contrasted to the

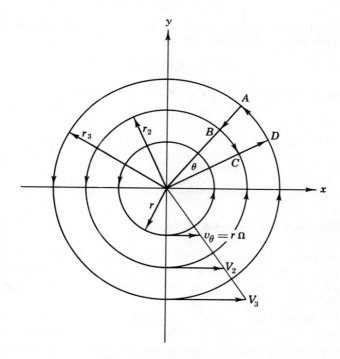

**Illustrative Example 3-2**

free vortex motion to be discussed in the following section. Physically, this fluid motion is caused by the rotation of a body of fluid; $\Omega \mathbf{k}$ is then the angular velocity of the rotation.

The circulation for this flow can be calculated by applying Eq. 3–7 to a circular streamline of radius $r$:

$$\Gamma = \oint_C \mathbf{V} \cdot d\mathbf{L} = \oint_C r\Omega \, dL = 2\pi r^2 \Omega$$

since $\Omega$ is a constant for the flow field and the line integral around the closed circular path is simply the circumference of the circle.

The circulation around any closed path, not including the center of the vortex, can be similarly calculated. This is done by taking the closed path $ABCDA$ as shown in the figure. Proceeding in a counterclockwise direction, we obtain

$$\Gamma_{ABCDA} = \Gamma_{AB} + \Gamma_{BC} + \Gamma_{CD} + \Gamma_{DA}$$

Both $\Gamma_{AB}$ and $\Gamma_{CD}$ along the two radii lines $AB$ and $CD$ are zero since the dot product $V \cdot dL$ equals zero for these two paths. Therefore,

$$\Gamma_{ABCDA} = 0 - V_2 r_2 \theta + 0 + V_3 r_3 \theta$$
$$= r_3^2 \Omega \theta - r_2^2 \Omega \theta = \Omega \theta (r_3^2 - r_2^2)$$

If we divide both $\Gamma$ and $\Gamma_{ABCDA}$ just derived by their respective areas enclosed in the closed paths, the circulation per unit area is then

$$\frac{\Gamma}{A} = 2\Omega \quad \text{(perpendicular to } A\text{)}$$

We may also calculate the circulation per unit area in this flow by using Eq. 3–10:

$$\frac{\delta \Gamma}{\delta A} = (\nabla \times V)_z = \frac{1}{r} \frac{\partial (r v_\theta)}{\partial r} - \frac{1}{r} \frac{\partial v_r}{\partial \theta}$$
$$= \frac{1}{r} \frac{\partial (r^2 \Omega)}{\partial r} = 2\Omega$$

which is identical to the result obtained by line integration.

### 3-4  Circulation in Irrotational Flows

When the flow is irrotational, $\nabla \times V = 0$ and the circulation about every closed curve in the flow must also vanish. However, there are exceptions to this rule. There are irrotational flows in which circulation does exist.

To discuss circulation in irrotational flows, it is useful to introduce the concept of simply-connected regions and multiply-connected regions. A *simply-connected* region is one wherein every closed curve can be shrunk continuously to a point of the region without ever passing outside the region. For example, the region inside the sphere in Fig. 3–7 is simply-connected, because the closed curve $C$ can be shrunk continuously to a point inside the sphere. Unbounded space is another example of a simply-connected region. On the other hand, a region not having this property is called a *multiply-connected* region. For example, a region including a cylinder of infinite length (Fig. 3–8) is multiply-connected, since it contains paths, such as $C'$, which cannot be shrunk continuously to a point. However, the region excluding the cylinder of infinite length is simply-connected. The path $C''$ not enclosing the cylinder can be shrunk continuously to a point.

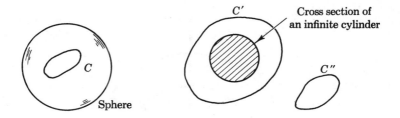

**Fig. 3-7.** A simply connected region inside a sphere.     **Fig. 3-8.** Region outside an infinite cylinder.

In simply-connected regions of irrotational flow, any closed path encloses a surface on which $(\nabla \times \mathbf{V})_n$ is zero. Thus, by Stokes' theorem, circulation around such a path is also zero.

In multiply-connected regions, circulation around certain paths, such as $C'$ in Fig. 3–8, cannot be ascertained by means of Stokes' theorem, because the surface enclosed by the path $C'$ must include the cylinder about which the vorticity condition is unknown. Circulation for such paths as $C'$ may have a finite value even though the flow in the region is irrotational. Indeed, as will be shown in Chapter 4, the theory of aerodynamic lift is intimately related to the existence of circulation in multiply-connected regions of an irrotational flow.

A simple example of an irrotational flow with circulation is the two-dimensional free vortex motion shown in Fig. 3–9. The streamlines in a free vortex motion are concentric circles, and the velocity components at any point in such a flow field can be readily expressed in polar coordinates $(r, \theta)$ as

$$v_\theta = \frac{K}{r} \quad \text{and} \quad v_r = 0 \qquad (3\text{–}24)$$

where $K$ is called the *vortex constant* and is a measure of the strength of the free vortex. At the vortex center where $r = 0$, Eq. 3–24 would give $v_\theta = \infty$. Such points are called *singular points*, which have no physical counterpart. Therefore, the free vortex motion would have a physical meaning only when the region enclosing the singular point is excluded from its flow region. Regions containing singular points are considered multiply-connected.

To show that this two-dimensional free vortex motion is irrotational, we simply use the criterion of irrotationality:

$$(\nabla \times \mathbf{V})_z = 0$$

which, in polar coordinates $(r, \theta)$, can be written as

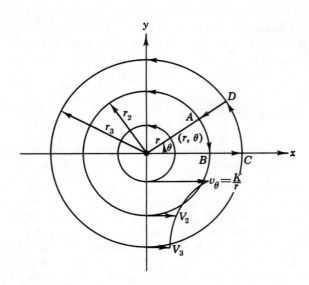

**Fig. 3-9.** A two-dimensional free vortex motion.

$$(\nabla \times \mathbf{V})_z = \frac{\partial v_r}{\partial \theta} - \frac{\partial (rv_\theta)}{\partial r} = 0 \qquad (3\text{-}25)$$

The velocity components in Eq. 3-24 are seen to satisfy Eq. 3-25, thus proving the irrotationality of the two-dimensional free vortex motion with the exclusion of the region containing the singular point.

The circulation around any streamline of the free vortex motion enclosing the singular point is easily calculated, since $\mathbf{V}$ is tangent to and has a constant magnitude along any one of the concentric circular stream-lines. Thus,

$$\oint_C \mathbf{V} \cdot d\mathbf{L} = v_\theta \oint_C dL$$

and the line integral of $dL$ around any closed circular path is simply the circumference of the circle. Therefore,

$$\Gamma = \oint_C \mathbf{V} \cdot d\mathbf{L} = v_\theta \oint_C dL = V_1(2\pi r_1) = V_2(2\pi r_2) = \cdots$$

which, after substitution of Eq. 3-24, $V_1 r_1 = V_2 r_2 = Vr = K$, becomes

$$\Gamma = 2\pi K \qquad (3\text{-}26)$$

Thus the circulation $\Gamma$ of a given free vortex motion is seen to depend only on the vortex constant $K$. Indeed, we shall show later in this section that, in an irrotational flow containing a singular point, the circulation for all closed paths enclosing the singular point are of equal magnitude.

On the other hand, the circulation has zero value when calculated along any closed path which excludes the singular point. This may be shown by taking the closed path $ABCDA$ in Fig. 3–9. Proceeding counterclockwise, we obtain

$$\Gamma_{ABCDA} = \Gamma_{AB} + \Gamma_{BC} + \Gamma_{CD} + \Gamma_{DA}$$

Both $\Gamma_{BC}$ and $\Gamma_{DA}$ along the two radial lines $\overline{BC}$ and $\overline{DA}$ are zero since $\mathbf{V}$ and $d\mathbf{L}$ are mutually perpendicular for these two paths. Along the two circular segments, $\Gamma_{AB} = -V_2\theta r_2$ and $\Gamma_{CD} = V_3\theta r_3$. Therefore

$$\Gamma_{ABCDA} = -V_2\theta r_2 + 0 + V_3\theta r_3 + 0 = 0$$

which proves that, in a free vortex motion, the circulation is everywhere zero except at the center which is a singular point.

We shall now demonstrate that the circulations are of equal value for all closed paths enclosing a singular point in an irrotational flow. The two arbitrary closed paths in Fig. 3–10 are drawn in an irrotational flow

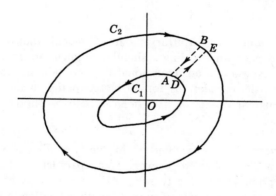

**Fig. 3-10.** Two arbitrary closed paths in an irrotational flow.

field enclosing a singular point $O$. The region between these two paths is simply-connected because it does not include the singular point. Introducing two parallel lines $\overline{AB}$ and $\overline{DE}$, we form another closed path $AC_1DEC_2BA$. The region enclosed by this closed path is also simply-connected, and the circulation around the path must be zero. Therefore, starting at point $A$ and performing line integrations in the direction as indicated by the arrows in the diagram, we may write

$$\Gamma_{AC_1DEC_2BA} = \int_{\substack{A \\ C_1}}^{D} \mathbf{V} \cdot d\mathbf{L} + \int_{D}^{E} \mathbf{V} \cdot d\mathbf{L} + \int_{\substack{E \\ C_2}}^{B} \mathbf{V} \cdot d\mathbf{L} + \int_{B}^{A} \mathbf{V} \cdot d\mathbf{L} = 0$$

If the distance between the two parallel lines $\overline{AB}$ and $\overline{DE}$ is made very small, the line integrations along these two lines become equal in magnitude but opposite in sign. The sum of these two integrations equals zero; i.e., $\int_D^E \mathbf{V} \cdot d\mathbf{L} + \int_B^A \mathbf{V} \cdot d\mathbf{L} = 0$. At the same time, the line integral $\int_{A}^{D}{}_{C_1} \mathbf{V} \cdot d\mathbf{L}$ is practically equal to that around the closed path $C_1$ in the counterclockwise direction, whereas the line integral $\int_{E}^{B}{}_{C_2} \mathbf{V} \cdot d\mathbf{L}$ is practically equal to that around the closed path $C_2$ in the clockwise direction. By denoting the counterclockwise direction as positive, the above equation then becomes

$$\Gamma_{AC_1DEC_2BA} = \int_A^D{}_{C_1} \mathbf{V} \cdot d\mathbf{L} + 0 + \int_E^B{}_{C_2} \mathbf{V} \cdot d\mathbf{L} + 0$$

$$= \oint_{C_1} \mathbf{V} \cdot d\mathbf{L} - \oint_{C_2} \mathbf{V} \cdot d\mathbf{L} = 0$$

or, after transposing terms,

$$\oint_{C_1} \mathbf{V} \cdot d\mathbf{L} = \oint_{C_2} \mathbf{V} \cdot d\mathbf{L}$$

Since paths $C_1$ and $C_2$ are arbitrary, we may conclude that the circulation for any closed path surrounding a singular point in an irrotational flow is invariant. Likewise, in an irrotational flow containing more than one singular point, the circulations for all closed paths enclosing the same number of singular points of fixed identity can be shown to have the same magnitude.

**Vortex filament.** The point vortex in the two-dimensional flow of Fig. 3–9 must be duplicated in every plane parallel to the $xy$ plane. Therefore, a point vortex in a two-dimensional flow may be regarded as a cross section of a line vortex of infinite length extending in the direction perpendicular to the plane of the two-dimensional flow. A line vortex is also called a *vortex filament*. A vortex filament does not necessarily have to be a straight line. In a three-dimensional flow a vortex filament may be a curve of any shape, as shown in Fig. 3–11. Hence, a vortex filament is defined as an axis of rotation of successive fluid elements.

When a vortex filament occurs in an irrotational flow, the circulation around any closed path, such as $C$ in Fig. 3–11, which links with the vortex filament is different from zero, because the curve $C$ cannot be shrunk continuously to a point without touching the vortex filament. The circulation around any closed path which does not link with a vortex filament is zero.

All closed paths which link with a single vortex filament have the same circulation. This statement can be proved in the following manner:

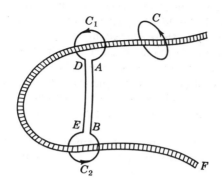

**Fig. 3-11.**   Vortex filament.

In Fig. 3–11, let the two closed curves $C_1$ and $C_2$ which link with the vortex filament be cut, and let the cuts be connected by the two parallel line segments $\overline{AB}$ and $\overline{DE}$ which lie very close together. The closed path $AC_1DEC_2BA$ does not link with the vortex filament so that the circulation around this closed path is zero. The line integrals of the velocities along the path segments $\overline{BA}$ and $\overline{DE}$ cancel each other, since these two segments are arbitrarily close to each other and their directions of line integration are opposite. Hence the line integrals of the velocities on the paths $C_1$ and $C_2$ also cancel each other. However, paths $C_1$ and $C_2$ in Fig. 3–11 are described in opposite directions; consequently, when they are described in the same sense, they have the same circulation. Since paths $C_1$ and $C_2$ are arbitrary, it can be concluded that all closed curves which link with the same vortex filament have the same circulation. This phenomenon is called the *law of conservation of vorticity* and can be written mathematically as

$$\Gamma = \iint_A (\nabla \times \mathbf{V}) \cdot d\mathbf{A} \qquad (3\text{--}27)$$

where $d\mathbf{A}$ denotes any cross-sectional area of a given vortex filament and $(\nabla \times \mathbf{V})$ is the vorticity vector at the same section. Note that Eq. 3–27 is analogous to the equation of continutiy for fluid flow in a stream filament. Hence, for a given vortex filament, the vorticity is inversely proportional to the cross-sectional area along the filament. For example, a tornado, which has the shape of a funnel, can be regarded as an enlarged vortex tube. The swirling motions of air particles are fastest at the tip (i.e., the smallest cross section) of the tornado funnel, which frequently touches the ground. The circular motion of air flow outside the tornado funnel is essentially irrotational.

A vortex filament cannot end at any point in the flow. If the vortex filament in Fig. 3–11 should come to an end at point $F$, the closed path $C_2$ could be slipped over the end, leaving the path $C_1$ in its original position still linked with the filament. Since the circulation around $C_2$ now becomes zero, the circulation around the closed path $AC_1DEC_2BA$ is no longer zero. This condition is clearly inconsistent with the law of conservation of vorticity. Therefore, a vortex filament may end at a solid boundary, it may extend to infinity, or it may form a closed curve.

**Vortex sheet.** A vortex sheet is formed by a large number of vortex filaments placed side by side, as shown in Fig. 3–12. Physically,

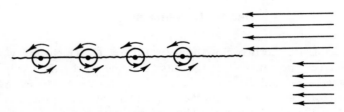

**Fig. 3-12.** Vortex sheet.

the vortex sheet forms a surface of discontinuity across which the velocity component parallel to the sheet changes by a finite amount.

### 3-5  Velocity Potential

Let $A$ and $B$ be two arbitrary paths that connect a fixed point $P_0(x_0, y_0, z_0, t)$ with a variable point $P(x, y, z, t)$ in an irrotational flow field at some time $t$, as is shown in Fig. 3–13. If the closed path $P_0APBP_0$ is simply-connected, then the circulation around this path equals zero, i.e.,

$$\Gamma_{P_0APBP_0} = \oint \mathbf{V} \cdot d\mathbf{L} = \int_{P_0 \atop A}^{P} \mathbf{V} \cdot d\mathbf{L} + \int_{P \atop B}^{P_0} \mathbf{V} \cdot d\mathbf{L} = 0$$

Whence, after transposing the second integral and reversing the limits on it, we have

$$\int_{P_0 \atop A}^{P} \mathbf{V} \cdot d\mathbf{L} = \int_{P_0 \atop B}^{P} \mathbf{V} \cdot d\mathbf{L}$$

Since paths $A$ and $B$ were chosen arbitrarily, we may conclude from the above equation that, in an irrotational flow, the line integral $\int_{P_0}^{P} \mathbf{V} \cdot d\mathbf{L}$

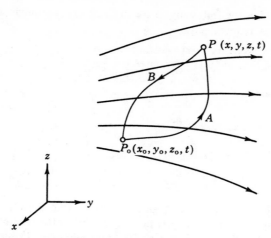

**Fig. 3-13.** Two arbitrary paths connecting a fixed point $P_0$ with a variable point $P$ in an irrotational flow field.

is independent of the path. This means that the quantity $\mathbf{V} \cdot d\mathbf{L}$ is an exact differential which may be considered as the differential of a point function. The value of this point function depends on the position $(x, y, z)$ and time $t$. This point function is called the *velocity potential* $\phi$ and is defined as

$$\mathbf{V} \cdot d\mathbf{L} = d\phi \tag{3–28}$$

so that

$$\int_{P_0}^{P} \mathbf{V} \cdot d\mathbf{L} = \int_{P_0}^{P} d\phi = \phi(x, y, z, t) - \phi_0(x_0, y_0, z_0, t) \tag{3–29}$$

where $\phi(x, y, z, t)$ is a point function with continuous derivatives and $\phi_0(x_0, y_0, z_0, t)$ is a constant. Hence a displacement of the fixed point $P_0$ merely alters the value of the constant $\phi_0$.

The total differential $d\phi$ in Eq. 3–28 may also be expressed in terms of the infinitesimal displacement $d\mathbf{L}$ as

$$d\phi = \nabla\phi \cdot d\mathbf{L}$$

since the projection of the gradient on any direction equals the derivative in that direction. Thus, Eq. 3–28 may also be expressed as

$$\mathbf{V} \cdot d\mathbf{L} = \nabla\phi \cdot d\mathbf{L}$$

or

$$\mathbf{V} = \nabla\phi \tag{3–30}$$

That is, the velocity field of an irrotational flow is always expressible in terms of the gradient of some scalar function $\phi$.

Eq. 3–30 takes the following forms in Cartesian, cylindrical, and spherical coordinates, respectively:

$$\mathbf{V} = u\mathbf{i} + v\mathbf{j} + w\mathbf{k}$$
$$= \nabla\phi = \frac{\partial\phi}{\partial x}\mathbf{i} + \frac{\partial\phi}{\partial y}\mathbf{j} + \frac{\partial\phi}{\partial z}\mathbf{k} \tag{3-31a}$$

$$\mathbf{V} = v_r\boldsymbol{\epsilon}_r + v_\theta\boldsymbol{\epsilon}_\theta + v_z\boldsymbol{\epsilon}_z$$
$$= \nabla\phi = \frac{\partial\phi}{\partial r}\boldsymbol{\epsilon}_r + \frac{1}{r}\frac{\partial\phi}{\partial\theta}\boldsymbol{\epsilon}_\theta + \frac{\partial\phi}{\partial z}\boldsymbol{\epsilon}_z \tag{3-31b}$$

$$\mathbf{V} = v_R\boldsymbol{\epsilon}_R + v_\theta\boldsymbol{\epsilon}_\theta + v_\phi\boldsymbol{\epsilon}_\phi$$
$$= \nabla\phi = \frac{\partial\phi}{\partial R}\boldsymbol{\epsilon}_R + \frac{1}{R}\frac{\partial\phi}{\partial\theta}\boldsymbol{\epsilon}_\theta + \frac{1}{R\sin\theta}\frac{\partial\phi}{\partial\phi}\boldsymbol{\epsilon}_\phi \tag{3-31c}$$

It is easy to show, by using Cartesian notations, that the velocity potential $\phi$ satisfies the condition of irrotationality by substituting the velocity components into Eqs. 3–5, which are mathematical criteria of irrotationality. Thus,

$$\frac{\partial w}{\partial y} - \frac{\partial v}{\partial z} = \frac{\partial^2\phi}{\partial z\,\partial y} - \frac{\partial^2\phi}{\partial y\,\partial z} = 0$$
$$\frac{\partial u}{\partial z} - \frac{\partial w}{\partial x} = \frac{\partial^2\phi}{\partial x\,\partial z} - \frac{\partial^2\phi}{\partial z\,\partial x} = 0 \tag{3-32}$$
$$\frac{\partial v}{\partial x} - \frac{\partial u}{\partial y} = \frac{\partial^2\phi}{\partial y\,\partial x} - \frac{\partial^2\phi}{\partial x\,\partial y} = 0$$

since each partial derivative of $\phi$ is a continuous function; hence, the order of partial differentiations becomes immaterial.

In the vector form, when the velocity field is expressed as the gradient of $\phi$, it automatically satisfies the condition of irrotationality (Eq. 3–4):

$$\nabla \times \mathbf{V} = \nabla \times \nabla\phi = 0 \tag{3-33}$$

since the cross product of two parallel vectors, $\nabla \times \nabla$, is zero.

Thus, we have proved that the conditions for irrotational flow are the necessary and sufficient conditions for the existence of a velocity potential and that the existence of a velocity potential implies irrotational flow. For this reason the terms *irrotational flow* and *potential flow* are often used interchangeably.

**Laplace equation.** To represent a possible case of potential flow, the function $\phi$ is, however, not arbitrary, for it must conform to the equation of continuity at every point in the flow field excepting singular points. If the fluid is incompressible,[1] then substitution of Eq. 3–30 into

---

[1] The equation satisfied by $\phi$ for a compressible flow is considerably more complex than for an incompressible flow. The potential equation for compressible flow will be derived and discussed in Chapter 9.

the equation of continuity (Eq. 2–17) leads to what is known as the *Laplace equation*:

$$\nabla \cdot \mathbf{V} = \nabla \cdot \nabla \phi = \nabla^2 \phi = 0 \qquad (3\text{–}34)$$

where the symbol $\nabla^2$ (called "del squared") is the famous *Laplace operator* or *Laplacian*. It has the dimensions of $L^{-2}$. The Laplace equation is also encountered in many other aspects of physics, such as theory of elasticity, heat transfer, electricity, etc. The Laplace operator $\nabla^2$ for different coordinate systems can be written as follows:
Cartesian coordinates $(x, y, z)$:

$$\nabla^2 \equiv \frac{\partial^2}{\partial x^2} + \frac{\partial^2}{\partial y^2} + \frac{\partial^2}{\partial z^2} \qquad (3\text{–}35a)$$

Cylindrical coordinates $(r, \theta, z)$:

$$\nabla^2 \equiv \frac{1}{r} \frac{\partial}{\partial r}\left(r \frac{\partial}{\partial r}\right) + \frac{1}{r^2} \frac{\partial^2}{\partial \theta^2} + \frac{\partial^2}{\partial z^2} \qquad (3\text{–}35b)$$

Spherical coordinates $(R, \theta, \phi)$:

$$\nabla^2 \equiv \frac{1}{R^2} \frac{\partial}{\partial R}\left(R^2 \frac{\partial}{\partial R}\right) + \frac{1}{R^2 \sin \theta} \frac{\partial}{\partial \theta}\left(\sin \theta \frac{\partial}{\partial \theta}\right) + \frac{1}{R^2 \sin \theta} \frac{\partial^2}{\partial \phi^2} \qquad (3\text{–}35c)$$

Since the Laplace equation embodies both the condition of irrotationality and the equation of continuity, any function $\phi$ which satisfies it represents a possible case of irrotational flow. The pattern of irrotational flow for a given set of boundary conditions is therefore determined by finding the solution of the Laplace equation in $\phi$ which satisfies the given boundary conditions. Once the $\phi$-function is known for a particular irrotational flow, the velocity field can be immediately determined by taking the gradient of $\phi$. Solutions of the Laplace equation are known as *harmonic functions*.[2] Mathematical solutions have been found for a number of relatively simple irrotational flow patterns by the inverse procedure of investigating known harmonic functions and determining the particular boundary conditions which these functions fulfill. Since $\nabla^2 \phi = 0$ is a linear, homogeneous differential equation, the sum of any two solutions is also a solution. Therefore, if we establish $\phi_1$ and $\phi_2$ to be harmonic, then the functions $C\phi_1$, $C + \phi_1$, $\phi_1 + \phi_2$, $C\phi_1 + \phi_2$, etc. are also harmonic. Thus, we may combine simple harmonic functions to obtain new ones of more complex nature. We shall discuss some of these irrotational flow patterns in Chapter 4.

In many problems, however, the boundary conditions are specified in advance. It then becomes necessary to find a proper velocity potential which satisfies both the Laplace equation and the prescribed boundary conditions of a given problem. The direct procedure of finding a $\phi$-function which satisfies the prescribed boundary conditions is rather difficult.

---

[2] See Louis A. Pipes, *Applied Mathematics for Engineers and Physicists*, 2nd ed. (New York: McGraw-Hill Book Company, 1958) pp. 488–490.

Several alternative methods of approach are available other than the direct method of finding a $\phi$-function from the boundary condition equations. These include the graphical trial-and-error method, the numerical approximate method, and the experimental analogy method.[3] These methods yield only a particular solution for the problem at hand. In general, the solution is approximate, but its precision can be refined to any desired degree. Consequently, these approximate methods have been widely used for engineering purposes.

Note also that the Laplace equation $\nabla^2\phi = 0$ does not involve $t$; hence its solution $\phi$ is determined for each instant $t$ by the boundary conditions which exist at that particular instant. Clearly the solution of an unsteady irrotational flow with continuously changing boundary conditions can be extremely complicated.

Since all hamonic functions are continuous, we may construct surfaces in irrotational flow fields over each of which the value of potential function $\phi$ is constant. Such surfaces are called *equipotential surfaces*. The gradient of $\phi$ along an elementary displacement on any one of those equipotential surfaces must equal zero; that is, there can be no velocity component tangent to equipotential surfaces. The velocity vectors must therefore be normal to all equipotential surfaces. Hence, surfaces which are constructed tangent to velocity vectors are orthogonal to equipotential surfaces. These surfaces are called *stream surfaces*, and the mathematical expressions representing stream surfaces are known as *stream functions*. We shall discuss stream functions and the relationship between velocity potentials and stream functions in Chapter 4.

**Illustrative Example 3–3.** Show that the function

$$\phi = \frac{a}{2}(x^2 + y^2 - 2z^2)$$

is a possible velocity potential for a three-dimensional, irrotational fluid flow.

*Solution:* If the given function represents a velocity potential of an irrotational flow, it must satisfy both the Laplace equation (which is the continuity equation of flow) and condition of irrotationality. Therefore,

$$\nabla^2\phi = \frac{\partial^2\phi}{\partial x^2} + \frac{\partial^2\phi}{\partial y^2} + \frac{\partial^2\phi}{\partial z^2}$$

$$= \frac{\partial^2}{\partial x^2}\left[\frac{a}{2}(x^2 + y^2 - 2z^2)\right]$$

$$+ \frac{\partial^2}{\partial y^2}\left[\frac{a}{2}(x^2 + y^2 - 2z^2)\right]$$

$$+ \frac{\partial^2}{\partial z^2}\left[\frac{a}{2}(x^2 + y^2 - 2z^2)\right]$$

$$= a + a - 2a = 0$$

[3]H. R. Vallentine, *Applied Hydrodynamics* (London: Butterworths Scientific Publications, 1959) Chap. 3.

The Laplace equation is satisfied and the given function could represent a possible fluid flow.

The velocity field for this flow is

$$\mathbf{V} = \nabla\phi = ax\mathbf{i} + ay\mathbf{j} - 2az\mathbf{k}$$

which can be readily shown to satisfy the condition of irrotationality, $\nabla \times \mathbf{V} = 0$.

Consequently, the given function could represent a velocity potential for a three-dimensional, irrotational flow.

## 3-6  Boundary Conditions

As was mentioned in the preceding section, a velocity potential which is chosen to represent a possible irrotational flow must satisfy not only the equation of continuity (i.e., the Laplace equation) but also the prescribed boundary conditions of the given problem. Sufficient information must be known concerning all boundaries which the fluid encounters in the flow. At a given boundary, both kinematic and dynamic conditions must be satisfied.

**Kinematic boundary conditions.** When a fluid is in contact with a solid boundary, kinematic conditions require that the fluid does not penetrate the boundary and that there are no gaps between the boundary and the fluid. We shall investigate the kinematic boundary conditions at a solid boundary in terms of velocity components parallel to and normal to the solid surface. Since irrotational flow occurs outside of the boundary layer, the fluid in the irrotational flow "at" the solid boundary seems to slide past its "contacting" surface with complete freedom. Hence at a solid boundary an irrotational flow may have any finite velocity parallel to the surface. The only restriction is then on the normal component of the velocity at the solid boundary. The fluid particle and the solid boundary with which it is in contact must have the same velocity normal to the surface.

At a stationary boundary, the fluid particle on the surface has zero velocity normal to the boundary surface; that is, at every point of the stationary boundary,

$$\mathbf{V} \cdot \mathbf{n} = 0 \qquad (3\text{–}36)$$

where $\mathbf{V}$ is the velocity of the fluid particle at the boundary surface, and $\mathbf{n}$ is the unit vector normal to the surface. Here the fluid velocity is everywhere tangential to the stationary surface.

If the solid boundary is in motion, the fluid velocity component normal to the boundary surface equals the velocity component of the surface normal to itself. That is,

$$\mathbf{V} \cdot \mathbf{n} = \mathbf{U}_b \cdot \mathbf{n} \qquad (3\text{–}37)$$

where $U_b$ denotes the velocity of the point on the boundary with which the fluid particle is in contact. By transposing terms,

$$(\mathbf{V} - \mathbf{U}_b) \cdot \mathbf{n} = 0 \tag{3-37a}$$

It is seen that the fluid velocity relative to the boundary is everywhere tangential to the boundary.

When two fluids which do not mix form a common surface of contact, the relative velocity between the contacting particles of the fluids must be everywhere tangential to the surface of contact. However, the shape and motion of the surface of contact also form a part of the solution to be determined for any given problem.

**Dynamic boundary conditions.** In addition to the above kinematic boundary conditions, certain dynamic boundary conditions must also be satisfied. When an irrotational flow is in contact with a boundary, whether solid or fluid, there is no shear stress at the boundary, and the fluid pressure must be normal to it. In case two different fluids are in contact, the pressure variation must be continuous across the surface of contact. Otherwise, if a finite difference in pressure should be permitted to occur across the boundary, then the resultant finite force acting on an element of the boundary would produce infinite acceleration on the boundary. This condition is physically impossible. Thus, in the case of a liquid in contact with the atmosphere, the pressure of the liquid at the free surface equals the local atmospheric pressure.

When a finite force causes a submerged object to move about in a fluid which is supposed to extend to infinity, dynamic boundary conditions specify that the velocity of fluid at infinity remains unaffected by the motion of the object. This restriction is necessary, since a physically impossible situation would otherwise result, in that a finite force acting on a submerged object would impart kinetic energy to an infinite mass of fluid in a finite time.

*Illustrative Example 3-4.* Suppose that $F(x, y, z, t) = 0$ represents the equation of a moving boundary surface. The total differential of $F$

$$dF = \frac{\partial F}{\partial x} dx + \frac{\partial F}{\partial y} dy + \frac{\partial F}{\partial z} dz + \frac{\partial F}{\partial t} dt = 0 \tag{A}$$

will be used to derive a general kinematic boundary condition equation.

The unit vector $\mathbf{n}$ normal to the boundary surface at any point $(x, y, z)$ may be written as

$$\mathbf{n} = l\mathbf{i} + m\mathbf{j} + n\mathbf{k}$$

where $l, m, n$ are direction cosines of $\mathbf{n}$. We shall denote $U_{bn}$ as the velocity of the boundary surface normal to itself at point $(x, y, z)$. Hence Eq. 3-37 can be written as

$$ul + vm + wn = U_{bn} \qquad \text{(B)}$$

where $u$, $v$, $w$ are velocity components of the fluid particle which is in contact with the boundary surface at point $(x, y, z)$.

The displacement components $dx$, $dy$, $dz$ of the boundary surface at point $(x, y, z)$ are related to $U_{bn}$ as follows:

$$dx = U_{bn}l\, dt$$
$$dy = U_{bn}m\, dt \qquad \text{(C)}$$
$$dz = U_{bn}n\, dt$$

which may be substituted into Eq. (A) to yield

$$U_{bn}\left(l\frac{\partial F}{\partial x} + m\frac{\partial F}{\partial y} + n\frac{\partial F}{\partial z}\right) + \frac{\partial F}{\partial t} = 0 \qquad \text{(D)}$$

The direction cosines of $\mathbf{n}$ can also be expressed in terms of gradients of $F$ as†

$$l = \frac{1}{R}\frac{\partial F}{\partial x}, \qquad m = \frac{1}{R}\frac{\partial F}{\partial y}, \qquad n = \frac{1}{R}\frac{\partial F}{\partial z} \qquad \text{(E)}$$

where

$$R = \sqrt{\left(\frac{\partial F}{\partial x}\right)^2 + \left(\frac{\partial F}{\partial y}\right)^2 + \left(\frac{\partial F}{\partial z}\right)^2}$$

Hence substitution of Eqs. (E) into Eq. (D) yields

$$U_{bn} = -\frac{1}{R}\frac{\partial F}{\partial t} \qquad \text{(F)}$$

We then introduce Eqs. (E) and (F) into Eq. (B) to obtain

$$u\frac{\partial F}{\partial x} + v\frac{\partial F}{\partial y} + w\frac{\partial F}{\partial z} + \frac{\partial F}{\partial t} = \frac{DF}{Dt} = 0 \qquad \text{(G)}$$

which is the general kinematic boundary condition equation. This equation must be satisfied at all points on a boundary surface (except at singular points).

Let us demonstrate the application of Eq. (G) by considering a sphere $x^2 + y^2 + z^2 = r^2$ whose center is moving along the $z$-axis with a uniform velocity $W\mathbf{k}$. The equation of the moving boundary surface of the sphere at any time $t$ is

$$F = x^2 + y^2 + (z - Wt)^2 - r^2 = 0$$

The partial derivatives of $F$ are

$$\frac{\partial F}{\partial x} = 2x, \qquad \frac{\partial F}{\partial y} = 2y, \qquad \frac{\partial F}{\partial z} = 2(z - Wt),$$

$$\frac{\partial F}{\partial t} = -2W(z - Wt)$$

Substituting these values into Eq. (G), we have

$$\frac{DF}{Dt} = u(2x) + v(2y) + w\,[2(z - Wt)] - 2W(z - Wt) = 0$$

---

†See V. L. Streeter, *Fluid Dynamics* (New York: McGraw-Hill Book Company, 1948) pp. 17–18.

which, upon simplifying, reduces to

$$ux + vy + (w - W)(z - Wt) = 0$$

This is the required kinematic boundary condition equation which must be satisfied for every point on the boundary surface of the moving sphere.

## 3-7  Bernoulli's Equation for an Irrotational Flow

The Bernoulli equation, which was derived in Sec. 2-13, is applicable only to points along any one streamline in a frictionless incompressible steady flow. According to that derivation, it cannot be applied to points on different streamlines in the same flow. However, if the flow further becomes irrotational, the applicability of Bernoulli's equation can be extended to all points (except singular points) in the entire irrotational flow field.

Let us again start with Euler's equation:

$$-\nabla p + \rho \mathbf{g} = \rho \left[ (\mathbf{V} \cdot \nabla) \mathbf{V} + \frac{\partial \mathbf{V}}{\partial t} \right] \tag{3-38}$$

We shall modify Euler's equation in the following manner. First, if we assume the $z$-axis to be in a vertical position with its positive direction pointed upward, the second term $\rho \mathbf{g}$ becomes $-\rho g \nabla z$. Next, we use the following familiar formula in vector analysis to replace the term $(\mathbf{V} \cdot \nabla) \mathbf{V}$ inside the bracket by its identity:

$$(\mathbf{V} \cdot \nabla)\mathbf{V} = \nabla \left( \frac{V^2}{2} \right) - \mathbf{V} \times (\nabla \times \mathbf{V}) \tag{3-39}$$

In an irrotational flow the **curl** of $\mathbf{V}$ is zero[4] so that the last term in the above equation vanishes leaving

$$(\mathbf{V} \cdot \nabla)\mathbf{V} = \nabla \left( \frac{V^2}{2} \right) \tag{3-40}$$

Finally, we may write the $\partial \mathbf{V}/\partial t$ term of Eq. 3-38 as

$$\frac{\partial \mathbf{V}}{\partial t} = \frac{\partial}{\partial t}(\nabla \phi) = \nabla \left( \frac{\partial \phi}{\partial t} \right) \tag{3-41}$$

since $\mathbf{V} = \nabla \phi$ in an irrotational flow, and the order of operators $\nabla$ and $\partial/\partial t$ may be interchanged for a continuous $\phi$-function. We then substitute Eqs. 3-40 and 3-41 into Eq. 3-38, transpose terms, and divide the equation through by $\rho$ to obtain the following form of Euler's equation for an irrotational flow:

---

[4]Note that the term $\mathbf{V} \times (\nabla \times \mathbf{V})$ may also be equal to zero if the $\mathbf{V}$-vector and the $(\nabla \times \mathbf{V})$-vector are parallel. In such a special case the flow field is no longer irrotational, but the streamlines are parallel to vortex lines.

$$\frac{\nabla p}{\rho} + g \, \nabla z + \nabla \left(\frac{V^2}{2}\right) + \nabla \left(\frac{\partial \phi}{\partial t}\right) = 0 \qquad (3\text{--}42)$$

The next step is to take the dot product of each term in the above equation with an arbitrary infinitesimal displacement $d\mathbf{r}$. By recalling from vector analysis that $\nabla p \cdot d\mathbf{r} = dp$, $\nabla z \cdot d\mathbf{r} = dz$, $\nabla(V^2/2) \cdot d\mathbf{r} = d(V^2/2)$, and $\nabla(\partial\phi/\partial t) \cdot d\mathbf{r} = d(\partial\phi/\partial t)$, the above equation becomes

$$\frac{dp}{\rho} + g \, dz + d\left(\frac{V^2}{2}\right) + d\left(\frac{\partial \phi}{\partial t}\right) = 0 \qquad (3\text{--}43)$$

where the differentials represent differential changes of the quantities in the direction of $d\mathbf{r}$. With $\rho$ and $g$ constant, we may integrate Eq. 3-43 along the direction $d\mathbf{r}$ to obtain

$$\frac{p}{\rho} + gz + \frac{V^2}{2} + \frac{\partial \phi}{\partial t} = B(t) \qquad (3\text{--}44)$$

where the Bernoulli function, $B(t)$ is an arbitrary function of time. In a steady flow the time-varying terms vanish and the above equation simplifies to the following familiar form:

$$\frac{p}{\rho} + gz + \frac{V^2}{2} = B \qquad (3\text{--}45)$$

In this derivation the infinitesimal displacement $d\mathbf{r}$ is arbitrary in direction. As a result, there is no directional restriction on the differentials in Eq. 3-43. Therefore, Eqs. 3-44 and 3-45 are valid everywhere (except at singular points) in an irrotational flow. The value of the Bernoulli constant $B$ in Eq. 3-45 is determined by the known conditions of pressure, position, and velocity at some point in the flow.

Although the resulting Bernoulli equations here and those in Sec. 2-13 are of the same form, it is extremely important to recognize that the two derivations are based on fundamentally different assumptions. Thus, by applying Euler's equation to an irrotational flow field, we are able to eliminate the earlier requirement of confining Bernoulli's equations to a particular streamline and to extend its application to the entire irrotational flow field.

*Illustrative Example 3–5.* A two-dimensional, irrotational flow is to be formed by the following function:

$$\phi = \frac{k}{2}(x^2 - y^2)$$

If the pressure is zero at position $\mathbf{r}_1 = 2\mathbf{i} + 3\mathbf{j}$, calculate the maximum pressure in this flow field.

*Solution:* It is easy to ascertain that the given function represents a velocity potential for a two-dimensional, irrotational flow, since the function can be shown to satisfy both the Laplace equation and the condition of irrotationality.

The gradient of $\phi$ then yields the velocity field for the flow:

$$\mathbf{V} = \nabla\phi = kx\mathbf{i} - ky\mathbf{j}$$

At position $\mathbf{r}_1$ where the pressure is zero, the velocity is clearly

$$\mathbf{V}_1 = 2k\mathbf{i} - 3k\mathbf{j}$$

and the magnitude of this velocity is

$$V_1 = \sqrt{u^2 + v^2} = \sqrt{(2k)^2 + (-3k)^2} = \sqrt{13}\,k$$

For a two-dimensional, irrotational flow, the maximum pressure occurs at the point where the velocity is zero. The point of zero velocity is obviously located at $(0, 0)$. The maximum pressure in the flow field can be determined by Bernoulli's equation written between the point $(0, 0)$ and position $\mathbf{r}_1$. Thus, by using the subscript 0 for conditions at point $(0, 0)$,

$$\frac{p_0}{\rho} + \frac{V_0^2}{2} = \frac{p_1}{\rho} + \frac{V_1^2}{2}$$

and, by substituting known values into the above equation,

$$\frac{p_0}{\rho} + 0 = 0 + \frac{13k^2}{2}$$

Therefore,

$$p_0 = \frac{13}{2}k^2\rho$$

which is the maximum pressure in this flow field.

## 3-8   Kinetic Energy in Irrotational Flows

An expression for the kinetic energy in an irrotational flow which can be obtained by Gauss' theorem has been found very useful in establishing some important theorems for irrotational flow. Gauss' theorem was earlier introduced in Sec. 2–4 in connection with the equation of continuity. The theorem is restated here for convenience:

$$\iiint_V (\nabla \cdot \mathbf{B})\, dV = \oiint_A \mathbf{B} \cdot d\mathbf{A} \tag{3–46}$$

where the only restriction placed on the vector function $\mathbf{B}$ is that it and its derivatives must be continuous throughout the volume $V$. This volume is completely bounded by one or more surfaces whose total area is $A$, of which $d\mathbf{A}$ is an element.

An expression for the kinetic energy can be obtained if we let

$$\mathbf{B} = \phi\nabla\phi$$

where $\phi$ is the velocity potential. Hence the integrand on the left-hand side of Eq. 3–46 becomes

$$(\nabla \cdot \mathbf{B})\, dV = \nabla \cdot (\phi \nabla \phi)\, dV = (\phi \nabla^2 \phi + \nabla \phi \cdot \nabla \phi)\, dV$$
$$= (\phi \nabla^2 \phi + V^2)\, dV \tag{3-47}$$

The last step is accomplished because in an irrotational flow $\mathbf{V} = \nabla \phi$ and the dot product $\mathbf{V} \cdot \mathbf{V}$ equals $V^2$. The integrand on the right-hand side of Eq. 3–46 can be expressed as

$$\mathbf{B} \cdot d\mathbf{A} = \phi \nabla \phi \cdot \mathbf{n}\, dA = \phi \frac{\partial \phi}{\partial n}\, dA \tag{3-48}$$

where $\mathbf{n}$ is the outward unit vector normal to $dA$. Multiplying the final results of Eqs. 3–47 and 3–48 by $\rho/2$ and substituting them into Eq. 3–46, we then have

$$\frac{\rho}{2} \iiint_V (\phi \nabla^2 \phi + V^2)\, dV = \frac{\rho}{2} \oiint_A \phi \frac{\partial \phi}{\partial n}\, dA$$

In an irrotational flow, $\nabla^2 \phi$ equals zero. Hence the remaining triple integral term is clearly the total kinetic energy of the fluid inside the volume $V$. Therefore, we may say

$$\mathrm{KE} = \frac{\rho}{2} \oiint_A \phi \frac{\partial \phi}{\partial n}\, dA \tag{3-49}$$

That is, in an irrotational flow the kinetic energy of the fluid inside a volume $V$ can be computed in terms of $\phi$ and $\partial \phi / \partial n$ over its entire boundary surface. Equation 3–49 applies only to velocity potentials which are single-valued.

If the fluid under consideration lies outside a solid object and extends throughout an infinite region, and if the velocity of flow is zero at infinity, the kinetic energy of the fluid external to the solid object is also given by Eq. 3–49.[5] In this case, the positive direction of $\mathbf{n}$ is pointed toward the interior of the solid object whose boundary surface has an area $A$.

**Uniqueness theorems.** The kinetic energy expression (Eq. 3–49) leads to several important conclusions regarding irrotational flows known as *uniqueness theorems*. These theorems are valid only for irrotational flows in which the velocity potential is both harmonic and single-valued. The uniqueness theorems and their proofs are as follows:

THEOREM 1: Irrotational motion is impossible in a fluid bounded entirely by fixed rigid boundaries.

*Proof*: On the fixed rigid boundary, $\partial \phi / \partial n = 0$ at every point. Therefore, $\mathrm{KE} = 0$ by virtue of Eq. 3–49, and $\mathbf{V}$ must be everywhere zero since $V^2$ cannot be negative.

---

[5]L. M. Milne-Thomson, *Theoretical Hydrodynamics*, 4th ed. (New York: The Macmillan Company, 1960) pp. 92–97.

THEOREM 2: Irrotational motion which satisfies the Laplace equation and the prescribed boundary conditions is uniquely determined by the prescribed motion of the boundaries.

*Proof*: If two harmonic functions $\phi_1$ and $\phi_2$ are both solutions of $\nabla^2\phi = 0$, then at every point on the boundary the velocity normal to the boundary surface must be the same for both functions. Hence

$$\frac{\partial\phi_1}{\partial n} = \frac{\partial\phi_2}{\partial n} \quad \text{or} \quad \frac{\partial\phi_1}{\partial n} - \frac{\partial\phi_2}{\partial n} = 0$$

Since $\nabla^2\phi = 0$ is a linear, homogeneous equation, the difference of any two harmonic functions, i.e., $\phi_1 - \phi_2$ in this case, is also a solution. Thus,

$$\frac{\partial(\phi_1 - \phi_2)}{\partial n} = \frac{\partial\phi_1}{\partial n} - \frac{\partial\phi_2}{\partial n} = 0$$

or

$$\phi_1 - \phi_2 = \text{constant}$$

indicating that $\phi_1$ and $\phi_2$ can differ only by a constant quantity. The velocity fields given by $\phi_1$ and $\phi_2$ are identical, since the addition of a constant to a potential does not change the value of the gradient of the potential.

THEOREM 3: Irrotational motion is impossible in a fluid at rest at infinity if the internal boundaries are simultaneously at rest.

*Proof*: The proof is essentially the same as that for Theorem 1, except that this is an external case.

THEOREM 4: Irrotational motion of a fluid at rest at infinity is uniquely determined by the motion of the internal boundaries.

*Proof*: The proof is essentially the same as that for Theorem 2, except that this is also an external case.

THEOREM 5: Irrotational motion of a fluid moving at a uniform velocity at infinity is uniquely determined by the motion of the internal boundaries.

*Proof*: If we superimpose a uniform velocity of equal magnitude and opposite sense to that at infinity on the entire flow field, this case is then reduced to that of Theorem 4.

***Illustrative Example 3-6.*** When a sphere of radius $R_0$ is moving uniformly with a velocity $V_0$ in a fluid which is initially at rest, the velocity potential for the resulting flow field can be written in spherical coordinates as

$$\phi = \frac{1}{2} V_0 \frac{R_0^3}{R^2} \cos\theta$$

Calculate the kinetic energy of all the fluid in this flow field.

*Solution:* The kinetic energy of all the fluid in this flow field can be calculated by means of Eq. 3–49:

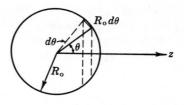

**Illustrative Example 3-6**

$$KE = \frac{\rho}{2} \oiint_A \phi \frac{\partial \phi}{\partial n} \, dA = -\frac{\rho}{2} \oiint_A \phi \frac{\partial \phi}{\partial R}$$

$$= \frac{\rho}{2} \oiint_A \frac{1}{2} V_0^2 \frac{R_0^6}{R^5} \cos^2 \theta \, dA$$

where the integration is performed over the surface of the sphere $R = R_0$ and $dA = 2\pi R_0 \sin \theta R_0 \, d\theta$, as shown in the figure. Substitution into the above equation yields

$$KE = \frac{\rho}{2} V_0^2 \pi R_0^3 \int_0^\pi \cos^2 \theta \sin \theta \, d\theta$$

$$= \frac{1}{2} \left( \frac{2}{3} \pi R_0^3 \rho \right) V_0^2$$

The kinetic energy of all the fluid in the flow field is seen to be equal to the kinetic energy of one-half the displaced mass of fluid if it were moving with the velocity $V_0$.

# PROBLEMS

**3–1.** Determine which of the following two-dimensional velocity fields represent possible examples of irrotational flow.

(a) $u = Ax/(x^2 + y^2)$

$v = Ay/(x^2 + y^2)$

(b) $v_r = A \cos \theta \left( 1 - \dfrac{B}{r^2} \right)$

$v_\theta = A \sin \theta \left( 1 - \dfrac{B}{r^2} \right)$

(c) $u = A (y^2 - x^2)$

$v = 2Axy$

(d) $u = Ax^2 yt$

$v = y^2 - Axy^2 t$

**3–2.** Calculate the unknown velocity component so that the two velocity components satisfy the conditions of two-dimensional irrotational flow.

(a) $u = 3x^2 - 3y^2$

$v = ?$

(b) $u = ?$

$v = -Ay + Axe^{-At}$

(c) $u = A \cos y + x \ln y$

$v = ?$

(d) $v_r = \dfrac{1}{2} r^{-1/2} \cos \dfrac{\theta}{2}$

$v_\theta = ?$

**3–3.** Do the velocity fields given in Problems 1–8, 1–10, 1–11, 1–12, 1–13, 1–14, 1–16, and 1–17 satisfy the conditions of irrotationality?

**3–4.** A steady, two-dimensional, incompressible flow occurs between two fixed surfaces spaced at a distance $b$ apart. The velocity profile is a parabola with vertex at the centerline. Using the notations shown in Fig. 3–14, determine an expression which describes the variation of vorticity in the flow field.

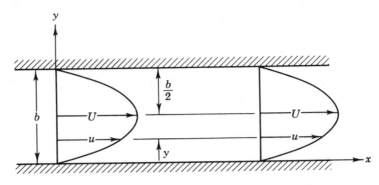

**Fig. 3-14.**

**3–5.** Given a velocity field

$$V = x\mathbf{i} - y\mathbf{j} + 8\mathbf{k}$$

Evaluate the circulation about a rectangular path in the xy-plane as shown in Fig. 3–15.

**3–6.** Using the path shown in the preceding problem, calculate the circulation for the following flow field.

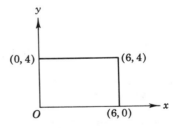

**Fig. 3-15.**

$$V = (5x^2 + 3y)\mathbf{i} + (12 + 4z)\mathbf{j} + 2yz^2\mathbf{k}$$

Compare the result with that obtained by integrating the z-component of the **curl** over the surface of the rectangle in the xy-plane.

**3–7.** Calculate the circulation about the square enclosed by $x = \pm 1$ and $y = \pm 1$ in the xy-plane for the two-dimensional flow given by

$$V = (3x^2 + y)\mathbf{i} - (6xy + x)\mathbf{j}$$

**3–8.** Use Stokes' theorem to evaluate the circulation along a circle $x^2 + y^2 = 1$ of the velocity field

$$V = x^2y\mathbf{i} - xy^2\mathbf{j} + 5\mathbf{k}$$

**3–9.** Use Stokes' theorem to evaluate the circulation along an ellipse $4x^2 + 9y^2 = 36$ of the velocity field

$$V = 3y\mathbf{i} + 2x\mathbf{j} - 4\mathbf{k}$$

**3–10.** Determine the velocity fields for the following velocity potentials:

(a) $\phi = x^2 + y^2 + z^2$

(b) $\phi = x^2 - x + y^2 + 5t^3 + 4zt$

(c) $\phi = \ln [(x + a)^2 - y^2]$

(d) $\phi = y - \arctan (y/x)$

(e) $\phi = e^x \cos y$

Which of these flow fields satisfy the equation of continuity?

3–11. Given a velocity field:

$$V = (x^2 - y^2 + x)i - (2xy + y)j$$

(a) Show that this field represents a possible irrotational flow. (b) Determine the velocity potential for this flow. (c) Determine the velocity component in the direction along a straight line joining points (0, 0) and (1, 2).

3–12. Repeat the same calculations as in Problem 3–11 for the following velocity fields:

(a) $V = (x^2 + y^2)i + 2xy^2j$

(b) $V = \dfrac{A \cos \theta}{r^2} \epsilon_r + \dfrac{A \sin \theta}{r^2} \epsilon_\theta$

3–13. Given: $V = 3i + 4j - 5k$. Find $\phi$.

3–14. The velocity potential of a steady flow field is given by the equation:

$$\phi = x^2 + y^2 - 2z^2$$

The temperature of the field is described by the following expression:

$$T = x + 3xy + z^2 + 5xyz$$

Determine the time rate of change of temperature of a fluid element as it passes through the point $(1, -2, 3)$.

3–15. Show that $\nabla \times (\nabla \phi) = 0$.

3–16. The parabolic profile $y = -x^2$ moves steadily with a velocity $V = 2j$ through an initially stationary fluid. If the time $t$ is measured from the instant that the vertex of the profile was at the origin of the coordinate system, determine (a) the equation of the moving profile at any time $t$, and (b) the kinematic boundary condition equation which must be satisfied for every point on the surface of the moving profile.

3–17. A sphere of radius $r$ moves steadily with a velocity $V = 3i + 2j - 5k$ through an initially stationary fluid. If the time $t$ is measured from the instant that the center of the sphere was at the origin of the coordinate system, determine (a) the equation of the moving boundary surface of the sphere at any time $t$, and (b) the kinematic boundary condition equation which must be satisfied for every point on the boundary surface of the moving sphere.

3–18. Work Problem 3–17 if, in addition, the sphere is also accelerating at $a = 4j$.

**3-19.** Show that $(V \cdot \nabla)V = \nabla\left(\frac{V^2}{2}\right) - V \times (\nabla \times V)$.

**3-20.** Derive a form of the integrated Euler's equation which applies to an unsteady, irrotational, compressible flow. State all the assumptions and restrictions involved in arriving at the final equation.

**3-21.** For each of the following velocity potentials:

(a) $\phi = 2xy + y$          (b) $\phi = x^2 + x - y^2$

(c) $\phi = 5x/(x^2 + y^2)$          (d) $\phi = e^x \cos y$

(e) $\phi = 10 \ln r + 20\,\theta$

Find the pressure gradient at point $(3, 4, 0)$ if the fluid is water.

**3-22.** An incompressible flow field is described by

$$\phi = x^2 - 2y^2 + z^2$$

(a) Calculate the pressure difference between points $(3, 6, 5)$ and $(5, -3, 8)$. (b) If the pressure is zero at point $(2, 1, 3)$, calculate the maximum pressure in this flow field.

**3-23.** When a cylinder of radius $r_0$ is moving uniformly with a velocity $V_0$ in a fluid which is initially at rest, the velocity potential for the resulting flow field can be written in cylindrical notations as

$$\phi = V_0 \frac{r_0^2}{r} \cos \theta$$

Calculate the kinetic energy, per unit length of cylinder, of all the fluid outside the cylinder.

# 4

# Incompressible
# Potential Flows

## 4-1  Introduction

The problem of determining a particular irrotational flow amounts mathematically to finding a velocity potential which satisfies both the Laplace equation and the given boundary conditions of the flow in question. A velocity potential does exist for every possible type of irrotational motion with its prescribed boundary conditions. Once the velocity potential is known for an irrotational flow, the velocity field of the flow can be determined by taking the gradient of the velocity potential, and the pressure field can, in turn, be calculated from the Bernoulli equation. This procedure sounds simple, but it is rather complicated mathematically to carry out. Indeed, the solution of the Laplace equation to satisfy simultaneously the prescribed boundary conditions requires a thorough knowledge of partial differential equations.

However, progress in potential flow theory has evolved from the reverse procedure of finding boundary conditions to which known harmonic functions would apply. These known functions are comparatively few in number and deal generally with two-dimensional planar flows and three-dimensional axially symmetric flows around bodies of revolution. Since the derivations are different for two-dimensional and three-dimensional potential flows, we shall treat them separately in this chapter.

## PART I. TWO-DIMENSIONAL PLANAR POTENTIAL FLOWS

### 4-2 Stream Function in Two-dimensional Flows

The stream function is a mathematical function representing the geometry of stream surfaces in both rotational and irrotational flow fields. In the two-dimensional steady flow of an incompressible fluid, the stream function can be related to the velocity field in a comparatively simple manner. Using Cartesian notations, we shall define the stream function $\psi(x, y)$ as a point function which has the following relations with the two velocity components:

$$u = \frac{\partial \psi}{\partial y} \qquad v = -\frac{\partial \psi}{\partial x} \qquad (4\text{-}1)$$

When these two expressions are substituted into the equation of continuity:

$$\nabla \cdot \mathbf{V} = \frac{\partial u}{\partial x} + \frac{\partial v}{\partial y} = \frac{\partial}{\partial x}\left(\frac{\partial \psi}{\partial y}\right) + \frac{\partial}{\partial y}\left(-\frac{\partial \psi}{\partial x}\right) = 0 \qquad (4\text{-}2)$$

it is seen that the assumption of a stream function as a point function identically satisfies the equation of continuity, since the order of differentiation of a point function is immaterial. In other words, the equation of continuity for the steady two-dimensional flow of an incompressible fluid is mathematically the necessary and sufficient condition for the existence of a point function called the *stream function*. Furthermore, the term *two-dimensional* here means that two space coordinates are necessary to describe the motion. Therefore, it includes both planar flows and axially symmetrical flows of three-dimensional nature. The treatment in this part is for planar flows only; three-dimensional axially symmetrical flows will be discussed in Part II of this chapter.

The physical meaning of the stream function will become clear when we examine the relationship between the stream function and the streamline. From the definition of the streamline given in Sec. 1-5, the differential equation of the streamline for a two-dimensional planar flow is clearly

$$\frac{dx}{u} = \frac{dy}{v} \qquad \text{or} \qquad u\,dy - v\,dx = 0 \qquad (4\text{-}3)$$

Substituting the values of $u$ and $v$ from Eqs. 4-1 into Eq. 4-3, we have

$$\frac{\partial \psi}{\partial y} dy + \frac{\partial \psi}{\partial x} dx = 0$$

The left-hand side of this equation is, by definition, equal to the total differential $d\psi$ when $\psi$ is a point function. Thus,

$$d\psi = \frac{\partial \psi}{\partial x} dx + \frac{\partial \psi}{\partial y} dy = 0$$

and

$$\psi = \text{constant (along a streamline)} \qquad (4\text{-}4)$$

which is the equation for a family of streamlines. Different numerical values of the constant in turn define different streamlines. A graphical representation of a flow pattern is obtained by plotting a series of streamlines differing by constant increments as shown in Fig. 4–1.

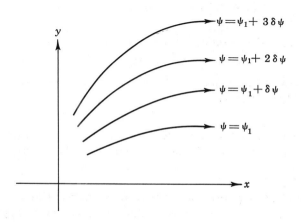

**Fig. 4-1.** A family of streamlines.

**Stream function and volume rate of flow.** Another physical interpretation of the stream function derives from its relationship with the volume rate of flow. Let us consider Fig. 4–2. The volume rate of flow $dq$ across any arbitrary surface $AB$ (of unit thickness normal to the $xy$ plane) connecting two adjacent stream surfaces is given by

$$dq = \mathbf{V} \cdot d\mathbf{L} = \mathbf{V} \cdot \mathbf{n} \, dL = \left( u \frac{\partial x}{\partial n} + v \frac{\partial y}{\partial n} \right) dL$$

With $u = \partial \psi / \partial y$, $v = -\partial \psi / \partial x$, $\partial x / \partial n = \partial y / \partial L$, and $\partial y / \partial n = -\partial x / \partial L$, the foregoing expression for $dq$ then becomes

$$dq = \left( \frac{\partial \psi}{\partial y} \frac{\partial y}{\partial L} + \frac{\partial \psi}{\partial x} \frac{\partial x}{\partial L} \right) dL$$

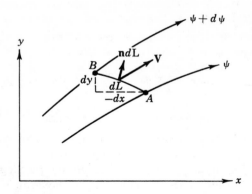

**Fig. 4-2.** Flow between two streamlines.

The right-hand side is evidently the equivalence of $d\psi$, so that

$$dq = d\psi \qquad (4\text{-}5)$$

Integrating the above equation between $A$ and $B$ on the two stream surfaces in Fig. 4–2 yields

$$q = \psi_B - \psi_A \qquad (4\text{-}6)$$

Hence the volume rate of flow between any two streamlines in a two-dimensional planar flow is numerically equal to the difference in their $\psi$-values.

**Stream function for two-dimensional irrotational flows.** The above attributes of the two-dimensional stream function $\psi(x, y)$ apply equally well to both rotational and irrotational flows. For irrotational flows, the condition of irrotationality, i.e.,

$$\frac{\partial u}{\partial y} - \frac{\partial v}{\partial x} = 0 \qquad (4\text{-}7)$$

must further be satisfied. Substitution of $\partial\psi/\partial y$ for $u$ and $-\partial\psi/\partial x$ for $v$ yields

$$\frac{\partial^2\psi}{\partial x^2} + \frac{\partial^2\psi}{\partial y^2} = 0 \qquad (4\text{-}8)$$

This is the two-dimensional Laplace equation in Cartesian coordinates. Just as the velocity potential $\phi$, the stream function $\psi$ in a two-dimensional irrotational flow is also the solution of the Laplace equation. Hence two-dimensional harmonic potentials are used to represent stream functions for analogous flows. Moreover, since the uniqueness theorems in Sec. 3–8 revealed that only one pattern of irrotational flow results from a given set of boundary conditions, hence only one $\psi$-function satisfies both the Laplace equation and the boundary conditions of a particular two-dimensional irrotational flow. This characteristic of the stream function of an irrotational flow forms the basis of graphical solution, called the *flow net*, for determining the pattern of flow once the form of the boundaries is known. The flow net is discussed in Sec. 4–4.

**Velocity components determined from the stream function in polar coordinates.** Polar coordinates are the same as cylindrical coordinates when $z$ is identically zero. The analytical treatment of many two-dimensional irrotational flows involving circular boundaries is greatly simplified through the use of polar coordinates. Figure 4–3 shows that

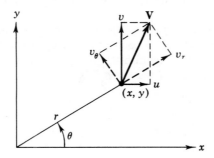

**Fig. 4-3.** Relationships between the Cartesian and polar coordinates of velocity components.

the tranformation formulas between the Cartesian and polar coordinates are:

$$x = r \cos \theta \qquad y = r \sin \theta \qquad (4\text{–}9)$$

Since $\psi = \psi(r, \theta)$ and the variables $r$ and $\theta$ are in turn related to $x$ and $y$ as shown in Eqs. 4–9, the partial differentiation of $\psi$ with respect to $r$ can be written as

$$\frac{\partial \psi}{\partial r} = \frac{\partial \psi}{\partial x}\frac{\partial x}{\partial r} + \frac{\partial \psi}{\partial y}\frac{\partial y}{\partial r} \qquad (4\text{–}10)$$

Using Eqs. 4–1 to substitute for the partial derivatives of $\psi$ and Eqs. 4–9 to replace the terms $\partial x/\partial r$ and $\partial y/\partial r$ in the above equation, we have

$$\frac{\partial \psi}{\partial r} = -(v \cos \theta - u \sin \theta) \qquad (4\text{–}11)$$

The two terms in the parentheses represent respectively the projections of the velocity components $v$ and $u$ in the tangential direction. Their sum then becomes the tangential component $v_\theta$ of the velocity vector as shown in Fig. 4–3. Thus, we may also write the above equation as

$$v_\theta = -\frac{\partial \psi}{\partial r} \tag{4-12}$$

Similar calculations will lead to an expression for the radial component of the velocity as

$$v_r = \frac{1}{r}\frac{\partial \psi}{\partial \theta} \tag{4-13}$$

## 4-3   Relationship Between the Stream Function and the Velocity Potential in Two-dimensional Irrotational Flows

The stream function and the velocity potential in a two-dimensional irrotational flow are related to each other by the velocity components of flow which can be derived from both of them through the use of partial differentiations. Thus, in Cartesian coordinates $(x, y)$,

$$u = \frac{\partial \psi}{\partial y} = \frac{\partial \phi}{\partial x} \qquad v = -\frac{\partial \psi}{\partial x} = \frac{\partial \phi}{\partial y} \tag{4-14}$$

and in polar coordinates $(r, \theta)$,

$$v_r = \frac{1}{r}\frac{\partial \psi}{\partial \theta} = \frac{\partial \phi}{\partial r} \qquad v_\theta = -\frac{\partial \psi}{\partial r} = \frac{1}{r}\frac{\partial \phi}{\partial \theta} \tag{4-15}$$

If either $\psi$ or $\phi$ is known for a particular two-dimensional irrotational flow, the other function can be determined from the above relationships. Equations 4–14 are known as the *Cauchy-Riemann equations*. Furthermore, in the two-dimensional irrotational flow both the stream function and the velocity potential must also satisfy their respective Laplace equations:

$$\nabla^2 \phi = 0 \tag{4-16}$$
$$\nabla^2 \psi = 0 \tag{4-17}$$

In view of the intimate relationships that exist between the stream function and the velocity potential, and the similar conditions that these two mathematical functions must satisfy in two-dimensional irrotational flows, it is instructive to summarize the restrictions of these two functions as follows:

(1) If $\nabla \times \mathbf{V} = 0$, then a velocity potential $\phi$ exists such that $\mathbf{V} = \nabla\phi$. Here the condition of irrotationality is the only restriction for the existence of $\phi$. Therefore, $\phi$ may also exist for compressible flows as long as they are irrotational.

(2) If $\nabla \times \mathbf{V} = 0$ and, in addition, if $\nabla \cdot \mathbf{V} = 0$, then $\phi$ also satisfies $\nabla^2 \phi = 0$. Note that we have introduced an additional restriction that the flow is incompressible.

(3) If $\nabla \cdot \mathbf{V} = 0$, then a stream function $\psi$ can be assumed to exist. The equation of continuity is the necessary and sufficient condition for the existence of $\psi$. Therefore, a $\psi$-function can be found to represent an incompressible flow, both rotational and irrotational, as long as it satisfies the equation of continuity.

(4) If $\nabla \cdot \mathbf{V} = 0$ and, in addition, if $\nabla \times \mathbf{V} = 0$, then $\psi$ also satisfies $\nabla^2 \psi = 0$.

It was shown in Sec. 3–5 that in an irrotational flow equipotential surfaces form an orthogonal system with stream surfaces. In a two-dimensional irrotational flow, equipotential surfaces and stream surfaces become respectively equipotential lines and streamlines. These two sets of lines intersect each other at right angles. Moreover, the Cauchy-Riemann equations stipulate that in a two-dimensional irrotational flow the rate of change of $\phi$ in one direction equals the rate of change of $\psi$ in an orthogonal direction. Thus, lines of constant $\phi$ and $\psi$ form an orthogonal grid system of squares called the *flow net*. We shall discuss the flow net after we establish the orthogonality relationship between equipotential lines and streamlines.

Figure 4–4 shows a system of equipotential lines and streamlines of a two-dimensional irrotational flow. To prove that the $\phi$-lines are orthogonal to the $\psi$-lines, it is necessary to show that, at any point such as $A$ which is a point of intersection of the lines $\phi = B_1$ and $\psi = C_1$, the slope of the $\phi = B_1$ line is the negative reciprocal of the $\psi = C_1$ line.

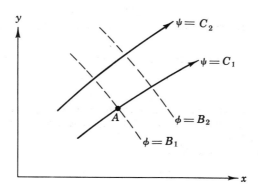

**Fig. 4-4.** Equipotential lines and streamlines of a two-dimensional irrotational flow.

Along these two lines the respective total changes of $\phi$ and $\psi$ are clearly equal to zero. Thus, we may write the total change of $\phi$ for the line $\phi = B_1$ as

$$d\phi = \frac{\partial \phi}{\partial x} dx + \frac{\partial \phi}{\partial y} dy = 0 \qquad (4\text{-}18)$$

and the total change of $\psi$ for the line $\psi = C_1$ as

$$d\psi = \frac{\partial \psi}{\partial x} dx + \frac{\partial \psi}{\partial y} dy = 0 \qquad (4\text{-}19)$$

Consequently, the slopes of the lines $\phi = B_1$ and $\psi = C_1$ are respectively

$$\left(\frac{dy}{dx}\right)_{\phi=B_1} = -\frac{\partial \phi/\partial x}{\partial \phi/\partial y} \qquad (4\text{-}20)$$

and

$$\left(\frac{dy}{dx}\right)_{\psi=C_1} = -\frac{\partial \psi/\partial x}{\partial \psi/\partial y} \qquad (4\text{-}21)$$

Since point $A$ is on both the lines $\phi = B_1$ and $\psi = C_1$, we may use Eqs. 4–14 to replace the partial derivatives of $\phi$ in Eq. 4–20 by the partial derivatives of $\psi$. Equation 4–20 then becomes

$$\left(\frac{dy}{dx}\right)_{\phi=B_1} = \frac{\partial \psi/\partial y}{\partial \psi/\partial x} = -\frac{1}{(dy/dx)_{\psi=C_1}} \qquad (4\text{-}22)$$

and the slopes of the two lines $\phi = B_1$ and $\psi = C_1$ are negative reciprocals of each other at point $A$. Since point $A$ was chosen arbitrarily, we may conclude that equipotential lines and streamlines in a two-dimensional irrotational flow form an orthogonal grid system.

***Illustrative Example 4-1.*** The stream function for a two-dimensional flow is

$$\psi = 2xy$$

Determine (a) the corresponding velocity potential, and (b) the pressure gradient at point $(1, 2)$.

*Solution:* (a) The velocity components for this flow are given by Eqs. 4-14:

$$u = \frac{\partial \psi}{\partial y} = 2x \qquad v = -\frac{\partial \psi}{\partial x} = -2y$$

It is easy to show that these velocity components satisfy both the continuity equation and the condition of irrotationality. Therefore, a velocity potential will exist for this flow.

By using the first of Eqs. 4-14,

$$\frac{\partial \phi}{\partial x} = \frac{\partial \psi}{\partial y} = 2x$$

Hence

$$\phi = \int 2x \, \partial x = x^2 + f(y) + C_1 \qquad (A)$$

and

$$\frac{\partial \phi}{\partial y} = \frac{\partial f(y)}{\partial y} \qquad\qquad \textbf{(B)}$$

From the second of Eqs. 4-14,

$$\frac{\partial \phi}{\partial y} = -\frac{\partial \psi}{\partial x} = -2y \qquad\qquad \textbf{(C)}$$

Equating the right-hand sides of Eqs. (B) and (C), we have

$$\frac{\partial f(y)}{\partial y} = -2y$$

Therefore,

$$f(y) = -y^2 + C_2$$

which may be substituted into Eq. (A) to yield the following desired velocity potential for this flow:

$$\phi = x^2 - y^2 + C$$

where the constant $C = C_1 + C_2$.

(b) The pressure gradient for this flow can be determined by using Euler's equation (Eq. 2-38):

$$\begin{aligned}
\nabla p &= -\rho(\mathbf{V} \cdot \nabla)\mathbf{V} \\
&= -\rho\left(u\frac{\partial u}{\partial x} + v\frac{\partial u}{\partial y}\right)\mathbf{i} - \rho\left(u\frac{\partial v}{\partial x} + v\frac{\partial v}{\partial y}\right)\mathbf{j} \\
&= -\rho[(2x)(2) + (-2y)(0)]\mathbf{i} - \rho[(2x)(0) + (-2y)(-2)]\mathbf{j} \\
&= -4\rho x\mathbf{i} - 4\rho y\mathbf{j}
\end{aligned}$$

At point (1, 2),

$$\nabla p = -4\rho\mathbf{i} - 8\rho\mathbf{j}$$

*Illustrative Example 4-2.* The function

$$\phi = -\frac{k}{r}\cos\theta$$

is expressed in polar coordinates. The symbol $k$ denotes a constant. Show that this function represents a velocity potential of a two-dimensional, irrotational flow defined everywhere except at the origin. Also determine the corresponding stream function.

*Solution:* If the given function represents a velocity potential of a two-dimensional, irrotational flow, it is necessary to show that this function satisfies both the continuity equation and the condition of irrotationality. The continuity equation is the Laplace equation for $\phi$. Thus, by using Eq. 3-35b,

$$\begin{aligned}
\nabla^2\phi &= \frac{1}{r}\frac{\partial}{\partial r}\left(r\frac{\partial \phi}{\partial r}\right) + \frac{1}{r^2}\frac{\partial^2 \phi}{\partial \theta^2} \\
&= \frac{1}{r}\frac{\partial}{\partial r}\left[r\frac{\partial}{\partial r}\left(-\frac{k}{r}\cos\theta\right)\right] + \frac{1}{r^2}\frac{\partial^2}{\partial \theta^2}\left(-\frac{k}{r}\cos\theta\right) \qquad \textbf{(A)} \\
&= \left(-\frac{k}{r^3}\cos\theta\right) + \left(\frac{k}{r^3}\cos\theta\right) = 0
\end{aligned}$$

The condition of irrotationality in polar coordinates is expressed in Eq. 3-2:

$$\nabla \times \nabla \phi = \left[ \frac{1}{r} \frac{\partial}{\partial r} \left( \frac{\partial \phi}{\partial \theta} \right) - \frac{1}{r} \frac{\partial}{\partial \theta} \left( \frac{\partial \phi}{\partial r} \right) \right] \epsilon_z$$

$$= \left\{ \frac{1}{r} \frac{\partial}{\partial r} \left[ \frac{\partial}{\partial \theta} \left( -\frac{k}{r} \cos \theta \right) \right] - \frac{1}{r} \frac{\partial}{\partial \theta} \left[ \frac{\partial}{\partial r} \left( -\frac{k}{r} \cos \theta \right) \right] \right\} \epsilon_z \quad \textbf{(B)}$$

$$= \left\{ \left( -\frac{k}{r^3} \sin \theta \right) - \left( -\frac{k}{r^3} \sin \theta \right) \right\} \epsilon_z = 0$$

The given function is seen to satisfy both the continuity equation and the condition of irrotationality; therefore, it could represent a velocity potential of a two-dimensional, irrotational flow.

The velocity components for this flow can be determined from Eqs. 4-15:

$$v_r = \frac{\partial \phi}{\partial r} = \frac{\partial}{\partial r} \left( -\frac{k}{r} \cos \theta \right) = \frac{k}{r^2} \cos \theta \quad \textbf{(C)}$$

$$v_\theta = \frac{1}{r} \frac{\partial \phi}{\partial \theta} = \frac{1}{r} \frac{\partial}{\partial \theta} \left( -\frac{k}{r} \cos \theta \right) = \frac{k}{r^2} \sin \theta \quad \textbf{(D)}$$

As $r \longrightarrow 0$, the velocity of flow approaches infinity. Therefore, the point $r = 0$ is a singular point at which the flow is not defined.

By using the first of Eqs. 4-15,

$$\frac{1}{r} \frac{\partial \psi}{\partial \theta} = \frac{\partial \phi}{\partial r} = \frac{k}{r^2} \cos \theta$$

Hence

$$\psi = \int \frac{k}{r} \cos \theta \, \partial \theta = \frac{k}{r} \sin \theta + f(r) + C_1 \quad \textbf{(E)}$$

and

$$\frac{\partial \psi}{\partial r} = -\frac{k}{r^2} \sin \theta + \frac{\partial f(r)}{\partial r} \quad \textbf{(F)}$$

From the second of Eqs. 4-15,

$$\frac{\partial \psi}{\partial r} = -\frac{1}{r} \frac{\partial \phi}{\partial \theta} = -\frac{k}{r^2} \sin \theta \quad \textbf{(G)}$$

Equating the right-hand sides of Eqs. (F) and (G), we have

$$\frac{\partial f(r)}{\partial r} = 0$$

Therefore

$$f(r) = \text{constant}$$

which may be substituted into Eq. (E) to obtain the desired stream function as

$$\psi = \frac{k}{r} \sin \theta + C$$

## 4-4 The Flow Net

The flow net serves as a graphical solution for a two-dimensional irrotational flow with given boundary conditions. It is a network of mutually perpendicular streamlines and equipotential lines, as shown in Fig. 4–5. The spacings of the streamlines are selected in such a way that

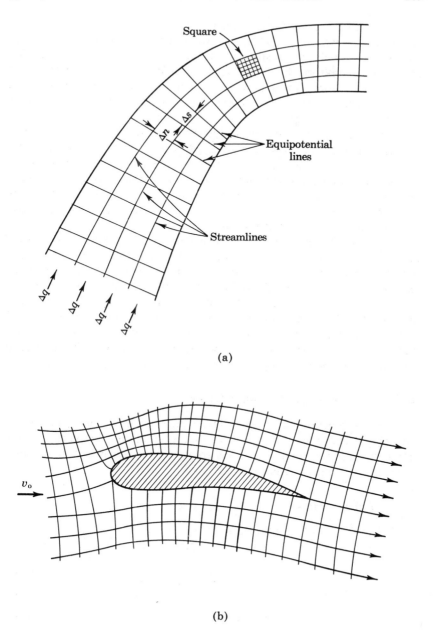

(a)

(b)

**Fig. 4-5.** Flow net (a) within a closed conduit, and (b) around a stream-lined object.

there is an equal rate of flow discharging through each space between any two adjacent streamlines. Then the equipotential lines are drawn everywhere perpendicular to the streamlines to form a network of small squares. In regions of uniform flow, the $\phi$- and $\psi$-lines form exact squares; and in regions of nonuniform flow, the $\phi$- and $\psi$-lines form approximate squares. Since no flow crosses a streamline, any solid boundary is always considered as a streamline.

According to the uniqueness theorems, there is only one possible pattern of irrotational flow for a given set of boundary conditions. Therefore, a flow net, if constructed correctly, represents a unique mathematical solution for an irrotational flow. For any given flow problem, once a flow net is completed, the velocity at any point in the flow field can be computed from the spacings of the $\phi$- and $\psi$-lines. Then the pressure may be determined from Bernoulli's equation.

The flow net method is useful for determining patterns of irrotational flows with boundary forms too complex for analytical treatment. However, for some simple boundary forms, it is possible to derive mathematical expressions for the $\phi$- and the $\psi$-functions. Indeed, mathematical methods are available for the analysis of irrotational flows. Two of the methods are introduced in this book. One, called the *conformal mapping method*, will be discussed in the next chapter. The other method, in which several patterns of irrotational flow of physical significance may be developed by combining simple flows, is the subject for the present chapter.

## 4-5   Two-dimensional Simple Flows

The two-dimensional simple flows which are to be presented in the following sections are uniform flow, source, sink, and free vortex. These simple flows can be used in various combinations to form more complex systems of practical significance.

## 4-6   Uniform Flow

Figure 4–6 shows a uniform flow with a velocity $V_0$ inclined at angle $\alpha$ to the $x$-axis. In Cartesian coordinates, the velocity components are:

$$u = V_0 \cos \alpha = \frac{\partial \psi}{\partial y} = \frac{\partial \phi}{\partial x} \tag{4-23}$$

and

$$v = V_0 \sin \alpha = -\frac{\partial \psi}{\partial x} = \frac{\partial \phi}{\partial y} \tag{4-24}$$

From Eq. 4–23

$$\phi = \int V_0 \cos \alpha \, \partial x = (V_0 \cos \alpha)x + f(y) + C_1$$

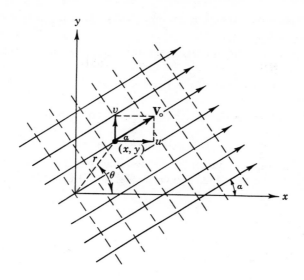

**Fig. 4-6.** Uniform flow inclined at an angle $\alpha$ to the x-axis.

The unknown function $f(y)$ is determined by first taking the partial derivative with respect to $y$ of the above expression and then using Eq. 4–24 to replace $\partial\phi/\partial y$ by $V_0 \sin \alpha$. Thus

$$\frac{\partial\phi}{\partial y} = \frac{\partial f(y)}{\partial y} = V_0 \sin \alpha$$

$$f(y) = (V_0 \sin \alpha)y + C_2$$

Substituting this into the $\phi$-equation above, we have

$$\phi = (V_0 \cos \alpha)x + (V_0 \sin \alpha)y + C_3 \tag{4-25}$$

where $C_3$ is the sum of $C_1$ and $C_2$.

Similarly, we can determine $\psi$ as follows:

$$\psi = \int V_0 \cos \alpha \, \partial y = (V_0 \cos \alpha)y + f(x) + C_4$$

$$\frac{\partial\psi}{\partial x} = \frac{\partial f(x)}{\partial x} = -V_0 \sin \alpha$$

$$f(x) = -(V_0 \sin \alpha)x + C_5$$

$$\psi = -(V_0 \sin \alpha)x + (V_0 \cos \alpha)y + C_6 \tag{4-26}$$

Constants $C_3$ and $C_6$ are to be omitted in a general treatment, since they do not affect the pattern and configuration of the $\phi$- and $\psi$-lines. In fact, we can make them vanish by arbitrarily assuming that the lines $\phi = 0$ and $\psi = 0$ pass through the origin of the coordinate axes. We shall omit such constants in the following development.

Using the polar coordinates, we recognize that $x = r \cos \theta$ and $y = r \sin \theta$, so that

$$\phi = (V_0 \cos \alpha) r \cos \theta + (V_0 \sin \alpha) r \sin \theta$$

or

$$\phi = V_0 r \cos (\theta - \alpha) \tag{4-27}$$

and

$$\psi = -(V_0 \sin \alpha) r \cos \theta + (V_0 \cos \alpha) r \sin \theta$$

or

$$\psi = V_0 r \sin (\theta - \alpha) \tag{4-28}$$

In most of our subsequent developments we shall use the uniform flow parallel to the x-axis, as shown in Fig. 4–7. In this case, $\alpha = 0$, and

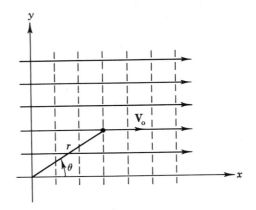

**Fig. 4-7.** Uniform flow parallel to the x-axis.

the above equations reduce to:
Cartesian coordinates:

$$\phi = V_0 x \tag{4-29}$$

$$\psi = V_0 y \tag{4-30}$$

Polar coordinates:

$$\phi = V_0 r \cos \theta \tag{4-31}$$

$$\psi = V_0 r \sin \theta \tag{4-32}$$

Since there are no singular points in this flow, the circulation must be zero for all paths in the flow by reason of Stokes' theorem.

### 4-7  Two-dimensional Source and Sink

Consider a two-dimensional flow with streamlines radiating from a central point as shown in Fig. 4–8. This flow is called a *source* if the

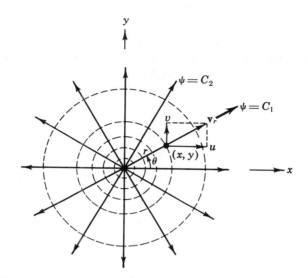

**Fig. 4-8.** A two-dimensional source.

velocity vectors are directed away from the center and a *sink* if they are directed toward the center. The center of a source may be thought of as a point from which flow issues at a constant rate along radial paths; and the center of a sink is then a point toward which flow disappears at a constant rate along radial paths. The magnitude of velocity in a source or sink flow is inversely proportional to the radial distance from the center.

Sources and sinks are useful mathematical concepts which, in combination with other simple flows, produce complex flow systems of physical significance. There are no exact physical situations which duplicate the flow phenomena of a source or a sink at their centers, for the velocities in the regions of their centers approach an infinite magnitude. The centers are singular points which must be kept outside the boundaries of the flow field considered. For example, when a source is combined with other simple flows to form a flow pattern around a body, the center of the source must lie inside the boundaries of the body so that it is outside the boundaries of the flow field.

Let us denote $q$ as the total volume rate of flow issuing from the center of a two-dimensional source. Since the flow is radial, the velocity components, using polar coordinates, at any radius $r$ from the center of the source are:

$$v_\theta = 0 = -\frac{\partial \psi}{\partial r} = \frac{1}{r}\frac{\partial \phi}{\partial \theta} \qquad (4\text{--}33)$$

$$v_r = \frac{q}{2\pi r} = \frac{1}{r}\frac{\partial \psi}{\partial \theta} = \frac{\partial \phi}{\partial r} \tag{4-34}$$

Note that as $r \to 0$, $v_r \to \infty$. The velocity potential and the stream function for a source can be obtained by the integration of velocity components in the above two equations. Hence, if constants of integration are omitted,

$$\phi = \frac{q}{2\pi}\ln r \tag{4-35}$$

and

$$\psi = \frac{q}{2\pi}\theta \tag{4-36}$$

The equation of equipotential lines is formed by equating the right-hand side of Eq. 4–35 to a constant:

$$\frac{q}{2\pi}\ln r = \text{constant}$$

whence

$$r = \text{constant} \tag{4-37}$$

This is the equation of a family of concentric circles as shown in Fig. 4–8. Next, we form the equation of streamlines as

$$\frac{q}{2\pi}\theta = \text{constant} \tag{4-38}$$

which represents a family of radial lines radiating from the center as shown in Fig. 4–8. Clearly these two families of lines are orthogonal to each other, a condition which was specified in Sec. 4–3.

Since the center of a source is a singular point, it is necessary to determine the circulation about the center by using a closed path surrounding it. Hence, following a circle of radius $r$, we have

$$\Gamma = \oint \mathbf{V} \cdot d\mathbf{s} = \int_0^{2\pi} v_\theta r\, d\theta = 0$$

since $v_\theta$ is zero.

In Cartesian notations (see Fig. 4–8), the velocity components in a two-dimensional source become

$$u = v_\theta \cos \theta = \frac{q}{2\pi r}\frac{x}{r} = \frac{q}{2\pi}\frac{x}{x^2 + y^2} \tag{4-39}$$

$$v = v_r \sin \theta = \frac{q}{2\pi r}\frac{y}{r} = \frac{q}{2\pi}\frac{y}{x^2 + y^2} \tag{4-40}$$

and the velocity potential and the stream function then take the following forms:

$$\phi = \frac{q}{4\pi}\ln (x^2 + y^2) \tag{4-41}$$

$$\psi = \frac{q}{4\pi} \arctan \frac{y}{x} \qquad (4\text{-}42)$$

For a sink, the flow rate becomes $-q$; so we simply replace $q$ in all the above equations by $-q$.

The magnitude of the flow rate $q$ is also used as a measure of the strength of a source or a sink.

## 4-8  Two-dimensional Free Vortex

The two-dimensional free vortex was discussed in Sec. 3–4. The streamlines in a free vortex flow are concentric circles about the center of the vortex and the velocity at any point in such a flow field is given by the following two components in polar coordinates:

$$v_\theta = \frac{K}{r} \qquad (4\text{-}43)$$

$$v_r = 0 \qquad (4\text{-}44)$$

where $K$ is called the *vortex constant* and is a measure of the strength of a free vortex motion. The free vortex motion is irrotational except at the center, where $v_\theta$ approaches infinity. Hence the center of a free vortex is a singular point.

The circulation $\Gamma$ about any closed path surrounding the center of a free vortex was found in Sec. 3–4 to be $\Gamma = 2\pi K$. Therefore, the velocity components may also be written as

$$v_\theta = \frac{\Gamma}{2\pi r} = -\frac{\partial \psi}{\partial r} = \frac{1}{r}\frac{\partial \phi}{\partial \theta} \qquad (4\text{-}45)$$

$$v_r = 0 = \frac{1}{r}\frac{\partial \psi}{\partial \theta} = \frac{\partial \phi}{\partial r} \qquad (4\text{-}46)$$

Whence

$$\phi = \frac{\Gamma}{2\pi}\theta \qquad (4\text{-}47)$$

$$\psi = -\frac{\Gamma}{2\pi}\ln r \qquad (4\text{-}48)$$

These two equations show that the flow net for a free vortex flow has the same form as that for a source or a sink flow except that the radial lines are now equipotential lines and the concentric circles become streamlines, as shown in Fig. 4–9. The counterclockwise direction of the free vortex motion shown in the figure is considered positive.

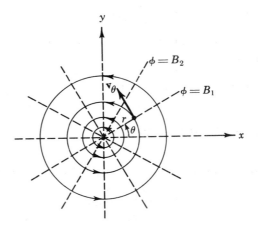

**Fig. 4-9.** A two-dimensional free vortex.

## 4-9 Superposition of Simple Flows

Potential flows of practical significance can be derived by superimposing the simple flows developed in the preceding sections in various combinations. The $\phi$- and $\psi$-functions of combined flows are obtained by adding respectively the $\phi$- and $\psi$-functions of various simple flows. This procedure of simple addition is possible because the $\phi$- and $\psi$-functions of simple flows are harmonic functions which satisfy the Laplace equations $\nabla^2\phi = 0$ and $\nabla^2\psi = 0$.

It is easy to demonstrate that the stream function of a combined flow is the sum of the stream functions of its component flows. Consider Fig. 4–10, in which two streamlines $\psi_A = A_1$ and $\psi_B = B_1$ are shown intersecting at point $P$. These two streamlines belong respectively to two different flow fields represented by stream functions $\psi_A$ and $\psi_B$. The velocities of the two component flows at point $P$ are shown as $\mathbf{V}_A$ and $\mathbf{V}_B$, which are respectively tangent to the two streamlines at point $P$. When these two flows are combined, the resulting velocity $\mathbf{V}$ of the combined flow at point $P$ must be the vector sum of the two velocities $\mathbf{V}_A$ and $\mathbf{V}_B$:

$$\mathbf{V} = \mathbf{V}_A + \mathbf{V}_B \tag{4-49}$$

Whence the component equations are

$$u = u_A + u_B$$

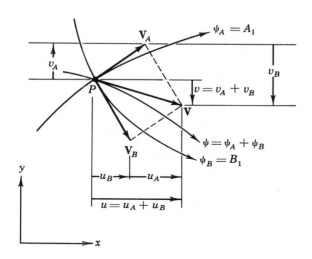

**Fig. 4-10.** Superposition of stream functions.

$$v = v_A + v_B$$

By using the relations of Eqs. 4–1, the last two equations are equivalent to

$$\frac{\partial \psi}{\partial y} = \frac{\partial \psi_A}{\partial y} + \frac{\partial \psi_B}{\partial y} = \frac{\partial}{\partial y}(\psi_A + \psi_B)$$

$$-\frac{\partial \psi}{\partial x} = -\frac{\partial \psi_A}{\partial x} + \left(-\frac{\partial \psi_B}{\partial x}\right) = -\frac{\partial}{\partial x}(\psi_A + \psi_B)$$

Hence

$$\psi = \psi_A + \psi_B \tag{4–50}$$

The $\psi$-line is tangent to the **V**-vector as shown in Fig. 4–10. We may follow the same procedure to show that the velocity potential of a combined flow is the sum of the velocity potentials of its component flows.

Figure 4–11 illustrates that point-to-point combination of two flow fields $\psi_A$ and $\psi_B$ yields a combined flow field $\psi$. Each of the $\psi$-lines is traced through points which have a constant value of the sum of $\psi_A + \psi_B$. For example, the line joining those intersections for which $\psi_A + \psi_B = 5$ is the resultant streamline marked $\psi = 5$. The graphical addition of equipotential lines can be carried out in a similar manner.

In the following sections, we shall discuss several combined flows of practical significance.

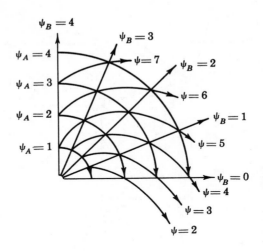

**Fig. 4-11.** Graphical addition of two flow fields; $\psi = \psi_A + \psi_B$.

## 4-10  Combined Flow Field of Source and Sink of Equal Strength

In Fig. 4–12(a), a source and a sink of equal strength $q$ are located at equal distances $a$ from the origin along the $x$-axis to form a combined source-sink flow field. An arbitrary field point $P(x, y)$ is shown at distances $r_1$ and $r_2$, respectively, from the source and the sink. The angles $\theta_1$ and $\theta_2$ are measured from the positive $x$-axis. Thus, for point $P$, the stream function of the combined flow field is the sum of the stream functions of the component flows:

$$\psi = \psi_{\text{source}} + \psi_{\text{sink}} = -\frac{q}{2\pi}(\theta_2 - \theta_1) \qquad (4\text{-}51)$$

From Fig. 4–12(a), it is seen that

$$\theta_1 = \arctan \frac{y}{x + a}$$

$$\theta_2 = \arctan \frac{y}{x - a}$$

Using the following trigonometric identity

$$\arctan \alpha - \arctan \beta = \arctan \frac{\alpha - \beta}{1 + \alpha\beta}$$

we may write

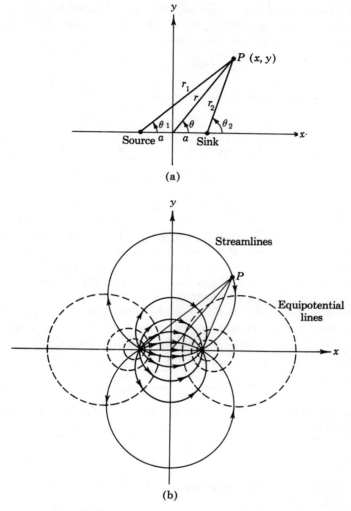

**Fig. 4-12.** Two-dimensional source-sink flow.

$$\theta_2 - \theta_1 = \arctan\left[y/(x - a)\right] - \arctan\left[y/(x + a)\right]$$

$$= \arctan\frac{2ay}{x^2 + y^2 - a^2}$$

The right-hand side of the above equation may now be substituted into Eq. 4–51 to express the stream function in Cartesian notations as

$$\psi = -\frac{q}{2\pi} \arctan\frac{2ay}{x^2 + y^2 - a^2} \tag{4-52}$$

To develop an equation for the family of streamlines in this flow, let us set $\psi = C$ (constant) in Eq. 4-52 and then take the tangent on both sides of the equation. The result is

$$-\tan\frac{2\pi C}{q} = \frac{2ay}{x^2 + y^2 - a^2}$$

which, after transposing terms, becomes

$$x^2 + y^2 + 2ay\cot\frac{2\pi C}{q} = a^2$$

We then complete the square for the terms containing $y^2$ and $y$ to obtain

$$x^2 + \left(y + a\cot\frac{2\pi C}{q}\right)^2 = a^2 + \left(a\cot\frac{2\pi C}{q}\right)^2 \tag{4-53}$$

From analytical geometry the above equation is recognized as an equation for circles. Thus, all the streamlines in this flow are circles with their radii equal to $a\csc(2\pi C/q)$ and with their centers at $[0, -a\cot(2\pi C/q)]$ on the $y$-axis. Moreover, if we set $y = 0$ in Eq. 4-53, we obtain $x = \pm a$ for all values of $C$, indicating that all the circular streamlines have the line joining the source and sink as a common chord. Streamlines for the source-sink flow are shown in Fig. 4-12(b). It is seen that flow originates at the source and terminates in the sink. Note the similarity of this flow field to the flux lines between the poles of a magnet.

Likewise, we may write the velocity potential for the combined flow field as

$$\phi = \phi_{\text{source}} + \phi_{\text{sink}} = \frac{q}{2\pi}\ln\frac{r_1}{r_2} \tag{4-54}$$

Referring again to Fig. 4-12(a), we can easily relate $r_1$ and $r_2$ with the Cartesian coordinates of the point $P(x, y)$ as follows:

$$r_1^2 = (x + a)^2 + y^2$$
$$r_2^2 = (x - a)^2 + y^2$$

We then use these relations to express the velocity potential of Eq. 4-54 in Cartesian notations as

$$\phi = \frac{q}{2\pi}\ln\sqrt{\frac{(x + a)^2 + y^2}{(x - a)^2 + y^2}} \tag{4-55}$$

The equation for a family of equipotential lines is obtained by setting $\phi = B$ (constant). Thus, taking antilog on both sides of the above equation with $\phi = B$, we have

$$\frac{(x + a)^2 + y^2}{(x - a)^2 + y^2} = e^{4\pi B/q}$$

This equation, after some algebraic manipulations, can be written as

$$y^2 + \left[x + a\left(\frac{1 + e^{4\pi B/q}}{1 - e^{4\pi B/q}}\right)\right]^2 = \left[a\,\frac{2}{e^{-2\pi B/q} - e^{2\pi B/q}}\right]^2 \quad \text{(4-55a)}$$

Using the following mathematical identities for hyperbolic functions,

$$\coth \alpha = \frac{e^\alpha + e^{-\alpha}}{e^\alpha - e^{-\alpha}} = \frac{1 + e^{-2\alpha}}{1 - e^{-2\alpha}}$$

$$\operatorname{csch} \alpha = \frac{2}{e^\alpha - e^{-\alpha}}$$

we may readily write Eq. 4-55a for a family of equipotential lines as

$$y^2 + \left(x - a \coth \frac{2\pi B}{q}\right)^2 = \left(-a \operatorname{csch} \frac{2\pi B}{q}\right)^2 \quad \text{(4-56)}$$

Clearly all the equipotential lines for this flow are circles with their radii equal to $a \operatorname{csch} (2\pi B/q)$ and with their centers at $[a \coth (2\pi B/q),\, 0]$ on the $x$-axis. Equipotential lines are also shown in Fig. 4–12(b). Note that the streamlines and equipotential lines form an orthogonal grid system.

## 4-11   Two-dimensional Doublet

A two-dimensional doublet is formed by the limit of the source-sink flow of Fig. 4–12(a) that as $a$ approaches zero, $q$ approaches infinity such that the product $2aq$ approaches a constant value $m$. Hence the stream function for a doublet is obtained by the limit of Eq. 4–52 as follows:

$$\psi = \lim_{\substack{a \to 0 \\ 2aq \to m}} -\frac{q}{2\pi} \arctan \frac{2ay}{x^2 + y^2 - a^2}$$

Since the term $2ay/(x^2 + y^2 - a^2)$ becomes small as $a$ approaches zero, we may make use of the infinite series expansion

$$\arctan \alpha = \alpha - \frac{\alpha^3}{3} + \frac{\alpha^5}{5} - \frac{\alpha^7}{7} + \cdots \qquad -1 < \alpha < 1$$

to express the stream function as

$$\psi = \lim_{\substack{a \to 0 \\ 2aq \to m}} -\frac{q}{2\pi}\left[\frac{2ay}{x^2 + y^2 - a^2} - \frac{1}{3}\left(\frac{2ay}{x^2 + y^2 - a^2}\right)^3 + \cdots\right]$$

In the limit, this stream function becomes

$$\psi = -\frac{m}{2\pi}\frac{y}{x^2 + y^2} \quad \text{(4-57)}$$

from which the equation of streamlines for a doublet is then

$$-\frac{m}{2\pi}\frac{y}{x^2 + y^2} = C \text{ (constant)} \quad \text{(4-58)}$$

The geometrical form of streamlines becomes evident by first rearranging
the above equation in the following form:

$$x^2 + y^2 + \frac{m}{2\pi C} y = 0$$

and then completing the square for the $y$-terms to obtain

$$x^2 + \left(y + \frac{m}{4\pi C}\right)^2 = \left(\frac{m}{4\pi C}\right)^2 \tag{4-59}$$

The streamlines for a doublet are, therefore, a family of circles with
their radii equal to $m/4\pi C$ and with their centers at $(0, -m/4\pi C)$ on the
$y$-axis. Note that when $y = 0$ in Eq. 4–59, $x = 0$ for all values of $C$.
Hence all circular streamlines must pass through the center of the doublet.
The pattern of streamlines for a doublet is shown in Fig. 4–13. Since this
doublet is formed by a source located on the negative $x$-axis and a sink

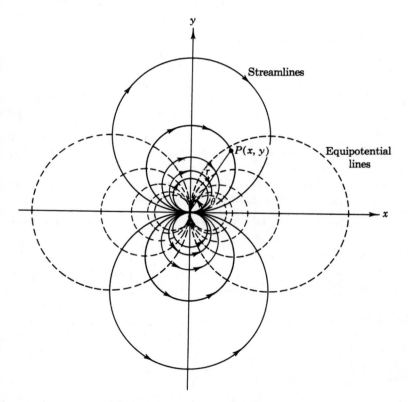

**Fig. 4-13.** Two-dimensional doublet.

on the positive $x$-axis, flow must issue from the center of the doublet in the negative $x$-direction and then return to the center from the positive $x$-direction, as is shown in Fig. 4–13.

To derive the velocity potential for the doublet, it is convenient to express the $\psi$-function of Eq. 4–57 in polar form (see Fig. 4–13):

$$\psi = -\frac{m}{2\pi}\frac{\sin\theta}{r} \tag{4-60}$$

Using the partial differential relations between the stream function and velocity potential in Eqs. 4–15, we may readily establish the velocity potential for the doublet from Eq. 4–60 as

$$\phi = \frac{m\cos\theta}{2\pi r} \tag{4-61}$$

From Fig. 4–13, the velocity potential for the doublet in Cartesian notations is clearly

$$\phi = \frac{m}{2\pi}\frac{x}{x^2 + y^2} \tag{4-62}$$

whence the equation of equipotential lines for the doublet becomes

$$\frac{m}{2\pi}\frac{x}{x^2 + y^2} = B \text{ (constant)} \tag{4-63}$$

This equation can be rearranged as

$$y^2 + x^2 - \frac{m}{2\pi B}x = 0 \tag{4-64}$$

Thus, equipotential lines are also circles touching the origin, as shown in Fig. 4–13. The centers of these circles are on the $x$-axis. The equipotential lines and streamlines are evidently orthogonal to one another at their points of intersection.

## 4-12  Combined Flow Field of a Uniform Flow and a Doublet— Uniform Flow Past a Circular Cylinder Without Circulation

Combination of a uniform flow and a doublet will yield a physical situation of flow past a circular cylinder with no circulation. Figure 4–14(a) shows the streamlines of both flows. The uniform flow has its velocity $V_0$ in the direction of the positive $x$-axis, and the doublet is located at the origin of the coordinate axes. In this combined flow the main problem is to find a streamline which will serve as the boundary of a circular cylinder in the flow field.

In polar coordinates, the stream function for the combined flow field of a uniform flow and a doublet is obviously the sum of Eqs. 4–32 and 4–60:

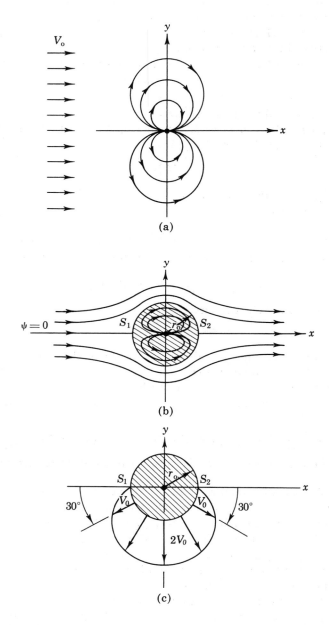

**Fig. 4-14.** Uniform flow past a cylinder without circulation.

$$\psi = \underbrace{V_0 r \sin \theta}_{\psi_{\text{uniform flow}}} - \underbrace{\frac{m}{2\pi} \frac{\sin \theta}{r}}_{\psi_{\text{doublet}}} \tag{4-65}$$

from which the equation of streamlines for the combined flow is obtained by setting $\psi = C$ (constant):

$$V_0 r \sin \theta - \frac{m}{2\pi} \frac{\sin \theta}{r} = C \tag{4-66}$$

The pattern of streamlines for this combined flow field, shown in Fig. 4-14(b), may be produced graphically by assigning different numerical values for $C$ in the above equation. Note that there is a streamline in the form of a circle. This circular streamline may be regarded as the boundary of a two-dimensional cylinder, and is formed by having $\psi = 0$. Hence the equation of the circle is

$$\left( V_0 r - \frac{m}{2\pi r} \right) \sin \theta = 0 \tag{4-67}$$

Mathematically, there are two conditions for which the above equation can be satisfied:

(1) Equation 4-67 is satisfied when $\theta = 0$ and $\theta = \pi$, indicating that the $x$-axis in Fig. 4-14(b) is also a part of the streamline.

(2) Equation 4-67 is also satisfied when

$$V_0 r - \frac{m}{2\pi r} = 0$$

whence

$$r = \sqrt{\frac{m}{2\pi V_0}} \tag{4-68}$$

That is, the circular cylinder has a radius of $\sqrt{m/2\pi V_0}$. We shall designate the radius of the circular cylinder by the symbol $r_0$.

The stream function for this combined flow field is frequently expressed in terms of $r_0$ instead of the strength of the doublet. Thus, substitution of $m = 2\pi r_0^2 V_0$ into Eq. 4-65 yields

$$\psi = V_0 \left( r - \frac{r_0^2}{r} \right) \sin \theta \tag{4-69}$$

At any point in this flow field the velocity components may be determined by applying Eqs. 4-15 to Eq. 4-69. Thus,

$$v_r = \frac{1}{r} \frac{\partial \psi}{\partial \theta} = V_0 \left( 1 - \frac{r_0^2}{r^2} \right) \cos \theta \tag{4-70}$$

$$v_\theta = -\frac{\partial \psi}{\partial r} = -V_0 \left( 1 + \frac{r_0^2}{r^2} \right) \sin \theta \tag{4-71}$$

since $r_0$ is a constant. On the surface of the cylinder where $r = r_0$, Eq.

4–70 shows that $v_r = 0$, indicating that the velocity is everywhere tangent to the surface of the cylinder and has a magnitude of

$$V_b = v_\theta = -2V_0 \sin \theta \qquad (4\text{-}72)$$

where the subscript $b$ denotes the boundary of the cylinder. The variation of velocity along the surface has been plotted along the lower half of the cylindrical surface in Fig. 4–14(c). Note that at points $S_1$ and $S_2$ where $\theta$ equals $\pi$ and zero, respectively, $V_b$ equals zero. These points of zero velocity in a flow field are called *stagnation points*.

Since the circulation is everywhere zero for each of the component flows of this combined flow field, the circulation for any path in the combined flow field must also be zero.

**Drag and lift for an immersed cylinder with no circulation.** When a cylinder is immersed in a fluid flow, experience tells us that the flowing fluid exerts a force on the immersed cylinder. We define the *drag* and *lift* as forces per unit length on the cylinder in directions parallel and perpendicular, respectively, to the uniform flow.

To evaluate the drag and lift on the immersed cylinder of Fig. 4–15, it is necessary to determine the pressure on the boundary surface of the

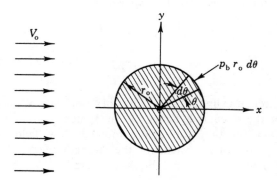

**Fig. 4-15.** Pressure on the surface of a cylinder in a uniform flow.

cylinder. At large distances from the cylinder, the effects of the doublet flow become negligibly small, and both the velocity $V_0$ and pressure $p_0$ in the approaching stream are practically uniform. Since the combined flow field is irrotational, we may employ Bernoulli's equation to relate $V_0$ and $p_0$ in the approaching stream and the velocity $V_b$ and pressure $p_b$ on the boundary of the cylinder. Thus,

$$\rho \frac{V_0^2}{2} + p_0 = \rho \frac{V_b^2}{2} + p_b$$

By substituting Eq. 4-72 for $V_b$ in the above equation, and solving for $p_b$, we obtain

$$p_b = p_0 + \rho \frac{V_0^2}{2} - \rho \frac{(-2V_0 \sin \theta)^2}{2} \qquad (4\text{-}73)$$

The drag force $dF_D$ acting on an elementary area per unit length of the cylinder $r_0 \, d\theta$ is $-p_b r_0 \, d\theta \cos \theta$. The negative sign indicates that pressure force is always directed toward the surface and contributes a negative increment of force when $\cos \theta$ is positive (see Fig. 4-15). The total drag acting on the cylinder per unit length is obtained by integration:

$$F_D = \int_0^{2\pi} - \left[ p_0 + \rho \frac{V_0^2}{2} - \rho \frac{(2V_0 \sin \theta)^2}{2} \right] r_0 \cos \theta \, d\theta = 0$$

In a similar manner the lift $F_L$ may be calculated to be also of zero magnitude.

The foregoing theoretical result for drag is evidently in complete disagreement with experimental results. This contradiction was first discovered by the French scientist Jean le Rond d'Alembert (1717–1783) in 1750, and is referred to as the *d'Alembert paradox*.[1] The reason for the disagreement is in the assumption of an irrotational flow in which the viscous stress is zero in the entire flow field. It is known that even in the flow of such fluids as water and air, which have a very small coefficient of viscosity and whose motion is nearly irrotational in regions remote from the solid boundary, the frictional effect of the fluid near a solid boundary cannot be neglected. The viscous action in the boundary layer flow becomes locally important. In Chapter 8 we shall attempt to show that the viscous action in the boundary layer flow is of great importance in the evaluation of drag forces. It is worth noting here that despite the apparent weakness of the irrotational flow theory in evaluating drag, the theory is, however, very useful in some respects, as we shall soon demonstrate.

**Kinetic energy and virtual mass.** Let us consider a cylinder moving with a uniform velocity $V_0$ through a fluid which is initially at rest. The flow pattern can be obtained by superimposing a flow with a uniform velocity $-V_0$ upon that of Fig. 4-14(b). The resulting streamline pattern is shown in Fig. 4-16. Here the cylinder is moving with a velocity $-V_0 \mathbf{i}$ in an initially stationary fluid. Note that this streamline pattern is simply the portion of that of a doublet flow outside the cylinder of radius $r_0$, as can be seen by comparing Figs. 4-16 and 4-13. The streamline pattern in Fig. 4-16 is unsteady, whereas that in Fig. 4-14(b) is steady. In many

[1] See H. Rouse and S. Ince, *History of Hydraulics* (Iowa City: Iowa Institute of Hydraulic Research, State University of Iowa, 1957) p. 102.

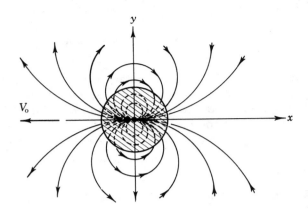

**Fig. 4-16.** Streamline pattern resulting from a cylinder moving uniformly in a stationary fluid.

fluid mechanics problems we can often, but not necessarily always, superimpose a uniform flow onto an unsteady flow field to make the resulting combined flow field steady. The stream function for this flow pattern is then obtained by adding $-V_0 r \sin \theta$ to Eq. 4–69. That is,

$$\psi = -V_0 \frac{r_0^2}{r} \sin \theta \qquad (4\text{–}74)$$

from which we may easily establish the velocity potential for this flow as

$$\phi = V_0 \frac{r_0^2}{r} \cos \theta \qquad (4\text{–}75)$$

The total kinetic energy imparted to the fluid by the motion of a unit length of cylinder can be calculated by means of Eq. 3–49:

$$(\text{KE})_{\text{fluid}} = \frac{\rho}{2} \iint_A \phi \frac{\partial \phi}{\partial n} \, dA = \frac{\rho}{2} \iint_A V_0^2 \frac{r_0^4}{r^3} \cos^2 \theta \, dA$$

where the integration is performed over the surface of the cylinder $r = r_0$ and $dA = r_0 \, d\theta$. Hence substitution into the above equation yields

$$(\text{KE})_{\text{fluid}} = \frac{\rho r_0^2 V_0^2}{2} \int_0^{2\pi} \cos^2 \theta \, d\theta = \frac{1}{2} \rho \pi r_0^2 V_0^2 \qquad (4\text{–}76)$$

The quantity $\rho \pi r_0^2$ is the mass of fluid displaced by the unit length of the cylinder; thus, the kinetic energy of all the fluid is equal to the kinetic energy of the displaced fluid mass if it were moving with the velocity $V_0$. We use the symbol $M'$ for this displaced fluid mass $\rho \pi r_0^2$ and call it the *virtual mass* of the cylinder.[2] If $M$ represents the mass of the cylinder per unit length, the total kinetic energy of the fluid and the cylinder is

$$(KE)_{\text{total}} = \tfrac{1}{2}(M + M')V_0^2 \qquad (4\text{-}77)$$

That is, when a stationary submerged cylinder is set to move at a velocity $\mathbf{V}_0$ in a fluid which is initially at rest, the whole body of fluid is set in motion at the same instant. The kinetic energy $M'V_0^2/2$ is required to set the fluid in motion. Likewise, if a moving submerged object is brought to rest, the whole body of fluid will also come to rest at the same instant. The work expended in bringing the moving submerged object to rest will be equal to the total kinetic energy of the fluid and the submerged object.

The virtual mass effect is also important in changing the motion of a submerged object. Let $\mathbf{F}$ be the external force applied to a sumberged object which is moving at a velocity $\mathbf{V}_0$. The rate at which $\mathbf{F}$ does work must be equal to the rate of change of the total kinetic energy. Thus,

$$\mathbf{F} \cdot \mathbf{V}_0 = \frac{d}{dt}(KE)_{\text{total}} = (M + M')\mathbf{V}_0 \cdot \frac{d\mathbf{V}_0}{dt}$$

since $V_0^2 = \mathbf{V}_0 \cdot \mathbf{V}_0$; and

$$\mathbf{F} = (M + M')\frac{d\mathbf{V}_0}{dt} \qquad (4\text{-}78)$$

in which the quantity $M'\, d\mathbf{V}_0/dt$ is the resistance offered by the entire fluid mass. The virtual mass concept is, therefore, useful in evaluating fluid resistance in the moving and maneuvering of ships and submarines.

The instantaneous response of fluid to the motion of a submerged object arises from the assumption of irrotational flow. In reality the frictional effect must be taken into consideration and there is a time lag between the change in the motion of submerged object and the response of the fluid medium.

## 4-13    Combined Flow Field of Uniform Flow, Doublet, and

### Vortex—Uniform Flow Past a Circular Cylinder

### With Circulation

When a vortex is superimposed onto the combined flow field of the uniform flow and the doublet of the preceding section, there results a physical situation of flow past a circular cylinder with circulation. We

---

[2]In general, the virtual mass for a moving submerged body is not always equal to the mass of fluid displaced by the submerged body; rather it is equal to a constant multiplied by the displaced fluid mass. For example, the virtual mass for a submerged sphere equals one half the mass of fluid displaced by the sphere.

shall demonstrate the effect of circulation in this combined flow field.

The stream function for the combined flow field of a uniform flow, a doublet, and a clockwise vortex, in polar notations, is

$$\psi = \underset{\psi_{\text{uniform flow}}}{V_0 r \sin \theta} - \underset{\psi_{\text{doublet}}}{\frac{m}{2\pi} \frac{\sin \theta}{r}} + \underset{\psi_{\text{vortex}}}{\frac{\Gamma}{2\pi} \ln r} \qquad (4\text{-}79)$$

The streamline patterns of the three component flows are shown in Fig. 4–17. Since the streamlines in a vortex flow are concentric circles

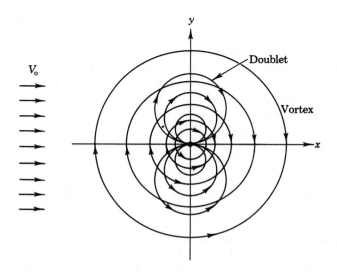

**Fig. 4-17.** Streamline patterns of a uniform flow, a doublet, and a clockwise vortex.

about the vortex center and the velocities in the vortex flow are entirely tangential to these circles, there are no radial components of velocities in the vortex flow to change the form of the circular cylinder contour. Therefore, Eq. 4–79 may also be written as

$$\psi = V_0 \left( r - \frac{r_0^2}{r} \right) \sin \theta + \frac{\Gamma}{2\pi} \ln r \qquad (4\text{-}80)$$

with $r_0 = \sqrt{m/2\pi V_0}$. The equation of streamlines for this combined flow field is formed by letting $\psi = C$ (constant):

$$V_0 \left( r - \frac{r_0^2}{r} \right) \sin \theta + \frac{\Gamma}{2\pi} \ln r = C \qquad (4\text{-}81)$$

In Fig. 4–18(a) we have plotted the streamline pattern for this combined flow field [with $(\Gamma/4\pi V_0)^2 < r_0^2$] by assigning different numerical values for $C$ in Eq. 4–81. The contour of the cylinder $r = r_0$ forms part of the

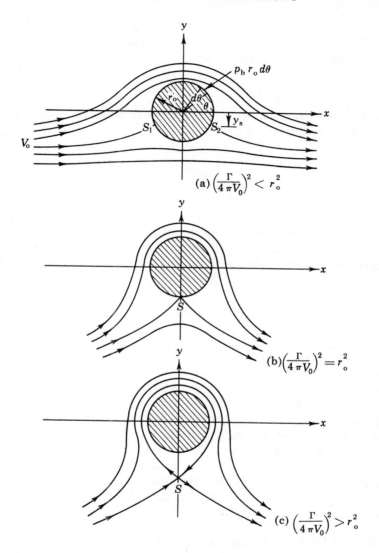

**Fig. 4-18.** Uniform flow past a cylinder with circulation.

streamline $\psi = C = (\Gamma/2\pi) \ln r_0$. The two stagnation points marked by the symbols $S_1$ and $S_2$ on the surface of the cylinder are located by the condition that $\mathbf{V} = 0$ at these two points.

The two velocity components at any point in this combined flow field are:

$$v_r = \frac{1}{r} \frac{\partial \psi}{\partial \theta} = V_0 \left(1 - \frac{r_0^2}{r^2}\right) \cos \theta \qquad \textbf{(4–82)}$$

$$v_\theta = -\frac{\partial \psi}{\partial r} = -V_0 \left(1 + \frac{r_0^2}{r^2}\right) \sin \theta - \frac{\Gamma}{2\pi r} \qquad (4\text{-}83)$$

On the surface of the cylinder $r = r_0$, $v_r = 0$ and

$$V_b = (v_\theta)_{r=r_0} = -2V_0 \sin \theta - \frac{\Gamma}{2\pi r_0} \qquad (4\text{-}84)$$

At the stagnation point, $v_\theta = 0$ and with the subscript $s$ denoting the stagnation position,

$$\sin \theta_s = -\frac{\Gamma}{4\pi r_0 V_0}$$
$$\theta_s = \arcsin \left(-\frac{\Gamma}{4\pi r_0 V_0}\right) \qquad (4\text{-}85)$$

indicating that the two stagnation points are in the third and foutth quadrants of the coordinate system of Fig. 4–18(a). The stagnation points are located symmetrically on both sides of the $y$-axis. Employing the trigonometric relation $\sin \theta_s = y_s/r_0$, we may also express the stagnation positions in Cartesian coordinates as

$$y_s = -\frac{\Gamma}{4\pi V_0} \qquad (4\text{-}86)$$

$$x_s = \pm\sqrt{r_0^2 - y_s^2} \qquad (4\text{-}87)$$

These two expressions indicate that the stagnation points move downward as $\Gamma$ becomes large, and that the two stagnation points coincide on the $y$-axis at $(0, -r_0)$ when $(\Gamma/4\pi V_0)^2$ equals $r_0^2$. For $(\Gamma/4\pi V_0)^2 > r_0^2$, the stagnation points leave the surface of the cylinder and Eqs. 4–86 and 4–87 are no longer valid. Figure 4–18 summarizes the positions of the stagnation points for different values of $\Gamma$.

In this combined flow field, the vortex is the only component flow which has a circulation $\Gamma$ about its singular point. Therefore, the circulation about the cylinder of this combined flow field is also equal to $\Gamma$. We shall now investigate the significance of the circulation in the production of lift on the cylinder.

**Drag and lift for a submerged cylinder with circulation.** The drag and lift exerted on the cylinder of Fig. 4–18(a) by the composite flow pattern may be determined by integrating over the surface of the cylinder the components of pressure forces on elementary surface areas parallel and normal to the direction of the uniform flow. At large distances from the cylinder, both the velocity $V_0$ and pressure $p_0$ in the approaching stream are uniform. Therefore, the equation for the pressure $p_b$ at any point on the boundary of the cylinder as obtained from Bernoulli's equation is

$$p_b = p_0 + \tfrac{1}{2}\rho V_0^2 - \tfrac{1}{2}\rho V_b^2$$

By substituting Eq. 4–84 for $V_b$ in this equation and rearranging terms, we obtain

$$p_b = p_0 + \frac{1}{2}\rho\left[V_0^2 - \left(2V_0\sin\theta + \frac{\Gamma}{2\pi r_0}\right)^2\right]$$ (4–88)

As can be seen from Fig. 4–18(a), the pressure $p_b$ is normal to the boundary of the cylinder and will produce a differential force $p_0 r_0\,d\theta$ on an elementary area $r_0\,d\theta$ per unit length of the cylinder. The total drag and lift forces are then

$$F_D = \int_0^{2\pi} -p_b r_0\cos\theta\,d\theta$$ (4–89)

$$F_L = \int_0^{2\pi} -p_b r_0\sin\theta\,d\theta$$ (4–90)

Because of the symmetry of the flow pattern about a vertical axis passing through the center of the cylinder, the integral for the total drag $F_D$ vanishes. The reason for zero drag can be traced to the assumption of irrotational flow. However, the total lift on the cylinder can be evaluated by substituting Eq. 4–88 into Eq. 4–90 and then integrating,

$$F_L = \int_0^{\pi} -\left\{p_0 + \frac{1}{2}\rho\left[V_0^2 - \left(2V_0\sin\theta + \frac{\Gamma}{2\pi r_0}\right)^2\right]\right\}r_0\,d\theta\sin\theta$$

which yields the following simple relationship:

$$F_L = \rho V_0\Gamma \quad \text{(per unit length)}$$ (4–91)

Equation 4–91 is known as the *Kutta-Joukowski theorem.*

Although the Kutta-Joukowski theorem was developed for a cylinder of circular cross section, it is also found to be true for a right cylinder of any cross-sectional shape provided there is a circulation around it. It will be shown in the next chapter that by the use of the mathematics of complex variables and conformal mapping it is possible to transform a two-dimensional irrotational incompressible flow about a cylinder of circular cross section to one about bodies resembling airfoils. Thus the Kutta-Joukowski theorem also provides mathematical methods for computing the lift on an airfoil.

The lift force produced by circulation may be experimentally approximated by rotating a circular cylinder in a fluid stream. This phenomenon was first observed by the German scientist Magnus in 1852 and is commonly referred to as the *Magnus effect.* A familiar example of the Magnus effect may be found in the curved pitch of a baseball; the ball must be "spun" in order for the curve to be produced.

## 4-14  Method of Images

The method of superposition leads to another well-known method, called the *method of images*, in the study of potential flows. In this method the boundary conditions of a given problem are to be satisfied by the introduction of a number of the so-called "mirror image" flow fields, as is illustrated in the following example.

Consider a two-dimensional sink of strength $-q$ located at a distance $a$ from a solid wall as shown in Fig. 4-19(a). It is desired that the potential flow pattern of the sink flow in the vicinity of the wall be determined. Since the wall is a solid surface and may be regarded as a streamline, the velocity of flow at the wall must be parallel to the wall. Therefore, it is necessary to devise a method to eliminate the component of velocity normal to the wall for the flow at the wall. The easiest way to accomplish this task is to introduce another sink of equal strength located on the other side of the wall and at a position directly opposite the original sink as shown in Fig. 4-19(b). This additional sink would appear to be the mirror image of the original sink if the solid wall were a mirror. In the combined flow field due to these two sinks, the solid wall becomes a streamline, as is evident in the streamline pattern shown in Fig. 4-19(c).

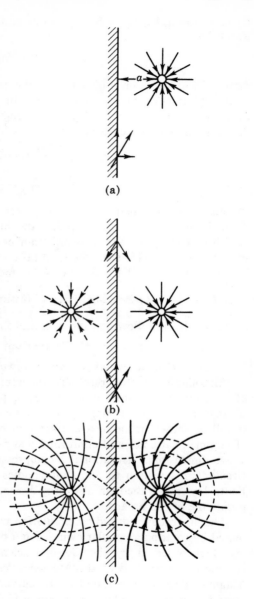

**Fig. 4-19.** Method of images. (a) A sink near a solid wall; (b) the sink and its mirror image; (c) the streamline pattern.

## PART II. THREE-DIMENSIONAL AXIALLY SYMMETRIC POTENTIAL FLOWS

### 4-15 Stokes' Stream Function for Three-dimensional Axially Symmetric Flows

Fluid motion in three dimensions is indeed a complicated phenomenon. In this part we shall study the simplest type of three-dimensional fluid motion in which the flow pattern is identical in every plane which passes through a given line. This line is called an *axis of symmetry*. This type of motion, which has the unique characteristic of being axially symmetric, occurs when a solid of revolution, such as a blimp, missile, or submarine, moves in a fluid in the direction of its axis of revolution. The axis of revolution coincides with the axis of symmetry. An axially symmetric flow is somewhat analogous to a two-dimensional flow in that a stream function can be defined, and, whenever the motion is irrotational, a velocity potential also exists.

In order to be consistent with the cylindrical and spherical coordinates which we defined in Chapter 1 (see Fig. 1–5), we shall choose the $z$-axis as the axis of symmetry as shown in Fig. 4–20.

The Stokes stream function for an axially symmetric flow is formulated in the following manner. Let us select a fixed point $A$ on the axis of symmetry and a variable field point $P$ in any axial plane as shown in

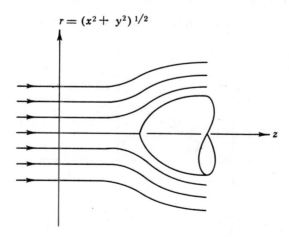

$$r = (x^2 + y^2)^{1/2}$$

**Fig. 4-20.** Coordinates for three-dimensional axially symmetric flows.

Fig. 4–21. The line joining $A$ and $P$ then represents a surface generated by the revolution of the line about the axis of symmetry. The rate of

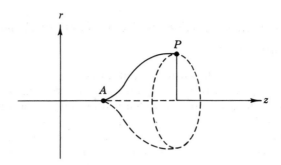

**Fig. 4-21.** Trace of a surface of revolution on an axially symmetric plane.

flow $q$ through this surface of revolution is defined as

$$q = 2\pi\Psi \qquad (4\text{-}92)$$

where $\Psi$ is the Stokes stream function, and is a function of the position of the point $P$ and time $t$. The loci $\Psi = C$ (constant), whose traces in an axial plane are streamlines, represent stream surfaces.

We may express the position of the point $P$ either in cylindrical coordinates as $P(z, r)$ or in spherical coordinates as $P(R, \theta)$, as shown in Fig. 4–22. Hence Eq. 4–92 should, in fact, be written as:

$$q = 2\pi\Psi(z, r, t) \quad \text{cylindrical coordinates} \qquad (4\text{-}92a)$$

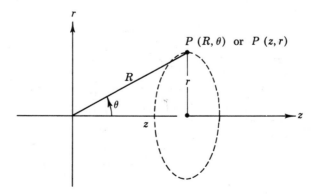

**Fig. 4-22.** Definition of cylindrical and spherical notations for a field point $P$ on an axially symmetric plane.

or

$$q = 2\pi\Psi(R, \theta, t) \quad \text{spherical coordinates} \qquad \textbf{(4–92b)}$$

depending on the coordinate system used in a particular problem.

It is instructive at this point to show that the rate of flow through the surface of revolution generated by the line $AP$ is independent of the path between the two end points $A$ and $P$. In Fig. 4–23 are two arbitrary surfaces of revolution formed by revolving lines $\widehat{A1P}$ and $\widehat{A2P}$ about the

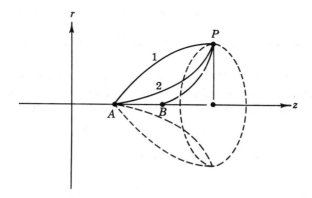

**Fig. 4-23.** Two surfaces of revolution generated by two lines joining two end points $A$ and $P$.

axis of symmetry. These two surfaces may be considered as control surfaces for a control volume in the shape of an annulus, as shown in Figure 4–23. By reason of conservation of mass flow for incompressible flow, the rate of flow through each of these two surfaces must be the same. Since these two generating paths ($\widehat{A1P}$ and $\widehat{A2P}$) are arbitrary, we may conclude that the rate of flow remains invariant for all surfaces generated by paths between $A$ and $P$. Furthermore, as can be seen from Fig. 4–23, the same rate of flow is associated with the path joining $P$ and another point $B$ which is also on the axis of symmetry. It follows that in an axially symmetric flow the value of $\Psi$ at any field point $P$ depends solely on the position of $P$.

## 4-16   Relationships Between the Stokes Stream Function and the Velocity Field

Let $\Psi_P$ and $\Psi_{P'}$ denote the values of the Stokes stream function at field points $P$ and $P'$, which are at an infinitesimal distance $\delta s$ apart,

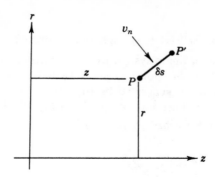

**Fig. 4-24.** Definition of the velocity $v_n$ normal to $PP'$.

as shown in Fig. 4–24. The rate of flow from left to right across the surface generated by revolving $PP'$ about the $z$-axis is $q = 2\pi(\Psi_{P'} - \Psi_P)$, which is related to the normal velocity $v_n$ from left to right across $PP'$ as

$$q = 2\pi r\, \delta s\, v_n = 2\pi(\Psi_{P'} - \Psi_P)$$

In the limit, the above expression is reduced to

$$v_n = \frac{1}{r}\frac{\partial \Psi}{\partial s} \tag{4–93}$$

We have adopted the sign conventions that the velocity $v_n$ in Fig. 4–24 is considered positive.

A similar procedure may be used to find the relationship between $\Psi$ and the velocity components $v_z$ and $v_r$ in cylindrical coordinates for an axially symmetric flow. In Fig. 4–25, let $PP'$ be an infinitesimal displacement $\delta r$ parallel to the $r$-axis and $PP''$ be $\delta z$ parallel to the $z$-axis. The resulting relations between $\Psi$ and the velocity components, using the sign conventions of the preceding derivation, are given by:

$$q_z = 2\pi r\, \delta r\, v_z = 2\pi\, \delta \Psi$$

and

$$q_r = -2\pi r\, \delta z\, v_r = 2\pi\, \delta \Psi$$

from which we obtain

$$v_z = \frac{1}{r}\frac{\partial \Psi}{\partial r} \tag{4–94}$$

and

$$v_r = -\frac{1}{r}\frac{\partial \Psi}{\partial z} \tag{4–95}$$

When the axially symmetric flow is irrotational, a velocity potential

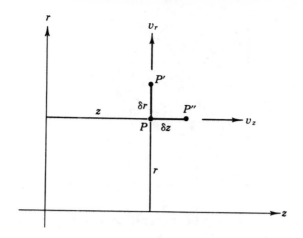

**Fig. 4-25.** Definition of $v_r$ and $v_z$.

$\Phi$ also exists. The Stokes stream function and the velocity potential, in cylindrical coordinates, are then related as follows:

$$v_z = \frac{1}{r}\frac{\partial \Psi}{\partial r} = \frac{\partial \Phi}{\partial z} \qquad (4\text{-}96)$$

and

$$v_r = -\frac{1}{r}\frac{\partial \Psi}{\partial z} = \frac{\partial \Phi}{\partial r} \qquad (4\text{-}97)$$

The condition of irrotationality for an axially symmetric flow in cylindrical coordinates is

$$\frac{\partial v_z}{\partial r} - \frac{\partial v_r}{\partial z} = 0 \qquad (4\text{-}98)$$

Using Eqs. 4–94 and 4–95 to substitute for $v_z$ and $v_r$ in the above equation, we obtain

$$\frac{\partial}{\partial r}\left(\frac{1}{r}\frac{\partial \Psi}{\partial r}\right) - \frac{\partial}{\partial z}\left(-\frac{1}{r}\frac{\partial \Psi}{\partial z}\right) = 0 \qquad (4\text{-}99)$$

which shows that the Stokes stream function for an axially symmetric, irrotational flow does not satisfy the Laplace equation in cylindrical coordinates.

In spherical coordinates, the relationships between $\Psi$ and the velocity components $v_R$ and $v_\theta$ can be established in the same manner. Referring to Fig. 4–26, we may write

$$q_R = 2\pi R \sin \theta R\, \delta\theta\, v_R = 2\pi\, \delta\Psi$$

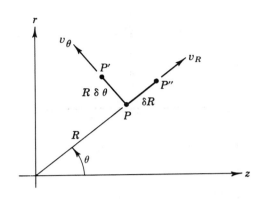

**Fig. 4-26.**  Definition of $v_\theta$ and $v_R$.

and
$$q_\theta = -2\pi R \sin \theta \, \delta R \, v_\theta = 2\pi \, \delta \Psi$$

whence

$$v_R = \frac{1}{R^2 \sin \theta} \frac{\partial \Psi}{\partial \theta} \qquad (4\text{--}100)$$

and

$$v_\theta = -\frac{1}{R \sin \theta} \frac{\partial \Psi}{\partial R} \qquad (4\text{--}101)$$

For irrotational flows, we may establish the following relations between the Stokes stream function and the velocity potential in spherical coordinates by equating the corresponding expressions for $v_R$ and $v_\theta$:

$$v_R = \frac{1}{R^2 \sin \theta} \frac{\partial \Psi}{\partial \theta} = \frac{\partial \Phi}{\partial R} \qquad (4\text{--}102)$$

$$v_\theta = -\frac{1}{R \sin \theta} \frac{\partial \Psi}{\partial R} = \frac{\partial \Phi}{R \, \partial \theta} \qquad (4\text{--}103)$$

The condition of irrotationality for an axially symmetric flow in spherical coordinates is

$$\frac{1}{R} \frac{\partial v_R}{\partial \theta} - \frac{\partial v_\theta}{\partial R} = 0 \qquad (4\text{--}104)$$

and, in terms of $\Psi$,

$$\frac{1}{R} \frac{\partial}{\partial \theta} \left( \frac{1}{R^2 \sin \theta} \frac{\partial \Psi}{\partial \theta} \right) - \frac{\partial}{\partial R} \left( -\frac{1}{R \sin \theta} \frac{\partial \Psi}{\partial R} \right) = 0 \qquad (4\text{--}105)$$

indicating that the Stokes stream function for an axially symmetric, irrotational flow does not satisfy the Laplace equation in spherical coordinates.

Equations 4–96, 4–97, 4–102, and 4–103 are useful in the analysis of axially symmetric flows. They enable us to solve for either the $\Psi$- or the $\Phi$-function, once the other is known. We shall demonstrate the application of these equations in the remainder of this chapter. But before we do so, we shall investigate the nature of the Stokes stream function and the velocity potential for axially symmetric flows in connection with the equation of continuity.

## 4-17    Equations of Continuity for Axially Symmetric Flows

When there is axial symmetry, the differential equation of continuity can be modified from Eq. 2–19 to take the following form, using cylindrical coordinates:

$$\nabla \cdot \mathbf{V} = \frac{1}{r}\frac{\partial}{\partial r}(rv_r) + \frac{\partial}{\partial z}v_z = 0 \qquad (4\text{-}106)$$

If we substitute the partial derivatives of the stream function in place of the velocity components into the above equation by using Eqs. 4–94 and 4–95, we have

$$\frac{1}{r}\frac{\partial}{\partial r}\left[r\left(-\frac{1}{r}\frac{\partial \Psi}{\partial z}\right)\right] + \frac{\partial}{\partial z}\left(\frac{1}{r}\frac{\partial \Psi}{\partial r}\right) = 0$$

This equation shows that the continuity equation is identically satisfied, as is to be expected when we consider how Eqs. 4–94 and 4–95 were developed. Now, if we replace the velocity components of Eq. 4–106 with proper expressions involving the velocity potential, using Eqs. 4–96 and 4–97, we obtain

$$\frac{1}{r}\frac{\partial}{\partial r}\left(r\frac{\partial \Phi}{\partial r}\right) + \frac{\partial}{\partial z}\left(\frac{\partial \Phi}{\partial z}\right) = 0 \qquad (4\text{-}107)$$

This equation is indeed the Laplace equation of $\Phi$ in cylindrical coordinates. Solutions of this equation are called *cylindrical harmonics*.

In a similar way we may modify Eq. 2–20 to get the following differential equation of continuity for an axially symmetric flow in spherical coordinates:

$$\nabla \cdot \mathbf{V} = \frac{1}{R^2}\frac{\partial}{\partial R}(R^2 v_R) + \frac{1}{R\sin\theta}\frac{\partial}{\partial \theta}(v_\theta \sin\theta) = 0 \qquad (4\text{-}108)$$

Substitution of the partial differentiations of the stream function in place of the velocity components into the above equation by using Eqs. 4–100 and 4–101 yields

$$\frac{1}{R^2}\frac{\partial}{\partial R}\left(R^2 \frac{1}{R^2\sin\theta}\frac{\partial \Psi}{\partial \theta}\right) + \frac{1}{R\sin\theta}\frac{\partial}{\partial \theta}\left(-\frac{1}{R\sin\theta}\frac{\partial \Psi}{\partial R}\sin\theta\right) = 0$$

indicating again that the Stokes stream function satisfies identically the continuity equation. But, if we replace the velocity components of Eq. 4–108 with proper expressions involving the velocity potential by using Eqs. 4–102 and 4–103, the result is

$$\frac{1}{R^2}\frac{\partial}{\partial R}\left(R^2\frac{\partial\Phi}{\partial R}\right) + \frac{1}{R\sin\theta}\frac{\partial}{\partial\theta}\left(\frac{\partial\Phi}{R\,\partial\theta}\sin\theta\right) = 0 \qquad (4\text{-}109)$$

This equation is the Laplace equation in spherical coordinates; solutions of this equation are called *spherical harmonics*.

It was shown in the preceding section that the Stokes stream function for axially symmetric flows does not satisfy the Laplace equation as does the stream function for two-dimensional flows. However, the velocity potential for axially symmetric flows satisfies the Laplace equation and is, therefore, harmonic. For this reason, in analyzing an axially symmetric flow we generally solve for a velocity potential which is harmonic. The general solution of axially symmetric flows is often more difficult than the two-dimensional flows because in axially symmetric flows we are unable to use such mathematical techniques as complex variables and conformal mapping, which are used exclusively for two-dimensional planar flows. In the following sections we shall develop a procedure, similar to the one used in Part I of this chapter, in which several simple known harmonic functions are superimposed to yield flow fields of practical significance.

*Illustrative Example 4-3.* The velocity potential for a three-dimensional, axially symmetric flow, expressed in spherical coordinates, is

$$\Phi = \frac{k}{R^2}\cos\theta$$

where $k$ is a constant. Determine the corresponding Stokes stream function for this flow.

*Solution:* The given function must satisfy the Laplace equation in spherical coordinates. That is,

$$\frac{1}{R^2}\frac{\partial}{\partial R}\left(R^2\frac{\partial\Phi}{\partial R}\right) + \frac{1}{R\sin\theta}\frac{\partial}{\partial\theta}\left(\sin\theta\frac{\partial\Phi}{R\,\partial\theta}\right) = \frac{1}{R^2}\frac{\partial}{\partial R}\left[R^2\frac{\partial}{\partial R}\left(\frac{k}{R^2}\cos\theta\right)\right]$$

$$+ \frac{1}{R\sin\theta}\frac{\partial}{\partial\theta}\left[\sin\theta\frac{\partial}{R\,\partial\theta}\left(\frac{k}{R^2}\cos\theta\right)\right] = \left(\frac{2k}{R^4}\cos\theta\right) + \left(-\frac{2k}{R^4}\cos\theta\right) = 0 \qquad (A)$$

By using Eq. 4-102, we have

$$\frac{1}{R^2\sin\theta}\frac{\partial\Psi}{\partial\theta} = \frac{\partial\Phi}{\partial R} = \frac{\partial}{\partial R}\left(\frac{k}{R^2}\cos\theta\right) = -\frac{2k}{R^3}\cos\theta$$

Hence

$$\Psi = \int -\frac{2k}{R}\sin\theta\cos\theta\,\partial\theta = -\frac{k}{R}\sin^2\theta + f(R) + C_1 \qquad (B)$$

and

$$\frac{\partial \Psi}{\partial R} = \frac{k}{R^2} \sin^2 \theta + \frac{\partial f(R)}{\partial R} \tag{C}$$

From Eq. 4-103,

$$-\frac{1}{R \sin \theta} \frac{\partial \Psi}{\partial R} = \frac{1}{R} \frac{\partial \Phi}{\partial \theta} = \frac{1}{R} \frac{\partial}{\partial \theta} \left( \frac{k}{R^2} \cos \theta \right) = -\frac{k}{R^3} \sin \theta$$

which, upon multiplying through by $-R \sin \theta$, becomes

$$\frac{\partial \Psi}{\partial R} = \frac{k}{R^2} \sin^2 \theta \tag{D}$$

Equating the right-hand sides of Eqs. (C) and (D), we have

$$\frac{\partial f(R)}{\partial R} = 0$$

Therefore,

$$f(R) = \text{constant}$$

Substitution of this value into Eq. (B) yields the following desired Stokes stream function for this flow:

$$\Psi = -\frac{k}{R} \sin^2 \theta + C$$

## 4-18   Axially Symmetric Simple Flows

The axially symmetric simple flows to be developed here are uniform flow, source, and sink. These simple flows are then superimposed in various combinations to form more complex systems of practical significance.

## 4-19   Uniform Flow

Consider a uniform stream of fluid having a velocity $V_0$ in the positive $z$-direction. The cylindrical components of this velocity may be expressed as

$$v_z = V_0 \tag{4-110}$$

$$v_r = 0 \tag{4-111}$$

Replacing $v_z$ and $v_r$ by the partial derivatives of $\Phi$, we get

$$\frac{\partial \Phi}{\partial z} = V_0 \tag{4-112}$$

$$\frac{\partial \Phi}{\partial r} = 0 \tag{4-113}$$

Integrating the above equations and omitting the constants of integration, we have at once the following desired velocity potential for the uniform flow in cylindrical coordinates:

$$\Phi = V_0 z \tag{4-114}$$

The corresponding Stokes stream function may be readily established by integrating Eqs. 4–96 and 4–97 for the above velocity potential. Hence

$$\Psi = \tfrac{1}{2} V_0 r^2 \tag{4-115}$$

In spherical coordinates, the components of velocity for the uniform flow can be written as

$$v_R = V_0 \cos \theta \tag{4-116}$$
$$v_\theta = -V_0 \sin \theta \tag{4-117}$$

The $\Phi$- and $\Psi$-functions for the uniform flows can then be found in the same manner as above to be

$$\Phi = RV_0 \cos \theta \tag{4-118}$$
$$\Psi = \tfrac{1}{2} V_0 R^2 \sin^2 \theta \tag{4-119}$$

Traces of equipotential surfaces and stream surfaces for the uniform flow on a symmetric plane are shown in Fig. 4–27 for constant increments of $\Phi$ and $\Psi$.

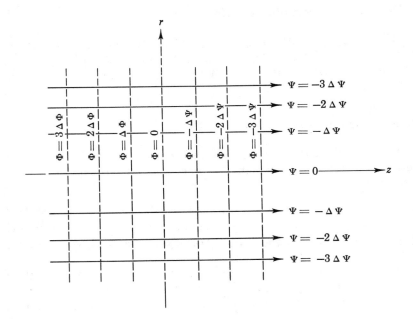

**Fig. 4-27.** Uniform flow in an axially symmetric plane.

## 4-20   Three-dimensional Sources and Sinks

Consider a three-dimensional source of strength $\hat{Q}$ with its center located at the origin of the coordinate axes, as shown in Fig. 4–28. At a radial distance $R$, the surface area of the spherical shell is $4\pi R^2$, and the velocity components, using spherical coordinates, are therefore

$$v_R = \frac{\hat{Q}}{4\pi R^2} \tag{4-120}$$

$$v_\theta = 0 \tag{4-121}$$

We may replace $v_R$ and $v_\theta$ in the above equations by the partial differentiations of $\Phi$ to obtain

$$\frac{\partial \Phi}{\partial R} = \frac{\hat{Q}}{4\pi R^2} \tag{4-122}$$

$$\frac{\partial \Phi}{R\,\partial \theta} = 0 \tag{4-123}$$

from which the velocity potential for the three-dimensional source may be determined by integration. The result is

$$\Phi = -\frac{\hat{Q}}{4\pi R} \tag{4-124}$$

The corresponding Stokes stream function may be established by the integration of Eqs. 4–102 and 4–103 in conjunction with Eqs. 4–122 and 4–123. Thus

$$v_R = \frac{1}{R^2 \sin\theta}\frac{\partial \Psi}{\partial \theta} = \frac{\partial \Phi}{\partial R} = \frac{\hat{Q}}{4\pi R^2} \tag{4-125}$$

$$v_\theta = -\frac{1}{R \sin\theta}\frac{\partial \Psi}{\partial R} = \frac{\partial \Phi}{R\,\partial \theta} = 0 \tag{4-126}$$

Integrating, we obtain

$$\Psi = -\frac{\hat{Q}}{4\pi}\cos\theta \tag{4-127}$$

as the Stokes stream function for a source at the origin.

Equations 4–124 and 4–127 indicate that equipotential surfaces form a family of concentric spherical surfaces about the center of the source and that stream surfaces are represented by a family of concentric cones about the $z$-axis with the apex at the center of the source. A trace of these surfaces on an axially symmetric plane is shown in Fig. 4–28.

For a sink the strength is $-\hat{Q}$; and so we simply replace $\hat{Q}$ in all the above equations by $-\hat{Q}$.

As in two-dimensional planar flows, we can develop three-dimensional

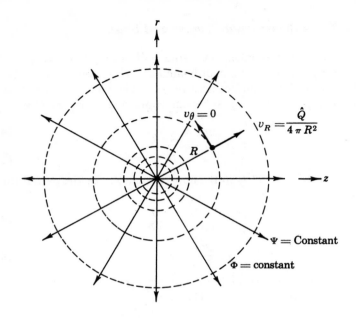

**Fig. 4-28.** A three-dimensional source.

axially symmetric potential flows of practical significance by superimposing the simple flows just derived in various combinations.

## 4-21 Combined Flow Field of Three-dimensional Source and Sink of Equal Strength

A three-dimensional source and a sink of equal strength $\hat{Q}$ are located at $(-a, 0)$ and $(a, 0)$, respectively, on the z-axis to form a combined source-sink flow field as shown in Fig. 4-29(a), which represents an axially symmetric plane. An arbitrary field point $P(z, r)$ is shown at distances $R_1$ and $R_2$, respectively, from the source and the sink. The angles $\theta_1$ and $\theta_2$ are measured from the positive z-axis. Thus, the velocity potential of the source at point $P$ is given by Eq. 4–124 to be

$$\Phi_{\text{source}} = -\frac{\hat{Q}}{4\pi R_1}$$

and that of the sink is

$$\Phi_{\text{sink}} = \frac{\hat{Q}}{4\pi R_2}$$

Since both $\Phi_{\text{source}}$ and $\Phi_{\text{sink}}$ are spherical harmonics, their sum also satisfies the Laplace equation. Hence

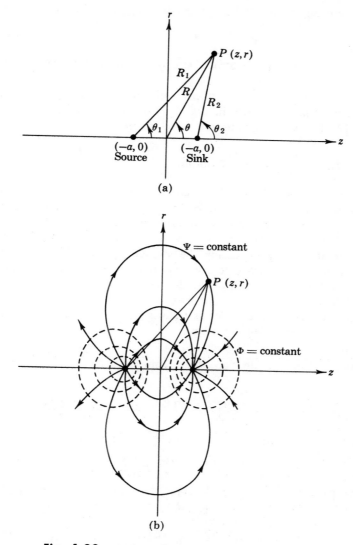

**Fig. 4-29.** A three-dimensional source-sink flow.

$$\Phi = -\frac{\hat{Q}}{4\pi R_1} + \frac{\hat{Q}}{4\pi R_2} = -\frac{\hat{Q}}{4\pi}\left(\frac{1}{R_1} - \frac{1}{R_2}\right)$$
$$\underbrace{\phantom{-\frac{\hat{Q}}{4\pi R_1}}}_{\Phi_{source}} \quad \underbrace{\phantom{\frac{\hat{Q}}{4\pi R_2}}}_{\Phi_{sink}}$$
$$= -\frac{\hat{Q}}{4\pi}\left(\frac{1}{\sqrt{(z+a)^2 + r^2}} - \frac{1}{\sqrt{(z-a)^2 + r^2}}\right)$$

$$(4\text{-}128)$$

represents the velocity potential of the combined source-sink flow field of Fig. 4–29(a).

The corresponding Stokes stream function may be evaluated to be

$$\Psi = -\frac{\hat{Q}}{2\pi} (\cos \theta_1 - \cos \theta_2) \qquad (4\text{–}129)$$

which is the sum of the Stokes stream functions for the source and the sink.

Traces of equipotential surfaces and stream surfaces on an axially symmetric plane are shown in Fig. 4–29(b) as plotted from Eqs. 4–128 and 4–129 by assigning constant values to $\Phi$ and $\Psi$.

### 4-22   Three-dimensional Doublet

As in the case of two-dimensional doublet in Sec. 4–11, a three-dimensional doublet is also developed by a similar limiting process. The limit process is carried out by bringing the source and sink of Fig. 4–29(a) together (that is, by making the distance $2a$ approach zero), while simultaneously increasing the strength $\hat{Q}$ indefinitely so that in the limit the product $2a\hat{Q}$ attains a constant value of $4\pi\mu$. The constant $\mu$ is defined as the strength of the doublet.

We shall now develop the velocity potential and the stream function of a three-dimensional doublet as follows. Applying the law of sines to the triangle of Fig. 4–29(a), we have

$$\frac{R_1}{\sin \theta_2} = \frac{R_2}{\sin \theta_1} = \frac{2a}{\sin (\theta_2 - \theta_1)} = \frac{2a}{2 \sin \frac{1}{2}(\theta_2 - \theta_1) \cos \frac{1}{2}(\theta_2 + \theta_1)}$$

whence

$$R_1 - R_2 = \frac{a(\sin \theta_2 - \sin \theta_1)}{\sin \frac{1}{2}(\theta_2 - \theta_1) \cos \frac{1}{2}(\theta_2 + \theta_1)} = \frac{2a \cos \frac{1}{2}(\theta_2 + \theta_1)}{\cos \frac{1}{2}(\theta_2 - \theta_1)}$$

which may be substituted into Eq. 4–128 to obtain

$$\Phi = -\frac{\hat{Q}}{4\pi} \frac{R_2 - R_1}{R_1 R_2} = \frac{2a\hat{Q}}{4\pi} \frac{\cos \frac{1}{2}(\theta_2 + \theta_1)}{R_1 R_2 \cos \frac{1}{2}(\theta_2 - \theta_1)}$$

In the limit as $2a \to 0$, $2a\hat{Q} \to 4\pi\mu$, $\theta_2 \to \theta$, $\theta_1 \to \theta$, $R_1 \to R$, and $R_2 \to R$, the above equation becomes

$$\Phi = \frac{\mu}{R^2} \cos \theta \qquad (4\text{–}130)$$

which is the velocity potential for a three-dimensional doublet at the origin.

The corresponding Stokes stream function for the three-dimensional doublet at the origin can be obtained by the integration of Eqs. 4–102 and 4–103 in conjunction with Eq. 4–130. The result is

$$\Psi = -\frac{\mu}{R} \sin^2 \theta \qquad (4\text{–}131)$$

Traces of equipotential surfaces and stream surfaces for the three-dimensional doublet are shown in Fig. 4–30. They are obtained by assigning constant values of $\Phi$ and $\Psi$ to Eqs. 4–130 and 4–131, respectively.

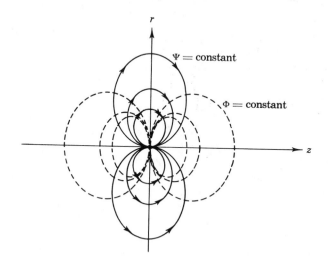

**Fig. 4-30.** A three-dimensional doublet.

## 4-23   Combined Flow Field of Uniform Flow and Three-dimensional Doublet—Uniform Flow Past a Sphere

When a uniform flow of velocity $V_0$ in the positive $z$-direction is superimposed on a three-dimensional doublet, the result is a physical situation of an irrotational flow past a sphere. The trace of the stream surfaces for each flow is shown in Fig. 4–31(a).

In spherical coordinates the velocity potential of the combined flow field is the sum of the velocity potentials of the two component flows:

$$\Phi = \underset{\Phi_{\text{uniform flow}}}{RV_0 \cos \theta} + \underset{\Phi_{\text{doublet}}}{\frac{\mu}{R^2} \cos \theta} \tag{4–132}$$

since the velocity potential is a spherical harmonic. The corresponding Stokes stream function for the combined flow field can be obtained by the integration of Eqs. 4–102 and 4–103 in conjunction with Eq. 4–132 to be

$$\Psi = \frac{1}{2} V_0 R^2 \sin^2 \theta - \frac{\mu}{R} \sin^2 \theta \tag{4–133}$$

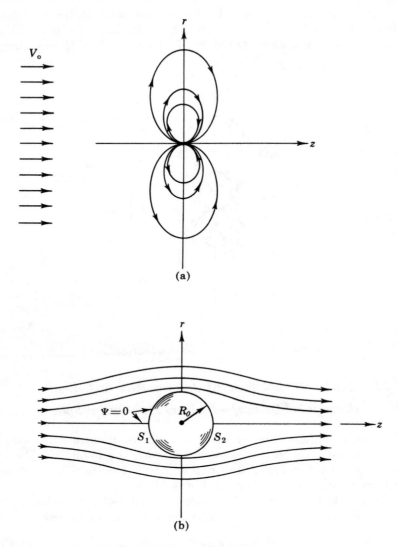

**Fig. 4-31.** Uniform flow past a sphere.

which is clearly the sum of the Stokes stream functions of the two component flows.

Since this combined flow pattern is a uniform flow past a sphere, the main problem is to develop the boundaries of a sphere in the flow field. We shall examine the stream surface corresponding to $\Psi = 0$, i.e.,

$$\frac{1}{2} V_0 R^2 \sin^2 \theta - \frac{\mu}{R} \sin^2 \theta = 0 \tag{4-134}$$

which can be rearranged as

$$\left( \frac{1}{2} V_0 R^2 - \frac{\mu}{R} \right) \sin^2 \theta = 0$$

This equation is satisfied by the following two conditions:

(1) The condition $\sin^2 \theta = 0$ which satisfies the above equations requires that $\theta = 0$ and $\theta = \pi$ for all values of $R$. Hence the axis of symmetry forms a part of this equation.

(2) The above equation is also satisfied by

$$\frac{1}{2} V_0 R^2 - \frac{\mu}{R} = 0$$

whence

$$R = \sqrt[3]{\frac{2\mu}{V_0}}$$

Since $\mu$ and $V_0$ are constant for any given combined flow, $R$ may be considered as the radius $R_0$ of the desired sphere in the uniform flow. The trace of the stream surface $\Psi = 0$ is shown in Fig. 4–31(b). Points $S_1$ and $S_2$ are the two stagnation points in this flow field.

By substituting the value of $\mu$ by $R_0^3 V_0/2$ into Eqs. 4–132 and 4–133, we can write the velocity potential and the Stokes stream function of this combined flow field in terms of $R_0$ as

$$\Phi = V_0 R \cos \theta \left( 1 + \frac{1}{2} \frac{R_0^3}{R^3} \right) \tag{4-135}$$

$$\Psi = \frac{1}{2} V_0 R^2 \sin^2 \theta \left( 1 - \frac{R_0^3}{R^3} \right) \tag{4-136}$$

In Fig. 4–31(b), the trace of stream surfaces outside of the spherical surface has been drawn by assigning various constant numerical values to $\Psi$ of Eq. 4–136.

## PROBLEMS

4-1. Determine the velocity components for the following stream functions:

   (a)  $\psi = x + y + x^2 + xy + y^2$

   (b)  $\psi = Ar \sin \theta$

   (c)  $\psi = Ar \left( 1 - \frac{B}{r^2} \right) \sin \theta$

   (d)  $\psi = -Ay + Be^{-y} \sin x$

Which of these stream functions represent possible irrotational flow fields?

**4-2.** Given a stream function $\psi = 3x^2 - xy^2 + 2t^3y$ for an unsteady two-dimensional flow. Calculate (a) the rate of flow across the circular arc $\widehat{AB}$, as shown in Fig. 4–32, at time $t = 4$ sec , and (b) the rates of flow across straight paths $\overline{OA}$ and $\overline{OB}$, respectively.

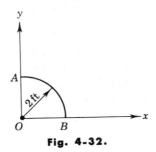

**Fig. 4-32.**

**4-3.** A parallel flow occurs in the $xy$ plane. The flow is in the positive $y$-direction and the velocity varies linearly from zero at $(-2, 0)$ to 20 ft/sec at $(+2, 0)$. Determine the expression for $\psi$. Is the flow irrotational?

**4-4.** A steady, two-dimensional, incompressible flow occurs between two fixed plane surfaces spaced at a distance $b$ apart. The velocity profile is a parabola with its vertex at the center line as shown in Fig. 4–33. Determine the stream function for the flow. Is this flow irrotational?

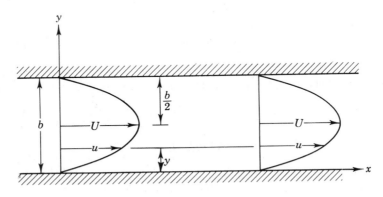

**Fig. 4-33.**

**4-5.** Derive an expression for $\omega_z$, the $z$-component of the vorticity vector $\boldsymbol{\omega}$, in terms of $\psi$.

**4-6.** Calculate the vorticity in the flow field of Problems 4-3 and 4-4.

**4-7.** Is the flow field represented by the stream function $\psi = x^3 + 3xy$ irrotational? If not, calculate the vorticity at the point $(4, 5)$.

**4-8.** A two-dimensional incompressible flow has the following velocity field: $\mathbf{V} = x\mathbf{i} - (3x + y)\mathbf{j}$. Check and see whether a stream function exists for this flow field. If so, find the expression for $\psi$.

**4-9.** A two-dimensional incompressible flow is represented by the following stream function:

$$\psi = x^3 - 3x^2 - 3xy^2 + 3y^2$$

(a) Determine the equation of the streamline passing through the point $(1, 2)$. (b) Calculate the velocity $\mathbf{V}$ at $(1, 2)$. (c) Show that the magnitude of $\mathbf{V}$ is identical to the absolute value of $\nabla\psi$ at $(1, 2)$. (d) Show that the direction of $\mathbf{V}$ is perpendicular to the direction of $\nabla\psi$ at $(1, 2)$.

**4-10.** The stream function for a uniform flow passing a circular cylinder is given by

$$\psi = 50y\left(1 - \frac{25}{r^2}\right) + \frac{107}{\pi}\ln\frac{r}{5}$$

Determine (a) the equation of the streamline which passes through the point $(5, 12)$, and (b) the velocity vector $\mathbf{V}$ at the point $(5, 12)$.

**4-11.** Show that the stream function $\psi = x^2 - y^2$ represents a two-dimensional irrotational flow. Calculate the pressure gradient at the point $(2, 3)$ if the fluid is water.

**4-12.** Which of the following velocity fields represent possible irrotational flows:
(a) $\mathbf{V} = 2xy\mathbf{i} + (x^2 - y^2)\mathbf{j}$
(b) $\mathbf{V} = (x^2 - y^2)\mathbf{i} - 2xy\mathbf{j}$
(c) $\mathbf{V} = (x^2 + x - y^2)\mathbf{i} - (2xy + y)\mathbf{j}$
(d) $\mathbf{V} = -(2xy + x)\mathbf{i} + (y^2 + y - x^2)\mathbf{j}$
Find the velocity potential and stream function for each irrotational flow field.

**4-13.** Find the stream function for the velocity potential $\phi = 2xy + y$. Sketch the streamlines and equipotential lines for this flow field.

**4-14.** Find the stream function for the velocity potential $\phi = 2x - 5xy + 3y + 4$. Determine the pressure gradient at the point $(-2, 5)$ in this flow field.

**4-15.** Show that $\phi = \ln(x^2 + y^2)^{1/2}$ represents a possible irrotational flow defined everywhere except at $(0, 0)$. Find the stream function for this flow.

**4-16.** Find the velocity potential for the stream function $\psi = x + x^2 - y^2$. Determine the pressure difference between points $(-2, 4)$ and $(3, 5)$.

**4-17.** Find the velocity potential for the stream function

$$\psi = \arctan\frac{2ay}{x^2 + y^2 - a^2}$$

Sketch the streamlines and equipotential lines for this flow field.

**4–18.** The stream function $\psi = r^{\pi/\alpha} \sin(\pi\theta/\alpha)$ represents a steady two-dimensional flow around a corner of angle $\alpha$ as shown in Fig. 4–34.

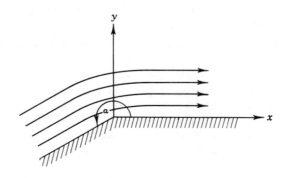

**Fig. 4-34.**

(a) Determine the velocity potential for this flow. (b) Show that if $\alpha = \pi$, the function represents a uniform flow. (c) Show that when $\alpha = \pi/2$, the function represents a flow at a corner of 90°. (d) Sketch the streamlines for the flow fields in (b) and (c).

**4–19.** Find the corresponding stream function for each of the following velocity potentials:
(a) $\phi = Ar \cos\theta$
(b) $\phi = B \ln r$
(c) $\phi = C\theta$
(d) $\phi = (D \cos\theta)/r$
(e) $\phi = Ar \cos\theta + C\theta + (D \cos\theta)/r$

**4–20.** Construct a flow net for a two-dimensional flow in a 90-degree bend. Determine and plot to scale the ratio of the outside boundary velocity and the velocity of approach for the resulting flow net.

**4–21.** A two-dimensional flow field is formed by combining a uniform flow with a velocity $\mathbf{V} = 5\mathbf{i}$ ft/sec and a source with $q = 20\pi$ ft³/sec/ft located at the origin of the coordinates. (a) Determine the stream function and velocity potential for this flow field. (b) Locate the stagnation point in this flow field. (c) Plot the body contour formed in this flow field and determine the equation which describes this body contour. This body contour is called a two-dimensional *half body*. (d) Determine the maximum thickness of this half body and the value of $\theta$ at which it occurs. (e) Show that the half body attains half its maximum thickness at its intersection with the $y$-axis. (f) Determine the velocity field for this flow and express $\mathbf{V}$ in polar notations.

**4–22.** Investigate the two-dimensional flow field which is formed by combining a uniform flow with $V = V_0 i$ and a source and a sink of equal strength q. The source is located at $(-a, 0)$ and the sink at $(a, 0)$. (a) Determine the stream function and velocity potential for this combined flow field. (b) Locate the stagnation points in this flow field. (c) Plot the body contour formed in this flow field and determine the equation which describes this body contour. This body contour is called the *Rankine oval*. (d) Determine the maximum thickness of this oval. (e) Determine the velocity field for this flow and express $V$ in polar notations.

**4–23.** A two-dimensional vortex pair is formed by two vortices of equal strength K but opposite sense in close proximity. The clockwise vortex is located at $(-a, 0)$ and the counterclockwise vortex at $(a, 0)$. (a) Determine the stream function and velocity potential of this combined flow field. (b) Locate any stagnation points in this flow field. (c) Determine the velocity field for this flow.

**4–24.** A uniform flow with a velocity $V = V_0 j$ is superimposed onto the vortex pair in Problem 4–23. (a) Determine the stream function and velocity potential of the combined flow field. (b) Locate any stagnation points in this flow field. (c) Plot the body contour formed in this flow field and determine the equation which describes this body contour. (d) Determine the width and length of this body contour at the $x$- and $y$-axis. (e) Determine the velocity field for this flow.

**4–25.** Investigate the two-dimensional flow field which is formed by combining a source of strength q and a vortex of strength K at the origin of the coordinates. Sketch the streamline pattern of the combined flow field.

**4–26.** If the $y$-axis of the coordinates is taken as a plane surface, show that the stream function for a two-dimensional source of strength q located at $(a, 0)$ is

$$\psi = \frac{q}{2\pi} \arctan \frac{2xy}{x^2 - y^2 - a^2}$$

Assuming the pressure to be zero at infinity, determine the pressure distribution along the plane surface.

**4–27.** A two-dimensional vortex of strength K is located at the point $(a, 0)$. If the $y$-axis is taken as the trace of a plane surface, find (a) the stream function for the flow field, and (b) the pressure distribution along the plane surface. The pressure is zero at infinity.

**4–28.** Find the stream function and velocity potential for the flow field of a source of strength q located at the point $(a, a)$, if the positive $x$- and $y$-axes are traces of plane surfaces. Sketch the streamlines for this flow.

**4–29.** Calculate the rate of flow through the surfaces of rotation by revolving the lines $BC$, shown in Fig. 4–35, about the $z$-axis when the Stokes stream function for the flow field is given as $\Psi = 5R^2 \sin^2 \theta$.

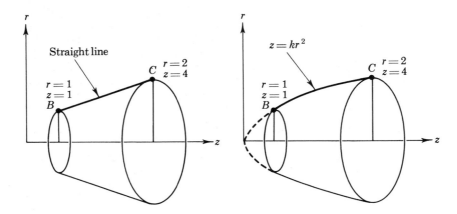

**Fig. 4-35.**

**4-30.** Work Problem 4–29 if the Stokes stream function for the flow field is

$$\Psi = -\frac{4}{R}\sin^2\theta$$

**4-31.** Show that

$$\Psi = \frac{1}{2} V_0 R^2 \sin^2\theta \quad \text{and} \quad \Phi = R V_0 \cos\theta$$

represent the same flow field. Express both the $\Psi$- and $\Phi$-functions in Cartesian notations.

**4-32.** Is $\Phi = 1/R$ harmonic? If so, determine the corresponding Stokes stream function.

**4-33.** Derive the velocity potential for the following Stokes stream function

$$\Psi = \frac{1}{R}\sin^2\theta - R^2\sin^2\theta$$

and show that the resulting velocity potential is harmonic.

**4-34.** Find the combined axially symmetric flow field which is formed by two three-dimensional sources of equal strength $\hat{Q}$ located at $(0, 0, -a)$ and $(0, 0, a)$, respectively. Show that this flow field is equivalent to that of a source $\hat{Q}$ located at $(0, 0, a)$ with the $xy$ plane as a rigid wall.

**4-35.** An axially symmetric flow field is formed by a three-dimensional source of strength $\hat{Q} = 60$ ft³/sec located at the origin of the coordinates and another source of $\hat{Q} = 30$ ft³/sec located at $(0, 0, 2)$. Determine the velocities at points $(-1, -2, 0)$ and $(1, 1, 1)$.

**4-36.** An axially symmetric flow field is formed by the superposition of a uniform flow with a velocity $\mathbf{V} = V_0\mathbf{k}$ ft/sec and a source with a strength $\hat{Q}$ ft³/sec located at the origin of the coordinates. (a) Determine the Stokes stream function and velocity potential for this flow field. (b) Locate the stagnation point in this flow field. (c) Find the value of the stream function passing through the stagnation point. (d) Plot the traces of the body contour formed in this flow field and determine the equation which describes this body contour. This body contour is called a *half body* as it extends to infinity surrounding the axis of symmetry.

4-37. By taking the pressure at infinity as zero, show that the pressure on the surface of the half body in Problem 4-36 is

$$p = \tfrac{1}{8}\rho V_0^2(1 + \cos\theta)(3\cos\theta - 1)$$

4-38. Show by integration that the drag on the half body of Problem 4-37 is zero.

4-39. Consider the superposition of a uniform flow with $\mathbf{V} = V_0\mathbf{k}$ and the three-dimensional source-sink flow of Sec. 4-21. (a) Determine the Stokes stream function and velocity potential for this combined axially symmetric flow field. (b) Locate the stagnation points in this flow field. (c) Plot the traces of the body contour formed in this flow field and determine the equation which describes this body contour. This body contour is the *Rankine body*. (d) Determine the velocity field for this flow.

4-40. Show that the drag on a sphere in a potential flow is equal to zero.

4-41. A sphere, 4 ft in diameter, is placed in a potential flow of air, in which the free-stream velocity is 75 ft/sec and the free-stream pressure is 14.7 lbf/in² abs. Calculate the maximum and minimum pressures on the surface of the sphere and locate the points at which these pressures occur. Use $\rho = 0.0024$ slug/ft³ for air.

4-42. A sphere, 2 ft in diameter, is towed at a uniform velocity $\mathbf{V} = V_0\mathbf{k}$ with its center submerged at a constant depth of 3 ft below the surface of water, as shown in Fig. 4-36. The atmospheric pressure is 14.7 lbf/in² abs.

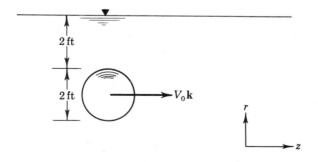

**Fig. 4-36.**

Assuming potential flow, calculate the magnitude of $V_0$ when *cavitation* starts on the surface of the sphere.

**4-43.** A sphere, 2 ft in diameter and having an average unit weight of 400 lbf/ft³, is released in water at rest. Assuming potential flow, calculate its velocity of descent after (a) 1 second, (b) 5 seconds, and (c) 10 seconds.

**4-44.** Figure 4–37 shows a line source along the z-axis. The strength of the line source is $q$ ft³/sec/ft. Show that the Stokes stream function for the flow field of this line source is

$$\Psi = -\frac{q}{4\pi}(R_0 - R_A)$$

Sketch the traces of stream surfaces and equipotential surfaces for this flow.

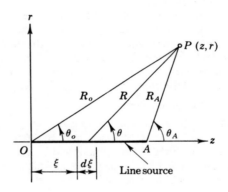

**Fig. 4-37.**

# 5 Application of Complex Variables and Conformal Transformations to Two-Dimensional Planar Potential Flows

## 5-1 Introduction

Two-dimensional planar potential flows can be most conveniently studied by a powerful mathematical technique—the theory of complex variables. Indeed, the study of potential flow has been greatly expanded as a result of the application of the theory of complex variables, since a large number of solutions to the two-dimensional Laplace equations are easily obtainable from functions of a complex variable. It will be shown in this chapter that the velocity potential and the stream function of every two-dimensional potential flow are respectively the real and imaginary parts of a function of a complex variable, and vice versa. Hence a considerably larger number of potential flows can be derived by considering various functions of a complex variable than would be possible by the method of superposition of simple flows of the preceding chapter. In fact, a large collection of such functions for two-dimensional potential flows has been made available in handbook form.[1] Furthermore, this theory enables us to find the velocity potential which satisfies the prescribed boundary conditions of a given flow problem by means of successive transformations.

Elements of the theories of complex variables and conformal transformations will be introduced in Secs. 5–2 through 5–6.

## 5-2 Complex Numbers

The solution of a quadratic equation with a negative discriminant is in the form of a complex number:

$$a + ib$$

where $a$ and $b$ are real numbers and $i$ is a unit defined by

$$i = \sqrt{-1} \quad \text{and} \quad i^2 = -1$$

The number $a$ is called the *real part* of the complex number, and the number $b$ is the *imaginary part*. The distinctive names of the two parts and the use of the unit $i$ may be regarded as devices for keeping the separate identities of the two parts in various mathematical manipulations involving complex numbers. Hence the two parts of a complex number may be regarded as similar to the two components of a vector in a plane.

It is seen that, when $b = 0$, the complex number becomes a real number. If $a = 0$, the complex number becomes a pure imaginary number. Two complex numbers $a_1 + ib_1$ and $a_2 + ib_2$ are identical when, and only when, $a_1 = a_2$ and $b_1 = b_2$.

Although complex numbers are essentially algebraic quantities, they may be given a convenient geometric representation called the *Argand diagram*, shown in Fig. 5–1. In the Argand diagram, the abscissa represents the real part of complex numbers and the ordinate represents the imaginary part. Any point in the Argand diagram is associated with a definite complex number whose real part and imaginary part form the coordinates of the point. In general, a complex number is written as

$$z = x + iy \tag{5-1}$$

---

[1] H. Kober, *Dictionary of Conformal Representations*. New York: Dover Publications, Inc., 1952.

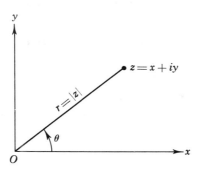

**Fig. 5-1.** Argand diagram.

which is shown in Fig. 5–1. This complex number may be more conveniently regarded as representing the directed line $\overline{Oz}$. The length of $z = x + iy$ is denoted by $r$ or $|z|$. That is,

$$r = |z| = \sqrt{x^2 + y^2} \tag{5–2}$$

and is called the *modulus* of $z$. The argument of $z$ is the angle $\theta$ between the positive real axis and the directed line $Oz$, measured in the counterclockwise direction (see Fig. 5–1). Thus,

$$\theta = \arg z = \tan^{-1} \frac{y}{x} \tag{5–3}$$

The argument of $z$ is not single-valued, for the angle $\theta \pm 2n\pi$ also represents an argument of $z$ for any integer $n$. For this reason, the principal value of arg $z$ is normally limited to the range $-\pi \leq \arg z \leq \pi$.

Clearly, every point in the Argand plane determines a complex number $z = x + iy$, and, conversely, every complex number $z = x + iy$ determines a unique point in the Argand plane. This correspondence between points of the Argand plane and the totality of complex numbers is a unique characteristic of the Argand plane. The Argand plane in Fig. 5–1 is called the *z-plane.*

Sometimes a complex number becomes more useful when it is expressed in the polar coordinate form or exponential form. From Fig. 5–1, $x = r \cos \theta$ and $y = r \sin \theta$, so that

$$z = r \cos \theta + ir \sin \theta = r (\cos \theta + i \sin \theta) \tag{5–4}$$

and

$$z = re^{i\theta} \tag{5–5}$$

The identity $e^{i\theta} = \cos \theta + i \sin \theta$ is called *DeMoivre's theorem* and can be easily established by the following series expansions of $e^{i\theta}$, cos $\theta$, and sin $\theta$:

$$e^{i\theta} = 1 + i\theta + \frac{(i\theta)^2}{2!} + \frac{(i\theta)^3}{3!} + \frac{(i\theta)^4}{4!} + \frac{(i\theta)^5}{5!} + \frac{(i\theta)^6}{6!} + \frac{(i\theta)^7}{7!} + \cdots$$

$$= 1 - \frac{\theta^2}{2!} + \frac{\theta^4}{4!} - \frac{\theta^6}{6!} + \cdots + i\left(\theta - \frac{\theta^3}{3!} + \frac{\theta^5}{5!} - \frac{\theta^7}{7!} + \cdots\right)$$

$$\cos\theta = 1 - \frac{\theta^2}{2!} + \frac{\theta^4}{4!} - \frac{\theta^6}{6!} + \cdots$$

$$\sin\theta = \theta - \frac{\theta^3}{3!} + \frac{\theta^5}{5!} - \frac{\theta^7}{7!} + \cdots$$

## 5-3 Mathematical Operations with Complex Numbers

Complex numbers obey the ordinary laws of algebra with the additional condition of $i^2 = -1$. Mathematical operations with complex numbers are summarized in this section.

**Addition and subtraction.** Because of the vectorial nature of complex numbers, addition of complex numbers obeys the parallelogram law of adding vectors, as indicated in Fig. 5–2. Hence

$$z = z_1 + z_2 = (x_1 + x_2) + i(y_1 + y_2)$$
$$z - z_1 = (x - x_1) + i(y - y_1) = z_2$$

as can be seen from Fig. 5–2.

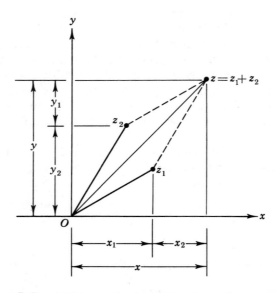

**Fig. 5-2.** Addition and subtraction of complex numbers.

**Multiplication and division.** The formula for multiplying two complex numbers in Cartesian form is

$$z_1 z_2 = (x_1 + iy_1)(x_2 + iy_2) = (x_1 x_2 - y_1 y_2) + i(x_1 y_2 + x_2 y_1)$$

However, when the two complex numbers are expressed in exponential form—$z_1 = r_1 e^{i\theta_1}$, and $z_2 = r_2 e^{i\theta_2}$—their product becomes

$$z_1 z_2 = (r_1 e^{i\theta_1})(r_2 e^{i\theta_2}) = r_1 r_2 e^{i(\theta_1 + \theta_2)}$$

The resulting complex number has a modulus which is the product of the moduli of $z_1$ and $z_2$, and an argument which is the sum of the arguments of $z_1$ and $z_2$. Hence we may regard the operation of multiplying $r_1 e^{i\theta_1}$ by $r_2 e^{i\theta_2}$ as a process of stretching (or shrinking) the modulus $r_1$ to $r_1 r_2$ and of increasing the argument $\theta_1$ to $\theta_1 + \theta_2$. This process is illustrated in Fig. 5–3.

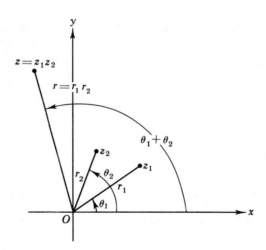

**Fig. 5-3.** Multiplication of complex numbers.

Division of one complex number by another in Cartesian form, such as

$$\frac{z_1}{z_2} = \frac{x_1 + iy_1}{x_2 + iy_2}$$

requires that the denominator be made real by multiplying both the numerator and denominator by $x_2 - iy_2$. We thus have

$$\frac{z_1}{z_2} = \frac{(x_1 + iy_1)(x_2 - iy_2)}{(x_2 + iy_2)(x_2 - iy_2)} = \frac{x_1 x_2 + y_1 y_2}{x_2^2 + y_2^2} + i\frac{x_2 y_1 - x_1 y_2}{x_2^2 + y_2^2}$$

When complex numbers are expressed in exponential form, division becomes a relatively simple operation:

$$\frac{z_1}{z_2} = \frac{r_1 e^{i\theta_1}}{r_2 e^{i\theta_2}} = \frac{r_1}{r_2} e^{i(\theta_1 - \theta_2)}$$

**Multiplication by $i$.** Since the complex number $i$ has a modulus of unity and an argument of $\pi/2$, it may be written as

$$i = \cos\frac{\pi}{2} + i\sin\frac{\pi}{2} = e^{i\pi/2}$$

Hence multiplying a complex number $z = re^{i\theta}$ by $i$, i.e.,

$$zi = (re^{i\theta})(e^{i\pi/2}) = re^{i(\theta + \pi/2)}$$

represents a process which simply rotates the directed line representing the complex number $z$ through an angle $\pi/2$ in the counterclockwise direction.

**Conjugate of a complex number.** The conjugate of a complex number $z = x + iy$ is defined as $\bar{z} = x - iy$. The bar over a complex number is used to denote its conjugate. Some properties of conjugate pairs are

$$z + \bar{z} = (x + iy) + (x - iy) = 2x \quad \text{a real number}$$

$$z - \bar{z} = (x + iy) - (x - iy) = i2y \quad \text{a pure imaginary number}$$

$$z\bar{z} = (x + iy)(x - iy) = x^2 + y^2 \quad \text{a real number} > 0$$

**Powers and roots.** If $z = x + iy$, the value of $z^n$, where $n$ is a positive integer, is found by applying the binomial theorem. For example,

$$z^2 = (x + iy)^2 = (x^2 - y^2) + i2xy$$

$$z^3 = (x + iy)^3 = (x^3 - 3xy^2) + i(3x^2y - y^3)$$

A simpler method of computing $z^n$ is to use the exponential form of $z$. Thus,

$$z^n = (re^{i\theta})^n = r^n e^{in\theta}$$

Using DeMoivre's theorem, we may also write the polar form of $z^n$ as

$$z^n = r^n(\cos n\theta + i\sin n\theta)$$

Similarly, the root $z^{1/n}$ can be conveniently determined in the following exponential and polar forms:

$$z^{1/n} = r^{1/n}e^{i\theta/n} = r^{1/n}\left(\cos\frac{\theta}{n} + i\sin\frac{\theta}{n}\right)$$

**Logarithm of a complex number.** Again we shall use the exponential form of complex number $z = re^{i\theta}$ to obtain the logarithm of $z$:

$$z = re^{i\theta} = x + iy$$

$$\ln z = \ln r + i\theta$$

$$= \ln \sqrt{x^2 + y^2} + i \tan^{-1}\frac{y}{x}$$

Clearly ln $z$ is another complex number whose real part is the logarithm of the modulus of $z$ and whose imaginary part is the argument of $z$.

## 5-4   Functions of a Complex Variable

The complex number $z = x + iy$, with variables $x$ and $y$, is commonly referred to as a *complex variable*.

Another variable $w$ may be introduced as a function of the complex variable $z = x + iy$. Mathematically, we can write

$$w = f(z) = f(x + iy) \tag{5–6}$$

as a general functional relationship between $w$ and $z$. For example,

$$w = 4z^2 = 4(x + iy)^2 = 4(x^2 - y^2) + i8xy$$

Clearly, $w$ can also be regarded as a complex variable with a real part and an imaginary part, such that

$$w = f(z) = f(x + iy) = \phi(x, y) + i\psi(x, y) \tag{5–6a}$$

in which $\phi(x, y)$ and $\psi(x, y)$ are both real functions of $x$ and $y$. In this example, $\phi(x, y) = 4(x^2 - y^2)$ and $\psi(x, y) = 8xy$.

Just as $z = x + iy$ defines a point on the $z$-plane for any given $xy$ pair, so $w = \phi + i\psi$ defines a point on another Argand plane which has $\phi$ as the real axis and $\psi$ as the imaginary axis for a given $\phi\psi$ pair. The $\phi\psi$ plane is called the $w$-plane. For each point representing given values of $x$ and $y$ in the $z$-plane, there will be, on the $w$-plane, a corresponding point whose $\phi$- and $\psi$-values can be determined from the given $xy$ pair and the functional relations $\phi(x, y)$ and $\psi(x, y)$. In the above example, for the point $z = x + iy = 3 + 2i$ in the $z$-plane, the coordinates of the corresponding point for $w = 4z^2$ in the $w$-plane are

$$\phi_{\substack{x=3 \\ y=2}} = 4(x^2 - y^2) = 20$$

$$\psi_{\substack{x=3 \\ y=2}} = 8xy = 48$$

Similarly, for any continuous line in the $z$-plane, there will be a corresponding line, though somewhat changed in form, in the $w$-plane, since a line is merely a continuous series of points. In this manner, we may use the functional relationship $w = f(z) = \phi + i\psi$ to transform any configuration from one plane into another configuration on a second plane. A transformation in which infinitesimal configurations in the two planes are similar is called *conformal transformation*, the details of which will be discussed in Secs. 5–6 through 5–9. At the present, we shall return to the discussion of functions of a complex variable.

Up to this point, we have interpreted the word *function* in its broadest sense. However, in the theory of functions of a complex variable, the word *function* is restricted to the so-called *analytic functions*. A single-valued function $f(z)$ of a complex variable is analytic within a region $R$ if the derivative of $f(z)$ exists uniquely at every point within the region $R$. Analytic functions are also called *regular* or *holomorphic* functions.

The derivative of a complex function $w = f(z)$ is defined as

$$\frac{dw}{dz} = f'(z) = \lim_{\Delta z \to 0} \frac{\Delta w}{\Delta z} \tag{5-7}$$

Since

$$w = \phi + i\psi \qquad z = x + iy$$

and

$$\Delta w = \Delta\phi + i\Delta\psi \qquad \Delta z = \Delta x + i\Delta y$$

Eq. 5–7 can then be written as

$$\frac{dw}{dz} = \lim_{\Delta z \to 0} \frac{\Delta\phi + i\Delta\psi}{\Delta x + i\Delta y} \tag{5-8}$$

Obviously, in the limiting process, there are many ways in which $\Delta z$ can approach zero in the complex plane. However, if $w = f(z)$ is analytic within the region $R$, $dw/dz$ must be single-valued at every point within the region $R$, independent of the way in which $\Delta z$ tends to zero. We shall consider two different paths by which $\Delta z$ may approach zero. For the first path, $\Delta z$ is allowed to approach zero along the $x$-axis; i.e., we first set $\Delta y = 0$ so that $\Delta z = \Delta x$. Equation 5–8 becomes

$$\frac{dw}{dz}\bigg|_{\text{along the } x\text{-axis}} = \lim_{\Delta x \to 0} \frac{\Delta\phi + i\Delta\psi}{\Delta x} = \frac{\partial\phi}{\partial x} + i\frac{\partial\psi}{\partial x} \tag{5-9}$$

For the second path, $\Delta z$ is allowed to approach zero in the $y$-direction by first letting $\Delta x = 0$; thus

$$\frac{dw}{dz}\bigg|_{\text{along the } y\text{-axis}} = \lim_{\Delta y \to 0} \frac{\Delta\phi + i\Delta\psi}{i\Delta y} = -i\frac{\partial\phi}{\partial y} + \frac{\partial\psi}{\partial y} \tag{5-10}$$

The existence of a single-valued $dw/dz$ for an analytic $f(z)$ at an arbitrary point in the region $R$ requires that the above two derivatives be the same. That is,

$$\frac{\partial\phi}{\partial x} + i\frac{\partial\psi}{\partial x} = -i\frac{\partial\phi}{\partial y} + \frac{\partial\psi}{\partial y} \tag{5-11}$$

By the definition of the equality of complex numbers, we must have

$$\frac{\partial \phi}{\partial x} = \frac{\partial \psi}{\partial y} \qquad \frac{\partial \phi}{\partial y} = -\frac{\partial \psi}{\partial x} \tag{5-12}$$

These relations are the *Cauchy-Riemann differential equations.*

Consequently, a necessary condition for the existence of the derivative $dw/dz$, and hence the analyticity of the function $f(z)$, in a region $R$ is that the function satisfies the Cauchy-Riemann equations at every point in this region, provided that the partial derivatives $\partial \phi/\partial x$, $\partial \phi/\partial y$, $\partial \psi/\partial x$, $\partial \psi/\partial y$ are continuous. Indeed this is not only a necessary condition but also a sufficient condition. The proof of sufficiency is given as follows. Using the chain rule of differentiation, we can obtain the total differential $dw$ of

$$w = \phi(x, y) + i\psi(x, y)$$

as

$$dw = \frac{\partial \phi}{\partial x} dx + \frac{\partial \phi}{\partial y} dy + i\frac{\partial \psi}{\partial x} dx + i\frac{\partial \psi}{\partial y} dy$$

From the Cauchy-Riemann equations (Eqs. 5–12), the above expression becomes

$$dw = \frac{\partial \phi}{\partial x} (dx + i\, dy) + i\frac{\partial \psi}{\partial x} (dx + i\, dy)$$

and the derivative

$$\frac{dw}{dz} = \frac{\partial \phi}{\partial x} + i\frac{\partial \psi}{\partial x}$$

is again independent of the path. Therefore, any complex function $w = f(z)$, which is defined throughout a region $R$ and which has a unique derivative at every point in $R$, satisfies the Cauchy-Riemann equations.

It must be noted here that singular points are excluded from the region $R$ within which a function is analytic, for the Cauchy-Riemann equations are not satisfied at such points.

Books on analysis show that derivatives of all orders exist for an analytic function in its region of analyticity. Consequently, we take the partial derivatives of the first of Eqs. 5–12 with respect to $x$ and of the second with respect to $y$ to obtain

$$\frac{\partial^2 \phi}{\partial x^2} = \frac{\partial^2 \psi}{\partial x\, \partial y} \quad \text{and} \quad \frac{\partial^2 \phi}{\partial y^2} = -\frac{\partial^2 \psi}{\partial y\, \partial x}$$

Adding these two equations gives

$$\frac{\partial^2 \phi}{\partial x^2} + \frac{\partial^2 \phi}{\partial y^2} = 0 \tag{5-13}$$

since, by the continuity of the partial derivatives, the mixed derivatives are equal. In a similar manner, we can obtain

$$\frac{\partial^2 \psi}{\partial x^2} + \frac{\partial^2 \psi}{\partial y^2} = 0 \qquad (5\text{-}14)$$

These two equations are the Cartesian forms of Laplace's equations in two dimensions. Functions $\phi(x, y)$ and $\psi(x, y)$ which satisfy Laplace's equations are called *harmonic functions*. Hence the real and imaginary parts of an analytic function are both harmonic functions, and they are called *harmonic conjugates*. The real part of an analytic function is said to be the conjugate of the purely imaginary part, or vice versa.

### 5-5    Representation of Two-dimensional Planar Potential Flows by Functions of a Complex Variable

It was shown in Sec. 4–3 that if $\phi$ and $\psi$ respectively denote the velocity potential and the stream function of a two-dimensional potential flow, they are related to each other in the following manner:

$$u = \frac{\partial \phi}{\partial x} = \frac{\partial \psi}{\partial y}$$

$$v = \frac{\partial \phi}{\partial y} = -\frac{\partial \psi}{\partial x}$$

Clearly these relationships indicate that $\phi$ and $\psi$ of a two-dimensional potential flow satisfy the Cauchy-Riemann equations. Furthermore, it was also shown in Sec. 4–3 that both $\phi$ and $\psi$ satisfy their respective Laplace equations; i.e., $\nabla^2 \phi = 0$ and $\nabla^2 \psi = 0$.

Consequently, if we use $\phi$ and $\psi$ of a two-dimensional potential flow to form a complex variable $w = \phi + i\psi$, $w$ is obviously an analytic function of $z = x + iy$. This proves the complete correspondence between two-dimensional potential flows and analytic functions of a complex variable. Hence the methods of the complex variable form an extremely powerful tool of mathematical analysis in the study of two-dimensional potential flows. Analytic functions of various types have been used to represent two-dimensional potential flows. A number of analytic functions will be presented in Sec. 5–7 representing those two-dimensional potential flows which were already treated in Chapter 4.

The complex variable $w = \phi + i\psi$ is called a *complex potential* when $\phi$ and $\psi$ are respectively the velocity potential and stream function of a two-dimensional potential flow. The derivative $dw/dz$ then takes on a physical meaning; that is, $dw/dz$ is directly related to the velocity components of flow as follows:

$$\frac{dw}{dz} = \frac{\partial \phi}{\partial x} + i\frac{\partial \psi}{\partial x} = u - iv \qquad (5\text{-}15)$$

since $u = \partial \phi / \partial x$ and $v = -\partial \psi / \partial x$ in a two-dimensional potential flow.

The derivative $dw/dz$ is called the *complex velocity*. The real part of $dw/dz$ is the velocity component in the $x$-direction, and the pure imaginary part is the negative of the velocity component in the $y$-direction. Clearly $dw/dz$ is the conjugate of the fluid velocity in the $z$-plane, and it is useful in determining the velocity of flow at any point in the flow field. The magnitude of the velocity $\mathbf{V}$ is given by

$$V = \left| \frac{dw}{dz} \right| = \sqrt{u^2 + v^2}$$

from which $dw/dz$ can also be expressed as

$$\frac{dw}{dz} = Ve^{-i\alpha} \tag{5–16}$$

where $\alpha$ is the angle between the velocity vector and the real axis measured in the counterclockwise direction.

## 5-6 Conformal Transformation and Its Application to Two-dimensional Potential Flow

In the preceding sections, we have discussed that if the two complex variables $z = x + iy$ and $w = \phi + i\psi$ are related by $w = f(z)$, this functional relationship defines a transformation or mapping of points in the $z$-plane into corresponding points in the $w$-plane, or vice versa. The locations of corresponding points in the two planes are determined by the values of $x$ and $y$ and the functional relations $\phi(x, y)$ and $\psi(x, y)$ in the complex function $w = f(z) = \phi(x, y) + i\psi(x, y)$.

If the function $w = f(z)$ is analytic, and if the derivative $dw/dz$ neither equals zero nor approaches infinity in a given region, the transformation is then called a *conformal transformation*. In a conformal transformation, infinitesimal configurations in one plane are transformed onto another plane without change of shape, although both their size and their orientation may be somewhat altered.

The derivative $dw/dz$ is used as a complex operator in the conformal transformation. An infinitesimal line element $\delta z$ in the $z$-plane is transformed into a corresponding line element $\delta w$ in the $w$-plane by the following relationship:

$$\delta w = \frac{dw}{dz} \delta z \quad \text{or} \quad \delta z = \frac{1}{dw/dz} \delta w = \frac{dz}{dw} \delta w \tag{5–17}$$

At a given point, the single-valued $dw/dz$ (which is neither zero nor infinite) may be regarded as a constant complex number; it can be written in the following exponential form:

$$\frac{dw}{dz} = ae^{i\beta}$$

where

$$a = \left| \frac{dw}{dz} \right| \quad \text{and} \quad \beta = \arg \frac{dw}{dz}$$

at this point. Equation 5-17 then becomes

$$\delta w = ae^{i\beta} \, \delta z \tag{5-18}$$

Hence in the neighborhood of this given point, all line elements in the w-plane are obtained from the corresponding line elements in the z-plane by multiplying their lengths by $a$ and turning them through an angle $\beta$. It thus follows that when an infinitesimal area element in the z-plane is transformed onto the w-plane, the new area element must have the same shape, since each line element is multiplied by $a$ and turned through a constant angle $\beta$.

In general, $dw/dz$ is a function of $z$ and its value varies as the value of $z$ varies from point to point. Both $a$ and $\beta$ in Eq. 5-18 take on different numerical values at different positions in the z-plane.

In the conformal representation of two-dimensional potential flows, whatever form the function $w = f(z)$ may take, the w-plane is always considered to have a rectangular grid system parallel to $\phi$- and $\psi$-axes. The $\phi$-lines are parallel to the $\psi$-axis and the $\psi$-lines are parallel to the $\phi$-axis. If we regard $\phi$ as the velocity potential and $\psi$ as the stream function of a two-dimensional potential flow, the pattern of $\phi$- and $\psi$-lines on the w-plane clearly represents a uniform flow in the positive $\phi$-axis. This rectangular grid system may be mapped onto the z-plane by an analytic function $w = f(z)$. The transformed $\phi$-lines and $\psi$-lines remain, respectively, equipotential lines and streamlines in the z-plane. The resulting flow net in the z-plane represents the physical pattern of the two-dimensional potential flow under investigation. The particular form of flow net in the z-plane depends entirely upon the form of $f(z)$, as the flow net in the w-plane is always in the form of a rectangular grid system. For any given analytic function $w = f(z) = \phi(x, y) + i\psi(x, y)$, equating the real part $\phi(x, y)$ to a constant yields the equation of the equipotential lines for the physical flow in the z-plane, and equating the imaginary part $\psi(x, y)$ to a constant yields the equation of the streamlines for the physical flow in the z-plane.

## 5-7  Examples of Simple Transformations

We now present analytic functions representing some of the two-dimensional potential flows which were discussed in Part I of Chapter 4. All examples are treated from the viewpoint of conformal transformations. They are discussed in sufficient detail to provide an understanding of the manipulations required to analyze simple functions. The $w$-plane is not usually shown because the flow net in it always consists of a rectangular grid system parallel to the $\phi$- and $\psi$-axes. Flow nets in the $z$-plane have been constructed in Chapter 4. The reader is urged to refer back to Chapter 4 for more detailed descriptions of these same flow fields.

The number of possible analytic functions for $w = f(z)$ is indeed large. All of the examples to be presented in the following sections are special cases of the following well-known function:

$$w = f(z) = \frac{1}{2\pi}(q + i\Gamma)\ln z + \sum_{-\infty}^{\infty}(a_n + ib_n)z^n \qquad (5\text{--}19)$$

where $q$, $\Gamma$, $a_n$, and $b_n$ are constants. The $\phi$- and $\psi$-functions for Eq. 5–19 can be written, respectively, as

$$\phi = \frac{q}{2\pi}\ln r - \frac{\Gamma}{2\pi}\theta + \sum_{-\infty}^{\infty}r^n(a_n\cos n\theta - b_n\sin n\theta) \qquad (5\text{--}20)$$

$$\psi = \frac{q}{2\pi}\theta + \frac{\Gamma}{2\pi}\ln r + \sum_{-\infty}^{\infty}r^n(a_n\sin n\theta + b_n\cos n\theta) \qquad (5\text{--}21)$$

## 5-8  Uniform Flow

The complex potential for a two-dimensional uniform flow is

$$w = V_0 z \qquad (5\text{--}22)$$

where the constant $V_0$ could be complex, real, or pure imaginary.

Let us consider the constant $V_0$ to be the conjugate of the complex number $a + ib$, i.e., $V_0 = a - ib$, where both $a$ and $b$ are constants; then

$$\frac{dw}{dz} = V_0 = a - ib = Re^{-i\alpha}$$

where

$$R = (a^2 + b^2)^{1/2} \quad \text{and} \quad \alpha = \tan^{-1}\frac{b}{a}$$

Hence

$$\delta z = \frac{dz}{dw}\,\delta w = \frac{1}{R}e^{i\alpha}\,\delta w$$

indicating that elements in the $w$-plane are multiplied by a constant factor $1/R$ and rotated through a constant angle $\alpha$ when transformed into the $z$-plane. Consequently, the flow net in the $z$-plane is that of a uniform flow inclined at an angle $\alpha$ with the positive $x$-axis (Fig. 5–4).

From Eq. 5–15,

$$\frac{dw}{dz} = V_0 = a - ib = u - iv$$

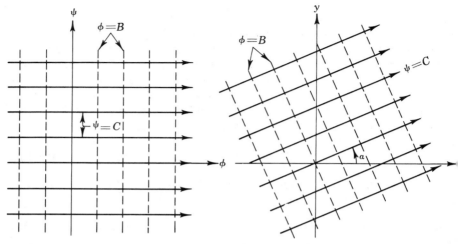

**Fig. 5-4.** The transformation $w = V_0 z$ ($V_0 = a - ib$) which transforms (a) a uniform flow in the $w$-plane into (b) another uniform flow in the $z$-plane.

so that

$$a = u \quad \text{and} \quad b = v$$

Equation 5–22 then becomes

$$w = V_0 z = (u - iv)(x + iy)$$
$$= (ux + vy) + i(uy - vx)$$
$$= \phi + i\psi$$

whence

$$\phi = ux + vy \quad \text{and} \quad \psi = uy - vx$$

which are the same results as those obtained in Sec. 4–5.

When $V_0$ is real, $\alpha = 0$. The flow net in the $z$-plane is that of the $w$-plane with its scale multiplied by $1/R$.

Finally, when $V_0$ is pure imaginary, the flow net in the $w$-plane is rotated through 90 degrees when transformed onto the $z$-plane.

Since $dw/dz = V_0$ (a constant), there are no singular points in the finite plane.

## 5-9   Two-dimensional Source

The complex potential for a two-dimensional source at $z = z_0$ is

$$w = \frac{q}{2\pi} \ln (z - z_0) \tag{5–23}$$

In this function, $z_0$ represents a fixed point with $(x_0, y_0)$ as its coordinates in the $z$-plane, as shown in Fig. 5–5(a). Using the notations in Fig. 5–5(a), we may write

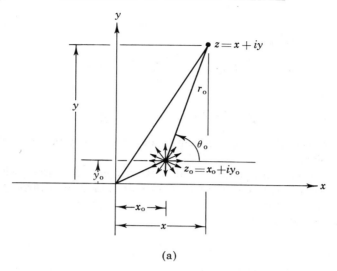

(a)

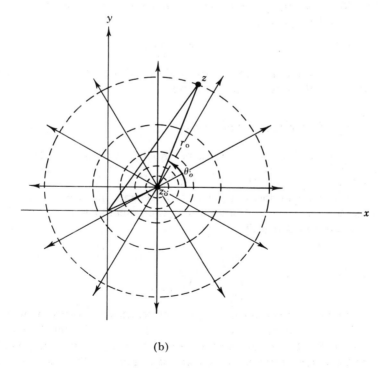

(b)

**Fig. 5-5.** A two-dimensional source at $z = z_0$ in the z-plane.

$$z - z_0 = r_0 e^{i\theta_0}$$

so that Eq. 5–23 becomes

$$w = \frac{q}{2\pi} \ln r_0 e^{i\theta_0} = \frac{q}{2\pi} \ln r_0 + i\frac{q}{2\pi} \theta_0 \qquad (5\text{–}24)$$

Hence

$$\phi = \frac{q}{2\pi} \ln r_0 \quad \text{and} \quad \psi = \frac{q}{2\pi} \theta_0$$

are respectively the velocity potential and stream function for this flow in the $z$-plane.

In the $z$-plane, the equipotential lines are concentric circles with their common center at $z_0$ and the streamlines are radial lines through $z_0$, as shown in Fig. 5-5(b).

Since the derivative

$$\frac{dw}{dz} = \frac{q}{2\pi} \frac{1}{z - z_0} \qquad (5\text{–}25)$$

is not defined at the point $z_0$, this point is a singular point which must be excluded from the region of transformation.

The complex potential for a source at the origin of the coordinate axes in the $z$-plane is

$$w = \frac{q}{2\pi} \ln z \qquad (5\text{–}26)$$

Adding minus signs to the right-hand side of Eqs. 5–23 and 5–26 yields complex potentials for a sink.

## 5-10  Two-dimensional Vortex

Consider the two complex potentials $w$ and $w_1$ such that

$$w_1 = iw = i(\phi + i\psi) = -\psi + i\phi \qquad (5\text{–}27)$$

Clearly the equipotential lines for $w$ become the streamlines for $w_1$, and the streamlines for $w$ become the equipotential lines for $w_1$. Therefore, the complex potential

$$w = -i\frac{\Gamma}{2\pi} \ln (z - z_0) = -i\frac{\Gamma}{2\pi} \ln r_0 e^{i\theta_0}$$
$$= \frac{\Gamma}{2\pi} \theta_0 - i\frac{\Gamma}{2\pi} \ln r_0 \qquad (5\text{–}28)$$

represents a two-dimensional counterclockwise vortex with a strength $\Gamma/2\pi$ and with its center at $z = z_0$. The flow net for this flow is also that of Fig. 5–5(b), except that the radial lines are now the equipotential lines and the concentric circles are the streamlines. The center of the vortex is a singular point, since the complex potential is not defined and is consequently not analytic at this point.

## 5-11   Combined Source-Sink Flow

It has been shown in Chapter 4 that the two parts of complex potentials—velocity potentials and stream functions—of various simple potential flows can each be superimposed to form those of new potential flows. It follows, then, that new complex potentials may be formed by adding simple complex potentials. Consequently, adding complex potentials for a source and a sink of equal strength yields the complex potential for a combined source-sink flow field. Let us consider a source and a sink of equal strength $q/2\pi$ located, for simplicity, at $(-a, 0)$ and $(a, 0)$, respectively, as shown in Fig. 5–6. The complex potential for this combined flow is

$$w = \underbrace{\frac{q}{2\pi} \ln (z + a)}_{w_{\text{source at } z_0 = -a}} - \underbrace{\frac{q}{2\pi} \ln (z - a)}_{w_{\text{sink at } z_0 = a}} = \frac{q}{2\pi} \ln \frac{z + a}{z - a} \qquad (5\text{–}29)$$

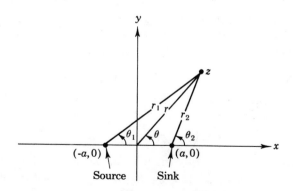

**Fig. 5-6.**  A two-dimensional source-sink flow in the z-plane.

Referring to Fig. 5–6, we may write

$$z + a = r_1 e^{i\theta_1} \quad \text{and} \quad z - a = r_2 e^{i\theta_2}$$

for any point $z$. Equation 5–29 then becomes

$$w = \frac{q}{2\pi} \ln \frac{z + a}{z - a} = \frac{q}{2\pi} \ln \frac{r_1 e^{i\theta_1}}{r_2 e^{i\theta_2}}$$
$$= \frac{q}{2\pi} \ln \frac{r_1}{r_2} + i \frac{q}{2\pi} (\theta_1 - \theta_2) \qquad (5\text{–}30)$$

whence

$$\phi = \frac{q}{2\pi} \ln \frac{r_1}{r_2} \quad \text{and} \quad \psi = \frac{q}{2\pi} (\theta_1 - \theta_2)$$

are respectively identical to Eqs. 4–54 and 4–51. The flow pattern for this combined source-sink flow is shown in Fig. 4–12(b).

Since the complex velocity

$$\frac{dw}{dz} = \frac{-qa}{\pi(z+a)(z-a)} \tag{5-31}$$

is not defined at $(-a, 0)$ and $(a, 0)$, these two points are singular points.

## 5-12  Doublet

The complex potential for a doublet can be derived by applying the limiting process to a source and a sink of equal strength in accordance with the definition of a doublet (see Sec. 4–11). If we take the source-sink combination of Fig. 5–6, the first step is to rearrange its complex potential (Eq. 5–29) in the following manner:

$$w = \frac{q}{2\pi} \ln(z+a) - \frac{q}{2\pi} \ln(z-a)$$

$$= \frac{q}{2\pi} \ln \frac{z+a}{z-a} = \frac{q}{2\pi} \ln \frac{1+a/z}{1-a/z} \tag{5-32}$$

We then make use of the following infinite series expansion:

$$\ln \frac{1+x}{1-x} = 2\left(x + \frac{x^3}{3} + \frac{x^5}{5} + \cdots\right) \qquad -1 < x < 1$$

to rewrite Eq. 5–32 as

$$w = \frac{2aq}{2\pi z}\left(1 + \frac{1}{3}\frac{a^2}{z^2} + \frac{1}{5}\frac{a^4}{z^4} + \cdots\right) \tag{5-33}$$

Finally, a doublet is formed by the limit of the source-sink flow that, as the distance $a$ in Fig. 5–6 approaches zero, $q$ approaches infinity such that the product $2aq$ approaches a constant value $m$. Equation 5–33 is in a form suitable for taking such a limit. Thus,

$$w = \lim_{\substack{a \to 0 \\ 2aq \to m}} \frac{2aq}{2\pi z}\left(1 + \frac{1}{3}\frac{a^2}{z^2} + \frac{1}{5}\frac{a^4}{z^4} + \cdots\right) = \frac{m}{2\pi z} \tag{5-34}$$

is the complex potential for a doublet at the origin of the $z$-plane. The real and imaginary parts of Eq. 5–34 can be readily formed by substituting $x + iy$ for $z$. Hence

$$w = \frac{m}{2\pi z} = \frac{m}{2\pi(x+iy)} = \frac{m}{2\pi}\frac{x-iy}{x^2+y^2}$$

giving

$$\phi = \frac{m}{2\pi}\frac{x}{x^2+y^2} \quad \text{and} \quad \psi = -\frac{m}{2\pi}\frac{y}{x^2+y^2}$$

These two expressions are respectively identical to Eqs. 4–62 and 4–57. The flow pattern for this doublet is shown in Fig. 4–13.

It is worthwhile to note that by comparing Eqs. 5–34 and 5–26, the complex potential for a doublet is the derivative of the complex potential for a source with respect to $z$ with the constant $q$ for a source changed to $m$ for a doublet.

## 5-13   Uniform Flow Past a Circular Cylinder Without Circulation

As was shown in Sec. 4–12, the superposition of a uniform flow and a two-dimensional doublet flow produces a uniform flow past a circular cylinder without circulation. When the uniform flow is in the positive $x$-direction and the doublet is at the origin of the $z$-plane, the complex potential is

$$w = \underset{\substack{w_{\text{uniform}} \\ \text{flow}}}{V_0 z} + \underset{\substack{w_{\text{doublet}} \\ \text{at } z_0 = 0}}{\frac{m}{2\pi z}} = V_0 \left( z + \frac{m}{2\pi V_0 z} \right) \tag{5–35}$$

By letting $\sqrt{m/2\pi V_0}$ equal a constant complex number $r_0$ which is the radius of the circular cylinder, we can write the above equation as

$$w = V_0 \left( z + \frac{r_0^2}{z} \right) = V_0 \left( r e^{i\theta} + \frac{r_0^2}{r} e^{-i\theta} \right) \tag{5–36}$$

We shall now employ DeMoivre's theorem, i.e., $e^{i\theta} = \cos\theta + i\sin\theta$, to rewrite Eq. 5–36 in the following polar form:

$$w = V_0 \left( r + \frac{r_0^2}{r} \right) \cos\theta + iV_0 \left( r - \frac{r_0^2}{r} \right) \sin\theta \tag{5–37}$$

Hence

$$\phi = V_0 \left( r + \frac{r_0^2}{r} \right) \cos\theta \quad \text{and} \quad \psi = V_0 \left( r - \frac{r_0^2}{r} \right) \sin\theta$$

give the same results as those derived in Sec. 4–12, and the same flow pattern as shown in Fig. 4–14(b).

On the surface of the cylinder, $r = r_0$ and Eq. 5–36 becomes

$$w = V_0 \left( r_0 e^{i\theta} + r_0 e^{-i\theta} \right) = 2 V_0 r_0 \cos\theta$$

indicating that the imaginary part of $w$ is zero; that is, $\psi = 0$. Therefore, the trace of the circular cylinder on the $z$-plane forms a part of the streamline with $\psi = 0$.

The complex velocity in this flow is

$$\frac{dw}{dz} = V_0 \left( 1 - \frac{r_0^2}{z^2} \right) \tag{5–38}$$

When $z$ is very large, the complex velocity approaches $V_0$; therefore, $V_0$ is the undisturbed velocity at a great distance from the cylinder. Equation 5–38 also indicates that the velocity is zero at $z = \pm r_0$ (i.e., $x = \pm r_0$, $y = 0$). These two points are stagnation points. The maximum velocity has a value of $2V_0$ and occurs at $z = \pm ir_0$ (i.e., $x = 0$, $y = \pm r_0$).

## 5-14   Uniform Flow Past a Circular Cylinder With Circulation

Superimposing a vortex onto the flow field of a uniform flow past a circular cylinder produces a circulation around the cylinder. Thus, the complex potential

$$w = V_0 \left( z + \frac{r_0^2}{z} \right) + i \frac{\Gamma}{2\pi} \ln z \qquad (5\text{–}39)$$

represents the flow field of a uniform flow past a circular cylinder of radius $r_0$ with a clockwise circulation $\Gamma$ around the cylinder. Since the streamlines in the vortex flow are concentric circles about the origin of the $z$-plane, adding the complex potential for a vortex to the uniform flow past a cylinder does not affect the satisfaction of boundary conditions on the surface of the cylinder. Moreover, the velocity of the vortex becomes increasingly small for large $z$; adding a vortex will not affect the uniform flow at infinity.

The two parts of the complex potential in Eq. 5–39 are:

$$\phi = V_0 \left( r + \frac{r_0^2}{r} \right) \cos \theta - \frac{\Gamma}{2\pi} \theta$$

$$\psi = V_0 \left( r - \frac{r_0^2}{r} \right) \sin \theta + \frac{\Gamma}{2\pi} \ln r$$

which agree with the expressions derived in Sec. 4–13.

## 5-15   Successive Transformations

There are many physical flow fields which cannot be obtained directly by means of a simple transformation from the $w$-plane to the $z$-plane, as was outlined in the preceding sections. The technique of *successive transformations* is required to provide solutions to many problems of two-dimensional planar potential flow. The $w$-plane uniform flow is first transformed into flows in intermediate planes and then into the desired flow field in the $z$-plane. The letter $z$ is reserved for the actual physical plane. We shall use the symbol $z_n$ to denote intermediate planes, where the subscript $n$ equals $1, 2, 3, \ldots$ and represents the number of intermediate planes required in the successive transformations for a particular problem.

The pattern of uniform flow past a circular cylinder, either with or without circulation, which was obtained by Eq. 5–35 or 5–39, can be further transformed into other patterns of flow, such as flow past plates, ellipses, struts, circular arcs, and airfoils. As will be shown later, in each case the trace of the physical object in the $z$-plane is obtained by the transformation of a circle in an intermediate plane by means of the *Joukowski transformation formula:*

$$z = z_1 + \frac{a^2}{z_1} \tag{5–40}$$

in which $a$ is real and positive.

The Joukowski transformation (Eq. 5–40) is obviously similar to the transformation $w = V_0(z_1 + r_0^2/z_1)$ in which the $z_1$-plane uniform flow past a circular cylinder of radius $r_0$ is transformed into the $w$-plane uniform flow. Therefore, Eq. 5–40 transforms the $z_1$-plane uniform flow past a circular cylinder into the $z$-plane uniform flow past a cylinder of some other cross sectional shape which is obtained by the transformation of a circle in the $z_1$-plane. The Joukowski transformation does not affect the following two boundary conditions: (1) the flow in the $z$-plane still has the uniform velocity at infinity, and (2) the trace of the physical object in the $z$-plane remains a streamline.

In mapping the flow field from the $z_1$-plane onto the $z$-plane, it is convenient to consider the Joukowski transformation as two separate transformations:

$$z_1' = \frac{a^2}{z_1} \quad \text{and} \quad z = z_1 + z_1'$$

The first transformation $z_1' = a^2/z_1$ can be carried out on the $z$-plane. With $z_1$ and $z_1'$ known, the second transformation $z = z_1 + z_1'$ simply states that any complex number $z$ in the $z$-plane is the vector sum of $z_1$ and $z_1'$. The graphical construction is shown in Fig. 5–7. The complex representation of any point $P_1$ outside the circle of radius $a$ in the $z_1$-plane is $\overline{OP_1} = r_1 e^{i\theta_1} = z_1$. Then

$$z_1' = \frac{a^2}{z_1} = \frac{a^2}{r_1 e^{i\theta_1}} = \frac{a^2}{r_1} e^{-i\theta_1} = \overline{OP_1'}$$

is a complex number with modulus $a^2/r_1$ and argument $-\theta_1$. The complex number $\overline{OP_1'}$ is the image of another complex number $\overline{OQ}$ in the real axis, since $|\overline{OP_1'}| = |\overline{OQ}|$ and $\angle QOx = \angle P_1'Ox$. The point $Q$ is on the line $\overline{OP_1}$, such that $|\overline{OQ}| = a^2/|\overline{OP_1}|$, and the complex number $\overline{OQ}$ is defined as the inverse of the complex number $\overline{OP_1}$. The second transformation $z = z_1 + z_1'$ is the vector addition of $\overline{OP_1}$ and $\overline{OP_1'}$, giving $\overline{OP}$ in the $z$-plane. Thus, the point $P_1$ in the $z_1$-plane is transformed into point $P$ in the $z$-plane by means of the Joukowski transformation

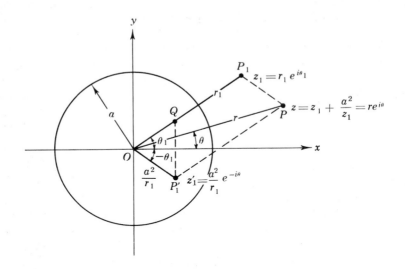

**Fig. 5-7.** Graphical construction of Joukowski transformation.

formula. In this manner, every point in the $z_1$-plane may be plotted onto the $z$-plane.

We shall now consider the transformation of circles in the $z_1$-plane into several shapes of physical significance in the $z$-plane by means of the Joukowski transformation. The $z_1$-plane is first obtained from the $w$-plane by the transformation formula $w = V_0(z_1 + r_0^2/z_1)$. The flow field in the $w$-plane is a uniform flow and the flow field in the $z_1$-plane is a uniform flow past a circular cylinder of radius $r_0$, as has been shown in Sec. 5–13; the center of the circle is at the origin of the $z_1$-plane.

## 5-16   Uniform Flow Past an Ellipse

The Joukowski transformation

$$z = z_1 + \frac{r_0^2}{z_1} \tag{5–41}$$

may be written as

$$x + iy = x_1 + iy_1 + \frac{r_0^2}{x_1 + iy_1} = x_1 + iy_1 + \frac{r_0^2(x_1 - iy_1)}{x_1^2 + y_1^2} \tag{5–42}$$

whence

$$x = x_1\left(1 + \frac{r_0^2}{x_1^2 + y_1^2}\right) \quad \text{and} \quad y = y_1\left(1 - \frac{r_0^2}{x_1^2 + y_1^2}\right)$$

Therefore, any concentric circle

$$x_1^2 + y_1^2 = a^2 \qquad a > r_0$$

in the $z_1$-plane is transformed into a confocal ellipse

$$\frac{x^2}{[1 + (r_0^2/a^2)]^2} + \frac{y^2}{[1 - (r_0^2/a^2)]^2} = a^2 \qquad (5\text{–}43)$$

with its foci located at $(-2r_0, 0)$ and $(2r_0, 0)$ on the real axis of the $z$-plane. The semi-major and semi-minor axes of the ellipse in the $z$-plane are respectively $(a^2 + r_0^2)/a$ and $(a^2 - r_0^2)/a$. Consequently, the size of the ellipse increases as the radius $a$ increases.

The graphical construction of the mapping of the physical object is shown in Fig. 5–8. Point $P_1$ is on the circumference of the $a$-circle (i.e.,

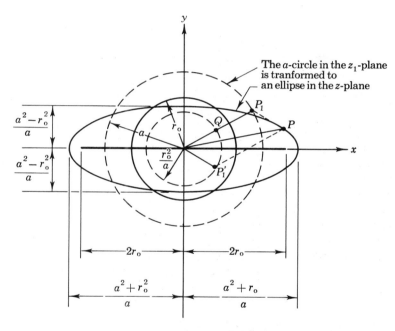

**Fig. 5-8.** Graphical construction of an ellipse by conformal mapping.

the circle with radius $a$) and point $P_1'$ describes a circle with a radius of $r_0^2/a$. Figure 5–9 shows the successive transformations from the $w$-plane to the intermediate $z_1$-plane and then to the physical $z$-plane. It is evident that all streamlines around the $a$-circle in the $z_1$-plane will undergo a corresponding transformation so that the final flow pattern in the $z$-plane will represent potential flow around an ellipse, as shown in Fig. 5–9(c).

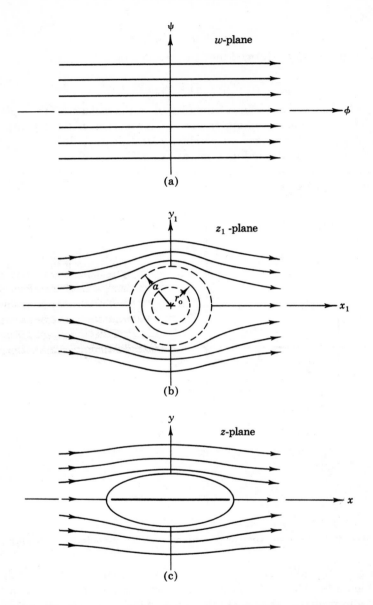

**Fig. 5-9.**  Successive transformations from (a) uniform flow in the w-plane
to (b) uniform flow past a circular cylinder in the $z_1$-plane,
and then to (c) uniform flow past an elliptical cylinder in the
z-plane.

## 5-17   Uniform Flow Past a Flat Plate

As $a$ approaches $r_0$, the ellipse degenerates to a line segment on the real axis of the $z$-plane extending from $(-2r_0, 0)$ to $(2r_0, 0)$. That is, the Joukowski transformation $z = z_1 + r_0^2/z_1$ transforms the circle of radius $r_0$ in the $z_1$-plane into a flat plate of length $4r_0$ and of negligible thickness in the $z$-plane.

The graphical construction of the mapping is shown in Fig. 5–10. In this case both points $P_1$ and $P_1'$ are on the circumference of the $r_0$-circle.

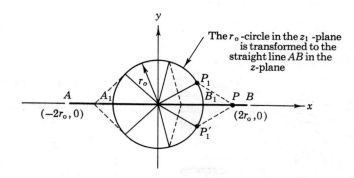

**Fig. 5-10.**   Graphical constructions of a flat plate by conformal mapping.

The complex velocity

$$\frac{dz}{dz_1} = 1 - \frac{r_0^2}{z_1^2} \tag{5-44}$$

is zero at $z_1 = \pm r_0$ on the $z_1$-plane and at $z = \pm 2r_0$ on the $z$-plane. Therefore, the two extremities $(-2r_0, 0)$ and $(2r_0, 0)$ of the flat plate in the $z$-plane are singular points.

## 5-18   Uniform Flow Past a Circular Arc

Again we start from the first intermediate plane, i.e., the $z_1$-plane [Fig. 5–11(b)], in which the flow pattern is the uniform flow past a circular cylinder of radius $r_0$. The transformation

$$z_2 = z_1 + me^{i\pi/2} = z_1 + im \tag{5-45}$$

moves the center of the $r_0$-circle from the origin of the $z_1$-plane in the direction of the positive imaginary axis to point $C_2(O, m)$ in the $z_2$-plane [Fig. 5–11(c)]. Note that $m = r_0 \sin \beta$. The next transformation

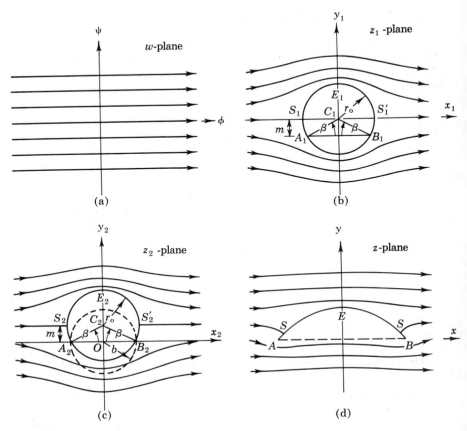

**Fig. 5-11.** Successive transformations for a uniform flow past a circular arc.

$$z = z_2 + \frac{b^2}{z_2} \qquad (5\text{-}46)$$

with $b = |\overline{OA_2}| = r_0 \cos \beta$ [Fig. 5–11(c)] transforms the $r_0$-circle in the $z_2$-plane into a circular arc $\overset{\frown}{AEB}$ in the $z$-plane [Fig. 5–11(d)]. Equation 5–46 also transforms the dotted $b$-circle in the $z_2$-plane into the chord $\overline{AB}$ of the circular arc in the $z$-plane.

Figure 5–12 shows the geometrical construction of mapping the $r_0$-circle in the $z_2$-plane into the circular arc in the $z$-plane. In the $r_0$-circle, $|\overline{OP_2}||\overline{OD_2}| = |\overline{OA_2}||\overline{OB_2}|$ where $|\overline{OP_2}| = r_2$ and $|\overline{OA_2}| = |\overline{OB_2}| = b$, so that $|\overline{OD_2}| = b^2/r_2$. By symmetry $|\overline{OP_2'}| = |\overline{OD_2}| = b^2/r_2$, showing that the image $P_2'$ of the inverse of the point $P_2$ and the point $P_2$ itself are both

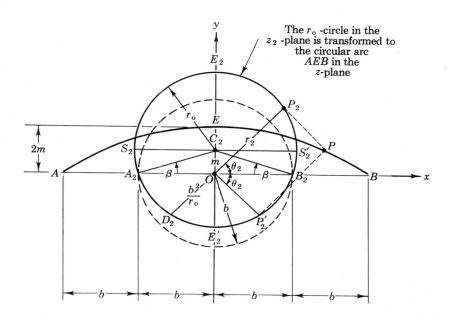

**Fig. 5-12.**   Graphical construction of a circular arc by conformal mapping.

on the circumference of the $r_0$-circle. Clearly $P_2$ can also be regarded as the image of the inverse of point $P_2'$. Thus, as $P_2$ moves in the $z_2$-plane in a counterclockwise direction around the $r_0$-circle starting at $B_2$, $P_2'$ moves in a clockwise direction around the same circle also starting at $B_2$, and the corresponding point $P$ in the $z$-plane describes the circular arc $\overset{\frown}{BEA}$. As $P_2$ passes $A_2$ in the $z_2$-plane and moves along the lower part of the $r_0$-circle to complete the circle, $P_2'$ also passes $A_2$ and moves along the upper part of the $r_0$-circle, and $P$ moves back along the same arc $\overset{\frown}{AEB}$ in the $z$-plane. From the mapping it is easy to find the maximum height $\overline{OE}$ of the transformed arc $\overset{\frown}{AEB}$ as

$$\overline{OE} = \overline{OE_2} - \overline{OE_2'} = (r_0 + m) - (r_0 - m) = 2m$$

The ratio of the maximum height to the chord of the arc is defined as the camber of the arc. The transformed arc in the $z$-plane is seen to have a camber of $2m/4b = \frac{1}{2}\tan\beta$.

## 5-19   Uniform Flow Past a Streamlined Strut

If the center of the $r_0$-circle in Fig. 5–13(b) is moved from the origin of the $z_1$-plane in the direction of the negative real axis to point $C_2(-m, 0)$

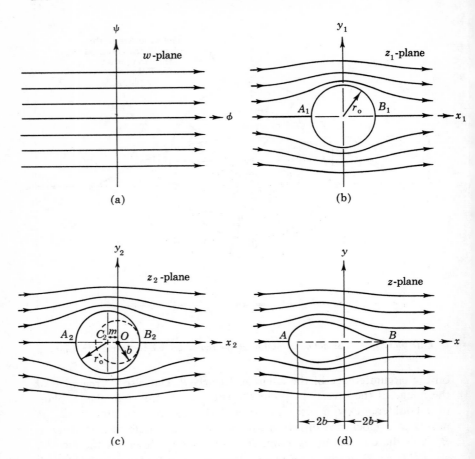

**Fig. 5-13.** Successive transformations for a uniform flow past a stream-lined strut.

in the $z_2$-plane [Fig. 5–13(c)] by the transformation

$$z_2 = z_1 - m \qquad (5\text{-}47)$$

the next transformation

$$z = z_2 + \frac{b^2}{z_2} \qquad (5\text{-}48)$$

with $b = |\overline{OB_2}| = r_0 - m$ [Fig. 5–13(c)] tranforms the $r_0$-circle in the $z_2$-plane into a streamlined strut in the $z$-plane [Fig. 5–13(d)]. The contour of the strut can be developed by the normal mapping procedure, as shown in Fig. 5–14. The image $P'_2$ of the inverse of $P_2$ describes a circle with

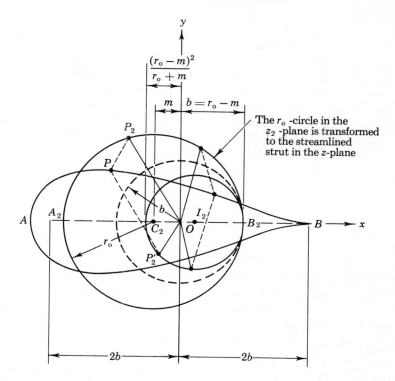

The $r_0$-circle in the $z_2$-plane is transformed to the streamlined strut in the $z$-plane

**Fig. 5-14.** Graphical construction of a streamlined strut by conformal mapping.

its center at $I_2$ as $P_2$ moves around the $r_0$-circle. The thickness of the strut increases as $m$ increases.

One of the singular points is located at $z = -2b$ and is inside the contour of the transformed strut. The other singular point is at $z = +2b$ where the $r_0$-circle touches the dotted $b$-circle at $B_2$ in the $z_2$-plane and transforms into a cusp of zero angle.

## 5-20   Uniform Flow Past a Cambered Airfoil

To obtain the contour of a cambered airfoil, it is first necessary to use the transformation

$$z_2 = z_1 + me^{i(\pi-\delta)} \qquad (5\text{–}49)$$

to move the center of the $r_0$-circle from the origin of the $z_1$-plane [Fig. 5–15(b)] to point $C_2$ in the $z_2$-plane [Fig. 5–15(c)]. The next transformation

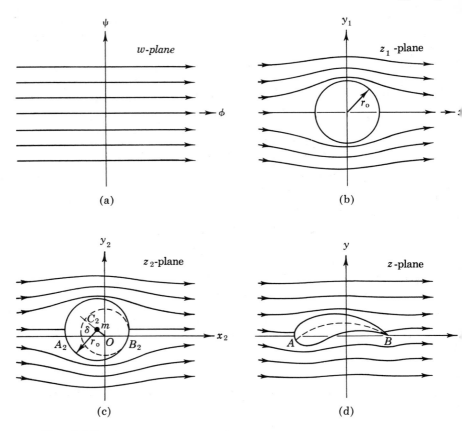

**Fig. 5-15.** Successive transformations for a uniform flow past a cambered airfoil.

$$z = z_2 + \frac{b^2}{z_2} \tag{5-50}$$

with $b = |\overline{OB_2}|$ [Fig. 5–15(c)] transforms the $r_0$-circle in the $z_2$-plane into a cambered airfoil in the $z$-plane [Fig. 5–15(d)]. The transformed airfoil is called the *Joukowski airfoil*.

The graphical mapping of the airfoil contour is shown in Fig. 5–16. As point $P_2$ moves around the $r_0$-circle, the image $P_2'$ of the inverse of the point $P_2$ describes a circle[2] with its center at $I_2$ and radius $\overline{I_2 B_2}$. The

---

[2]For the proof that the locus of $P_2'$ is a circle, see Victor L. Streeter, *Fluid Dynamics* (New York: McGraw-Hill Book Company, 1948) pp. 150–153.

center $I_2$ is located on the line $\overline{C_2 B_2}$ such that $\angle\ I_2 O B_2 = \angle\ C_2 O A_2 = \delta$. Note also that the line $\overline{C_2 B_2}$ intersects the imaginary axis at $F_2$. With these two circles known, points on the contour of the Joukowski airfoil can be easily constructed by drawing pairs of straight lines through $O$ to make equal angles $\theta_2$ with the real axis to intersect the two circles at $P_2$ and $P_2'$, which are then added vectorially to yield the point $P$ on the contour of the airfoil, as shown in Fig. 5–16.

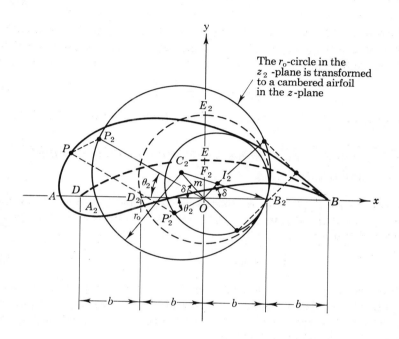

**Fig. 5-16.**   Graphical construction of a cambered airfoil by conformal mapping.

The camber of the Joukowski airfoil is indicated by the dotted circular arc $\overset{\frown}{DEB}$ which is transformed from the dotted circle with center at $F_2$ and radius $\overline{F_2 B_2}$ in the $z_2$-plane by Eq. 5–50. The thickness and shape of the transformed airfoil may be varied by varying the position of the point $C_2$ in the $z_2$-plane. The thickness of the airfoil increases with the increase in the distance $\overline{C_2 F_2}$, and the camber increases with the increase in $\overline{OF_2}$.

Just as in the case of a streamlined strut, the singular point $z = -2b$

is within the contour and does not need further consideration. The trailing edge $B$ (where $z = + 2b$) is a singular point; here a cusp of zero angle is formed. This condition creates a practical problem, for it is physically impossible to construct an airfoil with a cusp of zero angle at the trailing edge. Hence a transformation function which will produce a finite angle at the trailing edge of a transformed airfoil is of practical importance. The following transformation

$$\frac{z - nb}{z + nb} = \left(\frac{z_2 - b}{z_2 + b}\right)^n \qquad (5\text{--}51)$$

which has been proposed by Kármán and Trefftz,[3] will yield a modified airfoil with a finite angle $\tau$ at the trailing edge when $n$ is slightly less than 2. The angle $\tau$ equals $(2 - n)\pi$. Note that when $n = 2$, Eq. 5–51 becomes

$$\frac{z - 2b}{z + 2b} = \left(\frac{z_2 - b}{z_2 + b}\right)^2 \qquad (5\text{--}52)$$

which reduces to the ordinary Joukowski transformation of Eq. 5–50.

## 5-21  Uniform Flow Past an Airfoil With an Angle of Attack and a Circulation

Figure 5–17 summarizes the successive transformations from the uniform flow in the $w$-plane to the flow past an airfoil with an angle of attack $\alpha$ and a circulation $\Gamma$ around it. The first transformation is

$$w = V_0\left(z_1 + \frac{r_0^2}{z_1}\right) + i\frac{\Gamma}{2\pi}\ln z_1 \qquad (5\text{--}53)$$

which transforms the $w$-plane uniform flow [Fig. 5–17(a)] into a flow past a circular cylinder of radius $r_0$ with a clockwise circulation $\Gamma$ around it, the center of the cylinder being at the origin of the $z_1$-plane [Fig. 5–17(b)]. The second transformation

$$z_2 = z_1 e^{i\alpha} \qquad (5\text{--}54)$$

rotates the pattern of flow in the $z_1$-plane through an angle $\alpha$ with the positive real axis of the $z_2$-plane [Fig. 5–17(c)], where $\alpha$ is the angle of attack. The third transformation

$$z_3 = z_2 + me^{i(\pi - \delta)} \qquad (5\text{--}55)$$

moves the center of the $r_0$-circle from the origin of the $z_2$-plane to point $C_3$ in the $z_3$-plane [Fig. 5–17(d)]. The final transformation

---

[3]For the proof that the Kármán-Trefftz transformation will yield an airfoil with a finite angle $\tau$ at the trailing edge, see Manfred Rauscher, *Introduction to Aeronautical Dynamics* (New York: John Wiley & Sons, Inc., 1953) pp. 304–319.

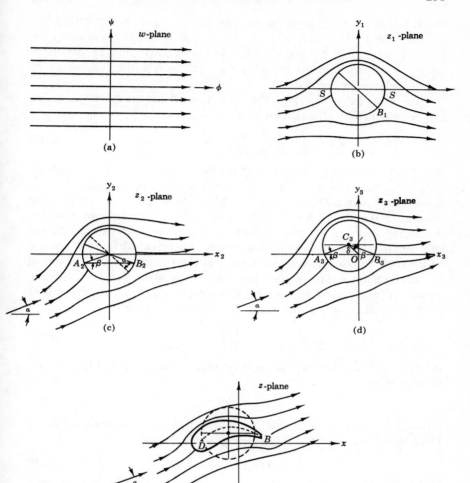

**Fig. 5-17.** Successive transformations for a uniform flow past an airfoil with an angle of attack and a circulation.

$$z = z_3 + \frac{b^2}{z_3} \qquad (5\text{-}56)$$

where $b = |\overline{OB_3}|$, as shown in Fig. 5–17(d), transforms the flow pattern past the $r_0$-circle in the $z_3$-plane into a flow past an airfoil in the physical $z$-plane [Fig. 5–17(e)]. In the $z$-plane, the uniform stream approaches the airfoil at an angle of attack $\alpha$, and the flow around the airfoil has a circulation $\Gamma$. The value of $\Gamma$ can be determined by the *Joukowski hypothesis*, which will be discussed in the next paragraph. The details of graphical construction for mapping the $r_0$-circle into the contour of an airfoil is shown in Fig. 5–16.

The complex velocity for the flow around the transformed airfoil can be obtained by chain differentiation as

$$\frac{dw}{dz} = \frac{dw}{dz_1}\frac{dz_1}{dz_2}\frac{dz_2}{dz_3}\frac{dz_3}{dz} = \frac{dw}{dz_1}\frac{e^{-i\alpha}}{1 - (b^2/z_3^2)} \qquad (5\text{–}57)$$

which indicates that $dw/dz$ approaches infinity at $z_3 = \pm b$ in the $z$-plane, unless $dw/dz_1$ equals zero at these two points. These two points are transformed into points $D$ and $B$ in the $z$-plane. Since point $D$ is within the contour of the airfoil, it is therefore necessary to consider only point $B$. According to the Joukowski hypothesis which has been verified by experimental results, the circulation around an actual airfoil will always adjust itself so that the velocity is finite at the trailing edge of the airfoil by turning point $B$ into a stagnation point, as shown in Fig. 5–18. That is, $dw/dz = 0$ at point $B$ in the $z$-plane or, from Eq. 5–57, $dw/dz_1 = 0$ at point $B_1$ in the $z_1$-plane. By using Eq. 5–53, we obtain

$$\frac{dw}{dz_1} = V_0\left(1 - \frac{r_0^2}{z_1^2}\right) + i\frac{\Gamma}{2\pi z_1} = 0 \qquad (5\text{–}58)$$

in which $z_1$ refers to point $B_1$ in the $z_1$-plane. Referring to Fig. 5–17(b), we may write $z_1$ as

$$z_1 = r_0 e^{-i(\alpha+\beta)}$$

Substitution of this value into Eq. 5–58 yields the following value for $\Gamma$ which makes point $B$ a stagnation point in the $z$-plane:

$$\Gamma = 4\pi r_0 V_0 \sin(\alpha + \beta) \qquad (5\text{–}59)$$

Hence the Joukowski hypothesis not only removes the singular point at the trailing edge where theoretically the velocity is infinite, but it also provides a means of calculating the magnitude of the circulation around an airfoil.

In the foregoing mathematical development the existence of a circulation $\Gamma$ around the transformed airfoil in the physical $z$-plane can be ascribed to the inclusion of the complex potential of a clockwise vortex in Eq. 5–53. However, the development of circulation around an actual airfoil is a complicated physical process which needs explanation. The establishment of a circulation around an actual airfoil is associated with the formation of vortices of definite strength at the trailing edge of an airfoil. The strength of the circulation around the airfoil is, in fact, equal

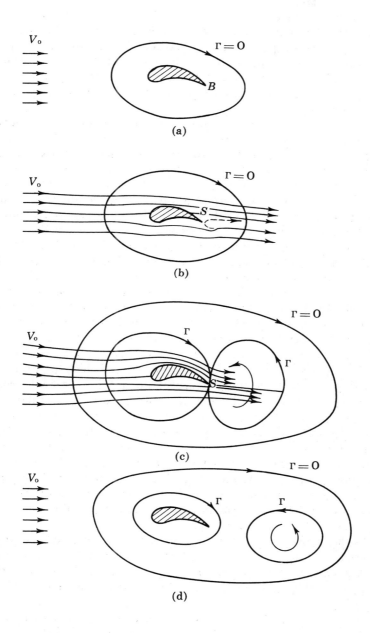

**Fig. 5-18.** Development of a circulation around an airfoil.

and opposite to that of the vortex at the trailing edge. This is in accordance with Thomson's theorem of invariance of circulation (Sec. 3–3). Thomson's theorem states that in a potential flow the circulation around any path which is composed of the same fluid particles remains invariant with time. The process of vortex formation at the trailing edge and the development of a circulation around an airfoil will be described in the following paragraphs.[4]

Figure 5–18 illustrates the successive stages in the development of a circulation around an airfoil. Before the motion starts the circulation is obviously zero [Fig. 5–18(a)]. As the uniform motion begins, the flow pattern is at first seen to be essentially irrotational, as shown in Fig. 5–18(b), and there can be no circulation around the airfoil; the rear stagnation point is on the upper surface upstream from the tip of the trailing edge. This means that flow from the undersurface has to flow around the sharp trailing edge, which is essentially an arc of zero radius, to meet that from the upper surface at the stagnation point. Since the velocity around an arc of zero radius would mean an infinite acceleration, it is physically impossible to maintain the flow from the lower surface around the trailing edge. Hence flow simply slides tangentially past the trailing edge on the underside. At the same time, the flow on the upper surface pushes the stagnation point toward the tip of the trailing edge. The two layers of flow that pass over the upper surface and undersurface of the airfoil meet at the trailing edge with slightly different velocities. The result is the formation of a surface of discontinuity across which there is a sharp velocity gradient at the trailing edge of the airfoil. The fluid viscosity immediately causes the formation of a counterclockwise starting vortex which is shed from the trailing edge of the airfoil, as shown in Fig. 5–18(c). A starting vortex has a definite strength of circulation associated with it. In order to counterbalance the counterclockwise circulation of the starting vortex at the trailing edge, a clockwise circulation of the same strength is formed around the airfoil. Thus the sum of circulation in the flow field is zero, in accordance with Thomson's theorem of invariance of circulation. The clockwise circulation around the airfoil is usually referred to as the *boundary circulation.*

As the strength of the starting vortex at the trailing edge increases, the strength of the boundary circulation around the airfoil also increases; the flow pattern also changes until a steady state is finally established. With the establishment of a steady flow pattern, the strength of both

---

[4]The reader is also referred to an excellent visual description of the formation of vortices at the trailing edge of an airfoil in Figs. 42 through 55 in L. Prandtl and O. G. Tietjens, *Applied Hydro- and Aeromechanics* (New York: Dover Publications, Inc., 1957) pp. 296–301.

th: starting vortex and the boundary circulation attains a constant limit-ing value. The starting vortex breaks away from the airfoil and moves downstream with the general flow, leaving behind only the boundary circulation around the airfoil. This condition is shown in Fig. 5–18(d).

Whenever the boundary circulation around the airfoil changes, the strength of the trailing vortices must necessarily change. For example, when an airplane encounters an upward gust, its wing will shed addi-tional counterclockwise vortices because the upward lift of an airplane increases the clockwise boundary circulation. As soon as the gust subsides, the wing will subsequently shed clockwise vortices in order to reduce its boundary circulation to its normal value. A repeated shedding of vortices alternating in opposite senses will set a wing in flutter.

Figure 5–19 illustrates the fluid motion in the vicinity of an airfoil as the fluid stream approaching the airfoil stops. A clockwise terminating

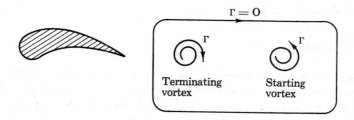

**Fig. 5-19.** Shedding of terminating vortex as the stream approaching an airfoil stops.

vortex with a strength equal to that of the starting vortex is shed from the trailing edge. Hence the total circulation is still zero for a path en-circling both the starting and terminating vortices.

## 5-22   Lift on an Airfoil

When an airfoil is placed in a uniform stream at an angle of attack, the moving fluid exerts a force on the airfoil. This force may be resolved into components parallel and perpendicular to the direction of the motion of the approaching stream, as shown in Fig. 5–20. The component which is parallel to the fluid motion is called the *drag* $F_D$ and the perpendicular component is the *lift* $F_L$. As will be discussed in Chapter 8, the drag is caused by fluid viscosity and fluid compressibility. In an irrotational flow the drag force is obviously equal to zero. However, the circulation around an airfoil produces a lift force on it. The lift force produced by

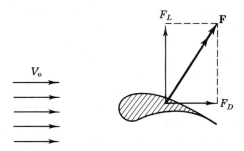

**Fig. 5-20.** Forces on an airfoil.

a circulation around a circular cylinder in a two-dimensional irrotational flow was discussed briefly in Sec. 4–13. To determine the lift force on an airfoil, it is necessary to use the Blasius theorem which will be presented in the following section.

### 5-23  Blasius Theorem

The Blasius theorem provides a method for determining the force and the moment[5] exerted by the fluid on a cylinder of any cross-sectional shape in a steady two-dimensional potential flow when the complex function $w = f(z)$ for the flow field is known. Figure 5–21 shows the trace

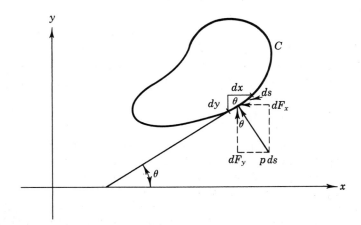

**Fig. 5-21.** The cross section of a cylinder.

---

[5]The moment equation of the Blasius theorem will not be derived here. See Victor L. Streeter, ed., *Handbook of Fluid Dynamics* (New York: McGraw-Hill Book Company, 1961) pp. 4–62, 4–63.

$C$ of a cylinder in a two-dimensional potential flow. The pressure force acting on the surface element $ds$ (which has a unit thickness perpendicular to the $xy$ plane) is $p\,ds$ and is perpendicular to $ds$. The two components of the pressure force $dF_x$ and $dF_y$ in the positive $x$- and $y$-directions are

$$dF_x = -p\,ds\,\sin\theta = -p\,dy$$
$$dF_y = +p\,ds\,\cos\theta = +p\,dx$$

where $\theta$ is the angle that $ds$ makes with the positive $x$-axis. These two differential force components may be written in complex form as

$$dF_x - i\,dF_y = -p(dy + i\,dx) = -ip\,d\bar{z} \tag{5-60}$$

in which $d\bar{z}(= dx - i\,dy)$ is the conjugate of $dz$.

In a steady two-dimensional potential flow, the pressure $p$ on the surface element $ds$ can be determined from the Bernoulli theorem as

$$p = B - \tfrac{1}{2}\rho V^2 \tag{5-61}$$

where the Bernoulli constant $B$ may be evaluated from the known conditions at a reference point in the flow field and $V$ is the magnitude of velocity at $ds$. Since the contribution from the constant part $B$ of the pressure to forces is zero and

$$\frac{dw}{dz}\frac{d\bar{w}}{d\bar{z}} = (u - iv)(u + iv) = u^2 + v^2 = V^2$$

we can take

$$p = -\frac{1}{2}\rho\,\frac{dw}{dz}\frac{d\bar{w}}{d\bar{z}} \tag{5-62}$$

so that Eq. 5-60 becomes

$$dF_x - i\,dF_y = i\frac{1}{2}\rho\,\frac{dw}{dz}\frac{d\bar{w}}{d\bar{z}}\,d\bar{z} \tag{5-63}$$

The trace of the surface of the cylinder in Fig. 5–21 is a streamline, and the equation of this surface can be written as $\psi = $ constant. On the surface, $d\psi = 0$, yielding $dw = d\bar{w}$ since

$$w = \phi + i\psi \qquad dw = d\phi + id\psi = d\phi$$
$$\bar{w} = \phi - i\psi \qquad d\bar{w} = d\phi - id\psi = d\phi$$

Therefore, Eq. 5-63 can also be written as

$$dF_x - i\,dF_y = i\frac{1}{2}\rho\left(\frac{dw}{dz}\right)^2 dz \tag{5-64}$$

which, upon integrating around the trace $C$ of the cylinder surface, becomes

$$F_x - iF_y = \oint_c i\frac{1}{2}\rho\left(\frac{dw}{dz}\right)^2 dz \tag{5-65}$$

This equation and the moment equation constitute the Blasius theorem.

We now apply Eq. 5–65 to the flow past a circular cylinder with circulation. The complex potential for this flow was given in Sec. 5–14 in the form of Eq. 5–39:

$$w = V_0\left(z + \frac{r_0^2}{z}\right) + i\frac{\Gamma}{2\pi}\ln z$$

The complex velocity is

$$\frac{dw}{dz} = V_0\left(1 - \frac{r_0^2}{z^2}\right) + i\frac{\Gamma}{2\pi z} \tag{5–66}$$

so that

$$
\begin{aligned}
\left(\frac{dw}{dz}\right)^2 &= V_0^2\left(1 - \frac{r_0^2}{z^2}\right)^2 + 2V_0\left(1 - \frac{r_0^2}{z^2}\right)\frac{i\Gamma}{2\pi z} + \left(\frac{i\Gamma}{2\pi z}\right)^2 \\
&= V_0^2 + \frac{iV_0\Gamma}{\pi z} - \left(2V_0^2 r_0^2 + \frac{\Gamma^2}{4\pi^2}\right)\frac{1}{z^2} \\
&\quad - \frac{iV_0 r_0^2\Gamma}{\pi z^3} + \frac{V_0^2 r_0^4}{z^4} \\
&= A_0 + \frac{A_1}{z} + \frac{A_2}{z^2} + \cdots
\end{aligned}
\tag{5–67}
$$

in which

$$A_0 = V_0^2$$

$$A_1 = \frac{iV_0\Gamma}{\pi}$$

$$A_2 = -\left(2V_0^2 r_0^2 + \frac{\Gamma^2}{4\pi^2}\right)$$

etc.

Substitution of Eq. 5–67 into Eq. 5–65 yields

$$
\begin{aligned}
F_x - iF_y &= \oint_C i\frac{1}{2}\rho\left(\frac{dw}{dz}\right)^2 dz \\
&= i\frac{\rho}{2}\left[A_0 z + A_1\ln z - \frac{A_2}{z} - \cdots\right]_{z=r_0 e^{i\theta_0}}^{z=r_0 e^{i(\theta_0 + 2\pi)}}
\end{aligned}
\tag{5–68}
$$

The above line integral starts from an arbitrary point $(r_0, \theta_0)$ on the contour $C$ and returns to the same point after the radius has swept through an angle $2\pi$, as shown in Fig. 5–22. Now, when the limits are substituted into any $z^n$ term in Eq. 5–68,

$$
\begin{aligned}
[r_0 e^{i(\theta_0 + 2\pi)}]^n - [r_0 e^{i\theta_0}]^n &= (r_0 e^{i\theta_0})^n(e^{i2\pi n} - 1) \\
&= (r_0 e^{i\theta_0})^n(\cos 2\pi n + i\sin 2\pi n - 1)
\end{aligned}
$$

If $n$ is an integer, $\cos 2\pi n = 1$, $\sin 2\pi n = 0$, and $\cos 2\pi n + i\sin 2\pi n - 1 = 0$. Consequently, all the terms in Eq. 5–68 containing $z^n$, where $n$ is an integer, vanish. But the term with $\ln z$ does not vanish, since

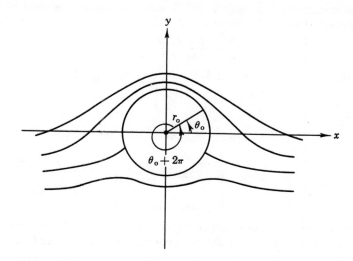

**Fig. 5-22.** Sketch illustrating the limits of line integral around a circular contour.

$$\ln z \Big|_{z=r_0 e^{i\theta_0}}^{z=r_0 e^{i(\theta_0+2\pi)}} = \ln r_0 e^{i(\theta_0+2\pi)} - \ln r_0 e^{i\theta_0}$$

$$= \ln \frac{r_0 e^{i(\theta_0+2\pi)}}{r_0 e^{i\theta_0}} = \ln e^{i2\pi}$$

$$= i2\pi$$

Thus, Eq. 5–68 becomes

$$F_x - iF_y = i\frac{\rho}{2} A_1 i2\pi = -\pi\rho A_1 = -\pi\rho \left(\frac{iV_0\Gamma}{\pi}\right)$$

$$= -i\rho V_0\Gamma \qquad (5\text{–}69)$$

so that

$$F_x = 0 \quad \text{and} \quad F_y = \rho V_0\Gamma$$

The force component $F_y$ is perpendicular to the direction of the approaching stream and is, therefore, the lift on the cylinder. These results are identical to the Kutta-Joukowski theorem derived in Sec. 4–13.

## 5-24    Lift on the Joukowski Airfoil

In order to apply the Blasius theorem (Eq. 5–65) to find the lift force on the Joukowski airfoil, it is necessary to express $dw/dz$ in terms of $z$. This can be accomplished by taking derivatives of the transformation functions (Eqs. 5–53 through 5–56)[6] since $dw/dz$ can be obtained by chain differentiation as

$$\frac{dw}{dz} = \frac{dw}{dz_1}\frac{dz_1}{dz_2}\frac{dz_2}{dz_3}\frac{dz_3}{dz} \tag{5-70}$$

By using Eqs. 5–53, 5–54, and 5–55, the derivative $dw/dz_1$ is

$$\frac{dw}{dz_1} = V_0\left(1 - \frac{r_0^2}{z_1^2}\right) + \frac{i\Gamma}{2\pi z_1}$$

$$= V_0 - V_0 r_0^2 e^{2i\alpha}\,[z_3 - me^{i(\pi-\delta)}]^{-2}$$

$$+ \frac{i\Gamma}{2\pi}\, e^{i\alpha}\,[z_3 - me^{i(\pi-\delta)}]^{-1}$$

Since

$$z_1 = z_2 e^{-i\alpha} = [z_3 - me^{i(\pi-\delta)}]\,e^{-i\alpha}$$

the last two terms on the right-hand side of $dw/dz_1$ can be expanded into binomial series, and the results are then rearranged in ascending powers of $1/z_3$ as

$$\frac{dw}{dz_1} = V_0 + \frac{1}{z_3}\frac{i\Gamma}{2\pi}\,e^{i\alpha} + \frac{1}{z_3^2}\left[\frac{i\Gamma m}{2\pi}\,e^{i(\pi+\alpha-\delta)} - V_0 r_0^2 e^{2i\alpha}\right]$$

$$+ \frac{1}{z_3^3}\left[\frac{i\Gamma m^2}{2\pi}\,e^{i(2\pi+\alpha-2\delta)} - 2V_0 r_0^2 m e^{i(\pi+\alpha-\delta)}\right] + \cdots$$

The other three derivatives are

$$\frac{dz_1}{dz_2} = e^{-i\alpha} \qquad \frac{dz_2}{dz_3} = 1$$

$$\frac{dz_3}{dz} = \left(1 - \frac{b^2}{z_3^2}\right)^{-1} = 1 + \frac{b^2}{z_3^2} + \frac{b^4}{z_3^4} + \cdots$$

Substituting the values of these four derivatives into Eq. 5–70 and expressing the result in series form, we have

$$\frac{dw}{dz} = \frac{dw}{dz_1}\frac{dz_1}{dz_2}\frac{dz_2}{dz_3}\frac{dz_3}{dz}$$

$$= V_0 e^{-i\alpha} + \frac{1}{z_3}\frac{i\Gamma}{2\pi} + \frac{1}{z_3^2}\left[V_0 b^2 e^{-i\alpha} + \frac{i\Gamma m}{2\pi}\,e^{i(\pi-\delta)} - V_0 r_0^2 e^{i\alpha}\right]$$

$$+ \cdots \tag{5-71}$$

From Eq. 5–56,

$$z_3 = z - \frac{b^2}{z} - \frac{b^4}{z^3} - \cdots$$

---

[6]An alternate method of determining the lift on the Joukowski airfoil, or indeed on any two-dimensional cylinder of any cross-sectional form, is by means of Cauchy's integral theorem. See Victor L. Streeter, ed., *op. cit.*, pp. 63–64.

whence

$$\frac{1}{z_3} = \frac{1}{z} + \frac{b^2}{z^3} + \cdots$$

and

$$\frac{1}{z_3^2} = \frac{1}{z^2} + \frac{2b^2}{z^4} + \cdots$$

These two series are then substituted into Eq. 5-71 to express $dw/dz$ in terms of $z$ as

$$\frac{dw}{dz} = V_0 e^{-i\alpha} + \frac{1}{z} \frac{i\Gamma}{2\pi} + \frac{1}{z^2} \left[ V_0 b^2 e^{-i\alpha} + \frac{i\Gamma m}{2\pi} e^{i(\pi-\delta)} - V_0 r_0^2 e^{i\alpha} \right] + \cdots$$

so that

$$\left(\frac{dw}{dz}\right)^2 = V_0 e^{-2i\alpha} + \frac{1}{z} \frac{iV_0\Gamma}{\pi} e^{-i\alpha}$$

$$+ \frac{1}{z^2} \left[ -\frac{\Gamma^2}{4\pi^2} + 2V_0^2 b e^{-2i\alpha} \right.$$

$$\left. + \frac{iV_0\Gamma m}{\pi} e^{i(\pi-\alpha-\delta)} - 2V_0^2 r_0^2 \right]$$

$$+ \cdots = A_0 + \frac{A_1}{z} + \frac{A_2}{z^2} + \cdots$$

where

$$A_0 = V_0 e^{-2i\alpha}$$

$$A_1 = \frac{iV_0\Gamma}{\pi} e^{-i\alpha}$$

etc.

Finally, we substitute the values of $A_1$ into Eq. 5-69 to obtain

$$F_x - iF_y = -\pi\rho A_1 = -i\rho V_0 \Gamma e^{-i\alpha}$$
$$= -i\rho V_0 \Gamma [\cos(-\alpha) + i\sin(-\alpha)]$$
$$= -i\rho V_0 \Gamma \cos \alpha - \rho V_0 \Gamma \sin \alpha$$

whence

$$F_x = -\rho V_0 \Gamma \sin \alpha \quad \text{and} \quad F_y = \rho V_0 \Gamma \cos \alpha \qquad \text{(5-72)}$$

Clearly $F_x$ and $F_y$ are the $x$- and $y$-components of a force $F_L$ which is perpendicular to the direction of the approaching stream, as shown in Fig. 5-23. Hence the lift on the Joukowski airfoil is

$$F_L = \sqrt{F_x^2 + F_y^2} = \rho V_0 \Gamma \quad \text{(per unit length)} \qquad \text{(5-73)}$$

This result is obviously the Kutta-Joukowski theorem.

In Sec. 5-21, an expression for $\Gamma$ was derived in the form of Eq. 5-59. If we substitute this value of $\Gamma$ into Eq. 5-73, the lift per unit length of the airfoil becomes

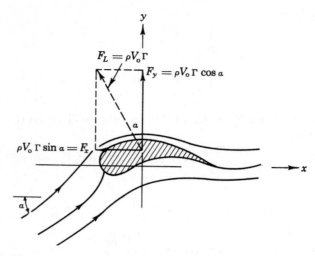

**Fig. 5-23.** Forces on a Joukowski airfoil inclined at an angle of attack $\alpha$ with respect to the direction of approaching stream.

$$F_L = \rho V_0 4\pi r_0 V_0 \sin(\alpha + \beta) \qquad (5\text{--}74)$$

In practice, the lift per unit length of an airfoil is customarily written as

$$F_L = C_L \, c \, \tfrac{1}{2} \rho V_0^2 \qquad (5\text{--}75)$$

in which $C_L$ is the dimensionless lift coefficient and $c$ is the chord length of the airfoil. Since the Joukowski airfoil has a chord length of approximately $4r_0$, its lift coefficient then becomes

$$C_L = 2\pi \sin(\alpha + \beta) \qquad (5\text{--}76)$$

In the conformal mapping in Sec. 5–21, $\beta$ is a measure of the camber of a Joukowski airfoil and is therefore a positive constant for a given airfoil. Hence the zero lift occurs at a negative angle of attack $\alpha_0$ equal to $\beta$, i.e., $\alpha_0 = -\beta$. Consequently, the angle $\alpha + \beta$ is usually considered as the angle of attack measured from the position of zero lift.

Figure 5–24 shows that the theoretical values of $C_L$ agree well with the experimental values for small angles of attack. As the angle of attack increases, a condition known as *stall* will be reached for an actual airfoil due to the separation of flow from the airfoil starting at the trailing edge (see the insert in Fig. 5–24). When the airfoil is stalled, the experimental values of $C_L$ depart rapidly from the theoretical values.

Although in the design of modern airfoils, profiles other than the Joukowski type are preferred in order to achieve better performance, and various methods have been devised for calculating the irrotational

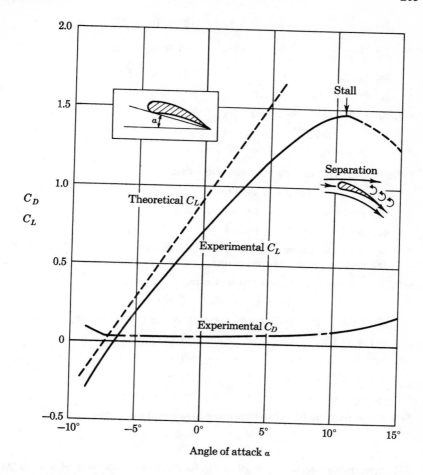

**Fig. 5-24.** Coefficients of drag and lift versus the angle of attack for a low-drag airfoil of infinite span.

flow with circulation for any arbitrary profile, the Kutta-Joukowski theorem must be considered as a contribution of major importance in the field of fluid mechanics as well as aeronautics.

## PROBLEMS

**5-1.** Given: $z_1 = 2 + 3i$, $z_2 = -1 + i$, and $z_3 = 4 - \sqrt{5}\,i$. Evaluate each of the following:

(a) $z_1 + z_2^2$                                                (b) $z_1 (z_2 + 2\bar{z}_1)$

(c) $\dfrac{z_1 + z_2}{z_3}$                                       (d) $\ln (z_1 + z_2)$

(e) $z_1 z_2 \bar{z}_3$                                          (f) $z_1 \bar{z}_2 + \bar{z}_1 z_2$

(g) $(z_1 + \bar{z}_2)^2 + (\bar{z}_1 + z_2)^2$                  (h) $z_1^3 - 2\bar{z}_1^2 + 3z_2$

**5-2.** Show that (a) $\overline{z_1 + z_2} = \bar{z}_1 + \bar{z}_2$

         (b) $\overline{z_1 z_2} = \bar{z}_1 \bar{z}_2$

         (c) $\overline{z_1/z_2} = \bar{z}_1/\bar{z}_2$

**5-3.** By using DeMoivre's theorem, show that

    (a) $\sin^3 \theta = \frac{3}{4} \sin \theta - \frac{1}{4} \sin 3\theta$

    (b) $\sin 3\theta = 3 \sin \theta - 4 \sin^3 \theta$

    (c) $\cos 4\theta = 8 \sin^4 \theta - 8 \sin^2 \theta + 1$

**5-4.** By using DeMoivre's theorem, find all five roots of $z^5 = -32$ and locate these values on an Argand diagram.

**5-5.** The complex function $w$ can be written as follows:

$$w = f(z) = \phi(x, y) + i\psi(x, y)$$

Find the $\phi$- and $\psi$-functions for each of the following $w$-functions

(a) $w = 1/z$                                                   (b) $\ln (z - 1)$

(c) $w = 2z^2 - 3iz$                                             (d) $w = z + 1/\bar{z}$

(e) $w = (1 - z)/(1 + z)$                                       (f) $w = z^{1/2}$

(g) $w = e^{-iz}$                                                (h) $w = \cos z$

**5-6.** Show that the Cauchy-Riemann equations in polar notations are

$$\frac{\partial \phi}{\partial r} = \frac{1}{r} \frac{\partial \psi}{\partial \theta}, \qquad \frac{1}{r} \frac{\partial \phi}{\partial \theta} = -\frac{\partial \psi}{\partial r}$$

**5-7.** Determine which of the following functions are functions of a complex variable:

(a) $2x (1 - y) + (2y + x^2 - y^2)i$    (b) $\dfrac{2xy}{x^2 + y^2} + \dfrac{x^2 - y^2}{x^2 + y^2} i$

(c) $r^{1/4} \cos 4\theta + ir^{1/4} \sin 4\theta$    (d) $e^x \cos y + ie^x \sin y$

**5-8.** (a) Prove that $\phi = \ln (x^2 + y^2)$ is harmonic in every region which does not include the origin of the coordinate system. (b) Find a function $\psi$ such that $w = \phi + i\psi$ is analytic.

**5-9.** Determine the velocity at $z = 4 + 3i$ in the $z$-plane for the following flow fields:

(a) $w = z + \ln z$                                             (b) $w = 3 i/z + z^2$

(c) $w = iz^2 + 2z$                                             (d) $w = 1/z + \ln z$

**5–10.** Sketch the streamlines and equipotential lines in the $z$-plane for the following complex potentials:

(a) $w = z^2 + 2z$          (b) $w = i \ln z + \ln z$

**5–11.** A uniform flow past a half body is formed by the combination of a uniform flow and a source. (a) Find the complex potential for a uniform flow past a half body formed by a uniform flow with $\mathbf{V} = V_0 \mathbf{j}$ and a two-dimensional source of strength $q$ located at the origin of the co-ordinates. (b) Determine the equation for the velocity on the surface of the half body. (c) Locate the stagnation point in this flow field.

**5–12.** A uniform flow past a Rankine oval is formed by the combination of a uniform flow and a source-sink flow. (a) Find the complex potential for a uniform flow past a Rankine oval formed by a uniform flow with $\mathbf{V} = -V_0 \mathbf{j}$, a two-dimensional source of strength $q$ at $(0, a)$, and a sink of strength $-q$ at $(0, -a)$. (b) Determine the equation for the velocity on the surface of the oval. (c) Locate the stagnation point in this flow field.

**5–13.** The complex potential for flow at a corner of walls is $w = Az^n$ where $A$ is a real and positive constant. Sketch the streamline patterns in the $z$-plane for the following complex potentials:

(a) $w = Az^3$      (b) $w = Az^2$      (c) $w = Az^{3/2}$

(d) $w = Az$      (e) $w = Az^{2/3}$      (f) $w = Az^{1/2}$

**5–14.** Write the successive transformation equations which are required to obtain a flow pattern in the $z$-plane representing a uniform flow with $\mathbf{V} = -V_0 \mathbf{j}$ past a normal plate. The plate lies on the $x$-axis extending from $(-2a, 0)$ to $(+2a, 0)$.

**5–15.** Write the successive transformation equations which are required to obtain a flow pattern in the $z$-plane representing a uniform flow with speed $V_0$ past an elliptic cylinder whose major axis is inclined at an angle $\alpha$ to the direction of the uniform stream.

**5–16.** Write the successive transformation equations which are required to obtain a flow pattern in the $z$-plane representing a uniform flow with speed $V_0$ past a flat plate with a circulation $\Gamma$ around the plate. The flat plate has a length of $4a$. The uniform flow approaches the plate with an angle of attack $\alpha$.

**5–17.** Write the successive transformation equations which are required to obtain a flow pattern in the $z$-plane representing a uniform flow with speed $V_0$ past a circular arc with a circulation $\Gamma$ around the arc. The arc has a camber of $2m/4b$. The uniform flow approaches the arc with an angle of attack $\alpha$.

**5–18.** Evaluate the lift on the flat plate and the circular arc of Problems 5–16 and 5–17 by means of the Blasius theorem.

**5–19.** Verify that the following transformation:

$$\frac{w - 2a}{w + 2a} = \left(\frac{z - a}{z + a}\right)^2$$

is identical to the Joukowski transformation:

$$w = z + \frac{a^2}{z}$$

**5-20.** Construct graphically a Joukowski airfoil by using the following data:

$$r = 3 \text{ in.} \qquad \delta = 70° \qquad m = 0.5 \text{ in.}$$

(a) Find the angle of zero lift for this airfoil. (b) Determine the lift on the airfoil with $V_0 = 300$ ft/sec and $\alpha = 5°$, assuming air flow at 70°F and 14.7 lbf/in² abs.

# 6

# Fluid Viscosity
# and Flow
# of Viscous Fluids

## 6-1  Some Characteristics of Flow of Viscous Fluids

In the preceding three chapters, we have investigated the characteristics of irrotational flow in which the viscous effect of fluids has been neglected. This idealization of the flow model greatly simplifies the mathematics involved in the analysis. For this reason, a rather extensive and elegant mathematical theory has been developed to account for irrotational flows. The theory of irrotational flow gives satisfactory explanation for some phenomena, such as the lift on an airfoil, but it fails to explain other phenomena, such as energy dissipation in the flow, skin friction, flow separation, form drag of an immersed body, shock waves, and many others. In order to obtain satisfactory explanations for these latter phenomena, it is necessary for us to examine the mechanics of the flow of viscous fluids.

Real fluids are both compressible and viscous. Fluid compressibility becomes important in the flow of gases. The density of gases changes considerably with the change in temperature and pressure of the gas media and, consequently, with the speed of flow. The effect of fluid compressibility must be taken into consideration in those high-speed flows which result from high temperature gradient or high pressure gradient. Since changes in fluid densities are always accompanied by temperature changes as well as heat transfer, we shall have to make use of thermodynamics in conjunction with mechanics of continuous media in the study of the flow of compressible fluids. The subject of compressible flow will be taken up in Chapter 9.

Fluid viscosity is principally due to molecular cohesion (in liquids) and molecular interaction (in gases). The viscosities of gases and liquids can be ascertained by means of molecular theory.[1] The Newtonian concept of the measurement of fluid viscosity was presented in Sec. 1–8. The reader is advised to refer to that section for a thorough review of the discussion on viscosity. In that same section are also presented curves showing the variations of viscosities as a function of temperature for some common fluids.

The viscosity plays an important role in fluid motion in that the viscous fluid offers frictional or shearing resistance to changes in form. The shearing resistance of a viscous fluid is directly proportional to the rate of deformation of fluid elements. Hence, in a viscous flow field, both the tangential and normal stresses must be taken into consideration. A part of the kinetic energy of the flow usually degenerates into heat as a result of the action of these viscous stresses.

Fluid motion has been observed experimentally to occur in two entirely different modes—laminar and turbulent flow. It was Osborne Reynolds[2] who discovered the phenomena of these two fundamentally different patterns of flow in his classical experiments on water in glass tubes, as shown in Fig. 6–1(a). At sufficiently low rate of flow, the dye streak is straight and parallel to the axis of the tube, and the flow is termed *laminar* [Fig. 6–1(b)]. When the flow rate is increased beyond a certain limit, the dye streak becomes wavy, as shown in Fig. 6–1(c). If the flow rate is increased still further, the dye streak will eventually break up and diffuse completely with water in the tube, and the flow is said to be *turbulent* [Fig. 6–1(d)].

In laminar flow the fluid appears to move in layers (or laminae), with one layer of fluid sliding over the other, although molecular motions do occur from one layer to the next. In turbulent flow the fluid mixes violently as it moves along the tube. The motion of fluid is apparently

---

[1] J. O. Hirschfelder, C. F. Curtiss, and R. B. Bird, *Molecular Theory of Gases and Liquids*. New York: John Wiley & Sons, Inc., 1954.

[2] Osborne Reynolds, "An Experimental Investigation of the Circumstances which Determine whether the Motion of Water will be Direct or Sinuous, and the Law of Resistance in Parallel Channels," *Phil. Trans. Roy. Soc.* (London), 1883; or *Scientific Papers* (London: Cambridge University Press, 1900–1903) Vol. II, 51–105.

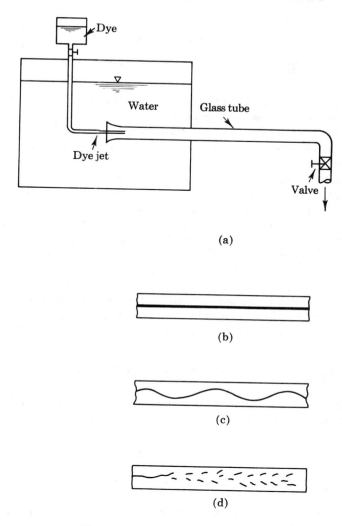

(a)

(b)

(c)

(d)

**Fig. 6-1.** Reynolds' experiment.

conditioned by the relative magnitude of the momenta of fluid particles and the viscous forces which are produced by the fluid viscosity. When velocities are low, the momenta of fluid particles are low and so the viscous forces tend to constrain the motion of fluid in parallel layers. When the momenta of fluid particles are large in comparison with the viscous forces, fluid layers break up into a turbulent flow.

A dimensionless quantity, called *Reynolds number R*, has been adopted as a quantitative measure for the occurrence of the laminar and turbulent modes of flow. The Reynolds number $R$ is defined as

$$R = \frac{VL\rho}{\mu} \tag{6–1}$$

where $V$ is the characteristic velocity, $L$ is a characteristic linear dimension, and $\rho$ and $\mu$ are, respectively, the fluid density and viscosity. For example, in a pipe flow, we use the pipe diameter as $L$ and the average velocity as $V$. The physical meaning of Reynolds number will be discussed further in Section 6–11.

The phenomena of laminar and turbulent flows are not restricted to water flows in tubes only. They have been observed in every type of flow of any fluid. In most engineering problems of fluid flow the flow is turbulent. It is, however, somewhat unfortunate that the true nature of turbulent flow is not yet fully understood. There is no completely satisfactory theory of turbulent flow that can be applied to engineering problems. Semiempirical theories supplemented by extensive experimental results have been found to agree fairly well with the action of the turbulent motion of fluids. Turbulent flow will be discussed in Chapter 7.

We shall now proceed to formulate the differential equations of motion for a viscous fluid element in a laminar flow.

### 6-2    Equations of Motion of a Viscous Fluid

The differential equation of motion for a fluid mass of unit volume subjected to an external force $\mathbf{f}$ was derived in Sec. 2–7 as

$$\rho \frac{D\mathbf{V}}{Dt} = \mathbf{f} \tag{6–2}$$

The external force $\mathbf{f}$ consists of two types of forces—body forces and surface forces.

In the absence of an electromagnetic field, gravity is the only body force encountered in fluid flow. The gravity force per unit volume is $\rho\mathbf{g}$, where $\mathbf{g}$ is the local gravitational acceleration.

To consider the surface forces, let us take an element of fluid which at time $t$ is a rectangular parallelepiped in a Cartesian coordinate system, as shown in Fig. 6–2. In order to avoid crowding the diagram, only stresses on the two faces of area $dy\,dz$ which are perpendicular to the $x$-axis are shown in this figure. The surface forces per unit area on these two faces are respectively $\mathbf{T}_x$ and $\mathbf{T}_x + (\partial \mathbf{T}_x/\partial x)\,dx$. The subscript $x$ denotes that

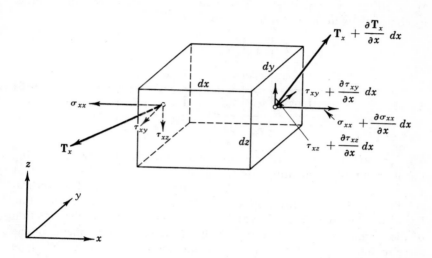

**Fig. 6-2.** A viscous fluid element.

these forces act on elementary areas which are perpendicular to the $x$-axis. Therefore, the resultant force on faces perpendicular to the $x$-axis is

$$\left(\mathbf{T}_x + \frac{\partial \mathbf{T}_x}{\partial x} dx\right) dy\, dz - \mathbf{T}_x\, dy\, dz = \frac{\partial \mathbf{T}_x}{\partial x} dx\, dy\, dz$$

Similarly, the resultant forces on faces perpendicular to the $y$- and $z$-axes are respectively

$$\frac{\partial \mathbf{T}_y}{\partial y} dy\, dx\, dz \quad \text{and} \quad \frac{\partial \mathbf{T}_z}{\partial z} dz\, dx\, dy$$

Hence the resultant surface force $\mathbf{f}_r$ per unit volume is then given by

$$\mathbf{f}_r = \frac{\partial \mathbf{T}_x}{\partial x} + \frac{\partial \mathbf{T}_y}{\partial y} + \frac{\partial \mathbf{T}_z}{\partial z} \tag{6-3}$$

The vectors $\mathbf{T}_x$, $\mathbf{T}_y$, and $\mathbf{T}_z$ can be expressed in terms of their components as

$$\mathbf{T}_x = \mathbf{i}\sigma_{xx} + \mathbf{j}\tau_{xy} + \mathbf{k}\tau_{xz} \tag{6-4a}$$

$$\mathbf{T}_y = \mathbf{i}\tau_{yx} + \mathbf{j}\sigma_{yy} + \mathbf{k}\tau_{yz} \tag{6-4b}$$

$$\mathbf{T}_z = \mathbf{i}\tau_{zx} + \mathbf{j}\tau_{zy} + \mathbf{k}\sigma_{zz} \tag{6-4c}$$

The double subscript notations for stresses were explained in Sec. 1–9.

The nine scalar component stresses in Eqs. 6–4 form a stress tensor. We shall use the capital letter **T** to denote this stress tensor and express its components in the following matrix form:

$$
\mathbf{T} =
\begin{array}{c|ccc}
 & \mathbf{i} & \mathbf{j} & \mathbf{k} \\
\hline
\mathbf{i} & \sigma_{xx} & \tau_{xy} & \tau_{xz} \\
\mathbf{j} & \tau_{yx} & \sigma_{yy} & \tau_{yz} \\
\mathbf{k} & \tau_{zx} & \tau_{zy} & \sigma_{zz}
\end{array}
=
\begin{array}{c|ccc}
 & \mathbf{i} & \mathbf{j} & \mathbf{k} \\
\hline
\mathbf{i} & \sigma_{xx} & \tau_{xy} & \tau_{xz} \\
\mathbf{j} & \tau_{xy} & \sigma_{yy} & \tau_{yz} \\
\mathbf{k} & \tau_{xz} & \tau_{yz} & \sigma_{zz}
\end{array}
\tag{6-5}
$$

The last step in the above equation was made possible by considering the moment of momentum for the fluid element in Fig. 6–2, so that $\tau_{yz} = \tau_{zy}$, $\tau_{xz} = \tau_{zx}$, and $\tau_{xy} = \tau_{yx}$. Each unit vector in the first vertical column denotes the direction of the stress components in the same horizontal row, and each unit vector of the top row indicates the direction of the normal to the surface on which all the stress components in the same column act. Mathematical manipulations concerning this type of matrix were worked out in Sec. 2–7.

Clearly the resultant surface force $\mathbf{f}_r$ per unit volume can also be expressed in terms of the stress tensor **T** as

$$
\mathbf{f}_r = [\nabla \cdot \mathbf{T}] \tag{6-6}
$$

It is easy to establish the identity between this equation and Eqs. 6–3 and 6–4 by carrying out the indicated mathematical operations.

Substituting the sum $\rho \mathbf{g} + [\nabla \cdot \mathbf{T}]$ for **f** in Eq. 6–2 yields

$$
\rho \frac{D\mathbf{V}}{Dt} = \rho \mathbf{g} + [\nabla \cdot \mathbf{T}] \tag{6-7}
$$

This is the vector-tensor form of the differential equation of motion for a viscous compressible fluid with gravity as the only body force.

If the fluid is nonviscous, all shear stresses vanish, and only the three normal stresses remain in the stress tensor. It was shown in Sec. 1–9 that these three normal stresses are equal to each other and their negative is defined as the pressure at point $(x, y, z)$ in the fluid; i.e.,

$$
\sigma_{xx} = \sigma_{yy} = \sigma_{zz} = -p
$$

Hence $[\nabla \cdot \mathbf{T}]$ becomes simply $-\nabla p$, and Eq. 6–7 reduces to Euler's equation (Eq. 2–38).

Equation 6–7 can be expressed in scalar component forms in any given coordinate system. Table 6–1 summarizes scalar component forms of Eq. 6–7 in different coordinate systems.

These equations of motion are expressed in terms of stress components which are in turn related to velocity gradients by Stokes' laws of

# TABLE 6–1. Component Equations of Motion Expressed in Terms of Stresses in Different Coordinate Systems

## 1. Cartesian coordinates $(x, y, z)$

$x$-component:

$$\rho \frac{Du}{Dt} = \rho\left(u\frac{\partial u}{\partial x} + v\frac{\partial u}{\partial y} + w\frac{\partial u}{\partial z} + \frac{\partial u}{\partial t}\right) = \rho g_x + \left(\frac{\partial \sigma_{xx}}{\partial x} + \frac{\partial \tau_{yx}}{\partial y} + \frac{\partial \tau_{zx}}{\partial z}\right) \quad \text{(A)}$$

$y$-component:

$$\rho \frac{Dv}{Dt} = \rho\left(u\frac{\partial v}{\partial x} + v\frac{\partial v}{\partial y} + w\frac{\partial v}{\partial z} + \frac{\partial v}{\partial t}\right) = \rho g_y + \left(\frac{\partial \tau_{xy}}{\partial x} + \frac{\partial \sigma_{yy}}{\partial y} + \frac{\partial \tau_{zy}}{\partial z}\right) \quad \text{(B)}$$

$z$-component:

$$\rho \frac{Dw}{Dt} = \rho\left(u\frac{\partial w}{\partial x} + v\frac{\partial w}{\partial y} + w\frac{\partial w}{\partial z} + \frac{\partial w}{\partial t}\right) = \rho g_z + \left(\frac{\partial \tau_{xz}}{\partial x} + \frac{\partial \tau_{yz}}{\partial y} + \frac{\partial \sigma_{zz}}{\partial z}\right) \quad \text{(C)}$$

## 2. Cylindrical coordinates $(r, \theta, z)$

$r$-component:

$$\rho \frac{Dv_r}{Dt} = \rho\left(v_r\frac{\partial v_r}{\partial r} + \frac{v_\theta}{r}\frac{\partial v_r}{\partial \theta} - \frac{v_\theta^2}{r} + v_z\frac{\partial v_r}{\partial z} + \frac{\partial v_r}{\partial t}\right)$$
$$= \rho g_r + \left(\frac{1}{r}\frac{\partial}{\partial r}r\sigma_{rr} + \frac{1}{r}\frac{\partial \tau_{r\theta}}{\partial \theta} - \frac{\sigma_{\theta\theta}}{r} + \frac{\partial \tau_{rz}}{\partial z}\right) \quad \text{(D)}$$

$\theta$-component:

$$\rho \frac{Dv_\theta}{Dt} = \rho\left(v_r\frac{\partial v_\theta}{\partial r} + \frac{v_\theta}{r}\frac{\partial v_\theta}{\partial \theta} + \frac{v_r v_\theta}{r} + v_z\frac{\partial v_\theta}{\partial z} + \frac{\partial v_\theta}{\partial t}\right)$$
$$= \rho g_\theta + \left(\frac{1}{r^2}\frac{\partial}{\partial r}r^2\tau_{r\theta} + \frac{1}{r}\frac{\partial \sigma_{\theta\theta}}{\partial \theta} + \frac{\partial \tau_{\theta z}}{\partial z}\right) \quad \text{(E)}$$

$z$-component:

$$\rho \frac{Dv_z}{Dt} = \rho\left(v_r\frac{\partial v_z}{\partial r} + \frac{v_\theta}{r}\frac{\partial v_z}{\partial \theta} + v_z\frac{\partial v_z}{\partial z} + \frac{\partial v_z}{\partial t}\right)$$
$$= \rho g_z + \left(\frac{1}{r}\frac{\partial}{\partial r}r\tau_{rz} + \frac{1}{r}\frac{\partial \tau_{\theta z}}{\partial \theta} + \frac{\partial \sigma_{zz}}{\partial z}\right) \quad \text{(F)}$$

## 3. Spherical coordinates $(R, \theta, \phi)$

$R$-component:

$$\rho \frac{Dv_R}{Dt} = \rho\left(v_R\frac{\partial v_R}{\partial R} + \frac{v_\theta}{R}\frac{\partial v_R}{\partial \theta} + \frac{v_\phi}{R\sin\theta}\frac{\partial v_R}{\partial \phi} - \frac{v_\theta^2 + v_\phi^2}{R} + \frac{\partial v_R}{\partial t}\right)$$
$$= \rho g_R + \left(\frac{1}{R^2}\frac{\partial}{\partial R}R^2\sigma_{RR} + \frac{1}{R\sin\theta}\frac{\partial}{\partial \theta}\tau_{R\theta}\sin\theta\right.$$
$$\left. + \frac{1}{R\sin\theta}\frac{\partial \tau_{R\phi}}{\partial \phi} + \frac{\sigma_{\theta\theta} + \sigma_{\phi\phi}}{R}\right) \quad \text{(G)}$$

$\theta$-component:

$$\rho \frac{Dv_\theta}{Dt} = \left(v_R\frac{\partial v_\theta}{\partial R} + \frac{v_\theta}{R}\frac{\partial v_\theta}{\partial \theta} + \frac{v_\phi}{R\sin\theta}\frac{\partial v_\theta}{\partial \phi} + \frac{v_R v_\theta}{R} - \frac{v_\phi^2\cot\theta}{R} + \frac{\partial v_\theta}{\partial t}\right)$$
$$= \rho g_\theta + \left(\frac{1}{R^2}\frac{\partial}{\partial R}R^2\tau_{R\theta} + \frac{1}{R\sin\theta}\frac{\partial}{\partial \theta}\sigma_{\theta\theta}\sin\theta\right.$$
$$\left. + \frac{1}{R\sin\theta}\frac{\partial \tau_{\theta\phi}}{\partial \phi} + \frac{\tau_{R\theta}}{R} - \frac{\sigma_{\phi\phi}\cot\theta}{R}\right) \quad \text{(H)}$$

$\phi$-component:

$$\rho \frac{Dv_\phi}{Dt} = \rho\left(v_R\frac{\partial v_\phi}{\partial R} + \frac{v_\theta}{R}\frac{\partial v_\phi}{\partial \theta} + \frac{v_\phi}{R\sin\theta}\frac{\partial v_\phi}{\partial \phi} + \frac{v_\phi v_R}{R} + \frac{v_\theta v_\phi}{R}\cot\theta + \frac{\partial v_\phi}{\partial t}\right)$$
$$= \rho g_\phi + \left(\frac{1}{R^2}\frac{\partial}{\partial R}R^2\tau_{R\phi} + \frac{1}{R}\frac{\partial \tau_{\theta\phi}}{\partial \theta} + \frac{1}{R\sin\theta}\frac{\partial \sigma_{\phi\phi}}{\partial \phi} + \frac{\tau_{R\phi}}{R} + \frac{2\tau_{\theta\phi}\cot\theta}{R}\right) \quad \text{(I)}$$

viscosity. We shall derive these laws in the following section and use them to replace the stress components by the velocity gradients so as to make the equations of motion more useful in the study of fluid flow.

## 6-3 Stokes' Laws of Viscosity

The derivation of Stokes' laws of viscosity is based on the postulates that the fluid is isotropic (i.e., its physical properties are the same in all directions) and that viscous stresses are linearly proportional to rates-of-strain. Since both the stress and the rates-of-strain at any point in a viscous flow field are tensor quantities, it is more convenient to establish, first, the stress-and-rate-of-strain relationships along the so-called "principal directions" and then to transform them to obtain the desired forms of Stokes' laws for the coordinate system under consideration. If a parallelepiped fluid element is taken with its orthogonal surfaces normal to the principal axes, all the shear stresses vanish over these surfaces, and the remaining normal stresses are called *principal stresses*. Likewise, all the rates-of-shear-strain associated with the principal axes also vanish, and the remaining rates-of-normal-strain are called *rates-of-principal-strain*.

**Relationships between rates-of-principal-strain and scalar components of rate-of-strain tensor.** Let us denote the principal axes by $x'$, $y'$, and $z'$. The directions of the principal axes and the $x$- , $y$- , and $z$-axes are related by the following table of direction cosines:

|        | $x$       | $y$       | $z$       |
|--------|-----------|-----------|-----------|
| $x'$   | $a_{x'x}$ | $a_{x'y}$ | $a_{x'z}$ |
| $y'$   | $a_{y'x}$ | $a_{y'y}$ | $a_{y'z}$ |
| $z'$   | $a_{z'x}$ | $a_{z'y}$ | $a_{z'z}$ |

Each $a$ denotes the direction cosine between the two axes which appear as double subscripts for the $a$. For example, $a_{y'z}$ is the cosine of the angle between the $y'$-axis and the $z$-axis. These nine direction cosines are not entirely independent. The orthogonality of the $x$- , $y$- , and $z$-axes and the $x'$- , $y'$- , and $z'$-axes requires that

$$
a_{x'x}a_{x'y} + a_{y'x}a_{y'y} + a_{z'x}a_{z'y}
$$
$$
= a_{x'y}a_{x'z} + a_{y'y}a_{y'z} + a_{z'y}a_{z'z}
$$
$$
= a_{x'z}a_{x'x} + a_{y'z}a_{y'x} + a_{z'z}a_{z'x} = 0
$$

and

$$a_{x'x}a_{y'x} + a_{x'y}a_{y'y} + a_{x'z}a_{y'z}$$
$$= a_{y'x}a_{z'x} + a_{y'y}a_{z'y} + a_{y'z}a_{z'z}$$
$$= a_{z'x}a_{x'x} + a_{z'y}a_{x'y} + a_{z'z}a_{x'z} = 0$$

Also, the sum of the squares of the direction cosines is equal to unity, so that

$$a_{x'x}^2 + a_{y'x}^2 + a_{z'x}^2 = a_{x'y}^2 + a_{y'y}^2 + a_{z'y}^2$$
$$= a_{x'z}^2 + a_{y'z}^2 + a_{z'z}^2 = 1$$

and

$$a_{x'x}^2 + a_{x'y}^2 + a_{x'z}^2 = a_{y'x}^2 + a_{y'y}^2 + a_{y'z}^2$$
$$= a_{z'x}^2 + a_{z'y}^2 + a_{z'z}^2 = 1$$

The transformation equations for coordinates in these two Cartesian systems can be written as follows:

$$x' = a_{x'x}x + a_{x'y}y + a_{x'z}z$$
$$y' = a_{y'x}x + a_{y'y}y + a_{y'z}z$$
$$z' = a_{z'x}x + a_{z'y}y + a_{z'z}z$$

and

$$x = a_{x'x}x' + a_{y'x}y' + a_{z'x}z'$$
$$y = a_{x'y}x' + a_{y'y}y' + a_{z'y}z'$$
$$z = a_{x'z}x' + a_{y'z}y' + a_{z'z}z'$$

If $u$, $v$, $w$ denote the velocity components in the directions of $x$, $y$, $z$, respectively, and $u'$, $v'$, $w'$, the velocity components along the $x'$-, $y'$-, $z'$-axis, respectively, the velocity components in the two Cartesian systems will transform in exactly the same manner as the coordinates. It is only necessary to replace $x$, $y$, $z$ by $u$, $v$, $w$, and $x'$, $y'$, $z'$ by $u'$, $v'$, $w'$, respectively, in the above transformation equations for coordinates in order to obtain transformation equations for velocity components.

Let us look into the transformation equations for velocity gradients. For example, by chain rule of differentiation, we may write

$$\frac{\partial u}{\partial x} = \frac{\partial u}{\partial x'}\frac{\partial x'}{\partial x} + \frac{\partial u}{\partial y'}\frac{\partial y'}{\partial x} + \frac{\partial u}{\partial z'}\frac{\partial z'}{\partial x}$$

since $x$ is a function of $x'$, $y'$, and $z'$. By recognizing that

$$\frac{\partial x'}{\partial x} = a_{x'x}, \qquad \frac{\partial y'}{\partial x} = a_{y'x}, \qquad \frac{\partial z'}{\partial x} = a_{z'x}$$

we may also write the above equation for $\partial u/\partial x$ as

$$\frac{\partial u}{\partial x} = \left(a_{x'x}\frac{\partial}{\partial x'} + a_{y'x}\frac{\partial}{\partial y'} + a_{z'x}\frac{\partial}{\partial z'}\right)u$$

which indicates that the partial differential operators, $\partial/\partial x$, $\partial/\partial y$, $\partial/\partial z$, also transform like the coordinates.

Hence, by making use of the transformation equations for the coordinates, velocity components, and partial differential operators, as derived in the preceding paragraphs, we obtain the following formulas for the transformation of the rates-of-strain:

$$\frac{\partial u}{\partial x} = \left(a_{x'x}\frac{\partial}{\partial x'} + a_{y'x}\frac{\partial}{\partial y'} + a_{z'x}\frac{\partial}{\partial z'}\right)(a_{x'x}u' + a_{y'x}v' + a_{z'x}w')$$

$$= a_{x'x}^2\frac{\partial u'}{\partial x'} + a_{y'x}^2\frac{\partial v'}{\partial y'} + a_{z'x}^2\frac{\partial w'}{\partial z'}. \tag{6-8a}$$

$$\frac{\partial v}{\partial y} = a_{x'y}^2\frac{\partial u'}{\partial x'} + a_{y'y}^2\frac{\partial v'}{\partial y'} + a_{z'y}^2\frac{\partial w'}{\partial z'} \tag{6-8b}$$

$$\frac{\partial w}{\partial z} = a_{x'z}^2\frac{\partial u'}{\partial x'} + a_{y'z}^2\frac{\partial v'}{\partial y'} + a_{z'z}^2\frac{\partial w'}{\partial z'} \tag{6-8c}$$

$$\frac{\partial v}{\partial z} + \frac{\partial w}{\partial y} = 2\left(a_{x'y}a_{x'z}\frac{\partial u'}{\partial x'} + a_{y'y}a_{y'z}\frac{\partial v'}{\partial y'} + a_{z'y}a_{z'z}\frac{\partial w'}{\partial z'}\right) \tag{6-8d}$$

$$\frac{\partial w}{\partial x} + \frac{\partial u}{\partial z} = 2\left(a_{x'z}a_{x'x}\frac{\partial u'}{\partial x'} + a_{y'z}a_{y'x}\frac{\partial v'}{\partial y'} + a_{z'z}a_{z'x}\frac{\partial w'}{\partial z'}\right) \tag{6-8e}$$

$$\frac{\partial u}{\partial y} + \frac{\partial v}{\partial x} = 2\left(a_{x'x}a_{x'y}\frac{\partial u'}{\partial x'} + a_{y'x}a_{y'y}\frac{\partial v'}{\partial y'} + a_{z'x}a_{z'y}\frac{\partial w'}{\partial z'}\right) \tag{6-8f}$$

since all the rates-of-shear-strain are zero on the principal planes.

The sum of Eqs. 6-8a, 6-8b, and 6-8c is an invariant:

$$\frac{\partial u}{\partial x} + \frac{\partial v}{\partial y} + \frac{\partial w}{\partial z} = \frac{\partial u'}{\partial x'} + \frac{\partial v'}{\partial y'} + \frac{\partial w'}{\partial z'} = \nabla \cdot \mathbf{V} \tag{6-9}$$

where the local volumetric dilatation $\nabla \cdot \mathbf{V}$ is independent of the orientation of coordinates.

### Relationships between principal stresses and scalar components of stress tensor.

Let us consider the tetrahedron $OABC$ of Fig. 6-3. Faces $\overline{OBC}$, $\overline{OAC}$, and $\overline{OAB}$ are principal planes over which shear stresses are zero, and the inclined face $\overline{ABC}$ is normal to the $x$-axis. If we denote the area of $\overline{ABC}$ by $\delta A_0$, then $\overline{OBC} = a_{x'x}\,\delta A_0$, $\overline{OAC} = a_{y'x}\,\delta A_0$, and $\overline{OAB} = a_{z'x}\,\delta A_0$. Writing the equation of motion for this tetrahedron in the $x$-direction by neglecting both the gravity and inertia terms which contain differentials of high order, we obtain

$$\sigma_{xx}\,\delta A_0 = \sigma_{x'x'}(a_{x'x}\,\delta A_0)a_{x'x} + \sigma_{y'y'}(a_{y'x}\,\delta A_0)a_{y'x} + \sigma_{z'z'}(a_{z'x}\,\delta A_0)a_{z'x}$$

Two similar equations of motion can be written for this tetrahedron in the $y$- and $z$-directions. Then we may take two other tetrahedrons with their inclined planes normal to the $y$- and $z$-axes, respectively, and write

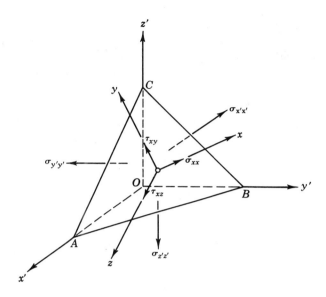

**Fig. 6-3.** A viscous fluid element in the form of a tetrahedron.

the remaining six equations of motion. These nine equations of motion, after $\delta A_0$ is canceled, become

$$\sigma_{xx} = a_{x'x}^2 \sigma_{x'x} + a_{y'x}^2 \sigma_{y'y'} + a_{z'x}^2 \sigma_{z'z'} \tag{6-10a}$$

$$\sigma_{yy} = a_{x'y}^2 \sigma_{x'x'} + a_{y'y}^2 \sigma_{y'y'} + a_{z'y}^2 \sigma_{z'z'} \tag{6-10b}$$

$$\sigma_{zz} = a_{x'z}^2 \sigma_{x'x'} + a_{y'z}^2 \sigma_{y'y'} + a_{z'z}^2 \sigma_{z'z'} \tag{6-10c}$$

$$\tau_{yz} = \tau_{zy} = a_{x'y} a_{x'z} \sigma_{x'x'} + a_{y'y} a_{y'z} \sigma_{y'y'} + a_{z'y} a_{z'z} \sigma_{z'z'} \tag{6-10d}$$

$$\tau_{zx} = \tau_{xz} = a_{x'z} a_{x'x} \sigma_{x'x'} + a_{y'z} a_{y'x} \sigma_{y'y'} + a_{z'z} a_{z'x} \sigma_{z'z'} \tag{6-10e}$$

$$\tau_{xy} = \tau_{yx} = a_{x'x} a_{x'y} \sigma_{x'x'} + a_{y'x} a_{y'y} \sigma_{y'y'} + a_{z'x} a_{z'y} \sigma_{z'z'} \tag{6-10f}$$

The sum of Eqs. 6–10a, 6–10b, and 6–10c is another invariant:

$$\sigma_{xx} + \sigma_{yy} + \sigma_{zz} = \sigma_{x'x'} + \sigma_{y'y'} + \sigma_{z'z'} = -3p \tag{6-11}$$

where $-p$ is the mean of normal stresses and is independent of the orientation of coordinates. We call $p$ the *average pressure* at the point under consideration.

*Relationships between stresses and rates-of-strain.* Postulation of the linear relationship between principal stresses and rates-of-principal-strain enables us to write

$$\sigma_{x'x'} = -p + \alpha\frac{\partial u'}{\partial x'} + \beta\frac{\partial v'}{\partial y'} + \gamma\frac{\partial w'}{\partial z'}$$

$$\sigma_{y'y'} = -p + \alpha\frac{\partial v'}{\partial y'} + \beta\frac{\partial w'}{\partial z'} + \gamma\frac{\partial u'}{\partial x'}$$

$$\sigma_{z'z'} = -p + \alpha\frac{\partial w'}{\partial z'} + \beta\frac{\partial u'}{\partial x'} + \gamma\frac{\partial v'}{\partial y'}$$

where $\alpha$, $\beta$, and $\gamma$ are constants. Because of isotropy, $\beta$ must equal $\gamma$. It is then more convenient to rewrite, for example, the first equation by adding and subtracting $\beta\,\partial u'/\partial x'$ in the following form:

$$\sigma_{x'x'} = -p + (\alpha - \beta)\frac{\partial u'}{\partial x'} + \beta\left(\frac{\partial u'}{\partial x'} + \frac{\partial v'}{\partial y'} + \frac{\partial w'}{\partial z'}\right)$$

Upon changing the constants by letting $\alpha - \beta = 2\mu$ and $\beta = \eta$, the above three equations may be written as

$$\sigma_{x'x'} = -p + 2\mu\frac{\partial u'}{\partial x'} + \eta\left(\frac{\partial u'}{\partial x'} + \frac{\partial v'}{\partial y'} + \frac{\partial w'}{\partial z'}\right)$$

$$\sigma_{y'y'} = -p + 2\mu\frac{\partial v'}{\partial y'} + \eta\left(\frac{\partial u'}{\partial x'} + \frac{\partial v'}{\partial y'} + \frac{\partial w'}{\partial z'}\right)$$

$$\sigma_{z'z'} = -p + 2\mu\frac{\partial w'}{\partial z'} + \eta\left(\frac{\partial u'}{\partial x'} + \frac{\partial v'}{\partial y'} + \frac{\partial w'}{\partial z'}\right)$$

Adding these three equations, we obtain $\eta = -2\mu/3$. We then substitute the values of $\sigma_{x'x'}$, $\sigma_{y'y'}$, and $\sigma_{z'z'}$ into Eqs. 6–10 to obtain the following set of equations:

$$\sigma_{xx} = -p + 2\mu\frac{\partial u}{\partial x} - \frac{2}{3}\mu\,\text{div }\mathbf{V} \qquad \text{(6–12a)}$$

$$\sigma_{yy} = -p + 2\mu\frac{\partial v}{\partial y} - \frac{2}{3}\mu\,\text{div }\mathbf{V} \qquad \text{(6–12b)}$$

$$\sigma_{zz} = -p + 2\mu\frac{\partial w}{\partial z} - \frac{2}{3}\mu\,\text{div }\mathbf{V} \qquad \text{(6–12c)}$$

$$\tau_{yz} = \tau_{zy} = \mu\left(\frac{\partial v}{\partial z} + \frac{\partial w}{\partial y}\right) \qquad \text{(6–12d)}$$

$$\tau_{zx} = \tau_{xz} = \mu\left(\frac{\partial w}{\partial x} + \frac{\partial u}{\partial z}\right) \qquad \text{(6–12e)}$$

$$\tau_{xy} = \tau_{yx} = \mu\left(\frac{\partial u}{\partial y} + \frac{\partial v}{\partial x}\right) \qquad \text{(6–12f)}$$

which are the desired forms of Stokes' laws of viscosity relating the viscous stress field and the velocity field.

The meaning of the constant $\mu$ becomes obvious when we consider the flow model which was used in the derivation of Newton's law of viscosity. For this simple flow, the fluid is incompressible and the velocity field is represented by $u = u(y)$. Then the three shear stress equations reduce to

$$\tau_{xy} = \tau_{yx} = \mu \frac{\partial u}{\partial y}$$

which is clearly Newton's law of viscosity derived in Sec. 1–8. Hence $\mu$ is the dynamic viscosity of fluid.

The Cartesian equations of Stokes' laws of viscosity are easily transformed into cylindrical and spherical coordinates. The results in these two coordinates are given in Table 6–2.

**TABLE 6–2. Equations of Stokes' Law of Viscosity in Cylindrical and Spherical Coordinates**

1. Cylindrical coordinates $(r, \theta, z)$

$$\tau_{r\theta} = \tau_{\theta r} = \mu \left[ r \frac{\partial}{\partial r} \left( \frac{v_\theta}{r} \right) + \frac{1}{r} \frac{\partial v_r}{\partial \theta} \right] \qquad \text{(A)}$$

$$\tau_{\theta z} = \tau_{z\theta} = \mu \left[ \frac{\partial v_\theta}{\partial z} + \frac{1}{r} \frac{\partial v_z}{\partial \theta} \right] \qquad \text{(B)}$$

$$\tau_{zr} = \tau_{rz} = \mu \left[ \frac{\partial v_z}{\partial r} + \frac{\partial v_r}{\partial z} \right] \qquad \text{(C)}$$

$$\sigma_{rr} = 2\mu \frac{\partial v_r}{\partial r} - \frac{2}{3} \mu \, \text{div} \, \mathbf{V} - p \qquad \text{(D)}$$

$$\sigma_{\theta\theta} = 2\mu \left( \frac{1}{r} \frac{\partial v_\theta}{\partial \theta} + \frac{v_r}{r} \right) - \frac{2}{3} \mu \, \text{div} \, \mathbf{V} - p \qquad \text{(E)}$$

$$\sigma_{zz} = 2\mu \frac{\partial v_z}{\partial z} - \frac{2}{3} \mu \, \text{div} \, \mathbf{V} - p \qquad \text{(F)}$$

2. Spherical coordinates $(R, \theta, \phi)$

$$\tau_{R\theta} = \tau_{\theta R} = \mu \left[ R \frac{\partial}{\partial R} \left( \frac{v_\theta}{R} \right) + \frac{1}{R} \frac{\partial v_R}{\partial \theta} \right] \qquad \text{(G)}$$

$$\tau_{\theta\phi} = \tau_{\phi\theta} = \mu \left[ \frac{\sin\theta}{R} \frac{\partial}{\partial \theta} \left( \frac{v_\phi}{\sin\theta} \right) + \frac{1}{R \sin\theta} \frac{\partial v_\theta}{\partial \phi} \right] \qquad \text{(H)}$$

$$\tau_{\phi R} = \tau_{R\phi} = \mu \left[ \frac{1}{R \sin\theta} \frac{\partial v_R}{\partial \phi} + R \frac{\partial}{\partial R} \left( \frac{v_\phi}{R} \right) \right] \qquad \text{(I)}$$

$$\sigma_{RR} = 2\mu \frac{\partial v_R}{\partial R} - \frac{2}{3} \mu \, \text{div} \, \mathbf{V} - p \qquad \text{(J)}$$

$$\sigma_{\theta\theta} = 2\mu \left( \frac{1}{R} \frac{\partial v_\theta}{\partial \theta} + \frac{v_R}{R} \right) - \frac{2}{3} \mu \, \text{div} \, \mathbf{V} - p \qquad \text{(K)}$$

$$\sigma_{\phi\phi} = 2\mu \left( \frac{1}{R \sin\theta} \frac{\partial v_\phi}{\partial \phi} + \frac{v_R}{R} + \frac{v_\theta \cot\theta}{R} \right) - \frac{2}{3} \mu \, \text{div} \, \mathbf{V} - p \qquad \text{(L)}$$

## 6-4 The Navier-Stokes Equations

Introduction of Eqs. 6–12 into Eqs. (A), (B), and (C) in Table 6–1 yields the following equations of motion for a Newtonian fluid with varying density and viscosity:

$$\rho \frac{Du}{Dt} = \rho g_x - \frac{\partial p}{\partial x} + \frac{\partial}{\partial x}\left[\mu\left(2\frac{\partial u}{\partial x} - \frac{2}{3}\operatorname{div} \mathbf{V}\right)\right]$$

$$+ \frac{\partial}{\partial y}\left[\mu\left(\frac{\partial u}{\partial y} + \frac{\partial v}{\partial x}\right)\right] + \frac{\partial}{\partial z}\left[\mu\left(\frac{\partial w}{\partial x} + \frac{\partial u}{\partial z}\right)\right] \tag{6–13a}$$

$$\rho \frac{Dv}{Dt} = \rho g_y - \frac{\partial p}{\partial y} + \frac{\partial}{\partial y}\left[\mu\left(2\frac{\partial v}{\partial y} - \frac{2}{3}\operatorname{div} \mathbf{V}\right)\right]$$

$$+ \frac{\partial}{\partial z}\left[\mu\left(\frac{\partial v}{\partial z} + \frac{\partial w}{\partial y}\right)\right] + \frac{\partial}{\partial x}\left[\mu\left(\frac{\partial u}{\partial y} + \frac{\partial v}{\partial x}\right)\right] \tag{6–13b}$$

$$\rho \frac{Dw}{Dt} = \rho g_z - \frac{\partial p}{\partial z} + \frac{\partial}{\partial z}\left[\mu\left(2\frac{\partial w}{\partial z} - \frac{2}{3}\operatorname{div} \mathbf{V}\right)\right]$$

$$+ \frac{\partial}{\partial x}\left[\mu\left(\frac{\partial w}{\partial x} + \frac{\partial u}{\partial z}\right)\right] + \frac{\partial}{\partial y}\left[\mu\left(\frac{\partial v}{\partial z} + \frac{\partial w}{\partial y}\right)\right] \tag{6–13c}$$

In vector notations, these equations can be consolidated into the following form:

$$\rho \frac{D\mathbf{V}}{Dt} = \rho\mathbf{g} - \nabla p + \frac{4}{3}\nabla(\mu\nabla\cdot\mathbf{V}) + \nabla(\mathbf{V}\cdot\nabla\mu) - \mathbf{V}\nabla^2\mu$$

$$+ \nabla\mu \times (\nabla \times \mathbf{V}) - (\nabla\cdot\mathbf{V})\nabla\mu \tag{6–14}$$

$$- \nabla \times (\nabla \times \mu\mathbf{V})$$

Equations 6–13, along with the equation of continuity $\nabla \cdot \rho\mathbf{V} + \partial\rho/\partial t = 0$, the energy equation (Eq. 6–27), the equation of state $p = p(\rho, T)$, and the empirical viscosity law $\mu = \mu(T)$ form a system of seven equations which are theoretically sufficient for solving the seven variables $u, v, w, p, \rho, T, \mu$ in many flow problems involving Newtonian fluids. Unfortunately, these equations are highly nonlinear and, consequently, they are seldom used in their complete form to set up flow problems. We shall now impose restrictions on the flow in order to simplify the motion equations.

**Flow of Newtonian fluid with varying density but constant viscosity.** When the variation in viscosity becomes negligible, Eq. 6–14 reduces to

$$\rho \frac{D\mathbf{V}}{Dt} = \rho\mathbf{g} - \nabla p + \frac{1}{3}\mu\nabla(\nabla\cdot\mathbf{V}) + \mu\nabla^2\mathbf{V} \tag{6–15}$$

**Flow of Newtonian fluid with constant density and constant viscosity.** When the density of fluid also remains constant, the flow is incompressible, and the equation of continuity becomes $\nabla \cdot \mathbf{V} = 0$. Hence Eq. 6–15 is further simplified to

$$\rho \frac{D\mathbf{V}}{Dt} = \rho\mathbf{g} - \nabla p + \mu\nabla^2\mathbf{V} \tag{6–16}$$

## TABLE 6–3. The Navier-Stokes Equations in Different Coordinate Systems

### 1. Cartesian coordinates $(x, y, z)$

$x$-component:

$$\rho\left(u\frac{\partial u}{\partial x} + v\frac{\partial u}{\partial y} + w\frac{\partial u}{\partial z} + \frac{\partial u}{\partial t}\right) = \rho g_x - \frac{\partial p}{\partial x} + \mu\left(\frac{\partial^2 u}{\partial x^2} + \frac{\partial^2 u}{\partial y^2} + \frac{\partial^2 u}{\partial z^2}\right) \quad \text{(A)}$$

$y$-component:

$$\rho\left(u\frac{\partial v}{\partial x} + v\frac{\partial v}{\partial y} + w\frac{\partial v}{\partial z} + \frac{\partial v}{\partial t}\right) = \rho g_y - \frac{\partial p}{\partial y} + \mu\left(\frac{\partial^2 v}{\partial x^2} + \frac{\partial^2 v}{\partial y^2} + \frac{\partial^2 v}{\partial z^2}\right) \quad \text{(B)}$$

$z$-component:

$$\rho\left(u\frac{\partial w}{\partial x} + v\frac{\partial w}{\partial y} + w\frac{\partial w}{\partial z} + \frac{\partial w}{\partial t}\right) = \rho g_z - \frac{\partial p}{\partial z} + \mu\left(\frac{\partial^2 w}{\partial x^2} + \frac{\partial^2 w}{\partial y^2} + \frac{\partial^2 w}{\partial z^2}\right) \quad \text{(C)}$$

### 2. Cylindrical coordinates $(r, \theta, z)$

$r$-component:

$$\rho\left(v_r\frac{\partial v_r}{\partial r} + \frac{v_\theta}{r}\frac{\partial v_r}{\partial \theta} - \frac{v_\theta^2}{r} + v_z\frac{\partial v_z}{\partial z} + \frac{\partial v_z}{\partial t}\right)$$
$$= \rho g_r - \frac{\partial p}{\partial r} + \mu\left[\frac{\partial}{\partial r}\left(\frac{1}{r}\frac{\partial}{\partial r}rv_r\right) + \frac{1}{r^2}\frac{\partial^2 v_r}{\partial \theta^2} - \frac{2}{r^2}\frac{\partial v_\theta}{\partial \theta} + \frac{\partial^2 v_r}{\partial z^2}\right] \quad \text{(D)}$$

$\theta$-component:

$$\rho\left(v_r\frac{\partial v_\theta}{\partial r} + \frac{v_\theta}{r}\frac{\partial v_\theta}{\partial \theta} + \frac{v_r v_\theta}{r} + v_z\frac{\partial v_\theta}{\partial z} + \frac{\partial v_\theta}{\partial t}\right)$$
$$= \rho g_\theta - \frac{1}{r}\frac{\partial p}{\partial \theta} + \mu\left[\frac{\partial}{\partial r}\left(\frac{1}{r}\frac{\partial}{\partial r}rv_\theta\right) + \frac{1}{r^2}\frac{\partial^2 v_\theta}{\partial \theta^2} + \frac{2}{r^2}\frac{\partial v_r}{\partial \theta} + \frac{\partial^2 v_\theta}{\partial z^2}\right] \quad \text{(E)}$$

$z$-component:

$$\rho\left(v_r\frac{\partial v_z}{\partial r} + \frac{v_\theta}{r}\frac{\partial v_z}{\partial \theta} + v_z\frac{\partial v_z}{\partial z} + \frac{\partial v_z}{\partial t}\right)$$
$$= \rho g_z - \frac{\partial p}{\partial z} + \mu\left[\frac{1}{r}\frac{\partial}{\partial r}\left(r\frac{\partial v_z}{\partial r}\right) + \frac{1}{r^2}\frac{\partial^2 v_z}{\partial \theta^2} + \frac{\partial^2 v_z}{\partial z^2}\right] \quad \text{(F)}$$

### 3. Spherical coordinates $(R, \theta, \phi)$

$R$-component:

$$\rho\left(v_R\frac{\partial v_R}{\partial R} + \frac{v_\theta}{R}\frac{\partial v_R}{\partial \theta} + \frac{v_\phi}{R\sin\theta}\frac{\partial v_R}{\partial \phi} - \frac{v_\theta^2 + v_\phi^2}{R} + \frac{\partial v_R}{\partial t}\right)$$
$$= \rho g_R - \frac{\partial p}{\partial R} + \mu\left(\nabla^2 v_R - \frac{2}{R^2}v_R - \frac{2}{R^2}\frac{\partial v_\theta}{\partial \theta} - \frac{2}{R^2}v_R\cot\theta - \frac{2}{R^2\sin\theta}\frac{\partial v_\phi}{\partial \phi}\right) \quad \text{(G)}$$

$\theta$-component:

$$\rho\left(v_R\frac{\partial v_\theta}{\partial R} + \frac{v_\theta}{R}\frac{\partial v_\theta}{\partial \theta} - \frac{v_\phi}{R\sin\theta}\frac{\partial v_\theta}{\partial \phi} + \frac{v_R v_\theta}{R} - \frac{v_\phi^2\cot\theta}{R} + \frac{\partial v_\theta}{\partial t}\right)$$
$$= \rho g_\theta - \frac{1}{R}\frac{\partial p}{\partial \theta} + \mu\left(\nabla^2 v_\theta + \frac{2}{R^2}\frac{\partial v_R}{\partial \theta} - \frac{v_\theta}{R^2\sin^2\theta} - \frac{2\cos\theta}{R^2\sin^2\theta}\frac{\partial v_\phi}{\partial \phi}\right) \quad \text{(H)}$$

$\phi$-component:

$$\rho\left(v_R\frac{\partial v_\phi}{\partial R} + \frac{v_\theta}{R}\frac{\partial v_\phi}{\partial \theta} + \frac{v_\phi}{R\sin\theta}\frac{\partial v_\phi}{\partial \phi} + \frac{v_\phi v_R}{R} + \frac{v_\theta v_\phi}{R}\cot\theta + \frac{\partial v_\phi}{\partial t}\right)$$
$$= \rho g_\phi - \frac{1}{R\sin\theta}\frac{\partial p}{\partial \phi} + \mu\left(\nabla^2 v_\phi - \frac{v_\phi}{R^2\sin^2\theta} + \frac{2}{R^2\sin^2\theta}\frac{\partial v_R}{\partial \phi} + \frac{2\cos\theta}{R^2\sin^2\theta}\frac{\partial v_\theta}{\partial \phi}\right) \quad \text{(I)}$$

This is the famous Navier-Stokes equation[3] in vector form. The component forms of the Navier-Stokes equation in different coordinate systems are presented in Table 6–3.

Clearly, by letting $\mu$ vanish, the Navier-Stokes equation reduces to Euler's equation of motion for an irrotational flow.

## 6-5   The Energy Equation

Before proceeding to carry out the integration of some of the simplified Navier-Stokes equations, we shall derive the energy equation for the viscous fluid element in Fig. 6–2. Application of the first law of thermodynamics to the element, with the absence of shaft work, yields the following rate equation:

$$\frac{dQ}{dt} = \frac{DE}{Dt} + \frac{dW_{\text{flow}}}{dt}$$
$$= \frac{D}{Dt}\left(\hat{u} + \frac{V^2}{2} + h_z\right)dx\,dy\,dz + \frac{dW_{\text{flow}}}{dt} \qquad (6\text{–}17)$$

where $Q$ is the quantity of heat transport into the given volume $dx\,dy\,dz$, $\hat{u}$ is the specific internal energy (i.e., internal energy per unit mass), $V$ is the speed of the fluid element, $h_z$ is the elevation of the fluid element above an arbitrary gravitational datum, and $W_{\text{flow}}$ represents the flow work transferred to the surrounding due to surface forces. We shall now evaluate each term in Eq. 6–17.

The rate of heat transport $dQ/dt$ into the volume can be calculated in accordance with the well-known Fourier's law of heat conduction. *Fourier's law* states that the heat flux crossing an area $dA$ is proportional to the temperature gradient $\partial T/\partial n$ normal to $dA$:

$$\frac{dQ}{dt\,dA} = -k\frac{\partial T}{\partial n}$$

where $k$ is the thermal conductivity (having the units of Btu/ft-sec-°R in the British system); the negative sign indicates that the direction of heat flow is opposite to that of the temperature gradient. With reference to Fig. 6–2, the rate of heat transport into the volume in the $x$-direction crossing the left surface $dy\,dz$ is $-(dy\,dz)k\,\partial T/\partial x$, and that crossing the right surface $dy\,dz$ is $-(dy\,dz)[k\,\partial T/\partial x + (\partial/\partial x)(k\,\partial T/\partial x)\,dx]$. Hence the

[3]The Navier-Stokes equations were first derived by Louis Marie Henri Navier in 1832 and perfected by George Gabriel Stokes in 1845. See L. M. H. Navier, "Memoire sur les lois du mouvement des fluides" (Memoir on the Laws of Motion of Fluids), *Mém. Acad. Roy. Sci.*, Vol. VI, 1823; and G. G. Stokes, "On the Theories of the Internal Friction of Fluids in Motion, and of the Equilibrium and Motion of Elastic Solids," *Trans. Cambridge Phil. Soc.*, Vol. VIII, 1845.

net rate of heat transport into the volume in the $x$-direction becomes

$$\frac{dQ_x}{dt} = -(dy\,dz)k\frac{\partial T}{\partial x} - \left\{-(dy\,dz)\left[k\frac{\partial T}{\partial x} + \frac{\partial}{\partial x}\left(k\frac{\partial T}{\partial x}\right)dx\right]\right\}$$

$$= \frac{\partial}{\partial x}\left(k\frac{\partial T}{\partial x}\right)dx\,dy\,dz$$

Similar expressions can be derived for the rate of heat transport in the $y$- and $z$-directions. The total rate of heat transport into the volume by conduction is then the sum of those in all three directions:

$$\frac{dQ}{dt} = \frac{dQ_x}{dt} + \frac{dQ_y}{dt} + \frac{dQ_z}{dt}$$

$$= \left[\frac{\partial}{\partial x}\left(k\frac{\partial T}{\partial x}\right) + \frac{\partial}{\partial y}\left(k\frac{\partial T}{\partial y}\right) + \frac{\partial}{\partial z}\left(k\frac{\partial T}{\partial z}\right)\right]dx\,dy\,dz \qquad \textbf{(6–18)}$$

$$= (\boldsymbol{\nabla}\cdot k\boldsymbol{\nabla}T)\,dx\,dy\,dz$$

By multiplying Eqs. A, B, and C in Table 6–1 by $u$, $v$, and $w$, respectively, and adding them together, we obtain:

$$\frac{D}{Dt}\left(\frac{V^2}{2} + gh_z\right) = u\left(\frac{\partial\sigma_{xx}}{\partial x} + \frac{\partial\tau_{yx}}{\partial y} + \frac{\partial\tau_{zx}}{\partial z}\right)$$

$$+ v\left(\frac{\partial\tau_{xy}}{\partial x} + \frac{\partial\sigma_{yy}}{\partial y} + \frac{\partial\tau_{zy}}{\partial z}\right) \qquad \textbf{(6–19)}$$

$$+ w\left(\frac{\partial\tau_{xz}}{\partial x} + \frac{\partial\tau_{yz}}{\partial y} + \frac{\partial\sigma_{zz}}{\partial z}\right)$$

since

$$\frac{D}{Dt}\left(\frac{V^2}{2}\right) = \frac{D}{Dt}\left(\frac{u^2 + v^2 + w^2}{2}\right) = u\frac{Du}{Dt} + v\frac{Dv}{Dt} + w\frac{Dw}{Dt}$$

and[4]

$$\frac{D}{Dt}(gh_z) = u\frac{\partial}{\partial x}(gh_z) + v\frac{\partial}{\partial y}(gh_z) + w\frac{\partial}{\partial z}(gh_z)$$

$$= -ug_x - vg_y - wg_z$$

Equation 6–19 may be written more compactly in vector-tensor notations as

$$\frac{D}{Dt}\left(\frac{V^2}{2} + gh_z\right) = \mathbf{V}\cdot[\boldsymbol{\nabla}\cdot\mathbf{T}] \qquad \textbf{(6–20)}$$

In considering the flow work which the normal and shear forces on the surfaces of the element perform on the surroundings, it is necessary to reverse the signs (i.e., the arrows) of all surface stresses shown in Fig.

---

[4]The gravitational field is a conservative field so that the gravity force in any direction equals the negative derivative of the gravitational potential with respect to that direction. For example, $\rho g_x = -\partial(\rho gh_z)/\partial x$.

6–2, since these stresses represent the action of the surrounding fluids on the surfaces of the element. By definition, [rate of doing work] = [force] × [velocity in the direction of the force]. Hence the rate of flow work done by the $\sigma_{xx}$-pair, for example, on the surroundings can be calculated as:

$$\sigma_{xx}dy\,dz\,u - \left(\sigma_{xx} + \frac{\partial \sigma_{xx}}{\partial x}dx\right)dy\,dz\left(u + \frac{\partial u}{\partial x}dx\right)$$

$$= -\left(\sigma_{xx}\frac{\partial u}{\partial x} + u\frac{\partial \sigma_{xx}}{\partial x} + \frac{\partial \sigma_{xx}}{\partial x}\frac{\partial u}{\partial x}dx\right)dx\,dy\,dz$$

$$= -\,dx\,dy\,dz\,\frac{\partial}{\partial x}(u\sigma_{xx})$$

where the term with higher order of differentials has been neglected in the last step. By carrying out similar calculations for the other eight pairs of surface stresses and then summing them up, we see that the total rate of flow work is

$$\frac{dW_{\text{flow}}}{dt} = -dx\,dy\,dz\left[\frac{\partial}{\partial x}(\sigma_{xx}u + \tau_{xy}v + \tau_{xz}\,w)\right.$$

$$+ \frac{\partial}{\partial y}(\tau_{yx}u + \sigma_{yy}v + \tau_{yz}w) \qquad (6\text{--}21)$$

$$\left. + \frac{\partial}{\partial z}(\tau_{zx}u + \tau_{zy}v + \sigma_{zz}w)\right]$$

This equation may be written in vector-tensor notations as

$$\frac{dW_{\text{flow}}}{dt} = -dx\,dy\,dz\,\boldsymbol{\nabla} \cdot [\mathbf{T} \cdot \mathbf{V}] \qquad (6\text{--}22)$$

We now substitute Eqs. 6–18, 6–20, and 6–22 into Eq. 6–17 and divide the resulting equation by $dx\,dy\,dz$ to obtain one form of the energy equation for a viscous compressible fluid particle:

$$\boldsymbol{\nabla} \cdot k\boldsymbol{\nabla}T = \rho\frac{D\hat{u}}{dt} + \mathbf{V} \cdot [\boldsymbol{\nabla} \cdot \mathbf{T}] - \boldsymbol{\nabla} \cdot [\mathbf{T} \cdot \mathbf{V}] \qquad (6\text{--}23)$$

The last two terms in the above equation can be combined as follows:

$$\mathbf{V} \cdot [\boldsymbol{\nabla} \cdot \mathbf{T}] - \boldsymbol{\nabla} \cdot [\mathbf{T} \cdot \mathbf{V}]$$

$$= -\left(\sigma_{xx}\frac{\partial u}{\partial x} + \tau_{xy}\frac{\partial v}{\partial x} + \tau_{xz}\frac{\partial w}{\partial x}\right)$$

$$- \left(\tau_{yx}\frac{\partial u}{\partial y} + \sigma_{yy}\frac{\partial v}{\partial y} + \tau_{yz}\frac{\partial w}{\partial y}\right) \qquad (6\text{--}24)$$

$$- \left(\tau_{zx}\frac{\partial u}{\partial z} + \tau_{zy}\frac{\partial v}{\partial z} + \sigma_{zz}\frac{\partial w}{\partial z}\right)$$

Applying Stokes' laws of viscosity (Eqs. 6–12) to the shear and normal stresses in the above equation, we have

$$\mathbf{V} \cdot [\boldsymbol{\nabla} \cdot \mathbf{T}] - \boldsymbol{\nabla} \cdot [\mathbf{T} \cdot \mathbf{V}] = p\boldsymbol{\nabla} \cdot \mathbf{V} - \mu\Phi_v \qquad (6\text{--}25)$$

where

$$\Phi_v = 2\left[\left(\frac{\partial u}{\partial x}\right)^2 + \left(\frac{\partial v}{\partial y}\right)^2 + \left(\frac{\partial w}{\partial z}\right)^2\right]$$
$$+ \left(\frac{\partial w}{\partial y} + \frac{\partial v}{\partial z}\right)^2 + \left(\frac{\partial u}{\partial z} + \frac{\partial w}{\partial x}\right)^2 + \left(\frac{\partial v}{\partial x} + \frac{\partial u}{\partial y}\right)^2 \quad (6\text{–}26)$$
$$+ \frac{2}{3}\left(\frac{\partial u}{\partial x} + \frac{\partial v}{\partial y} + \frac{\partial w}{\partial z}\right)^2$$

This is known as the *dissipation function*. The quantity $\mu\Phi_v$ represents an irreversible rate of degradation of mechanical to thermal energy by viscous dissipation.

Introducing Eq. 6–25 into Eq. 6–23, we obtain the following form of energy equation:

$$\nabla \cdot k\nabla T = \rho \frac{D\hat{u}}{Dt} + p\nabla \cdot \mathbf{V} - \mu\Phi_v \quad (6\text{–}27)$$

| Rate of heat transport by conduction into the fluid particle | Rate of increase in specific internal energy of the fluid particle | Reversible rate of flow work on the surroundings by the fluid particle | Irreversible rate of flow work on the surroundings due to viscous forces |
|---|---|---|---|

For most engineering applications, it is convenient to have the energy equation expressed in terms of the fluid temperature and heat capacity rather than the specific internal energy. The specific internal energy $\hat{u}$ for a perfect gas is a function of temperature only; that is, $d\hat{u} = c_v\,dT$, where $c_v$ is the specific heat at constant volume (having the units of Btu/lbm-°R in the British system). Thus, we may write

$$\rho \frac{D\hat{u}}{Dt} = \rho \frac{D}{Dt}(c_v T) \quad (6\text{–}28)$$

and introduce it into Eq. 6–27 to get the energy equation for a viscous perfect gas as

$$\nabla \cdot k\nabla T = \rho \frac{D}{Dt}(c_v T) + p\nabla \cdot \mathbf{V} - \mu\Phi_v \quad (6\text{–}29)$$

For those viscous perfect gases whose properties $k$ and $c_v$ are independent of time and position, the energy equation assumes the following simpler form:

$$k\nabla^2 T = \rho c_v \frac{DT}{Dt} + p\nabla \cdot \mathbf{V} - \mu\Phi_v \quad (6\text{–}30)$$

Finally, for a viscous incompressible fluid, $(\nabla \cdot \mathbf{V})$ vanishes, so that the energy equation further reduces to

$$k\nabla^2 T = \rho c_v \frac{DT}{Dt} - \mu\Phi_v \quad (6\text{–}31)$$

## me Exact Solutions of the Navier-Stokes Equations

nain mathematical difficulty in solving the Navier-Stokes equations lies in the presence of nonlinear terms. The nonlinearity is present in the convective terms, such as $u\, \partial u/\partial x$, $v\, \partial u/\partial y$, etc. Hence the principle of superposition which has worked well in the solution of the linear partial differential equations (i.e., Laplace equations) for potential flows is not generally applicable to viscous flows. As a result, no general method has yet become available for the solution of the complete Navier-Stokes equations. However, it has been found possible to obtain exact mathematical solutions for a limited number of laminar flows for which the Navier-Stokes equations can be simplified to such an extent that the nonlinear convective terms drop out in a natural way. In the following sections we shall show how to simplify the Navier-Stokes equations for several simple flows and then to obtain their mathematical solutions by using the boundary conditions in each flow. The standard procedure of simplifying the Navier-Stokes equations is to drop those terms which are negligibly small in the flow being studied.

### 6-7 Laminar Flow of an Incompressible Fluid Through Straight Channels with Parallel Boundaries

In a laminar flow, all fluid particles move parallel to the channel so that only one velocity component need be regarded as different from zero. For example, if the direction of flow is parallel to the $x$-axis of a Cartesian coordinate system, the velocity components $v$ and $w$ are everywhere equal to zero. Hence the equation of continuity for an incompressible flow specifies that $\partial u/\partial x = 0$, which means that $u$ is independent of $x$. Thus,

$$u = u(y, z, t), \qquad v = 0, \qquad w = 0$$

are the general expressions for the velocity field of this flow. Substitution of these expressions into Eqs. (A), (B), and (C) in Table 6–3 yields the following simplified equations of motion:

$x$-component: $\quad \rho \dfrac{\partial u}{\partial t} = \rho g_x - \dfrac{\partial p}{\partial x} + \mu\left(\dfrac{\partial^2 u}{\partial y^2} + \dfrac{\partial^2 u}{\partial z^2}\right)$ \hfill (6-32)

$y$-component: $\quad 0 = \rho g_y - \dfrac{\partial p}{\partial y}$ \hfill (6-33)

$z$-component: $\quad 0 = \rho g_z - \dfrac{\partial p}{\partial z}$ \hfill (6-34)

Equation 6–32 is a linear partial differential equation for $u = u(y, z, t)$.

Equations 6–33 and 6–34 indicate that the pressure varies hydrostatically in the $y$- and $z$-directions.

### Two-dimensional laminar flow between two fixed parallel flat plates.

A rather simple solution of Eq. 6–32 can be obtained for a two-dimensional steady flow between two fixed parallel flat plates separated by a distance $b$, as shown in Fig. 6–4. If the flow is in the $x$-direction, and

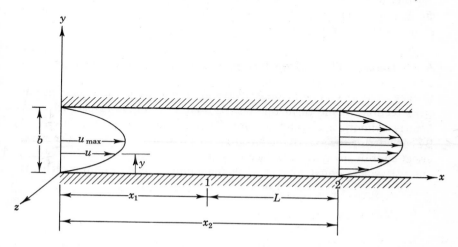

**Fig. 6-4.** Two-dimensional laminar flow between two fixed parallel flat plates.

the $x$-direction is taken as normal to the direction of the gravity so that $\rho g_x = 0$, Eq. 6–32 becomes simply

$$\frac{\partial p}{\partial x} = \mu\left(\frac{\partial^2 u}{\partial y^2}\right) \qquad (6\text{–}35)$$

Since $\partial p/\partial x$, the pressure gradient in the $x$-direction, is independent of $y$, this equation can be integrated twice with respect to $y$ to obtain the following general solution for the laminar flow within two parallel plates:

$$u = \frac{1}{2\mu}\frac{\partial p}{\partial x}y^2 + C_1 y + C_2 \qquad (6\text{–}36)$$

The two constants of integration $C_1$ and $C_2$ may be evaluated by means of the two boundary conditions, namely, no slip of fluid at the two solid boundary surfaces. For the two fixed plates

$$u = 0 \quad \text{at} \quad y = 0; \quad C_2 = 0$$

and

$$u = 0 \quad \text{at} \quad y = \underset{2}{b}; \qquad C_1 = -\frac{1}{2\mu}\frac{\partial p}{\partial x}b$$

Thus the resulting equation for $u$

$$u = \frac{1}{2\mu}\left(-\frac{\partial p}{\partial x}\right)(by - y^2) \tag{6-37}$$

together with $v = 0$ and $w = 0$ forms the complete solution for this steady laminar flow. The velocity profile for this flow is a parabola in the $xy$ plane, as shown in Fig. 6–4.

## 6-8   Laminar Flow of an Incompressible Fluid in Round Pipes

The axial flow of an incompressible fluid in a straight pipe of constant cross section, as shown in Fig. 6–5, is another example of parallel flow. Clearly cylindrical coordinates are the most appropriate for this flow. By considering the axis of the pipe to coincide with the $z$-axis of the cylindrical coordinate system, we see that the velocity components $v_r$ and $v_\theta$ are everywhere equal to zero. The remaining velocity component $v_z$ is

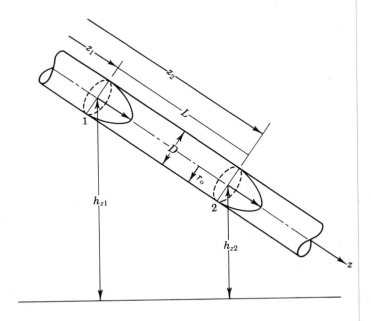

**Fig. 6-5.** Laminar flow of an incompressible fluid in a round pipe.

independent of $\theta$ because of axial symmetry. Furthermore, the equation of continuity for this incompressible flow is simply

$$\frac{\partial v_z}{\partial z} = 0$$

indicating that $v_z$ is also independent of $z$. Thus

$$v_r = 0, \qquad v_\theta = 0, \qquad v_z = v_z(r, t)$$

are the general expressions for the velocity field of this flow. Substitution of these expressions into Eqs. (D), (E), and (F) in Table 6–3 results in the following simplified equations of motion:

$r$-component:   $\quad 0 = \rho g_r - \dfrac{\partial p}{\partial r}$  \hfill (6–38)

$\theta$-component:   $\quad 0 = \rho g_\theta - \dfrac{1}{r}\dfrac{\partial p}{\partial \theta}$  \hfill (6–39)

$z$-component:   $\quad \rho\dfrac{\partial v_z}{\partial t} = \rho g_z - \dfrac{\partial p}{\partial z} + \mu\dfrac{1}{r}\dfrac{\partial}{\partial r}\left(r\dfrac{\partial v_z}{\partial r}\right)$  \hfill (6–40)

The first two equations indicate that the fluid pressure varies hydrostatically in the $r$- and $\theta$-directions. Equation 6–40 is a linear partial differential equation for $v_z = v_z(r, t)$.

By restricting this derivation to steady flow so that $\rho\partial v_z/\partial t = 0$ and recognizing that $\rho g_z$ may be written as $-\partial(\rho gh_z)/\partial z$, we may simplify Eq. 6–40 to

$$0 = -\frac{\partial}{\partial z}(\rho gh_z + p) + \mu\frac{1}{r}\frac{\partial}{\partial r}\left(r\frac{\partial v_z}{\partial r}\right) \qquad (6\text{–}41)$$

Integrating this equation twice with respect to $r$, we obtain the following solution for $v_z$:

$$v_z = \frac{1}{4\mu}\left[\frac{\partial}{\partial z}(\rho gh_z + p)\right]r^2 + C_1 \ln r + C_2 \qquad (6\text{–}42)$$

since $\partial(\rho gh_z + p)/\partial z$ is independent of $r$. To evaluate $C_1$ and $C_2$, it is necessary to find two boundary conditions. Only one is physically obvious; that is, $v_z = 0$ at $r = D/2$, where $D$ is the inside diameter of the pipe. However, by examining Eq. 6–42, we notice that the term $C_1 \ln r$ becomes infinite for $r = 0$ (that is, at the axis of the pipe); this is physically impossible. Consequently, the constant $C_1$ must be zero and the term $C_1 \ln r$ vanishes from Eq. 6–42 in order to render the equation physically meaningful for the entire flow field inside the pipe. Then the boundary condition $v_z = 0$ at $r = D/2$ gives

$$C_2 = \frac{1}{4\mu}\left[-\frac{\partial}{\partial z}(\rho gh_z + p)\right]\frac{D^2}{4}$$

and the final equation for the velocity profile becomes

$$v_z = \frac{1}{4\mu}\left[-\frac{\partial}{\partial z}(\rho g h_z + p)\right]\left(\frac{D^2}{4} - r^2\right) \tag{6-43}$$

which is an equation of parabola. The velocity varies parabolically along a diameter, and the velocity profile is a paraboloid of revolution over a cross section of the pipe.

The maximum velocity $(v_z)_{\max}$ occurs at the axis of the pipe and has the magnitude of

$$(v_z)_{\max} = \frac{1}{4\mu}\left[-\frac{\partial}{\partial z}(\rho g h_z + p)\right]\frac{D^2}{4} \tag{6-44}$$

The volumetric rate of flow $\hat{Q}$ through any cross section of diameter $D$ is

$$\begin{aligned}\hat{Q} &= \int_0^{D/2} \frac{1}{4\mu}\left[-\frac{\partial}{\partial z}(\rho g h_z + p)\right]\left(\frac{D^2}{4} - r^2\right)2\pi r\, dr \\ &= \frac{\pi}{8\mu}\left[-\frac{\partial}{\partial z}(\rho g h_z + p)\right]\frac{D^4}{16}\end{aligned} \tag{6-45}$$

and the average velocity $V$ is $\hat{Q}/A$, i.e.,

$$V = \frac{\hat{Q}}{\pi D^2/4} = \frac{1}{8\mu}\left[-\frac{\partial}{\partial z}(\rho g h_z + p)\right]\frac{D^2}{4} \tag{6-46}$$

Comparison of Eqs. 6–44 and 6–46 reveals that

$$V = \tfrac{1}{2}(v_z)_{\max} \tag{6-47}$$

for this flow.

Equation 6–46 may now be rearranged in the following form:

$$-\partial(\rho g h_z + p) = \frac{32\mu V}{D^2}\partial z$$

and then integrated with respect to $z$ for any straight stretch of pipe between $z_1$ and $z_2$; $z_2 - z_1 = L$, as shown in Fig. 6–5. The result of integration is

$$(\rho g h_{z1} + p_1) - (\rho g h_{z2} + p_2) = \frac{32\mu V L}{D^2} \tag{6-48}$$

This is the well-known Hagen-Poiseuille equation for laminar flow in straight pipes of circular cross section. Experimental observations indicate that this equation is valid for pipe flows with $V D \rho/\mu$ less than 2000.

*Illustrative Example 6-1.* Develop an expression for the $\hat{Q}$ discharged by laminar flow through the annular space between two concentric tubes of circular cross section. The inside diameter of the outer tube is $d_2$ and the outside diameter of the inner tube is $d_1$. Their respective radii are $r_2$ and $r_1$.

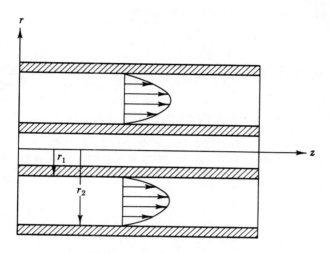

**Illustrative Example 6-1.**

*Solution:* The general solution for this flow is exactly the same as that for the Hagen-Poiseuille flow just derived, except that $\partial(\rho g h_z)/\partial z = 0$, since the flow is along a horizontal axis. Hence

$$v_z = \frac{1}{4\mu}\frac{\partial p}{\partial z} r^2 + C_3 \ln r + C_4 \tag{A}$$

The two constants of integration, $C_3$ and $C_4$, are to be determined by the following two boundary conditions for this flow: (1) $v_z = 0$ at $r = r_1$, and (2) $v_z = 0$ at $r = r_2$. Substitution of these values into Eq. (A) yields

$$0 = \frac{1}{4\mu}\frac{\partial p}{\partial z} r_1^2 + C_3 \ln r_1 + C_4 \tag{B}$$

$$0 = \frac{1}{4\mu}\frac{\partial p}{\partial z} r_2^2 + C_3 \ln r_2 + C_4 \tag{C}$$

from which

$$C_3 = -\frac{1}{4\mu}\frac{\partial p}{\partial z}\frac{r_2^2 - r_1^2}{\ln (r_2/r_1)} \tag{D}$$

$$C_4 = -\frac{1}{4\mu}\frac{\partial p}{\partial z}\left[r_2^2 - \frac{r_2^2 - r_1^2}{\ln (r_2/r_1)} \ln r_2\right] \tag{E}$$

Combining Eqs. (A), (D), and (E), we obtain the following expression for point velocity in this laminar flow:

$$v_z = \frac{1}{4\mu}\frac{\partial p}{\partial z}\left[r^2 - r_2^2 - \frac{r_2^2 - r_1^2}{\ln (r^2/r_1)} \ln \frac{r}{r_2}\right] \tag{F}$$

The discharge $\hat{Q}$ is then

$$\hat{Q} = \int_A v_z \, dA = \int_{r_1}^{r_2} v_z 2\pi r \, dr$$

$$= \frac{\pi}{8\mu}\left(-\frac{\partial p}{\partial z}\right)\left[r_2^4 - r_1^4 - \frac{(r_2^2 - r_1^2)^2}{\ln(r_2/r_1)}\right]$$

(G)

We write the result in this form by putting a minus sign in front of the pressure gradient in order to emphasize that the fluid pressure decreases in the direction of flow. Flow work must be performed on the fluid moving in an annulus to compensate for the viscous resistance of flow.

*Illustrative Example 6-2.* Laminar flow of an oil (sp. gr. 0.93 and $\mu = 1.55 \times 10^{-3}$ lbf-sec/ft²) occurs in an inclined pipe as shown in the accompanying sketch. (a) Determine the direction of flow, and (b) compute the rate of flow in gallons per minute.

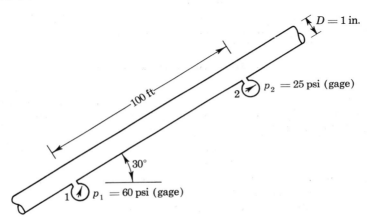

$D = 1$ in.

$p_2 = 25$ psi (gage)

100 ft

30°

$p_1 = 60$ psi (gage)

**Illustrative Example 6-2.**

*Solution:* (a) With the elevation datum at section 1 and the atmospheric pressure as pressure datum, the piezometric pressure at section 1 is

$$\rho g h_{z1} + p_1 = 0 + 60\frac{\text{lbf}}{\text{in.}^2} \times 144\frac{\text{in.}^2}{\text{ft}^2} = 8640\frac{\text{lbf}}{\text{ft}^2}$$

and the piezometric pressure at section 2 is

$$\rho g h_{z2} + p_2 = 0.93 \times 62.4\frac{\text{lbf}}{\text{ft}^3} \times 50\text{ ft} + 25\frac{\text{lbf}}{\text{in.}^2} \times 144\frac{\text{in.}^2}{\text{ft}^2} = 6500\frac{\text{lbf}}{\text{ft}^2}$$

Since $(\rho g h_{z1} + p_1) > (\rho g h_{z2} + p_2)$, the flow is in the upward direction from section 1 to section 2.

(b) From Eq. 6-48,

$$V = \frac{[(\rho g h_{z1} + p_1) - (\rho g h_{z2} + p_2)]D^2}{32\mu L}$$

$$= \frac{(8640 - 6500)\text{lbf/ft}^2 \times (\frac{1}{12}\text{ft})^2}{32(1.55 \times 10^{-3}\text{ lbf-sec/ft}^2)(100\text{ ft})}$$

$$= 3.0\text{ ft/sec}$$

The rate of flow is

$$\hat{Q} = VA = 3.0\,\frac{\text{ft}}{\text{sec}} \times \frac{\pi}{4} \times \left(\frac{1}{12}\text{ft}\right)^2 = 0.0164\,\frac{\text{ft}^3}{\text{sec}}$$

which may be converted to gallons per minute:

$$\hat{Q} = 0.0164\,\frac{\text{ft}^3}{\text{sec}} \times 7.48\,\frac{\text{gal}}{\text{ft}^3} \times 60\,\frac{\text{sec}}{\text{min}}$$

$$= 7.35\,\text{gal/min}$$

Finally, let us check $VD\rho/\mu$:

$$\frac{VD\rho}{\mu} = \frac{3.0\,\text{ft/sec} \times (\frac{1}{12}\,\text{ft}) \times 0.93 \times 62.4\,\text{lbf/ft}^3}{(1.55 \times 10^{-3}\,\text{lbf-sec/ft}^2)(32.174\,\text{ft/sec}^2)}$$

$$= 291 < 2000$$

**Entrance transition length.** Equation 6–48 applies only to the fully developed laminar pipe flow which occurs at a sufficient distance from the pipe entrance. When fluid enters a well-rounded entrance from a reservoir (Fig. 6–6), all fluid particles move with a uniform velocity

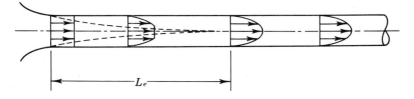

**Fig. 6-6.** Pipe entrance transition length.

because the flow in this region is essentially irrotational. However, fluid viscosity causes those particles next to the pipe wall to stick to the wall. Thus the velocity of flow is zero at the pipe wall and there the velocity gradient becomes extremely steep. The steep velocity gradient produces high frictional resistance in the flow near the pipe wall. The fluid motion slows down in the vicinity of the pipe wall as the fluid moves downstream. Since, for steady flow, the mass rate of flow remains constant, the fluid near the axis of the pipe must be accelerated convectively until an equilibrium condition is finally established for fully developed laminar flow with a parabolic distribution of velocity. Thus, we may consider that a laminar boundary layer is formed at the entrance and thickens downstream until the entire pipe cross section is occupied by this laminar boundary layer, as shown in Fig. 6–6.

The term *entrance transition length* $L_e$ is used for the distance between the pipe entrance and the section at which laminar flow is fully developed. In this transition length the convective acceleration term makes the motion equation nonlinear. Langhaar[5] developed the following formula for the theoretical laminar entrance transition length:

$$L_e = 0.058 \frac{VD\rho}{\mu} D \qquad (6\text{--}49)$$

which is in good agreement with experimental data.

## 6-9 Creeping Flow Around a Solid Sphere

The Navier-Stokes equations for incompressible flow can be solved when the velocity components become extremely small so that the inertia terms are negligible as compared to other terms. The very slow fluid motion is frequently characterized as the *creeping motion*. It is seen from Eq. 6–16 that by omitting the inertia term the incompressible Navier-Stokes equation for creeping motion becomes simply

$$\nabla(p + \rho g h_z) = \mu \nabla^2 \mathbf{V} \qquad (6\text{--}50)$$

The oldest known solution for a creeping motion is the very slow flow of an incompressible viscous fluid around a solid sphere of radius $R_0$ (or diameter $D$), as shown in Fig. 6–7. The flow approaches the sphere vertically upward along the $z$-axis with a uniform velocity $V_\infty$. Clearly the spherical coordinates are most appropriate for the spherical boundary.

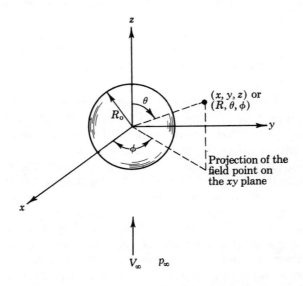

**Fig. 6-7.** Creeping flow around a solid sphere.

[5]H. L. Langhaar, "Steady Flow in the Transition Length of a Straight Tube," *J. Appl. Mech.*, Vol. X, 55, 1942.

The spherical components of the Navier-Stokes equations can be found in Table 6–3. We shall not attempt to show the rather lengthy steps in the solution of this problem.[6] The following field equations for pressure and velocity components represent the solution for this flow:

$$p = p_\infty - \rho g z - \frac{3}{2} \frac{\mu V_\infty}{R_0} \left(\frac{R_0}{R}\right)^2 \cos\theta \qquad (6\text{–}51)$$

$$v_R = V_\infty \left[1 - \frac{3}{2}\left(\frac{R_0}{R}\right) + \frac{1}{2}\left(\frac{R_0}{R}\right)^3\right] \cos\theta \qquad (6\text{–}52)$$

$$v_\theta = -V_\infty \left[1 - \frac{3}{4}\left(\frac{R_0}{R}\right) - \frac{1}{4}\left(\frac{R_0}{R}\right)^3\right] \sin\theta \qquad (6\text{–}53)$$

$$v_z = V_\infty \left[1 - \frac{1}{4}\frac{R_0}{R}\left(3 + \frac{R_0^2}{R^2}\right) + \frac{3}{4}\left(\frac{R_0^2}{R^2} - 1\right) \cos^2\theta\right] \qquad (6\text{–}54)$$

In the pressure equation (Eq. 6–51) the quantity $p_\infty$ is the pressure in the plane $z = 0$ far away from the sphere; the term $-\rho g z$ accounts for the hydrostatic effect since the negative $z$-axis is in the direction of gravity; and the last term represents the effect of the presence of the sphere.

The fact that these field equations do represent the solution for this flow can be readily established by substituting them into the equation of continuity and Eq. 6–50.

It is easy to show that these equations satisfy the boundary conditions for this flow. First, the pressure equation reduces to $p = p_\infty - \rho g z$, which is simply the hydrostatic equation, as the last term vanishes for large values of $R$. Then $v_R = v_\theta = 0$ on the surface of the sphere when $R = R_0$. Finally $v_z$ approaches $V_\infty$ in regions far away from the sphere where $R$ approaches infinity.

**Net force exerted by the fluid on the sphere.** To find the net force on the sphere, it is necessary to calculate the pressure and shear forces on every area element on the surface of the sphere and then to integrate them over the entire surface.

We shall first calculate the total pressure force on the sphere. The pressure $p_b$ on the surface of the sphere can be determined from Eq. 6-51 in the following manner:

$$p_b = p|_{R=R_0} = p_\infty - \rho g z - \frac{3}{2}\frac{\mu V_\infty}{R_0}\left(\frac{R_0}{R}\right)^2 \cos\theta$$

$$= p_\infty - \rho g z - \frac{3}{2}\frac{\mu V_\infty}{R_0}\cos\theta \qquad (6\text{–}55)$$

The pressure force $dF_p$ on a differential area element $R^2 \sin\theta \, d\theta \, d\phi$ of the surface of the sphere is

---

[6]See Sir Horace Lamb, *Hydrodynamics*, 6th ed. (New York: Dover Publications, Inc., 1945) pp. 597–604.

$$dF_p = p_b \, dA = \left( p_\infty - \rho gz - \frac{3}{2} \frac{\mu V_\infty}{R_0} \cos\theta \right) R^2 \sin\theta \, d\theta \, d\phi$$

This force acts perpendicularly to the area element. The component of $dF_p$ in the positive $z$-direction is $-dF_p \cos\theta$. Therefore, the resultant pressure force $F_{pz}$ in the positive $z$-direction can be obtained by the following integration:

$$F_{pz} = \int_0^{2\pi} \int_0^\pi - \left( p_\infty - \rho gz - \frac{3}{2} \frac{\mu V_\infty}{R_0} \cos\theta \right) R^2 \sin\theta \cos\theta \, d\theta \, d\phi$$

which yields

$$F_{pz} = \tfrac{4}{3} \pi R_0^3 \rho g + 2\pi \mu R_0 V_\infty \qquad (6\text{–}56)$$

The first term on the right-hand side is the buoyancy force. The second term is the drag force due to pressure difference and is referred to as the *form drag*, because the magnitude of this force depends on the form of the submerged object.

The resultant force due to viscous shear must be evaluated from the shear stress on the surface of the sphere:

$$(\tau_{R\theta})_b = \tau_{R\theta}|_{R=R_0} = \mu \left( \frac{1}{R} \frac{\partial v_R}{\partial\theta} + \frac{\partial v_\theta}{\partial R} \right)_{R=R_0} \qquad (6\text{–}57)$$

Thus,

$$\frac{\partial v_R}{\partial\theta}\bigg|_{R=R_0} = \frac{\partial}{\partial\theta} \left\{ V_\infty \left[ 1 - \frac{3}{2}\left(\frac{R_0}{R}\right) + \frac{1}{2}\left(\frac{R_0}{R}\right)^3 \right] \cos\theta \right\}_{R=R_0} = 0$$

and

$$\frac{\partial v_\theta}{\partial R}\bigg|_{R=R_0} = \frac{\partial}{\partial R} \left\{ -V_\infty \left[ 1 - \frac{3}{4}\left(\frac{R_0}{R}\right) - \frac{1}{4}\left(\frac{R_0}{R}\right)^3 \right] \sin\theta \right\}_{R=R_0}$$

$$= -\frac{3}{2} \frac{V_\infty}{R_0} \sin\theta$$

Substitution of these results into Eq. 6–57 yields

$$(\tau_{R\theta})_b = \tau_{R\theta}|_{R=R_0} = -\frac{3}{2} \frac{\mu V_\infty}{R_0} \sin\theta \qquad (6\text{–}58)$$

The shear force $dF_s$ on a differential area element $R^2 \sin\theta \, d\theta \, d\phi$ of the surface of the sphere is

$$dF_s = (\tau_{R\theta})_b \, dA = -\frac{3}{2} \frac{\mu V_\infty}{R_0} \sin\theta \, R^2 \sin\theta \, d\theta \, d\phi$$

This force acts at $dA$ in the $\theta$-direction. The component of $dF_s$ in the positive $z$-direction is $-dF_s \sin\theta$, and the resultant shear force in the positive $z$-direction is obtained by the integration:

$$F_{sz} = \int_0^{2\pi} \int_0^\pi - \frac{3}{2} \frac{\mu V_\infty}{R_0} R^2 \sin^3\theta \, d\theta \, d\phi = 4\pi \mu R_0 V \qquad (6\text{–}59)$$

This force is called the *shear drag*.

The total force $F_z$ on the sphere due to fluid flow is given by the sum of Eqs. 6–56 and 6–59:

$$F_z = \tfrac{4}{3}\pi R_0^3 \rho g + 2\pi \mu R_0 V_\infty + 4\pi \mu R_0 V_\infty \qquad (6\text{–}60)$$

$$\underset{\substack{\text{Buoyancy}\\\text{force}}}{\phantom{F}}\qquad \underset{\text{Form drag}}{\phantom{F}}\qquad \underset{\substack{\text{Viscous shear}\\\text{drag}}}{\phantom{F}}$$

or

$$F_z = \tfrac{4}{3}\pi R_0^3 \rho g + 6\pi \mu R_0 V_\infty \qquad (6\text{–}60a)$$

The equation for the total drag on the sphere

$$F_D = 6\pi \mu R_0 V_\infty \qquad (6\text{–}61)$$

is known as *Stokes' law*. We must remember that this law has been derived for very slow fluid motion. The law is valid for the numerical value of $V_\infty D\rho/\mu$ of about 0.1; at $V_\infty D\rho/\mu = 1$, Eq. 6–61 gives a drag force which is approximately 10 per cent too low.

Practical application of Stokes' law has been found in the study of sedimentation and of the motion of colloidal particles in an electric field.

## 6-10   Laminar Flow Near a Suddenly Accelerated Plane Surface

All the examples of exact solutions of simplified Navier-Stokes equations discussed so far have been for steady flow. We shall now investigate a simple unsteady parallel laminar flow.

A semi-infinite body of fluid with constant $\rho$ and $\mu$ is bounded by a flat plate, as shown in Fig. 6–8. The plate is in the $xy$ plane. The system is initially at rest. At time $t = 0$, the plate is suddenly set in motion in the $y$-direction with a constant velocity $V_0$. We shall attempt to find a

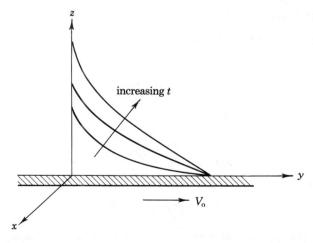

**Fig. 6-8.**  Laminar flow near a suddenly accelerated plane surface.

function which will describe the velocity of the fluid in the neighborhood of the flat surface.

Clearly the motion of the plate will induce the fluid to move in the $y$-direction only, leaving $u = 0$ and $w = 0$ for the entire flow field. Hence the equation of continuity for an incompressible fluid is

$$\frac{\partial v}{\partial y} = 0$$

which indicates that $v$ is independent of $y$. For parallel flow in the $y$-direction, $v$ is also independent of $x$, so that we may expect

$$v = v(z, t)$$

as the general form of the solution for this flow.

Let us assume for simplicity that the direction of gravity is along the negative $z$-axis. Therefore, for laminar flow the $y$-component of the Navier-Stokes equations reduces to

$$\rho \frac{\partial v}{\partial t} = \mu \frac{\partial^2 v}{\partial z^2} \quad \text{or} \quad \frac{\partial v}{\partial t} = \nu \frac{\partial^2 v}{\partial z^2} \tag{6–62}$$

where $\nu = \mu/\rho$. The boundary conditions for this flow are

1. $v = 0$ for all values of $z$ at $t \leqslant 0$
2. $v = V_0$ at $z = 0$ for $t > 0$
3. $v \rightarrow 0$ as $z \rightarrow \infty$ for $t > 0$

Since the solution of Eq. 6–62 must contain both $z$ and $t$, we shall guess the solution to have the following form:

$$v = V_0 f(\eta) \tag{6–63}$$

in which $\eta$ equals $z/\sqrt{4\nu t}$ which is a dimensionless variable, and $f(\eta)$ means a function of $\eta$. Thus,

$$\frac{\partial v}{\partial t} = \frac{\partial}{\partial t}[V_0 f(\eta)] = V_0 \frac{\partial f(\eta)}{\partial \eta} \frac{\partial \eta}{\partial t} = V_0 \frac{\partial f(\eta)}{\partial \eta} \left(-\frac{1}{2}\frac{\eta}{t}\right)$$

and

$$\frac{\partial^2 v}{\partial z^2} = \frac{\partial^2}{\partial z^2}[V_0 f(\eta)] = V_0 \frac{\partial}{\partial z}\left[\frac{\partial f(\eta)}{\partial \eta} \frac{\partial \eta}{\partial z}\right]$$

$$= V_0 \frac{\partial}{\partial z}\left[\frac{\partial f(\eta)}{\partial \eta} \frac{1}{\sqrt{4\nu t}}\right]$$

$$= \frac{V_0}{\sqrt{4\nu t}} \frac{\partial}{\partial \eta}\left[\frac{\partial f(\eta)}{\partial \eta}\right]\frac{\partial \eta}{\partial z} = V_0 \frac{\eta^2}{z^2} \frac{\partial^2 f(\eta)}{\partial \eta^2}$$

Substitution of these into Eq. 6–62 yields

$$-\frac{1}{2}\frac{\eta}{t} V_0 \frac{\partial f(\eta)}{\partial \eta} = \nu V_0 \frac{\eta^2}{z^2} \frac{\partial^2 f(\eta)}{\partial \eta^2}$$

Since the two partial differentiations are now both with respect to $\eta$, we may write them as total differentiations and then rearrange the above equation as

$$\frac{d^2 f(\eta)}{d\eta^2} + 2\eta \frac{df(\eta)}{d\eta} = 0 \qquad (6\text{–}64)$$

This is a second-order differential equation for $f(\eta)$. The boundary conditions for this equation accordingly are:

1. $f(\eta) = 1$   at   $\eta = 0$
2. $f(\eta) \to 0$   as   $\eta \to \infty$

Now if we introduce a new variable $\phi$ to replace $df(\eta)/d\eta$, Eq. 6–64 becomes a first-order differential equation with separable variables:

$$\frac{d\phi}{d\eta} + 2\eta\phi = 0$$

for which the solution is easily obtained as

$$\phi = \frac{df(\eta)}{d\eta} = C_1 e^{-\eta^2}$$

Integration of this equation with respect to $\eta$ then gives the function $f(\eta)$ in indefinite integral form

$$f(\eta) = C_1 \int_0^\eta e^{-\eta^2} \, d\eta + C_2 \qquad (6\text{–}65)$$

with an arbitrarily assigned value $\eta = 0$ as its lower limit because we are unable to evaluate the integral in closed form. The two constants of integration can be evaluated by the two boundary conditions. Thus, the first boundary condition

$$f(\eta) = 1 \quad \text{at} \quad \eta = 0 \quad \text{yields} \quad C_2 = 1$$

and the second boundary condition

$$f(\eta) \to 0 \quad \text{as} \quad \eta \to \infty \quad \text{yields} \quad C_1 = \frac{-1}{\displaystyle\int_0^\infty e^{-\eta^2} \, d\eta}$$

With these values of $C_1$ and $C_2$, Eq. 6–65 then becomes

$$f(\eta) = 1 - \frac{\displaystyle\int_0^\eta e^{-\eta^2} \, d\eta}{\displaystyle\int_0^\infty e^{-\eta^2} \, d\eta} = 1 - \frac{2}{\sqrt{\pi}} \int_0^\eta e^{-\eta^2} \, d\eta \qquad (6\text{–}66)$$

in which the ratio of the integrals is called the *error function*, erf $\eta$, which is a well-known function in the theory of probability. The numerical values of the error function have been tabulated elsewhere.[7] Hence the solution of Equation 6–62 for this unsteady flow may be written as

$$v = V_0 \left( 1 - \operatorname{erf} \frac{z}{\sqrt{4\nu t}} \right) \qquad (6\text{–}67)$$

---

[7]See, for example, H. B. Dwight, *Tables of Integrals and Other Mathematical Data*, 3rd ed. New York: The Macmillan Company, 1957.

This equation is plotted graphically in Fig. 6–9 in dimensionless form with $v/V_0$ as abscissa and $z/\sqrt{4\nu t}$ as ordinates.

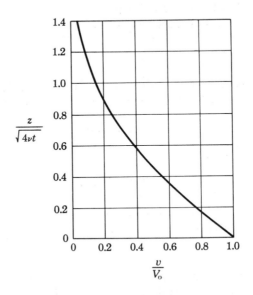

**Fig. 6-9.** Velocity distribution near a suddenly accelerated plane surface plotted in dimensionless form.

The interesting feature of this problem is the governing equation (Eq. 6–62) for this flow. Equation 6–62 is in the general form of the so-called "diffusion equation," which describes diffusion phenomena such as transient heat conduction in a solid or diffusion of one gas into another. Hence the solution (Eq. 6–67) may be considered as a description of diffusion of the viscosity effect from a solid plate surface into the fluid as the plate is moved impulsively. Here the diffusion phenomenon is manifested in the motion of initially stationary fluid particles as a result of the action of fluid viscosity. Diffusion of viscous effect from a solid boundary into the fluid is an important phenomenon in fluid mechanics.

## 6-11   Reynolds' Law of Dynamic Similarity of Flow of Viscous Fluids

In the preceding sections mathematical solutions for a few laminar flows were found possible on the basis of simplified flow models. In all these flows the type of fluid motion is relatively simple, and the nonlinear terms of the convective acceleration are everywhere zero. Nevertheless, the general solution of the Navier-Stokes equations with all nonlinear terms intact is not yet available. It was Osborne Reynolds who, at the beginning of this century, recognized this insurmountable mathematical difficulty and proposed a new approach to study the motion of viscous fluids by considering the dynamic similarity of flow characteristics.

Reynolds postulated that two flows can be considered dynamically similar if (1) they have geometrically similar boundaries, and, at the same time, (2) the forces acting on the fluid particles at all corresponding positions in the two flow fields have a constant ratio.

To insure geometric similarity for any two flows, it is necessary that the two flow boundaries have the same geometric shape and that the linear dimensions at corresponding parts of the two flow fields have a constant ratio. In considering similarity between forces, we find it convenient to consider the ratio of the inertia of fluid and each force at each point in the flow fields. Dynamic similarity for two flows requires that each ratio have a constant value at corresponding positions in the two flow fields.

Let us consider, for example, the dynamic similarity of two flow fields based on viscous forces only. Figure 6–10 shows a fluid particle in a steady

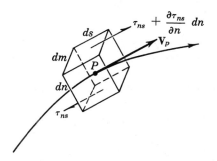

**Fig. 6-10.**  A fluid particle at point P in a viscous flow field.

viscous flow field. In the direction of flow the fluid inertia $F_I$ for this particle is

$$F_I = \rho \, ds \, dn \, dm \frac{dV_p}{dt} = \rho \, ds \, dn \, dm \, V_p \frac{\partial V_p}{\partial s}$$

and the viscous force on this particle is

$$F_V = \left(\tau_{ns} + \frac{\partial \tau_{ns}}{\partial n} dn\right) ds \, dm - \tau_{ns} \, ds \, dm$$

$$= \frac{\partial \tau_{ns}}{\partial n} ds \, dn \, dm = \mu \frac{\partial^2 V_p}{\partial n^2} ds \, dn \, dm$$

Therefore, two viscous flow fields will be dynamically similar if the ratio

$$\frac{F_I}{F_V} = \frac{\rho V_p(\partial V_p/\partial s)}{\mu \partial^2 V_p/\partial n^2}$$

at the corresponding points in the two flows is constant. For any given flow, we may express this ratio in terms of the variables associated with the flow. For example, if $l$ is the characteristic length and $V$ the reference velocity of a flow, the velocity $V_p$ is proportional to $V$, the velocity gradient $\partial V_p/\partial s$ is dimensionally proportional to $V/l$, and the term $\partial^2 V_p/\partial n^2$ is dimensionally proportional to $V/l^2$. The ratio

$$\frac{F_I}{F_V} = \frac{\rho V_p(\partial V_p/\partial s)}{\mu \partial^2 V_p/\partial n^2} = \frac{\rho V(V/l)}{\mu V/l^2} = \frac{Vl\rho}{\mu} = R \qquad (6\text{--}68)$$

is a dimensionless parameter called the *Reynolds number* $R$. Thus, two flows of different fluids moving at different velocities, having geometrically similar boundaries, and with viscous forces as the only forces present, are considered dynamically similar if the Reynolds numbers are the same at corresponding points in these two flows. This statement is, in essence, Reynolds' law of dynamic similarity.

The criteria of Reynolds' law can be extended to flows in which other forces, such as pressure, gravity, etc., are present in addition to viscous forces. We shall consider these effects in the following section.

### 6-12   Dynamic Similarity Derived From Dimensionless Equation of Motion

The preceding discussion is limited to the similarity of flows in which the viscous forces are the only forces present in the fluid motion. In order to obtain a more comprehensive picture of the dynamic similarity of flows when other forces are also present, we must investigate the differential equations which govern the flows. For this reason, we shall consider the Navier-Stokes equation, which is an equation of motion for Newtonian fluids of constant density and viscosity:

$$\rho \frac{D\mathbf{V}}{Dt} = \rho\mathbf{g} - \nabla p + \mu\nabla^2\mathbf{V} \qquad (6\text{--}69)$$

When this partial differential equation is used to study the fluid motion in a particular flow problem, each quantity in the equation must be expressed in a given system of units. However, we can transform this equation to a form in which each quantity becomes dimensionless. The resulting dimensionless form of the Navier-Stokes equation will shed more light on the conditions of dynamic similarity of flows.

If $l$, $V$, and $P$ represent respectively the characteristic reference magnitudes of length, velocity, and pressure, dimensionless variables and differential operators can be defined in the following manner:

Lengths:   $X^* = \dfrac{x}{l}$;   $Y^* = \dfrac{y}{l}$;   $Z^* = \dfrac{z}{l}$

Velocity:   $\mathbf{V}^* = \dfrac{\mathbf{V}}{V}$

Pressure:   $P^* = \dfrac{p}{P}$

Differential operations:

$$\frac{D}{Dt^*} = \frac{l}{V}\frac{D}{Dt}; \qquad \boldsymbol{\nabla}^* = l\boldsymbol{\nabla}; \qquad \boldsymbol{\nabla}^{*2} = l^2\boldsymbol{\nabla}^2$$

in which the symbols with a superscript $*$ represent dimensionless quantities. We now introduce these dimensionless quantities into Eq. 6–69 to obtain

$$\rho\frac{V}{l}\frac{D}{Dt^*}V\mathbf{V}^* = \rho\mathbf{g} - \frac{1}{l}\boldsymbol{\nabla}^*PP^* + \mu\frac{1}{l^2}\boldsymbol{\nabla}^{*2}V\mathbf{V}^*$$

which, after dividing through by $\rho V^2/l$, becomes

$$\frac{D\mathbf{V}^*}{Dt^*} = \left[\frac{lg}{V^2}\right]\frac{\mathbf{g}}{g} - \left[\frac{P}{\rho V^2}\right]\boldsymbol{\nabla}^*P^* + \left[\frac{\mu}{Vl\rho}\right]\boldsymbol{\nabla}^{*2}\mathbf{V}^* \qquad (6\text{–}70)$$

This is the dimensionless form of the Navier-Stokes equation. In this form the variables which describe the overall size ($l$) and speed ($V$) of the flow system and its physical properties ($\rho$ and $\mu$) are assembled in three dimensionless groups. These dimensionless groups occur very frequently in engineering studies and have been named after pioneering workers in fluid mechanics as

Froude number:   $F = \dfrac{V^2}{lg}$ $\qquad\qquad\qquad\qquad\qquad$ (6–71)

Euler number:   $E = \dfrac{\rho V^2}{P}$ $\qquad\qquad\qquad\qquad\qquad$ (6–72)

Reynolds number:   $R = \dfrac{Vl\rho}{\mu}$ $\qquad\qquad\qquad\qquad$ (6–73)

By introducing the dimensionless numbers, we may write Eq. 6–70 as

$$\frac{D\mathbf{V}^*}{Dt^*} = \frac{1}{F}\frac{\mathbf{g}}{g} - \frac{1}{E}\boldsymbol{\nabla}^*p^* + \frac{1}{R}\boldsymbol{\nabla}^{*2}\mathbf{V}^* \qquad (6\text{–}74)$$

Hence in two different flow systems if the Froude, Euler, and Reynolds numbers are respectively the same at the corresponding points in the flow fields, these two systems are described by identical dimension-less Navier-Stokes equations. If, in addition, these two systems are geometrically similar so that their dimensionless initial and boundary conditions are the same, the two systems are mathematically identical. Mathematically identical systems are said to be *dynamically similar.* Therefore, for the complete dynamic similarity of geometrically similar flows of Newtonian fluids of constant density and viscosity, the flows must have the same Froude number, same Euler number, and same Reynolds number at corresponding points.

If, in addition, the flow is compressible and heat transfer is involved, it is easy to show that dynamic similarity between flows also depends on the dimensionless Mach number $M = V/a$ and Prandtl number $P = c_p \mu / k$.

## 6-13    Dimensional Analysis and the Buckingham $\pi$-Method

Dynamic similarity can also be studied by the method of dimensional analysis. The theory of dimensional analysis is based on the fact that a complete physical equation must be dimensionally homogeneous and is, therefore, reducible to a functional equation among dimensionless parameters.

One of the most frequently used methods in dimensional analysis is the *Buckingham $\pi$-method.*[8] Let $B_1, B_2, \ldots, B_m$ be the $m$ variables involved in a physical problem. We may write their functional relationship as

$$F(B_1, B_2, \ldots, B_m) = C \text{ (constant)}$$

If $k$ dimensions (such as $F$, $L$, $T$, etc.) are required to define these variables, the above equation may be transformed to an equivalent equation relating $(m - k)$ dimensionless $\pi$-terms:

$$F_1(\pi_1, \pi_2, \ldots, \pi_{m-k}) = C_1 \text{(constant)}$$

Each dimensionless $\pi$-term is to be formed by combining $k$ primary $B$-variables and one of the other $B$-variables. Thus,

$$\pi_1 = B_1^{a_{11}} \quad B_2^{a_{12}} \quad \ldots \quad B_k^{a_{1k}} \quad B_{k+1}$$

$$\pi_2 = B_1^{a_{21}} \quad B_2^{a_{22}} \quad \ldots \quad B_k^{a_{2k}} \quad B_{k+2}$$

$$\cdot \qquad \cdot \qquad \cdot \qquad \ldots \qquad \cdot \qquad \cdot$$

$$\cdot \qquad \cdot \qquad \cdot \qquad \ldots \qquad \cdot \qquad \cdot$$

$$\pi_{m-k} = B_1^{a_{(m-k)1}} \quad B_2^{a_{(m-k)2}} \quad \ldots \quad B_k^{a_{(m-k)k}} \quad B_m$$

The $k$ primary $B$-variables are chosen on the basis of the following two

[8]E. Buckingham, "On Physically Similar Systems; Illustrations of the Use of Dimensional Equations," *Phys. Rev.*, Vol. IV, No. 4, (1914), 345.

criteria: (1) They must contain all the $k$-dimensions among themselves, and (2) they themselves must not form a dimensionless parameter. Numerical values for exponents $a_{11}, a_{12}, \ldots, a_{21}, a_{22}, \ldots$, etc. are to be found by an algebraic procedure which is best illustrated by the following example.

***Illustrative Example 6-3.*** It is desired that an expression for the pressure drop of a steady flow of a Newtonian liquid through a long, straight horizontal pipe of circular cross section be developed.

After careful consideration it is decided that the pressure drop $\Delta p$ depends on (a) the average velocity $V$ of the pipe flow, (b) the pipe length $L$, (c) the pipe diameter $D$, (d) the fluid density $\rho$, (e) the fluid viscosity $\mu$, and (f) the average pipe wall roughness $e$. We have not considered gravity, because the flow is horizontal and does not change in elevation. Since there is no free surface in this flow, surface tension does not enter into this problem. The effect of compressibility is, of course, not important in liquid flow.

We may then write the functional equation for this problem as

$$F(\Delta p, V, L, D, \rho, \mu, e) = C$$

All seven variables in this equation can be defined by the three fundamental dimensions of Newtonian mechanics, such as, for example, $MLT$. Hence these seven variables can be combined to form four dimensionless $\pi$-terms, and

$$F_1(\pi_1, \pi_2, \pi_3, \pi_4) = C_1$$

There are many possible combinations of three variables to be chosen as primary variables for forming $\pi$-terms. The proper choice would depend on the skill and experience of the problem solver. There is no easy rule for a beginner to follow. In order to obtain dimensionless quantities which are well-established in fluid mechanics, we shall choose $VD\rho$ as primary variables and form the $\pi$-terms as follows:

$$\pi_1 = V^{a_{11}} \quad D^{a_{12}} \quad \rho^{a_{13}} \quad \Delta p$$
$$\pi_2 = V^{a_{21}} \quad D^{a_{22}} \quad \rho^{a_{23}} \quad L$$
$$\pi_3 = V^{a_{31}} \quad D^{a_{32}} \quad \rho^{a_{33}} \quad \mu$$
$$\pi_4 = V^{a_{41}} \quad D^{a_{42}} \quad \rho^{a_{43}} \quad e$$

We shall work out the details of algebraic procedure for determining the exponents of the variables which form $\pi_1$ for the purpose of illustration. By using the dimensions $MLT$,

$$\pi_1 = M^0 L^0 T^0 = (LT^{-1})^{a_{11}} \quad (L)^{a_{12}} \quad (ML^{-3})^{a_{13}} \quad (ML^{-1}T^{-2})$$

$$
\begin{aligned}
M: \quad & 0 \quad = \quad && a_{13} + 1 \\
L: \quad & 0 \quad = +a_{11} + a_{12} - 3a_{13} - 1 \\
T: \quad & 0 \quad = -a_{11} && -2 \\
& a_{11} = -2 \quad a_{12} = 0 \quad a_{13} = -1
\end{aligned}
$$

and

$$\pi_1 = V^{-2} D^0 \rho^{-1} \Delta p = \frac{\Delta p}{\rho V^2}$$

In a similar manner, it is found that

$$\pi_2 = \frac{L}{D}, \qquad \pi_3 = \frac{\mu}{VD\rho} = \frac{1}{R}, \qquad \pi_4 = \frac{e}{D}$$

Thus

$$F_1(\pi_1, \pi_2, \pi_3, \pi_4) = F_1\left(\frac{\Delta p}{\rho V^2}, \frac{L}{D}, R, \frac{e}{D}\right) = C_1$$

or

$$\frac{\Delta p}{\rho V^2} = F_2\left(\frac{L}{D}, R, \frac{e}{D}\right)$$

## PROBLEMS

**6–1.** Expand $[\nabla \cdot \mathbf{T}]$ and show that it is identical to Equations 6–3 and 6–4.

**6–2.** The velocity field of a viscous incompressible flow is given by

$$\mathbf{V} = 5x^2 y\mathbf{i} + 3xyz\mathbf{j} - 8xz^2\mathbf{k} \quad \text{ft/sec}$$

The fluid viscosity is $\mu = 0.003$ lbf-sec/ft$^2$. At the position $(2, 4, -6)$, $\sigma_{yy} = -2.000$ lbf/ft$^2$. Calculate the other normal and shear stresses at the same position.

**6–3.** The velocity field of a viscous incompressible flow is given as

$$\mathbf{V} = 8x^2 z\mathbf{i} - 6y^2 z^2\mathbf{j} + (4yz^3 - 8xz^2)\mathbf{k} \quad \text{ft/sec}$$

The fluid density is 1.8 slugs/ft$^3$ and the fluid viscosity is $\mu = 0.1$ lbf-sec/ft$^2$. The negative $z$-axis is in the direction of gravity. Calculate the pressure gradient at the position $(1, 2, 3)$.

**6–4.** Evaluate the quantity of $\mu\Phi_v$ in Problems 6–2 and 6–3.

**6–5.** Use the Navier-Stokes equations to show that the stream function $\psi = \psi(x, y, t)$ for a two-dimensional incompressible laminar viscous flow satisfies the following equation:

$$\nabla^2 \frac{\partial \psi}{\partial t} + \frac{\partial \psi}{\partial y} \nabla^2 \frac{\partial \psi}{\partial x} - \frac{\partial \psi}{\partial x} \nabla^2 \frac{\partial \psi}{\partial y} = \frac{\mu}{\rho} \nabla^4 \psi$$

where

$$\nabla^4 \equiv \nabla^2(\nabla^2) \equiv \frac{\partial^4}{\partial x^4} + 2\frac{\partial^4}{\partial x^2 \partial y^2} + \frac{\partial^4}{\partial y^4}$$

**6–6.** Calculate the slope at which two fixed parallel flat plates 2.00 in. apart must be placed so that a steady laminar flow occurs between them with no change in pressure in the direction of flow. Given: $q = 2$ ft$^3$/sec per foot width, sp. gr. $= 0.78$, and $\mu = 0.05$ lbf-sec/ft$^2$.

**6–7.** A steady laminar flow of an oil occurs between two fixed horizontal parallel plates separated by a distance of 1.00 in. The oil has a density $\rho = 1.70$

slugs/ft³ and a viscosity $\mu = 0.002$ lbf-sec/ft². The pressure drop in the direction of flow is estimated to be 2 lbf/ft² per foot length of the channel. Calculate (a) the maximum velocity in the flow; (b) the rate of flow per foot width of the channel; and (c) the shear stress at the plate surface.

**6–8.** Water at 60 F° seeps out of the 0.1 in. deep crack in the 8 in. wide wall as shown in Fig. 6–11. Assuming laminar flow through the crack, estimate the rate of seepage per unit foot length of the wall.

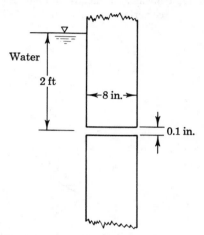

**Fig. 6-11.**

**6–9.** Derive an expression which describes the velocity distribution across the two fixed parallel plates for a steady laminar flow of two layers of fluid under a pressure gradient $\partial p / \partial x = -k$, as shown in Fig. 6–12.

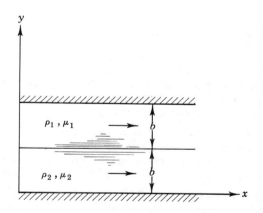

**Fig. 6-12.**

**6–10.** In Figure 6–4, if the top plate is moving uniformly in its own plane with a velocity $U_c\mathbf{i}$, show that the velocity distribution of flow is

$$u = \frac{U_c}{b} y - \frac{1}{2\mu} \frac{\partial p}{\partial x} (by - y^2)$$

**6–11.** Consider the steady laminar flow of a thin sheet of viscous liquid with a free surface as shown in Fig. 6–13. (a) Show that the velocity distribution

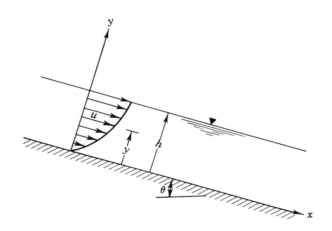

**Fig. 6-13.**

in this flow is given by the following formula:

$$u = \frac{\gamma}{\mu} y \left( h - \frac{y}{2} \right) \sin \theta$$

(b) Compute the rate of flow per unit width (perpendicular to the plane of paper). (c) Determine the depth below the free surface at which the point velocity is equal to the average velocity of flow.

**6–12.** Find the terminal thickness of a viscous liquid film which flows down a smooth plate inclined at 60 degrees with the horizontal when the maximum velocity at the free surface of the film is 1.5 ft/sec. The liquid has a density $\rho = 1.98$ slugs/ft³ and a viscosity $\mu = 1.5 \times 10^{-4}$ lbf-sec/ft².

**6–13.** If the liquid in Problem 6–12 flows down the same inclined surface with a film thickness of 0.1 in., what is the rate of flow per foot of width of the plate?

**6–14.** A viscous liquid flows laminarly down along the surface of a vertical circular cylinder as shown in Fig. 6–14. Determine the velocity distribution equation for the liquid flow. The density and dynamic viscosity of the liquid are respectively $\rho$ and $\mu$.

**Fig. 6-14.**

**6–15.** An oil is pumped through a 4 in. diameter pipeline at a rate of 3.5 ft³/sec. The specific weight of the oil is 56.0 lbf/ft³ and its dynamic viscosity is $2.6 \times 10^{-2}$ lbf-sec/ft². Assume the flow to be fully developed. (a) Calculate the shear stress at the pipe wall. (b) Determine the pump horsepower required to deliver the oil through 1000 ft of horizontal pipeline when the intake and discharge pressures are the same.

**6–16.** In Illustrative Example 6–1, if the inner pipe of the annulus system is moving uniformly with a velocity $V = W_c \mathbf{k}$ while the outside pipe is stationary, determine (a) the velocity distribution equation for the flow in the annulus and (b) the volume rate of flow in the annulus.

**6–17.** A viscous fluid flows laminarly upward in the inner pipe and downward in the annulus space as shown in Fig. 6–15. If the flow rate is 0.5 ft³/sec, find the ratio of the maximum velocities in the inner pipe and in the annulus.

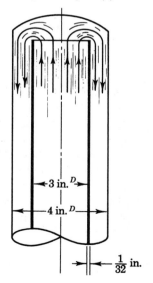

**Fig. 6-15.**

**6–18.** A laminar flow occurs through a horizontal annular system. (See Illustrative Example 6–1.) For the following given data:

$$r_2 = 1.5 \text{ in.}, \quad r_1 = 1.0 \text{ in.}$$

$$\frac{\partial p}{\partial z} = -450 \text{ lbf/ft}^2 \text{ per foot length}$$

$$\mu = 0.05 \text{ lbf-sec/ft}^2$$

$$\rho = 1.75 \text{ slugs/ft}^3$$

calculate the drag per foot of length on the inner tube.

**6–19.** Figure 6–16 shows the cross section of two long concentric circular cylinders. The annular space between the two cylinders is filled with a viscous fluid of density $\rho$ and dynamic viscosity $\mu$. The outer cylinder is rotated

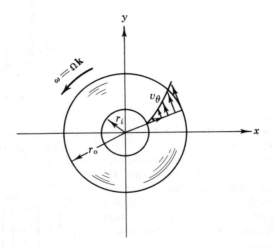

**Fig. 6-16.**

at a constant angular velocity $\boldsymbol{\omega} = \Omega\mathbf{k}$ while the inner cylinder is held stationary. The fluid motion in the annular space is axially symmetric. (a) Set up the differential equation of motion in cylindrical notations. (b) Show that the equation for the variation of tangential velocity is

$$v_\theta = \left(\frac{\Omega r_0^2}{r_0^2 - r_i^2}\right)\left(r - \frac{r_i^2}{r}\right)$$

(c) Determine the torque (per unit length) about the axis of the cylinders due to shear forces acting on the surface of the inner cylinder.

**6–20.** Show that the Stokes stream function for creeping flow around a solid sphere, shown in Figure 6–7, is

$$\Psi = \frac{3}{4} V_\infty R_0 R \left(1 - \frac{R_0^2}{3R^2}\right) \sin^2 \theta$$

Sketch the traces of the stream surfaces.

**6–21.** Show that the terminal velocity $V_t$ of a sphere of radius $R_0$ falling slowly in a very viscous fluid is

$$V_t = 2R_0^2(\rho_s - \rho)g/9\mu$$

where  $\rho_s \equiv$ average density of the sphere
  $\rho \equiv$ density of the fluid
  $\mu \equiv$ dynamic viscosity of the fluid
  $g \equiv$ gravitational acceleration.

**6–22.** Determine the largest diameter of sediment particle, having a specific weight $\gamma = 180$ lbf/ft³, which will settle in water at 50°F and obey Stokes' law.

**6–23.** A sphere of radius $R_0$ is falling in creeping motion through a stationary fluid of viscosity $\mu$ with a terminal velocity $V_t$. Find the horizontal distances from the center of the sphere in a plane perpendicular to the direction of fall where the velocity of the fluid is (a) $0.1 V_t$; and (b) $0.01 V_t$.

**6–24.** A long cylinder of radius $r_0$ is rotated about its axis with a constant angular speed $\Omega$ in an infinite body of viscous fluid of kinematic viscosity $\nu$. (a) Show that the steady motion induced in the fluid is an irrotational motion with $v_\theta = r_0^2 \Omega/r$. (b) When the rotational motion of the cylinder is suddenly stopped, the fluid motion becomes unsteady. By assuming the radius $r_0$ of the cylinder as infinitesimally small and the time $t = 0$ at the instant when the rotational motion of the cylinder is stopped, show that the tangential velocity of the unsteady motion of the fluid at any instant $t = t$ is

$$v_\theta = \frac{r_0 \Omega}{r} (1 - e^{-r^2/4\nu t})$$

**6–25.** By considering the differential equations of motion, what dimensionless parameters are significant in (a) three-dimensional potential flows, and (b) two-dimensional planar potential flows of incompressible fluid? Assume that the two-dimensional flow occurs on the plane perpendicular to the direction of gravity.

**6–26.** The dimensionless Prandtl number

$$P = c_p \mu/k$$

is a useful parameter in studies of heat transfer, where

  $c_p \equiv$ specific heat of a fluid at constant pressure

  $\mu \equiv$ dynamic viscosity of a fluid

  $k \equiv$ thermal conductivity of a fluid

Determine the dimensions of $k$ in both the $MLT$ and $FLT$ systems.

**6–27.** Suppose that the pressure $p$ in an ideal fluid flowing at a constant elevation varies with the velocity $V$ of flow, the density $\rho$ of the fluid, and the gravitational acceleration $g$. By dimensional analysis develop an expression for the pressure in terms of the variables mentioned.

**6–28.** The stagnation pressure $p_s$ at a stagnation point in an air stream depends on the pressure $p_0$, density $\rho_0$, and velocity $V_0$ in the free stream. Determine a dimensionless parameter on which the pressure ratio $p_s/p_0$ depends.

6–29. A pump of diameter $D$, rotating at an angular velocity $\Omega$ under a pumping head $H$, handles a rate of flow $\hat{Q}$ of a fluid of density $\rho$ and viscosity $\mu$. Using dimensional analysis, derive an expression for the power $P$ required in terms of these variables.

6–30. List all the variables involved in determining the drag on a jet airplane wing when the airplane is cruising at a speed which is three-fourth the speed of sound. Derive by dimensional analysis an expression for the drag.

# 7 Fluid Turbulence and Turbulent Flow of Incompressible Viscous Fluids

## 7-1 Transition Between Laminar and Turbulent Flow

Laminar and turbulent flows and the transition between them are familiar phenomena in our daily life. Most of us have observed these phenomena in the rising column of smoke from a burning cigarette. The smoke rises in smooth filament (i.e., laminar flow) for some distance immediately above the burning tip of the cigarette. It breaks down into turbulent motion at a height which depends on the condition of the surrounding air. If the surrounding air is still, the smooth smoke filament may persist to a considerable height. If the air is being stirred up, the smoke filament breaks down in the immediate neighborhood of the cigarette. This breakdown of the laminar filament is the phenomenon of transition from laminar to turbulent flow.

It has been established in very carefully controlled experiments that the dimensionless Reynolds number can be used as a measure for in-

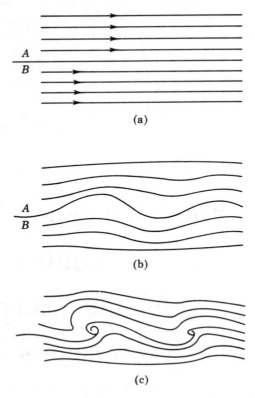

**Fig. 7-1.** Eddies formed in an unstable laminar flow.

dicating the occurrence of laminar and turbulent flows and the transition between them. For example, in pipe flows, laminar flow occurs at $R (= VD\rho/\mu) < 2000$ and transition normally takes place at Reynolds numbers between 2000 and 4000.

The mechanism of transition is rather complicated and is still not fully understood. For example, when extreme precautions were taken in minimizing the initial disturbances in the pipe flow, transition could be delayed until a Reynolds number of 50,000 had been attained. Thus, the transition Reynolds number seems to depend partly on the degree of turbulence in the flow; its numerical value always increases with a decrease in turbulence.

Transition phenomenon has been associated with the stability of laminar flow.[1] Under certain conditions, a laminar flow is stable; any local disturbances will be damped out by fluid viscosity. On the other

---

[1]C. C. Lin, *The Theory of Hydrodynamic Stability*. London: Cambridge University Press, 1955.

hand, laminar flow becomes unstable under other conditions, and a slight local disturbance will cause an initially laminar flow to become turbulent. Figure 7–1 illustrates how an unstable laminar flow may turn into a turbulent flow. Figure 7–1(a) shows that a local disturbance causes an increase in the velocity of particle $A$. This increase in velocity will cause the pressure at $A$ to fall below that at $B$. The pressure difference will further increase the velocity difference across the surface of discontinuity as shown in Fig. 7–1(b). The result is the formation of eddies at the surface of discontinuity and the initiation of turbulent flow.

A turbulent flow is characterized by rapid and chaotic mixing of macroscopic chunks of fluid. The violent mixing motion of fluid particles in a turbulent flow causes additional energy dissipation. For example, in laminar pipe flows the friction loss is proportional to the average velocity $V$, whereas in turbulent pipe flows the friction loss is proportional to $V^2$. The turbulent mixing also results in a more rapid transfer of momentum between different layers of fluid. Thus, the velocity distribution in a turbulent flow is more uniform than that in a laminar flow, as shown in Fig. 7–2.

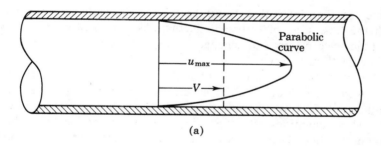

(a)

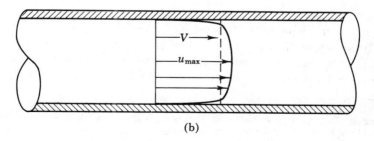

(b)

**Fig. 7-2.** Comparison of velocity distribution for (a) laminar, and (b) turbulent pipe flow.

## 7-2    Fluid Turbulence

At any given point in a turbulent flow, the instantaneous velocity and, indeed, all the instantaneous continuum properties are found to fluctuate rapidly and randomly about a mean value with respect to time and spatial direction. In the theoretical analysis of turbulent flow, it is convenient to consider an instantaneous quantity, such as $u$, as the sum of its time-average part $\bar{u}$ and momentary fluctuation part $u'$, as shown in Fig. 7–3:

$$u = \bar{u} + u' \tag{7–1}$$

In a steady flow $\bar{u}$ does not change with time.

By definition

$$\bar{u} = \frac{1}{\Delta t} \int_{t_0}^{t_0+\Delta t} u \, dt \tag{7–2}$$

and

$$\bar{u'} = \frac{1}{\Delta t} = \int_{t_0}^{t_0+\Delta t} u' \, dt = \frac{1}{\Delta t} \int_{t_0}^{t_0+\Delta t} (u - \bar{u}) \, dt = \bar{u} - \bar{u} = 0 \tag{7–3}$$

where the time interval $\Delta t$ must be taken sufficiently large compared with the time scale of turbulent fluctuations but small compared with the time scale of any slow changes in the flow field which are not associated with turbulence.

Although the time average of a fluctuation quantity is zero (e.g., $\bar{u'} = 0$), the quantities $\overline{u'^2}, \overline{u'v'}, \overline{u'w'}$, etc., which are time averages of the products of any two fluctuation components, will not necessarily equal zero. These quantities will appear in equations governing the turbulent motion of a fluid. They are used as a measure of the magnitude of turbulent fluctuations at any given point in a turbulent flow field, since the intensity of turbulence $I$ at a given point has been defined quantitatively by the expression:

$$I = \frac{\sqrt{(\overline{u'^2} + \overline{v'^2} + \overline{w'^2})/3}}{V} \tag{7–4}$$

where $V$ is the magnitude of the velocity at the same point.

Inasmuch as turbulent fluctuations are random, it seems logical to study turbulence by means of statistical methods. Indeed, a statistical theory of turbulence was developed by Sir G. I. Taylor[2] in 1935, and

[2] G. I. Taylor, "The Statistical Theory of Turbulence," Parts I-IV, *Proc. Roy. Soc.* (London), Vol. A151 (1935), 421–478. This paper and several others have been republished in S. K. Friedlander and Leonard Topper, eds., *Turbulence—Classical Papers on Statistical Theory.* New York: Interscience Publishers, Inc., 1961.

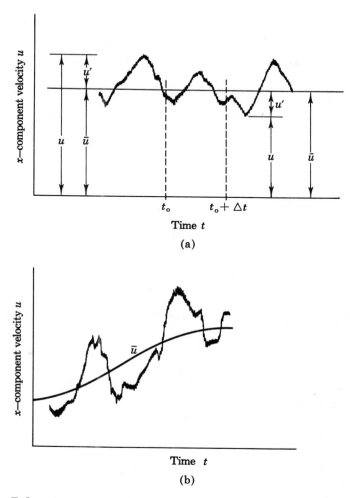

**Fig. 7-3.** Fluctuations of instantaneous velocity component with respect to time at a fixed point in (a) a steady flow, and (b) an unsteady flow.

considerable advances have been made in connection with Taylor's theory. However, the statistical theory of turbulence has not yet been able to yield results which can be used directly in engineering application.

We shall not attempt to present the mathematics of the statistical theory of turbulence; instead, we shall study turbulent flow by following the historical route taken by Osborne Reynolds. Reynolds reasoned that since the Navier-Stokes equations are essentially equations of motion for a viscous fluid, they must be valid for both laminar and turbulent flows. The instantaneous velocity components and pressure in a turbulent flow must also satisfy the Navier-Stokes equations.

## 7-3  Equations of Continuity and of Motion for Time-Average Turbulent Flow of an Incompressible Viscous Fluid

By following the previously adopted notations that $u = \bar{u} + u'$, etc., the equation of continuity for an incompressible turbulent flow can be written as

$$\frac{\partial}{\partial x}(\bar{u} + u') + \frac{\partial}{\partial y}(\bar{v} + v') + \frac{\partial}{\partial z}(\bar{w} + w') = 0 \tag{7-5}$$

Let us average each term in this equation over a time interval $\Delta t$. For example, by definition

$$\overline{\frac{\partial}{\partial x}(\bar{u} + u')} = \frac{1}{\Delta t} \int_{t_0}^{t_0 + \Delta t} \left[ \frac{\partial}{\partial x}(\bar{u} + u') \right] dt$$

Since the integration with respect to time is independent of differentiation with respect to space coordinates, the above equation can also be written as

$$\overline{\frac{\partial}{\partial x}(\bar{u} + u')} = \frac{\partial}{\partial x} \left[ \frac{1}{\Delta t} \int_{t_0}^{t_0 + \Delta t} (\bar{u} + u') \, dt \right]$$

The expression inside the square brackets is then $\bar{u}$ in accordance with Eqs. 7–1 and 7–2. Therefore, the time-average equation of continuity for an incompressible turbulent flow is simply

$$\frac{\partial \bar{u}}{\partial x} + \frac{\partial \bar{v}}{\partial y} + \frac{\partial \bar{w}}{\partial z} = 0 \tag{7-6}$$

By subtracting Eq. 7–6 from Eq. 7–5, we obtain

$$\frac{\partial u'}{\partial x} + \frac{\partial v'}{\partial y} + \frac{\partial w'}{\partial z} = 0 \tag{7-7}$$

Clearly both the time-average velocity field and the fluctuating velocity components satisfy the same form of equation of continuity as the actual velocity field.

Let us turn our attention to the equation of motion. It is necessary to consider only the $x$-component of the Navier-Stokes equations since the $y$- and $z$-components can be worked out in the same manner. Hence by substituting $\bar{u} + u'$ for $u$, $\bar{v} + v'$ for $v$, etc. in the following $x$-component of the Navier-Stokes equations:

$$\rho \left( u \frac{\partial u}{\partial x} + v \frac{\partial u}{\partial y} + w \frac{\partial u}{\partial z} + \frac{\partial u}{\partial t} \right) = \rho g_x - \frac{\partial p}{\partial x} + \mu \nabla^2 u \tag{7-8}$$

the resulting $x$-component equation of motion for the turbulent flow of an incompressible viscous fluid becomes

$$\rho(\bar{u} + u')\frac{\partial}{\partial x}(\bar{u} + u') + \rho(\bar{v} + v')\frac{\partial}{\partial y}(\bar{u} + u')$$

$$+ \rho(\bar{w} + w')\frac{\partial}{\partial z}(\bar{u} + u') + \rho\frac{\partial}{\partial t}(\bar{u} + u') \qquad (7\text{--}9)$$

$$= \rho g_x - \frac{\partial}{\partial x}(\bar{p} + p') + \mu\nabla^2(\bar{u} + u')$$

The next step is to take the time average of each term of the above equation according to Eq. 7–2. For example, the first term in the above equation can be expanded as

$$\rho(\bar{u} + u')\frac{\partial}{\partial x}(\bar{u} + u') = \rho\bar{u}\frac{\partial \bar{u}}{\partial x} + \rho\bar{u}\frac{\partial u'}{\partial x} + \rho u'\frac{\partial \bar{u}}{\partial x} + \rho u'\frac{\partial u'}{\partial x} \qquad (7\text{--}10)$$

Then the time-average process is applied to each of the four terms on the right-hand side of Eq. 7–10. The first term $\rho\bar{u}\,\partial\bar{u}/\partial x$ is not changed by the time-average process because all the variables in this term are time-average quantities that remain constant in the time interval $\Delta t$. In the second term $\rho\bar{u}$ are time-average quantities, and the time average of $\partial u'/\partial x$ is zero, thus making the entire term zero. Similarly, the time average of $\rho u'$ is zero and the third term $\rho u'\,\partial\bar{u}/\partial x$ becomes zero. The last term $\rho u'\,\partial u'/\partial x$ is the product of two fluctuating components; its time-average value is not necessarily zero and it is written as $\rho\overline{u'\,\partial u'/\partial x}$. By carrying out similar operations for all the remaining terms in Eq. 7–9, we see that Eq. 7–9 then becomes

$$\rho\left(\bar{u}\frac{\partial \bar{u}}{\partial x} + \bar{v}\frac{\partial \bar{u}}{\partial y} + \bar{w}\frac{\partial \bar{u}}{\partial z} + \bar{w}\frac{\partial \bar{u}}{\partial t}\right)$$

$$= \rho g_x - \frac{\partial \bar{p}}{\partial x} + \mu\nabla^2\bar{u} - \left(\rho\overline{u'\frac{\partial u'}{\partial y}} + \rho\overline{v'\frac{\partial u'}{\partial y}} + \rho\overline{w'\frac{\partial u'}{\partial z}}\right) \qquad (7\text{--}11)$$

It is easy to verify that

$$-\left(\rho\overline{u'\frac{\partial u'}{\partial x}} + \rho\overline{v'\frac{\partial u'}{\partial y}} + \rho\overline{w'\frac{\partial u'}{\partial z}}\right)$$

$$= \frac{\partial}{\partial x}(-\rho\overline{u'^2}) + \frac{\partial}{\partial y}(-\rho\overline{u'v'}) + \frac{\partial}{\partial z}(-\rho\overline{u'w'}) \qquad (7\text{--}12)$$

by carrying out the differentiations on the right-hand side and by making use of Eq. 7–7. With this identity, we finally obtain the following time-average $x$-component equation of motion for the turbulent flow of an incompressible viscous fluid:

$$\rho\left(\bar{u}\frac{\partial \bar{u}}{\partial x} + \bar{v}\frac{\partial \bar{u}}{\partial y} + \bar{w}\frac{\partial \bar{u}}{\partial z} + \frac{\partial \bar{u}}{\partial t}\right) = \rho g_x - \frac{\partial \bar{p}}{\partial x} + \mu\nabla^2\bar{u}$$

$$+ \frac{\partial}{\partial x}(-\rho\overline{u'^2}) + \frac{\partial}{\partial y}(-\rho\overline{u'v'}) + \frac{\partial}{\partial z}(-\rho\overline{u'w'}) \qquad (7\text{--}13\text{a})$$

In a similar manner, the time-average $y$- and $z$-component equations of motion are respectively

$$\rho\left(\bar{u}\frac{\partial\bar{v}}{\partial x} + \bar{v}\frac{\partial\bar{v}}{\partial y} + \bar{w}\frac{\partial\bar{v}}{\partial z} + \frac{\partial\bar{v}}{\partial t}\right) = \rho g_y - \frac{\partial\bar{p}}{\partial y} + \mu\nabla^2\bar{v}$$
$$+ \frac{\partial}{\partial x}(-\rho\overline{u'v'}) + \frac{\partial}{\partial y}(-\rho\overline{v'^2}) + \frac{\partial}{\partial z}(-\rho\overline{v'w'}) \tag{7-13b}$$

and

$$\rho\left(\bar{u}\frac{\partial\bar{w}}{\partial x} + \bar{v}\frac{\partial\bar{w}}{\partial y} + \bar{w}\frac{\partial\bar{w}}{\partial z} + \frac{\partial\bar{w}}{\partial t}\right) = \rho g_z - \frac{\partial\bar{p}}{\partial z} + \mu\nabla^2\bar{w}$$
$$+ \frac{\partial}{\partial x}(-\rho\overline{u'w'}) + \frac{\partial}{\partial y}(-\rho\overline{v'w'}) + \frac{\partial}{\partial z}(-\rho\overline{w'^2}) \tag{7-13c}$$

These equations are called the *Reynolds equations of motion for turbulent flow*. In these equations the additional terms over the Navier-Stokes equations are called the *Reynolds stresses* or *eddy stresses* due to turbulent fluctuations in the flow. The nine eddy stresses form the components of a second-order tensor $\mathbf{T}^{(e)}$ which is defined as

$$\mathbf{T}^{(e)} = \begin{pmatrix} \sigma_{xx}^{(e)} & \tau_{xy}^{(e)} & \tau_{xz}^{(e)} \\ \tau_{yx}^{(e)} & \sigma_{yy}^{(e)} & \tau_{yz}^{(e)} \\ \tau_{zx}^{(e)} & \tau_{zy}^{(e)} & \sigma_{zz}^{(e)} \end{pmatrix} = \begin{pmatrix} -\rho\overline{u'^2} & -\rho\overline{u'v'} & -\rho\overline{u'w'} \\ -\rho\overline{u'v'} & -\rho\overline{v'^2} & -\rho\overline{v'w'} \\ -\rho\overline{u'w'} & -\rho\overline{v'w'} & -\rho\overline{w'^2} \end{pmatrix} \tag{7-14}$$

where $\sigma^{(e)}$ represents eddy normal stresses and $\tau^{(e)}$ eddy shear stresses. Hence the Reynolds equations may be summarized in the following vector-tensor form:

$$\rho\frac{D\mathbf{V}}{Dt} = \rho\mathbf{g} - \nabla\bar{p} + \mu\nabla^2\bar{\mathbf{V}} + [\nabla\cdot\mathbf{T}^{(e)}] \tag{7-15}$$

Although the Reynolds equations describe the dynamic conditions of turbulent flow fields, it is obviously hopeless to obtain a mathematical solution for any practical turbulent flow problem from these equations. Aside from the fact that these equations are nonlinear, we have only four equations—namely, the three component equations of motion and the equation of continuity—for ten unknowns: $\bar{p}$, $\bar{u}$, $\bar{v}$, $\bar{w}$, and six Reynolds stresses. This is one of the main difficulties in the theoretical study of turbulent flow. Apparently, additional assumptions and hypotheses are necessary to simplify these equations so that we may obtain approximate solutions for some practical turbulent flow problems.

## 7-4  Semiempirical Theories of Turbulent Flow

Inasmuch as eddy stresses in a turbulent flow represent rates of momentum transfer across the corresponding surfaces as a result of macroscopic turbulent velocity fluctuations, it is reasonable to expect that these stresses are related to the time-average velocity field of the turbulent flow. Several semiempirical theories have been proposed along this line of thought in an attempt to solve some turbulent flow problems. These semiempirical theories are formulated for a rather simple flow model. In these theories certain numerical values must be determined experimentally and hence they are termed *semiempirical*. In each theory, a functional relationship is first established between, for example, the shear stress $\tau_{yx}$ and quantities, such as $\bar{u}$, $d\bar{u}/dy$, $d^2\bar{u}/dy^2$, etc., of the time-average turbulent velocity field. With these functions the solution of some simple turbulent flow problems can be carried out with moderate success.

Consider a steady two-dimensional turbulent flow parallel to a plane surface as shown in Fig. 7–4. In this flow the time-average velocity field is

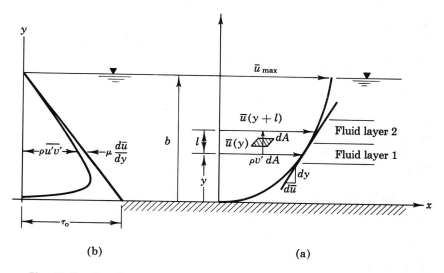

**Fig. 7-4.** Turbulent parallel flow past a plane boundary. (a) Velocity profile; (b) shear stress distribution.

$$\bar{u} = \bar{u}(y) \quad \text{and} \quad \bar{v} = \bar{w} = 0$$

and the eddy stresses can vary with respect to $y$ only. Hence the Reynolds equations for this flow are simply:

$$\frac{\partial}{\partial x}(\bar{p} + \rho g h_z) = \frac{\partial}{\partial y}\left(\mu \frac{\partial \bar{u}}{\partial y} - \rho \overline{u'v'}\right) \tag{7-16}$$

and

$$\frac{\partial}{\partial y}(\bar{p} + \rho g h_z + \rho \overline{v'^2}) = 0 \tag{7-17}$$

Let us first examine Eq. 7–17. Integration of Eq. 7–17 with respect to $y$ yields

$$\bar{p} + \rho g h_z + \rho \overline{v'^2} = C \tag{7–18}$$

This equation indicates that $\bar{p}$ no longer varies hydrostatically in the $y$-direction as it would if the flow had been laminar. The turbulent fluctuation $v'$ is obviously equal to zero at the solid wall. Therefore, the sum $\bar{p} + \rho g h_z$ must have a larger value in the region near the wall.

Integration of Eq. 7–16 with respect to $y$ yields

$$\mu \frac{d\bar{u}}{dy} - \rho \overline{u'v'} = y \frac{\partial}{\partial x}(\bar{p} + \rho g h_z) + C_1 \tag{7–19}$$

since $\partial(\bar{p} + \rho g h_z)/\partial x$ is a gradient in the $x$-direction and does not vary with $y$. The left-hand side of Eq. 7–19 represents the total shear stress which is the sum of the viscous shear stress $\mu \, d\bar{u}/dy$ and the eddy shear stress $-\rho \overline{u'v'}$ due to turbulent velocity fluctuations. This total shear stress varies linearly in the $y$-direction. The constant $C_1$ can be determined from the boundary conditions at the wall where $y = 0$ and the total wall shear stress is $\tau_0$. Therefore, Eq. 9–19 becomes

$$\mu \frac{d\bar{u}}{dy} - \rho \overline{u'v'} = y \frac{\partial}{\partial x}(\bar{p} + \rho g h_z) + \tau_0 \tag{7–20}$$

With this equation we are in a position to analyze some turbulent flow problems provided that we can express the eddy shear stress $-\rho \overline{u'v'}$ in terms of the quantities of the time-average velocity field in the turbulent flow.

The following four semiempirical theories have been chosen to demonstrate efforts toward this purpose. Each theory is useful for a particular group of flow systems.

A. *Boussinesq's eddy viscosity concept.* In analogy with Newton's law of viscosity: $\tau_{yx} = \rho v \, (du/dy)$, Boussinesq[3] introduced an eddy kinematic viscosity $\epsilon$ and proposed the following expression for eddy shear stress:

$$-\rho \overline{u'v'} = \rho \epsilon \frac{d\bar{u}}{dy} \tag{7–21}$$

It has been found that $\epsilon$ depends on both the fluid and the type of flow and that $\epsilon$ usually varies from point to point in a flow field. This theory has been successfully applied to such problems as atmospheric turbulent diffusion and jet mixing, in which a simple expression for $\epsilon$ can be derived.

---

[3] J. Boussinesq, "Essai sur la theorie des eaux courants" (Analysis Concerning the Theory of Flowing Water), *Memoires présentés par divers savants à l'Academie des Science*, Vol. XXIII, 1877.

B. *Prandtl's mixing length theory.* Consider Fig. 7–4. Fluid particles within layer 1 (at $y = y$) have a time-average velocity $\bar{u}(y)$. The time-average velocity of those fluid particles within layer 2 (at $y = y + l$) can be found by means of a Taylor series as

$$\bar{u}(y + l) = \bar{u}(y) + l\frac{d\bar{u}}{dy} + \frac{l^2}{2!}\frac{d^2\bar{u}}{dy^2} + \cdots$$

If $l$ is small, $\bar{u}(y + l) \approx \bar{u}(y) + l(d\bar{u}/dy)$. The transverse distance $l$ is called *Prandtl's mixing length.*

By Prandtl's hypothesis

$$u' = l\left|\frac{d\bar{u}}{dy}\right| \tag{7-22}$$

The absolute sign is necessary because the sign for $u'$ depends on both $d\bar{u}/dy$ and $v'$. For example, as shown in Fig. 7–4, a positive $v'$ means that fluid is carried from a region of lower $\bar{u}$ to a region of higher $\bar{u}$, and $u'$ is generally negative. The physical meaning of Eq. 7–22 is made clear if both sides of the equation are multiplied by $\rho$, that is, $\rho u' = l\,|d\rho\bar{u}/dy|$. The excess momentum $\rho u'$ in the $x$-direction produced by turbulent fluctuations is of the same magnitude as the quantity of momentum being exchanged when a fluid particle moves through a distance $l$ normal to the time-average flow. Prandtl further assumed $v'$ to be of the same order of magnitude as $u'$. That is, $v' = u' = l\,|d\bar{u}/dy|$. Hence

$$-\rho\overline{u'v'} = \rho l^2\left|\frac{d\bar{u}}{dy}\right|\frac{d\bar{u}}{dy} \tag{7-23}$$

This is the well-known Prandtl mixing length theory for parallel turbulent flow.[4]

Since $v'$ is zero at a solid wall, Prandtl assumed that near a wall $l$ is a linear function of the distance $y$ from the wall, i.e.,

$$l = \kappa y \tag{7-24}$$

in which $\kappa$ is the so-called *universal constant* and its numerical value is to be determined from experimental data.

C. *Von Kármán's similarity theory.* Since the mixing length is a linear element in a turbulent flow, von Kármán[5] assumed that it could be

---

[4]L. Prandtl, "Uber die ausgebildete Turbulenz" (Investigations on Turbulent Flow), *Z. angew. Math. u. Mech.*, Vol. V, 136, and *Proceedings of the Second International Congress of Applied Mechanics*, Zurich, 1926. Also translated as NACA TM 1231, 1949.

A result similar to Eq. 7–23 was also obtained by Taylor's vorticity transport theory. See G. I. Taylor, "The Transport of Vorticity and Heat through Fluids in Turbulent Motion," *Proc. Roy. Soc.* (London) Vol. A135 (1932), 685.

[5]Th. von Kármán, "Turbulence and Skin Friction," *J. Aeronaut. Sci.*, Vol. 1, No. 1 (1934) 1.

a function of $d\bar{u}/dy$, $d^2\bar{u}/dy^2$, etc., which are measures of local velocity variations. From the dimensional consideration, the simplest expression for $l$ is

$$l = \kappa \frac{d\bar{u}/dy}{d^2\bar{u}/dy^2} \qquad (7\text{-}25)$$

where $\kappa$ is the universal constant.

D. *Deissler's empirical formula for the turbulent flow in the immediate vicinity of a solid wall.* In the immediate vicinity of a solid wall where the Prandtl equation (Eq. 7–23) and the von Kármán equation (Eq. 7–25) become inadequate, Deissler[6] considered the turbulence to diminish toward the wall and proposed the following empirical formula for use in the immediate vicinity of a wall:

$$-\rho\overline{u'v'} = \rho n^2 \bar{u} y \left[ 1 - \exp\left(\frac{-n^2 \bar{u} y}{\nu}\right) \right] \frac{d\bar{u}}{dy} \qquad (7\text{-}26)$$

in which the constant $n$ was determined experimentally to be 0.124 by Deissler from the time-average velocity profiles measured in tube flows.

## 7-5   Time-Average Velocity Profile for Turbulent Parallel Flow Past a Plane Boundary

We now use Prandtl's mixing length theory to derive a time-average velocity distribution equation for the turbulent parallel flow past a plane boundary as shown in Fig. 7–4. Substitution of Eqs. 7–23 and 7–24 into Eq. 7–20 yields the following equation of motion for this flow:

$$\mu \frac{d\bar{u}}{dy} + \rho\kappa^2 y^2 \left(\frac{d\bar{u}}{dy}\right)^2 = y\frac{\partial}{\partial x}(\bar{p} + \rho g h_z) + \tau_0 \qquad (7\text{-}27)$$

in which $\tau_0$ is the shear stress at the wall and has a constant value for a given steady flow.

Equation 7–27 is difficult to solve. We shall examine the physical phenomena in the flow and find a way to simplify this equation. Figure 7–4(b) shows the relative magnitude of viscous shear stresses and eddy shear stresses as measured in a turbulent parallel flow past a smooth boundary. In the region near the wall, velocity fluctuations are suppressed by the presence of the wall, eddy stresses become negligibly small, and the flow is laminar. This region is called the *laminar sublayer*. The thickness $\delta_s$ of laminar sublayer is very small. With these conditions the equation

---

[6]Robert G. Deissler, "Analysis of Turbulent Heat Transfer, Mass Transfer, and Friction in Smooth Tubes at High Prandtl and Schmidt Numbers," NACA Report 1210, 1955.

of motion for the laminar sublayer flow becomes simply

$$\mu \frac{d\bar{u}}{dy} = \tau_0 \qquad (7\text{--}28)$$

Integrating this equation, with the boundary conditions at the wall that $\bar{u} = 0$ at $y = 0$, we obtain the following velocity distribution equation for the laminar sublayer flow:

$$\bar{u} = \frac{\tau_0}{\mu} y \qquad (7\text{--}29)$$

This equation may be transformed into a nondimensional form after both sides are divided by $\sqrt{\tau_0/\rho}$. Hence

$$\frac{\bar{u}}{\sqrt{\tau_0/\rho}} = \frac{\sqrt{\tau_0/\rho}\, y\rho}{\mu} \qquad (7\text{--}30)$$

The term $\sqrt{\tau_0/\rho}$ has the dimensions of velocity $(L/T)$ and is called the *shear velocity* or *friction velocity*. In the region away from the wall, turbulent motion is fully developed and the viscous shear stresses become negligibly small. It should be noted that there is a so-called *buffer zone* between the laminar sublayer and the fully developed turbulent flow. Within the buffer zone viscous shear stresses and eddy shear stresses are equally important. Although we have used experimental results from a turbulent flow past a smooth boundary in this discussion, the wall roughness will not affect the turbulent flow which occurs away from the wall. However, wall roughness does interfere with the formation of the laminar sublayer and the buffer zone.

Hence, for the turbulent region, we may neglect the viscous stress term $\mu\, d\bar{u}/dy$ in Eq. 7–27. If we further assume that the depth $b$ of the turbulent flow in Fig. 7–4 is small, the term $y\, \partial(\bar{p} + \rho g h_z)/\partial x$ becomes small compared with $\tau_0$. The equation of motion for the turbulent region then becomes

$$\rho \kappa^2 y^2 \left(\frac{d\bar{u}}{dy}\right)^2 = \tau_0 \qquad (7\text{--}31)$$

Taking square root on both sides, separating variables, and integrating the resulting expression, we obtain

$$\frac{\bar{u}}{\sqrt{\tau_0/\rho}} = \frac{1}{\kappa} \ln y + C \qquad (7\text{--}32)$$

The constant $C$ can be evaluated by taking a velocity measurement at any point in the turbulent flow. A useful expression for the velocity distribution of this turbulent flow can be obtained by considering the time-average $\bar{u}_{\max}$ to occur at $y = b$, as shown in Fig. 7–4. Thus,

$$C = \frac{\bar{u}_{\max}}{\sqrt{\tau_0/\rho}} - \frac{1}{\kappa} \ln b$$

and

$$\frac{\bar{u}}{\sqrt{\tau_0/\rho}} = \frac{\bar{u}_{max}}{\sqrt{\tau_0/\rho}} + \frac{1}{\kappa} \ln \frac{y}{b} \qquad (7\text{--}33)$$

This is the famous Prandtl's universal velocity distribution equation for turbulent flow past a plane boundary. Equation 7–33, with $\kappa = 0.4$, is in good agreement with experimental data in the expected region of two-dimensional turbulent parallel flows.

## 7-6  Velocity Distribution Equations for Turbulent Flow in Pipes of Circular Cross Section

Turbulent flow in pipes of circular cross section has been investigated rather thoroughly because of its practical importance. A voluminous quantity of experimental data on pipe flows can be found in technical literature. Experiments indicate that near a pipe entrance turbulent flow undergoes adjustment in the form of boundary layer formation, as shown in Fig. 7–5. The entrance transition length is much shorter for a turbulent

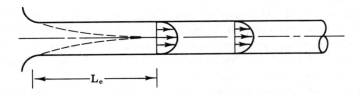

**Fig. 7-5.**  Boundary layer formation in the entrance transition length.

flow than for a laminar flow because the violent mixing action in a turbulent flow tends to speed up the establishment of a fully developed velocity profile. The entrance transition length for a turbulent flow is about 50 pipe diameters. In this section we shall discuss only the velocity profile of a fully developed turbulent flow which occurs downstream from the entrance transition length.

By coincidence Eq. 7–33, with slight modifications of notations, also agrees with experimental data for turbulent axisymmetric flows in pipes of circular cross section. To modify the parallel flow of Fig. 7–4 to a pipe flow, it is only necessary to consider $y$ as the radial distance from the pipe wall, $b$ as the radius $r_0$ of a pipe, and $\bar{u}_{max}$ as the maximum time-average velocity at the pipe axis. By substituting $r_0$ for $b$, setting $\kappa = 0.4$, and rearranging terms, we may express Eq. 7–33 in the following form:

$$\frac{\bar{u}_{max} - \bar{u}}{\sqrt{\tau_0/\rho}} = 2.5 \ln \frac{r_0}{y} \qquad (7\text{--}34)$$

This equation is plotted in Fig. 7–6 and is seen to agree well with Nikuradse's experimental data for turbulent flow in both smooth and rough pipes.[7] The terms $(\bar{u}_{max} - \bar{u})$ are frequently referred to as the *velocity defect*.

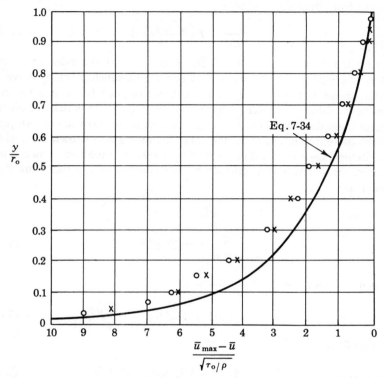

**Fig. 7-6.** Experimental verification of universal velocity distribution equation for turbulent pipe flow.

In using Eq. 7–34 it is necessary to measure $\bar{u}_{max}$ which occurs at the pipe axis. However, alternate equations for turbulent velocity distribution may be derived by considering the conditions at the pipe wall.

**Turbulent velocity distribution equations in smooth pipes.** For turbulent flows in smooth pipes, we may reasonably assume that the point time-average velocity $\bar{u}$ depends on (1) the fluid properties $\rho$ and $\mu$, (2) the distance $y$ of the point from the pipe wall, and (3) the pipe wall condition

[7]J. Nikuradse, "Strömungsgesetze in rauhen Röhren" (Laws of Flow in Rough Pipes), VDI-Forschungsheft 361; *Beilage zu Forschung auf dem Gebiete der Ingenieur-wesen*, Ausgabe B, Band IV, 1933. Also translated as NACA TM 1292, 1950.

represented by the wall shear stress $\tau_0$. Thus

$$\bar{u} = F(\rho, \mu, y, \tau_0) \qquad (7\text{--}35)$$

Dimensional analysis of the above equation will yield the following possible nondimensional equation:

$$\frac{\bar{u}}{\sqrt{\tau_0/\rho}} = F\left(\frac{\sqrt{\tau_0/\rho}\,y\rho}{\mu}\right) \qquad (7\text{--}36)$$

relating the nondimensional velocity $\bar{u}/\sqrt{\tau_0/\rho}$ and the nondimensional distance $\sqrt{\tau_0/\rho}\,y\rho/\mu$. The exact functional relationship must, however, be determined experimentally. The existence of such functional relationships throughout the entire pipe is shown in Fig. 7–7 in which are plotted experimental data from numerous tests of turbulent flow in smooth pipes under different conditions. In the same figure are also shown lines which best fit the experimental data as well as algebraic equations which represent the lines. The entire velocity profile consists of the following three segments:

Laminar sublayer:   $5 > \dfrac{\sqrt{\tau_0/\rho}\,y\rho}{\mu}$

$$\frac{\bar{u}}{\sqrt{\tau_0/\rho}} = \frac{\sqrt{\tau_0/\rho}\,y\rho}{\mu} \qquad (7\text{--}37)$$

Buffer zone:   $30 > \dfrac{\sqrt{\tau_0/\rho}\,y\rho}{\mu} > 5$

$$\frac{\bar{u}}{\sqrt{\tau_0/\rho}} = -3.05 + 11.5 \log_{10} \frac{\sqrt{\tau_0/\rho}\,y\rho}{\mu} \qquad (7\text{--}38)$$

Turbulent core:

$$\frac{\bar{u}}{\sqrt{\tau_0/\rho}} = 5.50 + 5.75 \log_{10} \frac{\sqrt{\tau_0/\rho}\,y\rho}{\mu} \qquad (7\text{--}39)$$

Equation 7–37 is identical to Eq. 7–30. The thickness $\delta_s$ of the laminar sublayer is, therefore,

$$\delta_s = 5\frac{\mu}{\sqrt{\tau_0/\rho}\,\rho} \qquad (7\text{--}40)$$

Equation 7–39 can be obtained by transforming Eq. 7–34 in the following manner. We first rearrange Eq. 7–34 and multiply both the numerator and denominator of the logarithmic term by $\sqrt{\tau_0/\rho}\,\rho/\mu$ to obtain

$$\frac{\bar{u}}{\sqrt{\tau_0/\rho}} = \frac{\bar{u}_{\max}}{\sqrt{\tau_0/\rho}} - 2.5 \ln \frac{\sqrt{\tau_0/\rho}\,r_0\rho/\mu}{\sqrt{\tau_0/\rho}\,y\rho/\mu}$$

$$= \frac{\bar{u}_{\max}}{\sqrt{\tau_0/\rho}} - 2.5 \ln \frac{\sqrt{\tau_0/\rho}\,r_0\rho}{\mu} + 2.5 \ln \frac{\sqrt{\tau_0/\rho}\,y\rho}{\mu}$$

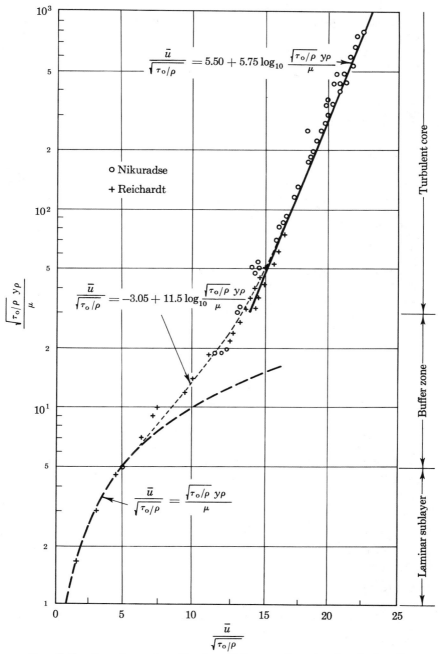

**Fig. 7-7.** Experimental verification of the nondimensional velocity distribution equations for turbulent flow in smooth pipes.

The first two terms on the right-hand side of the above equation have a constant value for any given turbulent pipe flow. This constant is found experimentally equal to 5.50 for all turbulent flows in smooth pipes. Hence the above equation becomes

$$\frac{\bar{u}}{\sqrt{\tau_0/\rho}} = 5.50 + 5.75 \log_{10} \frac{\sqrt{\tau_0/\rho}\, y\rho}{\mu} \qquad (7\text{--}41)$$

since $\ln = 2.30 \log_{10}$.

For the range $70 < \sqrt{\tau_0/\rho}\, y\rho/\mu < 700$, it has been found that the following simple equation also fits well the velocity profile in the turbulent core of Fig. 7–7.

$$\frac{\bar{u}}{\sqrt{\tau_0/\rho}} = 8.74 \left( \frac{\sqrt{\tau_0/\rho}\, y\rho}{\mu} \right)^{1/7} \qquad (7\text{--}42)$$

This is the famous Blasius' one-seventh-power velocity distribution equation for turbulent flow in smooth pipes.[8] Equation 7–42 is frequently used in engineering calculations because of its mathematical simplicity.

*Turbulent velocity distribution equations in rough pipes.* For turbulent flow in rough pipes, the average pipe wall roughness $e$ also affects the velocity profile, and the nondimensional velocity distribution equation then takes the following general form:

$$\frac{\bar{u}}{\sqrt{\tau_0/\rho}} = F\left( \frac{\sqrt{\tau_0/\rho}\, y\rho}{\mu}, \frac{y}{e} \right) \qquad (7\text{--}43)$$

Flow conditions in rough pipes depend on the relative magnitude of the wall roughness $e$ and the thickness $\delta_s$ of the laminar sublayer. If $e$ becomes large compared to $\delta_s$, the wall roughness interferes with the formation of the laminar sublayer and buffer zone. Such pipes are described as *fully rough*, because the velocity profile is a function of $y/e$ only, as shown in Fig. 7–8. The algebraic equation which best fits the experimental data for turbulent flow in fully rough pipes is shown in Fig. 7–8 and can be derived from Eq. 7–34 by first transposing terms and dividing the numerator and denominator of the logarithmic term by $e$ to obtain

$$\frac{\bar{u}}{\sqrt{\tau_0/\rho}} = \frac{\bar{u}_{max}}{\sqrt{\tau_0/\rho}} - 2.5 \ln \frac{r_0/e}{y/e}$$

$$= \frac{\bar{u}_{max}}{\sqrt{\tau_0/\rho}} - 2.5 \ln \frac{r_0}{e} + 2.5 \ln \frac{y}{e}$$

The terms $(\bar{u}_{max}/\sqrt{\tau_0/\rho} - 2.5 \ln r_0/e)$ have a constant value for any given

---

[8]H. Blasius, "Das Ähnlichkeitsgesetz bei Reibungsvorgängen in Flüssigkeiten" (The Law of Similarity for Frictional Processes in Fluids), *Forsch. Arb. Ing.-Wesen* (Berlin), No. 131, 1913.

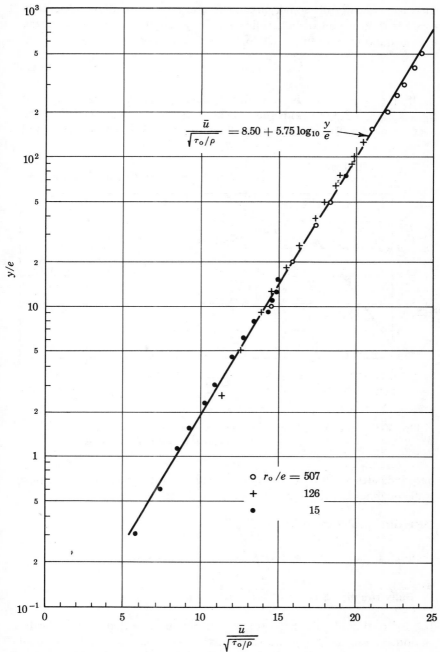

**Fig. 7-8.** Experimental verification of the nondimensional velocity distribution equation for turbulent flow in rough pipes.

turbulent flow in fully rough pipes. This constant is found experimentally equal to 8.50 for all turbulent flows in fully rough pipes. Therefore, the above equation, with $\ln = 2.30 \log_{10}$, may be written as

$$\frac{\bar{u}}{\sqrt{\tau_0/\rho}} = 8.50 + 5.75 \log_{10} \frac{y}{e} \tag{7-44}$$

If the pipe wall is not fully rough, the numerical value of $(\bar{u}_{max}/\sqrt{\tau_0/\rho} - 2.5 \ln r_0/e)$ is found experimentally to be a function of the average pipe wall roughness $e$, as shown in Fig. 7-9. The experimental

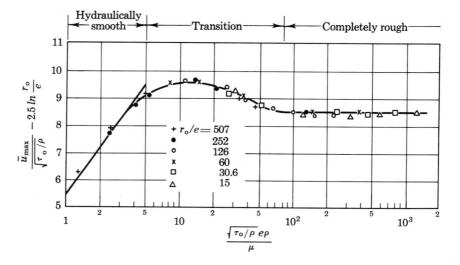

**Fig. 7-9.** The relationship between the numerical value of $(\bar{u}_{max}/\sqrt{\tau_0/\rho} - 2.5 \ln r_0/e)$ and the average pipe wall roughness.

data indicates the following limits for defining the conditions of the pipe wall roughness:

Hydraulically smooth:    $\dfrac{\sqrt{\tau_0/\rho}\,e\rho}{\mu} < 5$

Transitional:    $5 < \dfrac{\sqrt{\tau_0/\rho}\,e\rho}{\mu} < 80$

Fully rough:    $80 < \dfrac{\sqrt{\tau_0/\rho}\,e\rho}{\mu}$

It is interesting to note that a rough pipe may be considered hydraulically smooth as long as $\sqrt{\tau_0/\rho}\,e\rho/\mu$ is less than 5, and that the nondimensional velocity for turbulent flow in fully rough pipes is independent of fluid viscosity.

**Turbulent velocity distribution equation in both smooth and rough pipes.** When Eqs. 7–41 and 7–44 are expressed in terms of the average velocity of flow in the pipe, they can be transformed to an identical form.[9] By definition, the average velocity $V$ in a pipe flow is

$$V = \frac{\hat{Q}}{A} = \frac{\int_0^{r_0} \bar{u}(2\pi r)\, dr}{\pi r_0^2} = \frac{\int_{r_0}^0 \bar{u}\, 2\pi (r_0 - y)\, dy}{\pi r_0^2} \tag{7–45}$$

since $r = r_0 - y$ and $dr = -dy$.

For turbulent flow in smooth pipes, the velocity $\bar{u}$ can be written as

$$\bar{u} = \sqrt{\frac{\tau_0}{\rho}}\left(5.50 + 2.5 \ln\frac{\sqrt{\tau_0/\rho}\, y\rho}{\mu}\right) \tag{7–46}$$

By substituting this equation into Eq. 7–45, integrating, and then rearranging terms, we find the result to be

$$\frac{V}{\sqrt{\tau_0/\rho}} = 1.75 + 5.75 \log_{10}\frac{\sqrt{\tau_0/\rho}\, r_0\rho}{\mu} \tag{7–47}$$

Similar calculations can be carried out for Eq. 7–44. The result is

$$\frac{V}{\sqrt{\tau_0/\rho}} = 4.75 + 5.75 \log_{10}\frac{r_0}{e} \tag{7–48}$$

If we subtract either Eq. 7–47 from Eq. 7–41 for smooth pipes or Eq. 7–48 from Eq. 7–44 for rough pipes, the following identical equation is obtained for both cases:

$$\frac{\bar{u}}{\sqrt{\tau_0/\rho}} = \frac{V}{\sqrt{\tau_0/\rho}} + 3.75 + 5.75 \log_{10}\frac{y}{r_0} \tag{7–49}$$

It is indeed not surprising to find that the velocity distribution equation for the turbulent core is identical for both smooth and rough pipes, since the mechanism of turbulent motion in the region away from the pipe wall is independent of the conditions at the wall.

When Eq. 7–49 is used to plot velocity profile in rough pipes, it is not necessary to know the pipe wall roughness. We need only to determine the average velocity of flow in the pipe. In general, the average velocity is easier to determine than the pipe wall roughness. Thus, Eq. 7–49 has a definite advantage over the special equation 7–44 which is for fully rough pipes only.

---

[9]H. Rouse, *Elementary Mechanics of Fluids* (New York: John Wiley & Sons, Inc., 1946) pp. 196–197.

## 7-7  Friction Loss of Turbulent Flow in Straight Pipes of Circular Cross Section

Another pipe flow problem of importance in technological application is the determination of friction loss in turbulent flow. Unlike the laminar flow in pipes for which a closed-form mathematical solution can be worked out, as shown in Sec. 6–8, the friction loss in turbulent pipe flow must be determined with the aid of experimental data.

Pipe flow problems are generally assumed to be one-dimensional and can be solved by the application of (1) the one-dimensional energy equation and (2) the equation of friction loss. In Sec. 2–13 it was shown that the friction loss $h_L$ between any two sections in a steady one-dimensional incompressible flow is equal to the difference of total energies at these two sections:

$$h_L = \left( \frac{p_1}{\gamma} + z_1 + \frac{V_1^2}{2g} \right) - \left( \frac{p_2}{\gamma} + z_2 + \frac{V_2^2}{2g} \right) \tag{7–50}$$

The friction loss $h_L$ denotes the amount of energy dissipated from each unit weight of fluid as it flows from section 1 to section 2 in the pipe system. The energy dissipation occurs both in straight pipes and in pipe fittings, such as pipe connections and valves. With the present knowledge about turbulent flow, we can calculate the energy dissipation of flow through pipe fittings only by empirical formulas because of an incomplete understanding of the large-scale turbulence which is produced as the flow passes these fittings. Such empirical formulas will be developed in Sec. 7–9. The energy dissipation of flow in straight pipes of constant diameter can be evaluated by semiempirical theories which are to be developed in this section.

Let us refer to Fig. 7–10 in which a steady flow of an incompressible viscous fluid occurs in a straight pipe of constant diameter $D$. Since $V_1 = V_2$, Eq. 7–50 reduces to

$$h_L = \left( \frac{p_1}{\gamma} + z_1 \right) - \left( \frac{p_2}{\gamma} + z_2 \right) \tag{7–51}$$

The friction loss $h_L$ can be related to the pipe wall shear stress $\tau_0$ by considering the volume inside the pipe between the two normal sections at 1 and 2 as a control volume. The momentum equation for the steady flow through this control volume in the direction of flow may be written as

$$p_1 \frac{\pi D^2}{4} - p_2 \frac{\pi D^2}{4} + \gamma L \frac{\pi D^2}{4} \cos \theta - \tau_0 \pi D L = 0$$

whence

$$\tau_0 = \frac{D\gamma}{4L} \left( \frac{p_1 - p_2}{\gamma} + L \cos \theta \right) = \frac{D\gamma}{4L} h_L \tag{7–52}$$

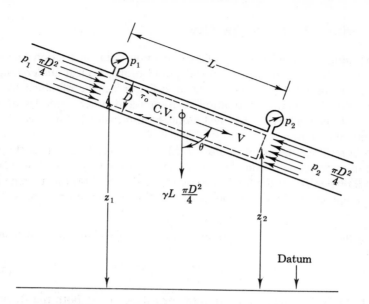

**Fig. 7-10.** A steady turbulent flow in a straight pipe.

The last step in the above equation is made possible by recognizing that $L \cos \theta = z_1 - z_2$ from Fig. 7–10, and then by using Eq. 7–51. Dividing the two sides of the above equation by $\rho V^2/8$, we obtain

$$\frac{\tau_0}{\rho V^2/8} = \frac{D\gamma h_L/4L}{\rho V^2/8} = f \qquad (7\text{–}53)$$

in which a dimensionless friction factor $f$ has been introduced and $V$ is the average velocity of flow through the pipe. This equation is commonly written as

$$h_L = f \frac{L}{D} \frac{V^2}{2g} \qquad (7\text{–}54)$$

which is the famous Darcy's equation[10] for friction loss.

---

[10]This equation is sometimes called the *Darcy-Weisbach equation*. See H. Darcy, "Sur des récherchés experimentales relatives au mouvement des eaux dans les tuyaux" (Experimental Researches on the Flow of Water in Pipes), *Comptes rendus*, Vol. XXXVIII, No. 11 (1854), 1109–1121; and Julius Weisbach, *Lehrbuch der Ingenieur- und Maschinenmechanik* (Textbook of Engineering Mechanics), Brunswick, Germany, 1845.

Equation 7–54 is also frequently written as

$$h_L = 4f_F \frac{L}{D} \frac{V^2}{2g}$$

which is called *Fanning's equation*. Obviously, Fanning's friction factor $f_F$ is one-fourth of Darcy's friction factor $f$. See J. T. Fanning, *A Practical Treatise on Hydraulic and Water Supply Engineering*. Princeton, N.J.: D. Van Nostrand Co., Inc., 1893.

## 7-8   Friction Factor in Pipe Flow

Although a large quantity of experimental data on friction factor in pipe flow can be found in technical publications, a clear understanding of the functional dependence of friction factor can be obtained by first establishing a functional equation relating $f$ and other variables of pipe flow and then applying the technique of dimensional analysis to that functional equation.

A careful examination of Eqs. 7–53 and 7–54 indicates that the pipe friction factor depends on (1) the average velocity $V$ of pipe flow, (2) the pipe diameter $D$, (3) the fluid properties $\rho$ and $\mu$, and (4) the average pipe wall roughness $e$. Hence the following functional equation may be written:

$$f = F(V, D, \rho, \mu, e)$$

Dimensional analysis of this equation yields the following nondimensional equation:

$$f = F_1\left(\frac{VD\rho}{\mu}, \frac{D}{e}\right) = F_2\left(\frac{VD\rho}{\mu}, \frac{r_0}{e}\right) \qquad (7\text{–}55)$$

which states that the pipe friction factor $f$ depends on both the Reynolds number $VD\rho/\mu$ of pipe flow and the relative pipe roughness $r_0/e$.

Based on Eq. 7–55, Moody[11] presented experimental data on pipe flow by means of a three-way logarithmic plot of $f$ versus $VD\rho/\mu$ with different $r_0/e$-values as variable parameters, as shown in Fig. 7–11. The curves in this diagram are for both laminar flow and turbulent flow in smooth and rough pipes. For any pipe flow, the friction factor is readily determined from Fig. 7–11 after the numerical values of $r_0/e$ and $VD\rho/\mu$ are calculated. Included in Fig. 7–11 is a tabulation of $e$-values for materials commonly used in the manufacture of commercial pipes. It is important to note that the tabulated $e$-values are for materials in new and clean condition. The $e$-values of such materials will increase with age because of the accumulation of rust and sedimentation on the pipe walls.[12]

Laminar pipe flow. The straight line on the far left-hand side of Fig. 7–11 represents the friction factor curve for laminar pipe flow. The theory of laminar flow in pipes of circular cross section was derived in Sec. 6–8 and the result was shown to be in the form of the Hagen-Poiseuille equation:

---

[11]L. F. Moody, "Friction Factors for Pipe Flow," *Trans. Am. Soc. Mech. Engrs.*, Vol. LXVI (1944), 671.

[12]C. F. Colebrook and C. M. White, "The Reduction of Carrying Capacity of Pipes with Age," *J. Inst. of Civil Engrs.* (London), Vol. VII (1937), 99; and P. A. Lamont, "The Reduction with Age of the Carrying Capacity of Pipelines," *J. Inst. Water Engrs.*, Vol. VIII (1954), 53.

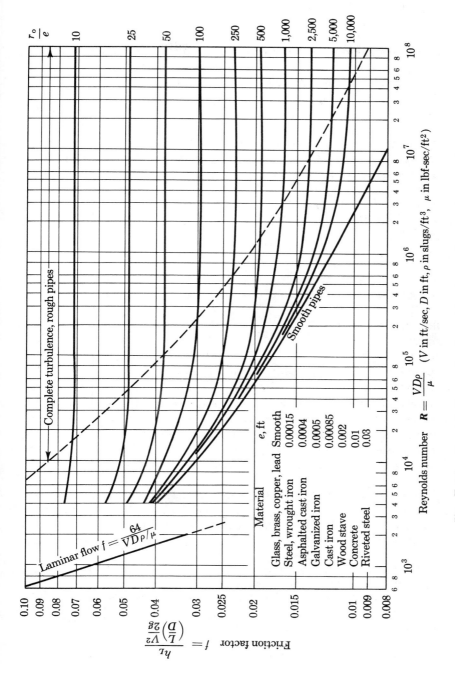

**Fig. 7-11.** Moody's diagram for determining friction factor in commercial pipes.

Reynolds number $R = \dfrac{VD\rho}{\mu}$ ($V$ in ft/sec, $D$ in ft, $\rho$ in slugs/ft$^3$, $\mu$ in lbf-sec/ft$^2$)

Friction factor $f = \dfrac{h_L}{\left(\dfrac{L}{D}\right)\dfrac{V^2}{2g}}$

Laminar flow $f = \dfrac{64}{VD\rho/\mu}$

Complete turbulence, rough pipes

Smooth pipes

$\dfrac{r_o}{e}$

10
25
50
100
250
500
1,000
2,500
5,000
10,000

| Material | $e$, ft |
|---|---|
| Glass, brass, copper, lead | Smooth |
| Steel, wrought iron | 0.00015 |
| Asphalted cast iron | 0.0004 |
| Galvanized iron | 0.0005 |
| Cast iron | 0.00085 |
| Wood stave | 0.002 |
| Concrete | 0.01 |
| Riveted steel | 0.03 |

$$h_L = \frac{32\mu VL}{\gamma D^2} \tag{7-56}$$

Equating this equation to Darcy's equation (Eq. 7–54), we obtain

$$\frac{32\mu VL}{\gamma D^2} = f \frac{L}{D} \frac{V^2}{2g}$$

The friction factor $f$ for laminar flow is found to be

$$f = \frac{64}{VD\rho/\mu} \tag{7-57}$$

which indicates that $f$ varies inversely with the Reynolds number of laminar pipe flow. This relationship is in good agreement with experimental data for pipe flow with $VD\rho/\mu < 2000$.

**Turbulent flow in smooth pipes.** The lowest curve in Fig. 7–11 represents experimental data for turbulent flow in smooth pipes. The algebraic equation for this curve can be derived by combining Eqs. 7–47 and 7–53 to yield

$$\frac{1}{\sqrt{f}} = -0.91 + 2.03 \log_{10}\left(\frac{VD\rho}{\mu}\sqrt{f}\right)$$

However, it is necessary to change the constants in this equation in order for the equation to fit experimental data. The following equation has been found in good agreement with experimental data of turbulent flow in smooth pipes:

$$\frac{1}{\sqrt{f}} = -0.8 + 2.0 \log_{10}\left(\frac{VD\rho}{\mu}\sqrt{f}\right) \tag{7-58}$$

Equation 7–58 is frequently referred to as the *Kármán-Prandtl universal friction factor equation for turbulent flow in smooth pipes.*

For turbulent flow in smooth pipes with $VD\rho/\mu < 60{,}000$, the following simple friction factor equation can be derived from Blasius' one-seventh-power velocity distribution equation (Eq. 7–42):

$$f = \frac{0.3164}{(VD\rho/\mu)^{1/4}} \tag{7-59}$$

This equation is frequently used in engineering calculations because of its simplicity.

**Turbulent flow in rough pipes.** The family of curves in Fig. 7–11 labeled with different $r_0/e$-values are obtained from experimental data on turbulent flow in rough pipes. These curves have been divided into two portions by a broken line. To the right of this broken line, the curves are horizontal straight lines indicating that $f$ is a function of $r_0/e$ only and is independent of the Reynolds number. These horizontal straight lines represent experimental data for turbulent flow in fully rough pipes. The algebraic equation for this family of horizontal lines can be derived by combining Eqs. 7–48 and 7–53 to yield

$$\frac{1}{\sqrt{f}} = 1.68 + 2.03 \log_{10} \frac{r_0}{e}$$

Again, a comparison of this equation with experimental data on turbulent flow in fully rough pipes indicates that slight modification of constants in this equation will improve the agreement with test data. The modified universal friction factor equation for turbulent flow in fully rough pipes is

$$\frac{1}{\sqrt{f}} = 1.74 + 2.0 \log_{10} \frac{r_0}{e} \qquad (7\text{--}60)$$

which indicates a constant value of $f$ for any given $r_0/e$-value; $f$ is independent of the fluid viscosity in fully rough pipes.

The portion of rough-pipe curves to the left of the broken line in Fig. 7–11 represents the turbulent flow in the transitional region between hydraulically smooth and rough pipes in which both fluid viscosity and pipe wall roughness are important. Colebrook[13] developed the following empirical equation from experimental data for this portion of curves for commercial rough pipes:

$$\frac{1}{\sqrt{f}} - 2.0 \log_{10} \frac{r_0}{e} = 1.74 - 2.0 \log_{10} \left( 1 + 18.7 \frac{r_0/e}{\sqrt{f}\, VD\rho/\mu} \right) \qquad (7\text{--}61)$$

## 7-9   Empirical Formulas for Turbulent Pipe Flow

Because of axisymmetry, semiempirical theories have been formulated successfully for predicting the velocity profile and friction loss of turbulent flow in straight pipes of circular cross section. In the case of turbulent flow in closed conduits of noncircular cross section and in pipe fittings, only empirical formulas are available at the present time.

**Turbulent flow in closed conduits of noncircular cross sections.** Figure 7–12 shows velocity distribution patterns for some turbulent flows along the lengths of conduits of rectangular and triangular cross sections as obtained by experimental measurements. The lines in each flow are traces of equal time-average point velocities. These longitudinal velocity distribution patterns are further complicated by the existence of secondary

---

[13]C. F. Colebrook, "Turbulent Flow in Pipes with Particular Reference to the Transition Region between the Smooth and Rough Pipe Laws," *J. Inst. Civil Engrs.* (London), Vol. XI (1938–1939), 133–156.

flow at any flow section. In the secondary flow, fluid particles move away from the central portion of the conduit walls and toward the corners of the conduit, as shown in Fig. 7–13. Secondary flows are superimposed onto the main flow to further complicate the resulting flow pattern.

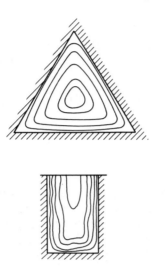

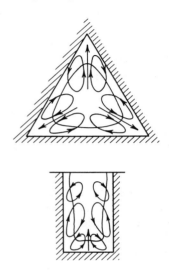

**Fig. 7-12.** Traces of equal time-average point velocities in closed conduits of noncircular cross sections.

**Fig. 7-13.** Secondary flows in closed conduits of noncircular cross sections.

For turbulent flow in conduits of noncircular cross sections for which the velocity distribution is reasonably uniform, it has been found that a modified form of Darcy's equation may be derived to evaluate the friction loss. Let us assume that the pipe in Fig. 7–10 has a noncircular cross section with a cross-sectional area $A$ and a wetted perimeter $P$. The momentum equation for the steady flow through the indicated control volume may then be written as

$$p_1 A - p_2 A + \gamma L A \cos \theta - \tau_0 P L = 0$$

from which

$$\tau_0 = \frac{A}{PL} (p_1 - p_2 + \gamma L \cos \theta) = \frac{A}{PL} h_L \gamma$$

By following Eq. 7–53, we see that

$$f = \frac{\tau_0}{\rho V^2/8} = \frac{A h_L \gamma}{P L \rho V^2/8}$$

The ratio $A/P$ is defined as the *hydraulic radius* $R_h$. The above equation can be rearranged into the following form:

$$h_L = f \frac{L}{4R_h} \frac{V^2}{2g} \qquad (7\text{-}62)$$

since $\gamma/\rho = g$. This is the modified Darcy's equation for evaluating turbulent friction loss in conduits of noncircular cross sections. It is easy to show that for a circular pipe of diameter $D$ the hydraulic radius is $D/4$. Therefore, in using Eq. 7–62 to calculate the friction loss for turbulent flow in conduits of noncircular cross section, the numerical value of $f$ may also be found from Fig. 7–11 with the modified Reynolds number and relative roughness computed as follows:

$$R = \frac{V4R_h\rho}{\mu} \qquad (7\text{-}63)$$

and

$$\frac{r_0}{e} = \frac{2R_h}{e} \qquad (7\text{-}64)$$

**Turbulent friction losses in pipe fittings.** When flow passes a pipe fitting, additional energy is dissipated from the flow due to local disturbances. Local disturbances can generally be attributed to a change of flow direction (such as an elbow), a change in flow section (such as a reducer or an enlargement), or an obstruction (such as a valve) in a pipe line. These local disturbances frequently generate additional eddying turbulence which will normally persist for a considerable distance downstream and is eventually damped out by the fluid viscosity. Therefore, a certain amount of useful energy is expended in the generation and subsequent decaying of eddying turbulence.

The magnitude of local disturbance depends on the abruptness of the change of velocity through a pipe fitting. If a pipe fitting is carefully streamlined, the local disturbance may be kept at a minimum. If, on the other hand, the pipe fitting is not properly streamlined, the resulting local disturbance will cause excessive dissipation of energy.

Friction losses in pipe fittings have been found to vary approximately with the velocity head of flow. Thus,

$$h_L = C_L \frac{V^2}{2g} \qquad (7\text{-}65)$$

in which $C_L$ is called the *loss coefficient* and $V$ is the average velocity of flow. In general, experimental measurements are necessary to determine the numerical value of loss coefficient for each type of pipe fitting. The empirical values of $C_L$ for several pipe fittings are presented in Table 7–1. It is important to note that the tabulated values are statistical averages of experimental results from a number of tests. The numerical value of $C_L$ for any individual pipe fitting may be somewhat different from that given in the table.

## TABLE 7-1. Loss Coefficient due to Fittings and Valves

| Fittings and Valves | $C_L$ |
|---|---|

Sudden enlargement

$$h_L = C_L \frac{V_1^2}{2g}$$

$$\left(1 - \frac{A_1}{A_2}\right)^2$$

Sudden contraction

$$h_L = C_L \frac{V_2^2}{2g}$$

| $A_2/A_1 =$ 0.1 | 0.41 |
|---|---|
| 0.3 | 0.36 |
| 0.5 | 0.26 |
| 0.7 | 0.14 |
| 0.9 | 0.06 |

| | |
|---|---|
| Sharp-cornered entrance | 0.50 |
| Rounded-cornered entrance | 0.25 |
| Globe valve, fully open | 10.0 |
| Gate valve, fully open | 0.2 |
| Closed return bend | 2.2 |
| Standard tee | 1.8 |
| Standard 90-degree elbow | 0.9 |
| 45-degree elbow | 0.4 |

*Illustrative Example* 7–1. A flow of 3 cubic feet per second is being pumped through the steel pipeline shown in the accompanying sketch. The pump is

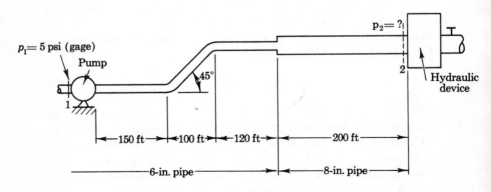

**Illustrative Example 7-1.**

delivering 90 horsepower to the pipe flow. The liquid has a specific weight $\gamma = 60.0$ lbf/ft³ and a dynamic viscosity $\mu = 3.5 \times 10^{-5}$ lbf-sec/ft². The globe valve is fully open. Calculate the pressure at station 2.

*Solution:* Using the pipe axis at station 1 as elevation datum and including all losses, we may write the energy equation from station 1 to station 2 as follows:

$$\underbrace{\frac{(5\,\text{lbf/in.}^2)(144\,\text{in.}^2/\text{ft}^2)}{60.0\,\text{lbf/ft}^3}}_{p_1/\gamma} + \underbrace{0}_{z_1} + \frac{V_1^2}{2g}$$

$$+ \underbrace{\frac{(90\,\text{hp})(550\,\text{ft-lbf/sec/hp})}{(3\,\text{ft}^3/\text{sec})(60.0\,\text{lbf/ft}^3)}}_{\text{pump head}} - f_1 \underbrace{\frac{411.4\,\text{ft}}{6/12\,\text{ft}}\frac{V_1^2}{2g}}_{\text{6-in. pipe line}}$$

$$- \underbrace{2 \times 0.4\frac{V_1^2}{2g}}_{\text{two 45° elbows}} - \underbrace{0.2\frac{V_1^2}{2g}}_{\substack{\text{sudden}\\\text{enlargement}}} - f_2 \underbrace{\frac{200\,\text{ft}}{8/12\,\text{ft}}\frac{V_2^2}{2g}}_{\text{8-in. pipe line}}$$

$$= \underbrace{\frac{p_2}{\gamma} + 100.0\,\text{ft}}_{z_2} + \frac{V_2^2}{2g}$$

This equation can be simplified and solved for $p_2/\gamma$:

$$\frac{p_2}{\gamma} = 187.0\,\text{ft} - 822.8\,f_1\frac{V_1^2}{2g} - (1 + 300\,f_2)\frac{V_2^2}{2g}$$

For the 6-in. pipe,

$$V_1 = \frac{3\,\text{ft}^3/\text{sec}}{(\pi/4)(6/12\,\text{ft})^2} = 15.3\,\text{ft/sec}$$

$$R = \frac{(15.3\,\text{ft/sec})(\tfrac{6}{12}\,\text{ft})(60.0\,\text{lbf/ft}^3)}{(3.5 \times 10^{-5}\,\text{lbf-sec/ft}^2)(32.2\,\text{ft/sec}^2)} = 4.0 \times 10^5$$

$$\frac{r_0}{e} = \frac{\tfrac{3}{12}\,\text{ft}}{0.00015\,\text{ft}} = 1670$$

From Fig. 7–11, $f_1 = 0.017$.

For the 8-in. pipe,

$$V_2 = \frac{3\,\text{ft}^3/\text{sec}}{(\pi/4)(8/12\,\text{ft})^2} = 8.6\,\text{ft/sec}$$

$$R = \frac{(8.6\,\text{ft/sec})(\tfrac{8}{12}\,\text{ft})(60.0\,\text{lbf/ft}^3)}{(3.5 \times 10^{-5}\,\text{lbf-sec/ft}^2)(32.2\,\text{ft/sec}^2)} = 3.1 \times 10^5$$

$$\frac{r_0}{e} = \frac{\tfrac{4}{12}\,\text{ft}}{0.00015\,\text{ft}} = 2220$$

From Fig. 7–11, $f_2 = 0.0165$.

Substituting the calculated values of $V_1$, $V_2$, $f_1$, and $f_2$ into the $p_2/\gamma$-equation, we obtain

$$\frac{p_2}{\gamma} = 129.4\,\text{ft}$$

and

$$p_2 = \frac{(129.4\,\text{ft})(60.0\,\text{lbf/ft}^3)}{(144\,\text{in.}^2/\text{ft}^2)} = 53.9\,\text{lbf/in.}^2\,\text{gage}$$

*Illustrative Example* 7–2. This example illustrates a transient pipe flow problem. It is desired to determine the time required for the establishment of a steady pipe flow in a pipeline under a constant head $H$ when a valve is suddenly opened, as shown in the accompanying sketch. In the first instant after the valve is opened,

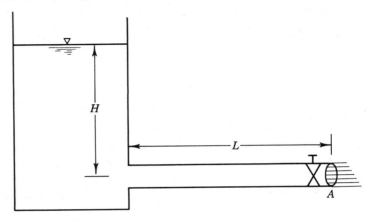

**Illustrative Example 7-2.**

the available head $H$ causes flow to accelerate in the pipeline. As the velocity increases, the available head is gradually reduced by friction losses in the pipe and the fittings until a steady flow is established.

The steady-state velocity $V_0$ in the pipeline can be determined by writing the energy equation between the liquid surface in the reservoir and the pipe outlet. Thus,

$$H = f\frac{L}{D}\frac{V_0^2}{2g} + C_L\frac{V_0^2}{2g} + \frac{V_0^2}{2g} = f\frac{L_e}{D}\frac{V_0^2}{2g} \tag{A}$$

where $L_e$ is called the *equivalent length* of the pipe line to account for fitting losses and the velocity head at the pipe outlet.

The equation of motion for the pipe flow during the transient period is

$$\gamma A\left(H - f\frac{L_e}{D}\frac{V^2}{2g}\right) = \frac{\gamma AL}{g}\frac{dV}{dt} \tag{B}$$

where $V$ is the transient velocity in the pipeline. Equations (A) and (B) can be combined to yield

$$\gamma A\left(f\frac{L_e}{D}\frac{V_0^2}{2g} - f\frac{L_e}{D}\frac{V^2}{2g}\right) = \frac{\gamma AL}{g}\frac{dV}{dt}$$

which may be simplified and rearranged into the following form:

$$\frac{gH}{LV_0^2}(V_0^2 - V^2) = \frac{dV}{dt}$$

whence

$$\int_0^t dt = \frac{LV_0^2}{gH}\int_0^V \frac{dV}{V_0^2 - V^2}$$

which is readily integrated as

$$t = \frac{LV_0}{2gH} \ln \frac{V_0 + V}{V_0 - V}$$

This equation indicates that $V$ will approach $V_0$ only when $t$ approaches infinity; that is, mathematically $V$ approaches $V_0$ asymptotically. Therefore, for practical purposes, we may consider, for example, that a steady flow is established in the pipeline when $V$ reaches $0.99\,V_0$. The time required for $V$ to reach $0.99\,V_0$ is then

$$t = \frac{LV_0}{2gH} \ln \frac{1.99}{0.01} = \frac{LV_0}{2gH} \quad (5.293)$$

## 7-10  Turbulent Flows in Open Channels

An *open channel* is a conduit in which liquid flows with a free surface and under the influence of gravity. Because open channels are usually irregular in cross section and in other hydraulic properties and because the depth of an open-channel flow varies with respect to time and space, the mechanics of open-channel flow is much more complicated than that of pipe flow. A wide variety of problems may be encountered in open-channel flows. In this section we shall consider only the friction resistance of a steady uniform flow in a prismatic open channel laid on a uniform slope, as shown in Fig. 7–14.

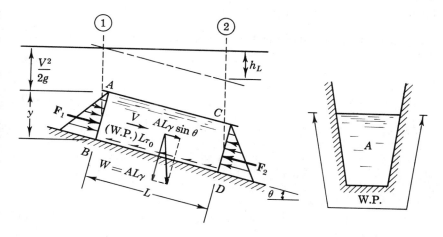

**Fig. 7-14.** Condition of equilibrium in a uniform open-channel flow.

The forces acting on the liquid inside the indicated control volume are shown in Fig. 7–14. For a steady uniform flow the hydrostatic forces $F_1$ and $F_2$ are equal to each other. The momentum equation for this control volume in the direction of flow can be written as

$$AL\gamma \sin \theta - PL\tau_0 = 0$$

since there is no change of momentum in a steady uniform flow. Note that $\sin \theta = h_L/L = S$, where $S$ is the slope of the channel. Solving the above equation for $\tau_0$, we obtain

$$\tau_0 = \gamma \frac{A}{P} \sin \theta = \gamma R_h S \qquad (7\text{--}66)$$

where $R_h$ is the hydraulic radius.

The wall shear stress in an open-channel flow has undoubtedly the same mechanism as that in a pipe flow. Therefore, it seems reasonable to express $\tau_0$ for an open-channel flow in the following form which is similar to Eq. 7–53 of a pipe flow:

$$\tau_0 = f_c \frac{\rho V^2}{2} \qquad (7\text{--}67)$$

where $f_c$ is a friction factor for an open-channel flow.

Equations 7–66 and 7–67 may be combined to eliminate $\tau_0$. Thus,

$$\gamma R_h S = f_c \frac{\rho V^2}{2}$$

from which

$$V = \sqrt{2\gamma/\rho f_c} \sqrt{R_h S} = \sqrt{2g/f_c} \sqrt{R_h S}$$

since $\gamma/\rho = g$. This expression is customarily written as

$$V = C\sqrt{R_h S} \qquad (7\text{--}68)$$

by setting

$$C = \sqrt{2g/f_c} \qquad (7\text{--}69)$$

Equation 7–68 is the famous Chézy formula.[14]

From the discussion of friction factor in pipe flow, we may conclude that the friction factor $f_c$ for open-channel flow and, consequently, Chézy's $C$ is a function of Reynolds number and relative channel wall roughness. A friction factor diagram similar to Fig. 7–11 could be constructed from experimental data for open-channel flows. However, since most open channels have rather rough surfaces, the effect of Reynolds number on Chézy's $C$ may be neglected, and the effect of wall roughness can be expressed empirically. Many empirical formulas for Chézy's $C$ have been proposed for engineering calculations. The Manning formula is probably the best known for this purpose.

---

[14]Clemens Herschel, "On the Origin of the Chézy Formula," *J. Assoc. Eng. Soc.*, Vol. XVIII (1887), 363–369.

*The Manning formula.* The Manning formula,[15] expressed in British units, is written as

$$V = \frac{1.486}{n} R_h^{2/3} S^{1/2} \tag{7-70}$$

where $n$ is a roughness factor. This empirical formula was derived from experimental data on water flow and has been widely used in engineering calculations mainly because of its simple form as well as the satisfactory results it yields in practical application. Suggested values of Manning's $n$ for different surface materials are given in Table 7–2.

**TABLE 7-2.  Values of Manning's *n* for Various Surface Materials**

| Surface | n |
|---|---|
| Smooth | 0.010 |
| Neat cement | 0.011 |
| Finished concrete, planed wood, or steel | 0.012 |
| Mortar, clay, or glazed brick | 0.013 |
| Vitrified clay | 0.014 |
| Brick lined with cement mortar | 0.015 |
| Unfinished cement | 0.017 |
| Rubber masonry or corrugated metal | 0.020 |
| Earth channel with gravel bottom | 0.025 |
| Earth channel with dense weed | 0.035 |
| Natural channel with clean bottom, brush on sides | 0.050 |
| Flood plain with dense brush | 0.100 |

Comparison of the Manning formula and the Chézy formula indicates that

$$C = 1.486 \frac{R_h^{1/6}}{n} \tag{7-71}$$

Thus, the ratio $R_h^{1/6}/n$ may be taken as a relative roughness factor for open-channel flow comparable to $r_0/e$ for pipe flow.

## PROBLEMS

**7–1.** Estimate the maximum rate of flow, in cubic feet per second, at which flow in a 2 in. diameter pipe can remain laminar if the fluid is (a) water, (b) glycerine, and (c) air, at a temperature of 80°F and a pressure of 14.7 lbf/in.² abs.

**7–2.** In the following table are shown the instantaneous values of the x-com-

---

[15]Robert Manning, "On the Flow of Water in Open Channels and Pipes," *Trans. Inst. Civil Engrs. Ireland*, Vol. XX (1891), 161–207.

ponent velocities measured at two points in a flow stream. Points $A$ and $B$ are 0.5 ft apart on the $x$-axis.

| $t$, seconds | $u_A$, ft/sec | $u_B$, ft/sec |
|:---:|:---:|:---:|
| 0 | 170 | 140 |
| 0.5 | 200 | 120 |
| 1.0 | 150 | 220 |
| 1.5 | 150 | 200 |
| 2.0 | 100 | 240 |
| 2.5 | 180 | 150 |

(a) Calculate the intensity of turbulence for $u$ at each point. (b) Estimate $\overline{\partial u/\partial x}$ and $\partial \bar{u}/\partial x$ at point $A$. (c) Calculate the correlation coefficient $R_{u_A u_B}$ for the instantaneous velocities at these two points where $R_{u_A u_B}$ is defined as

$$R_{u_A u_B} = \frac{\overline{u'_A u'_B}}{\sqrt{\overline{u'^2_A}}\sqrt{\overline{u'^2_B}}}$$

7-3. From the definition of time-average quantities, show that

(a) $\overline{u + v} = \bar{u} + \bar{v}$

(b) $\overline{\bar{u}v} = \bar{u}\bar{v}$

(c) $\dfrac{\overline{du}}{dx} = \dfrac{d\bar{u}}{dx}$

(d) $\dfrac{\overline{du}}{dt} = \dfrac{d\bar{u}}{dt}$

7-4. Express $Du(x, y, t)/Dt$ in terms of time-average and fluctuation velocity components and their derivatives.

7-5. Show that when a stagnation tube is placed in a turbulent flow and pointed in the $x$-direction, the total pressure that it measures amounts to

$$\bar{p} = p_0 + \frac{\rho \bar{u}^2}{2}\left(1 + \frac{\overline{u'^2} + \overline{v'^2} + \overline{w'^2}}{\bar{u}^2}\right)$$

7-6. Derive the equation of continuity, in cylindrical notations, for the time-average turbulent flow of an incompressible fluid by using substitutions, $v_r = \overline{v_r} + v'_r$, etc.

7-7. Derive the Reynolds equations, in cylindrical notations, for the time-average turbulent flow of an incompressible fluid by using substitutions, $v_r = \overline{v_r} + v'_r$, etc.

7-8. Write the Reynolds equations for the steady time-average turbulent flow (a) between two fixed horizontal parallel flat plates, and (b) in a round tube.

7-9. Assume that, for the turbulent parallel flow past a plane boundary in Figure 7-4, the velocity distribution is

$$\bar{u} = A\left(\frac{y}{b}\right)^{1/n}$$

where $A$ is a constant. (a) Derive an expression for the mixing length in this flow. (b) Calculate the rate of flow per unit width of the channel and the average velocity for this turbulent flow.

**7–10.** A liquid flows turbulently down an inclined plane surface as shown in Fig. 7–15. (a) Show that the shear stress $\tau_{yx}$ in the flow at a point which is

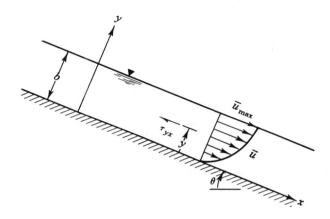

**Fig. 7-15.**

$y$ above the plane surface can be written as

$$\tau_{yx} = \tau_0 \left(1 - \frac{y}{b}\right) = \gamma(b - y) \sin \theta$$

where $\tau_0$ is the shear stress at the plane surface and $\gamma$ is the specific weight of the liquid. (b) Equate the above expression to Prandtl's mixing length formula to obtain

$$\gamma(b - y) \sin \theta = \rho \kappa^2 y^2 \left(\frac{d\bar{u}}{dy}\right)^2$$

and show that the equation for the time-average turbulent velocity distribution for this flow is given by

$$\bar{u} = \bar{u}_{\text{max}} + \frac{1}{\kappa} \sqrt{\frac{\gamma b \sin \theta}{\rho}} \left(2\sqrt{1 - \frac{y}{b}} + \ln \frac{\sqrt{b} - \sqrt{b - y}}{\sqrt{b} + \sqrt{b - y}}\right)$$

**7–11.** A turbulent flow occurs between two fixed horizontal parallel plates as shown in Fig. 7–16. The shear stresses in this flow are:

$$\tau_{yx} = \frac{b - y}{b} \tau_0 \quad \text{for} \quad 0 < y < b$$

$$\tau_{yx} = \frac{y - b}{b} \tau_0 \quad \text{for} \quad b < y < 2b$$

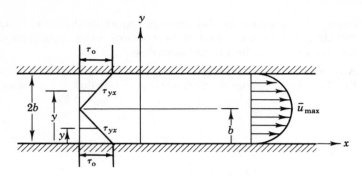

**Fig. 7-16.**

Using Prandtl's mixing length formula: $\tau_{yx} = \rho\kappa^2 y^2 (d\bar{u}/dy)^2$, derive the velocity distribution equations for this flow.

**7–12.** For a turbulent flow in a round pipe, the shear stress $\tau_{rz}$ varies linearly from zero at the pipe axis to a maximum value $\tau_0$ at the pipe wall. Thus we may write

$$\tau_{rz} = \tau_0 \left(1 - \frac{y}{r_0}\right)$$

When this expression is equated to von Kármán's eddy shear stress formula, we have

$$\tau_0 \left(1 - \frac{y}{r_0}\right) = \rho\kappa^2 \frac{(d\bar{u}/dy)^4}{(d^2\bar{u}/dy^2)^2}$$

Starting with this equation, show that von Kármán's universal velocity distribution equation for turbulent pipe flow is

$$\bar{u} = \bar{u}_{\max} + \frac{\sqrt{\tau_0/\rho}}{\kappa} [\sqrt{1 - y/r_0} + \ln(1 - \sqrt{1 - y/r_0})]$$

**7–13.** Turbulent flow occurs through an annulus formed by two concentric round pipes as shown in Fig. 7–17. The pipe surfaces are smooth. Assum-

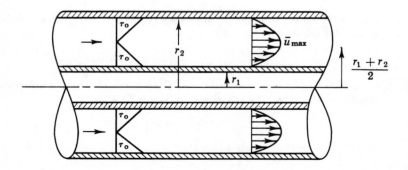

**Fig. 7-17.**

ing that the maximum time-average velocity $\bar{u}_{max}$ occurs at $r = (r_1 + r_2)/2$ and using Prandtl's mixing length formula, derive the equations for the velocity distribution in this flow through the annulus.

**7-14.** By using Equation 7-34, show that the average velocity $V$ of turbulent flow in a round pipe is

$$V = \bar{u}_{max} - 3.75\sqrt{\tau_0/\rho}$$

**7-15.** For turbulent flow in a smooth pipe with $VD\rho/\mu < 10^5$, the velocity profile in the turbulent core can be approximated by the following power equation:

$$\bar{u} = \bar{u}_{max}\left(\frac{y}{r_0}\right)^{1/7} = \bar{u}_{max}\left(\frac{r_0 - r}{r_0}\right)^{1/7}$$

where $y$ and $r$ are respectively the distances measured from the pipe wall and the pipe axis. Show that (a) the average velocity $V$ of this pipe flow is

$$V = \frac{49}{60}\bar{u}_{max}$$

and (b) Prandtl's mixing length $l$ becomes

$$l = 7r_0\frac{\sqrt{\tau_0/\rho}}{\bar{u}_{max}}\left(\frac{r_0 - r}{r_0}\right)^{6/7}\left(\frac{r}{r_0}\right)^{1/2}$$

**7-16.** For turbulent flow in a smooth round pipe with $VD\rho/\mu < 10^5$, the velocity profile in the turbulent core can be approximated by Eq. 7-42:

$$\frac{\bar{u}}{\sqrt{\tau_0/\rho}} = 8.74\left(\frac{\sqrt{\tau_0/\rho}\,y\rho}{\mu}\right)^{1/7}$$

Starting with this equation, show that (a) the wall shear stress $\tau_0$ is given by

$$\tau_0 = \frac{0.03955\,\rho V^2}{(VD\rho/\mu)^{1/4}}$$

and (b) the friction factor $f$ is

$$f = \frac{0.3164}{(VD\rho/\mu)^{1/4}}$$

where $V$ is the average velocity of the pipe flow and $D$ is the diameter of the pipe.

**7-17.** Water at 80°F flows through a horizontal, smooth pipe of 4 in. in diameter. At a point where $r = 1.50$ in., calculate the velocity $\bar{u}$, shear stress $\tau_{yx}$, kinematic eddy viscosity $\epsilon$, and mixing length $l$ when the average velocity of the pipe flow is (a) 20 ft/sec, (b) 2 ft/sec, and (c) 0.02 ft/sec.

**7-18.** For turbulent flow in a smooth pipe of diameter $D$, show that the thickness $\delta_s$ of laminar sublayer is

$$\delta_s = \frac{5\sqrt{8}}{(VD\rho/\mu)\sqrt{f}}D$$

where $f$ is the friction factor of the pipe flow.

**7-19.** Water at 80°F flows through a long, horizontal, straight stretch of 8-in. diameter smooth pipe with a pressure drop of 2.0 lbf/in.² per 100 ft of length. (a) Determine the thickness of the laminar sublayer and the buffer zone. (b) Calculate the velocities at $r/r_0 = 0.1, 0.2, 0.4, 0.6, 0.8, 0.9,$ and 1.0.

**7-20.** Air at a temperature of 70°F and a pressure of 14.7 lbf/in.² abs. flows in a horizontal 3-in. diameter smooth pipe with an average velocity of 50 ft/sec. (a) Determine the thickness of the laminar sublayer and the buffer zone. (b) Calculate the velocity and shear stress at $r = 0.90\, r_0$. (c) Find the ratio of viscous shear stress to eddy shear stress at $r = 0.90\, r_0$.

**7-21.** If the inside surface of the pipe in Prob. 7–20 has an equivalent roughness $e = 0.05$ in., calculate the velocity and shear stress at $r = 0.90\, r_0$.

**7-22.** Show that, for a turbulent pipe flow,

$$\frac{V}{\bar{u}_{max}} = \frac{1}{1 + 1.43\sqrt{f}}$$

where $V$ is the average velocity of a turbulent pipe flow, $\bar{u}_{max}$ is the maximum time-average velocity at the pipe axis, and $f$ is the friction factor for a turbulent pipe flow.

**7-23.** Pitot tube measurements in an air flow in a 6-in. diameter pipe indicate that the velocities at the pipe axis and at $r = 0.50\, r_0$ are respectively 95 ft/sec and 85 ft/sec. At this flow section, $p = 16.0$ lbf/in.² abs. and $T = 80°F$. Assuming incompressible flow, calculate (a) the friction factor and (b) the equivalent pipe roughness.

**7-24.** Water at 80°F flows through a horizontal rough pipe of 4 in. in diameter. At a point where $r = 1.50$ in., calculate the velocity $\bar{u}$, shear stress $\tau_{yx}$, kinematic eddy viscosity $\epsilon$, and mixing length $l$ when (a) $V = 20$ ft/sec and $r_0/e = 100$, (b) $V = 2$ ft/sec and $r_0/e = 100$, and (c) $V = 0.02$ ft/sec and $r_0/e = 100$.

**7-25.** Water at 70°F is being pumped from tank $A$ to tank $B$ at a rate of 1.5 ft³/sec

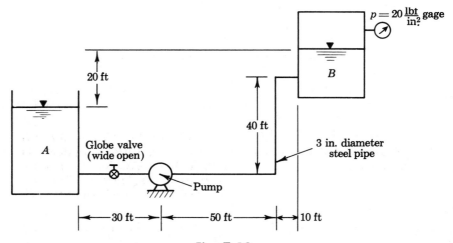

**Fig. 7-18.**

through a piping system as shown in Fig. 7–18. Estimate the power consumption when the pump is operating at an efficiency of 75 per cent.

7–26. In Prob. 7–25, if the pump is removed, what would be the rate of water flow, in gallons per minutes, by gravity from tank $B$ to tank $A$?

7–27. Water at 100°F flows from a constant-head tank through a 1.5-in. diameter steel pipeline and discharges freely into the atmosphere at its open end which is 50 ft below the water surface in the tank. The top of the tank is open to the atmosphere. The pipeline has an equivalent length of 200 ft. Estimate the rate of flow in gallons per minute.

7–28. Determine the minimum diameter of a pipe required to deliver 500 gallons per minute of water through a pipeline with an equivalent length of 500 ft. The intake end of the pipeline is to be connected to a large water main at a point where the pressure is 40 lbf/in.² gage. The discharge end of the pipeline is 30 ft above the main. Water discharges freely into the atmosphere at an average temperature of 70°F.

7–29. A 3-ft diameter riveted steel pipe with an equivalent length of 200 ft is embedded horizontally in a gravity dam to discharge flood water. Estimate the rate of flow, in cubic feet per second, when the reservoir water surface is 100 ft above the pipe axis and water is discharged as a submerged jet into a pool at a depth of 36 ft below the pool surface. What change in the rate of flow would result if two steel plates are riveted to the interior of the pipe throughout its entire length as shown in Fig. 7–19.

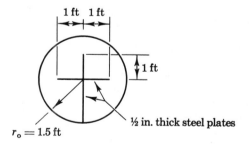

**Fig. 7-19.**

7–30. A vertical cylindrical tank, 10 ft in diameter and 20 ft high, is filled with water. A 2-in. diameter straight pipeline, 500 ft long, is connected to the bottom of the tank. The discharge end of the pipeline is 20 ft below the bottom of the tank, and the flow is regulated by a globe valve. The valve is opened completely when the tank is full. How long will it take to drain half the water in the tank? Use $f = 0.02$.

7–31. Two vertical rectangular tanks $A$ and $B$ are connected by a straight horizontal pipeline 100 ft long and 1 in. in diameter. There is a globe valve in the pipeline to control the flow rate between the two tanks. The cross sectional areas of tanks $A$ and $B$ are respectively 36 and 18 ft². The water level in $A$ is initially 16 ft and that in B is 8 ft above the pipe axis. Find the time required for the water to attain the same level in both tanks after the valve is fully open. Use $f = 0.02$.

**7–32.** A vertical cylindrical water tank, 4 ft in diameter, 10 ft high, and open to the atmosphere, is being filled with water which is pumped in through the horizontal pipeline as shown in Fig. 7–20. The pump maintains a

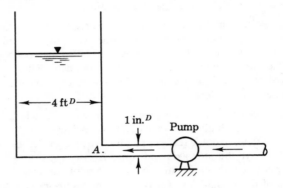

**Fig. 7-20.**

constant gage pressure of 5 lbf/in.² at point $A$. Find the time required to raise the water level in the tank from 3 ft to 6 ft above the pipe axis.

**7–33.** A finished concrete lined trapezoidal channel has a horizontal bottom of 10 ft and side walls of 30 degrees with the horizontal. The longitudinal slope of the channel is 0.0001. If water flows uniformly at a depth of 4 ft, calculate (a) the rate of flow in the channel and (b) the average shear stress over the wetted perimeter.

**7–34.** A 60-degree V-shaped concrete gutter is designed to carry a discharge of 40 ft³/sec of water. Calculate the depth of water if the gutter is laid on a longitudinal slope of 0.0009.

# 8 Boundary Layer Theory

## 8-1 Boundary Layer Flow

Boundary layer has been mentioned on several occasions in previous chapters. For example, in the pipe entrance transition length, the establishment of fully developed velocity profile was attributed to the formation of boundary layer at the pipe wall. At the pipe entrance, the initial velocity distribution is uniform across the pipe. As the flow proceeds downstream, it is retarded near the pipe wall by the wall shear stress. The portion of flow which is affected by the wall shear stress has been referred to as *boundary layer flow*. The boundary layer grows along the length of the pipe until it finally fills the entire pipe to form a fully developed velocity profile.

The boundary layer concept was first introduced by L. Prandtl[1] in 1904 and is probably one of the most important advances in modern fluid mechanics. When a fluid of small viscosity, such as air or water, flows past a streamlined solid body at a high Reynolds number, the effect of

---

[1]L. Prandtl, "Über Flüssigkeitsbewegungen bei sehr kleiner Reibung" (On Fluid Motions with Very Small Friction), *Verhandlungen des III. Internationalen Mathematiker Kongresses* (Heidelberg, 1904), Leipzig, 1905.

viscosity should be small since, in a high Reynolds-number flow, the inertia effect becomes large as compared to the viscous effect. Therefore, the flow may be regarded as frictionless. The theory of irrotational flow has been successful in predicting the correct flow pattern and pressure distribution in such flow fields. However, the theory of irrotational flow cannot be used to calculate the drag experienced by the submerged body because the drag is due primarily to viscous friction. It was Prandtl who proposed the idea that in such flows the effect of viscosity is confined to a very thin layer of flow in the immediate vicinity of the solid surface where the condition of no slip at the solid surface results in a rather high velocity gradient which in turn generates internal friction due to fluid viscosity. Prandtl used the term *boundary layer* to describe the thin layer of flow on the solid surface within which the effect of fluid viscosity must be taken into consideration. Figure 8-1 is a schematic diagram of boundary layer

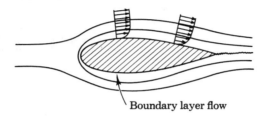

Boundary layer flow

**Fig. 8-1.** Boundary layer flow.

flow. At the outer edge of the boundary layer, the velocity is the same as the local free-stream velocity. The flow outside of the boundary layer is unaffected by the wall shear stress and may be regarded as frictionless so that the theory of irrotational flow can be used directly to determine the patterns of streamlines and pressure distribution. Then by proper matching of solutions from the boundary layer flow and the free-stream flow, it has been found possible to obtain solutions to many high Reynolds-number flow problems. As will be shown later, the boundary layer theory does not only enable us to calculate the frictional drag but also affords us with explanations for such phenomena as flow separation and the formation of vortices and wakes behind a submerged body.

In general, the phenomena of boundary layer flow on curved surfaces are complicated. For simplicity, we shall consider the boundary layer flow on a flat plate surface, as shown in Fig. 8-2. The flow which approaches the leading edge of the plate has a uniform velocity $U_0$. The formation of boundary layer starts at the leading edge of the plate and the thickness of boundary layer increases in the downstream direction. The outer

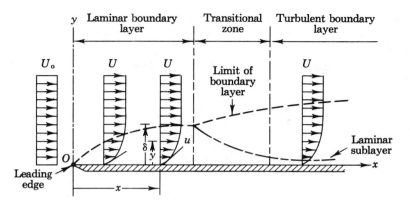

**Fig. 8-2.** Boundary layer flow on a flat plate.

edge of the boundary layer flow is indicated by the broken line shown in Fig. 8-2. On the leading-edge portion of the plate the boundary layer flow is laminar. As the laminar boundary layer grows to a certain thickness at some downstream position, instability sets in and the laminar flow inside the boundary layer will become turbulent. Transition from the laminar to the turbulent boundary layer flow occurs at a certain range of Reynolds number which is defined as $R_x = Ux\rho/\mu$, where $x$ is the distance from the leading edge of the plate and $U$ is the corresponding local free-stream velocity, as shown in Fig. 8-2. Transition between the two modes of flow occurs in a region called the *transitional boundary layer*. The flow in the transitional boundary layer is found experimentally to be partly laminar and partly turbulent; in fact, it often fluctuates from one to the other. Downstream from the transitional boundary layer flow, the boundary layer flow is turbulent. If a turbulent boundary layer is formed on a smooth surface, there is also a thin laminar sublayer next to the solid surface.

## 8-2   Boundary Layer Thickness

In Fig. 8-2 the position of the line marking the outer limit of the boundary layer flow is to a certain extent rather arbitrary, since the velocity of flow near the outer edge of the boundary layer approaches that of the local free-stream flow asymptotically. For practical purposes the boundary layer thickness $\delta$ is defined as the normal distance from the solid surface to the point where the velocity of the boundary layer flow differs from that of the local free-stream flow by one per cent.

Because of the ambiguous nature of defining the boundary layer thickness $\delta$, several other measures of boundary layer thickness have been found very useful in engineering calculations. One of these is the displacement thickness $\delta^*$, shown in Fig. 8-3. The displacement thickness

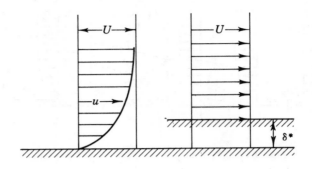

**Fig. 8-3.** Displacement thickness.

is the distance that the solid boundary would have to be displaced outward in order to account for the decrease of velocity in the boundary layer flow. Hence we may define the displacement thickness $\delta^*$ by the following mathematical expression:

$$\delta^* U = \int_0^\infty (U - u)\, dy$$

from which

$$\delta^* = \int_0^\infty \left(1 - \frac{u}{U}\right) dy \qquad (8\text{--}1)$$

Clearly the volume rate of irrotational flow outside of the displaced boundary is the same as the volume rate of real flow outside of the original boundary. By using this idea in the design of streamlined devices, it has been found that the calculated values based on an irrotational flow past the displaced boundaries are in better agreement with experimental data.

Following analysis similar to that presented above, we may define the momentum thickness $\theta$ as

$$\theta U^2 = \int_0^\infty u(U - u)\, dy \qquad \theta = \int_0^\infty \frac{u}{U}\left(1 - \frac{u}{U}\right) dy \qquad (8\text{--}2)$$

and the energy thickness $\delta^{**}$ as

$$\delta^{**} U^3 = \int_0^\infty u(U^2 - u^2)\, dy \qquad \delta^{**} = \int_0^\infty \frac{u}{U}\left(1 - \frac{u^2}{U^2}\right) dy \qquad (8\text{--}3)$$

## 8-3   Simplified Differential Equations for Two-dimensional Laminar Boundary Layer Flow

Let us consider a two-dimensional incompressible laminar boundary layer flow on a plane surface, as shown in Fig. 8-4. The surface lies in the

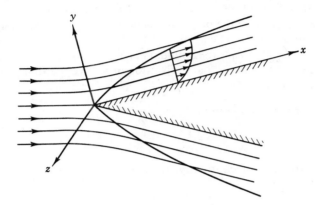

**Fig. 8-4.**   Two-dimensional laminar boundary layer flow on a plane surface.

*xz* plane and the free-stream flow is in the *x*-direction. The simplified equations of motion for the laminar boundary layer flow on the plane surface can be obtained by simplifying the Navier-Stokes equations in Cartesian coordinates (Eqs. A, B, and C in Table 6-3). If we neglect the body forces, the equations of motion for this two-dimensional flow are:

$$\rho \left( u \frac{\partial u}{\partial x} + v \frac{\partial u}{\partial y} + \frac{\partial u}{\partial t} \right) = -\frac{\partial p}{\partial x} + \mu \left( \frac{\partial^2 u}{\partial x^2} + \frac{\partial^2 u}{\partial y^2} \right) \qquad (8\text{-}4)$$
$$\quad\;\; 1\;\; 1 \qquad \delta\;\; 1/\delta \qquad 1 \qquad\qquad\qquad\quad 1 \qquad 1/\delta^2$$

$$\rho \left( u \frac{\partial v}{\partial x} + v \frac{\partial v}{\partial y} + \frac{\partial v}{\partial t} \right) = -\frac{\partial p}{\partial y} + \mu \left( \frac{\partial^2 v}{\partial x^2} + \frac{\partial^2 v}{\partial y^2} \right) \qquad (8\text{-}5)$$
$$\quad\;\; 1\;\; \delta \qquad \delta\;\; 1 \qquad \delta \qquad\qquad\qquad\quad \delta \qquad 1/\delta$$

The equation of continuity is simply

$$\frac{\partial u}{\partial x} + \frac{\partial v}{\partial y} = 0 \qquad (8\text{-}6)$$

Since Eqs. 8-4 and 8-5 are highly nonlinear, they cannot be solved in their present forms. Prandtl suggested that these equations can be further simplified by an order-of-magnitude analysis of individual terms in them. Some of the terms are found to be negligibly small compared with others and can be neglected, thus simplifying the equations considerably.

Since the thickness $\delta$ of the boundary layer is small everywhere, we can safely say that $\delta \ll x$ and $dy \ll dx$ except for the region near the leading edge of the surface where the boundary layer starts (i.e., $x \to 0$). We shall, therefore, choose a scale of measurement for the distance such that $x$ and $u$ both have the order of magnitude 1, which we designate as $x \equiv 0(1)$ and $u \equiv 0(1)$. The symbol "$\equiv 0(1)$" means "has the same order of magnitude as(1)". Inside the boundary layer, $y \equiv 0(\delta)$ where $0(\delta) \ll 0(1)$.

The first and second partial derivatives of $u$ have the following orders of magnitude:

$$\frac{\partial u}{\partial x} \equiv 0(1) \qquad \frac{\partial^2 u}{\partial x^2} \equiv 0(1)$$

$$\frac{\partial u}{\partial y} \equiv 0\left(\frac{1}{\delta}\right) \qquad \frac{\partial^2 u}{\partial y^2} \equiv 0\left(\frac{1}{\delta^2}\right)$$

From the equation of continuity, we have

$$\frac{\partial v}{\partial y} = -\frac{\partial u}{\partial x} \equiv 0(1)$$

Inside the boundary layer, the changes in $y$ are of $0(\delta)$; it follows that changes in $v$ in the $y$-direction must be also of $0(\delta)$. We may then say that

$$v \equiv 0(\delta)$$

$$\frac{\partial v}{\partial x} \equiv 0(\delta) \qquad \frac{\partial^2 v}{\partial x^2} \equiv 0(\delta^2)$$

$$\frac{\partial v}{\partial y} \equiv 0(1) \qquad \frac{\partial^2 v}{\partial y^2} \equiv 0\left(\frac{1}{\delta}\right)$$

The order of magnitude of each term in Eqs. 8-4 and 8-5 is indicated below these equations. The local acceleration $\partial u/\partial t$ must have the same order of magnitude as the convective acceleration $u\,\partial u/\partial x$; hence $\partial u/\partial t \equiv 0(1)$. Similar reasoning leads to $\partial v/\partial t \equiv 0(\delta)$.

If we examine the order of magnitude of each term in Eq. 8-4, we immediately discover that we can neglect the term $\partial^2 u/\partial x^2$, since it is negligibly small compared to $\partial^2 u/\partial y^2$. Then the remaining term $\mu\,\partial^2 u/\partial y^2$ represents the viscous forces which must have the same order of magnitude as the inertia term. Comparison of the inertia and viscous force terms indicates that the kinematic viscosity $\nu(=\mu/\rho)$ of the fluid must be of $0(\delta^2)$; that is, the fluid must have a very small coefficient of kinematic viscosity. This is in agreement with the basic hypothesis of Prandtl's boundary layer theory which is for fluids with small coefficient of viscosity.

Finally, let us turn our attention to the terms involving pressure gradients. Equations 8-4 and 8-5 require that $(1/\rho)\partial p/\partial x \equiv 0(1)$ and

$(1/\rho)\,\partial p/\partial y \equiv 0(\delta)$, respectively. Therefore, within the boundary layer the pressure gradient $\partial p/\partial y$ is negligibly small and $p$ is nearly independent of $y$. We may consider $p$ as invariable in the $y$-direction and equal to that of the local free-stream region at the outer edge of the boundary layer. This pressure can be determined from irrotational flow theory by neglecting the boundary layer.

From the foregoing analysis, we note that $v$ having $0(\delta)$ is negligibly small compared to $u$ having $0(1)$, and so we shall not need Eq. 8-5 which has $v$ as the principal dependent variable. Therefore, the following equation

$$\rho\left(u\frac{\partial u}{\partial x} + v\frac{\partial u}{\partial y} + \frac{\partial u}{\partial t}\right) = -\frac{dp}{dx} + \mu\frac{\partial^2 u}{\partial y^2} \qquad (8\text{-}7)$$

and Eq. 8-6 form the system of simplified differential equations for the two-dimensional laminar boundary flow. In Eq. 8-7, we have changed $\partial p/\partial x$ to $dp/dx$ since in the boundary layer flow $p$ varies with $x$ only. The boundary conditions for Eqs. 8-6 and 8-7 are:

(1) $u = v = 0$　at　$y = 0$.

(2) $u = U$, the velocity of the local free-stream flow at the outer edge of the boundary layer.

When the boundary layer flow is steady, $\partial u/\partial t = 0$, and Eq. 8-7 becomes

$$\rho\left(u\frac{\partial u}{\partial x} + v\frac{\partial u}{\partial y}\right) = -\frac{dp}{dx} + \mu\frac{\partial^2 u}{\partial y^2} \qquad (8\text{-}8)$$

The general solution for Eqs. 8-7 and 8-8 is difficult to obtain, especially for flows around a body of arbitrary shape. H. Blasius[2] obtained a solution of these equations for the velocity profile in a steady incompressible laminar boundary layer flow on a flat plate surface with no pressure gradient. The mathematical details of Blasius' solution are presented in Example 8-1. In addition, several approximate solutions for Eqs. 8-7 and 8-8 have also been obtained by integrating these equations over the boundary layer thickness. The resulting integral equations satisfy only the boundary conditions of the boundary layer flow at the plate surface and at the outer edge of the boundary layer flow. The most well-known approximate solution by Kármán[3] and Pohlhausen[4] is presented in Example 8-2.

[2]H. Blasius, "Grenzschichten in Flüssigkeiten mit kleiner Reibung" (Boundary Layers in Fluids of Small Friction), *Z. Math.-Physik*, Vol. LVI, 1908.

[3]Th. von Kármán, "Über laminare und turbulente Reibung" (On Laminar and Turbulent Friction), *Z. angew. Math. Mech.*, Vol. I (1921), 233–252. Also translated as NACA TM 1092, 1946.

[4]K. Pohlhausen, "Zur näherungsweisen Integration der Differentialgleichung der laminaren Reibungsschicht" (The Approximate Integration of the Differential Equation of the Laminar Boundary Layer), *Z. angew. Math. Mech.*, Vol. I (1921), 252–289.

***Illustrative Example 8-1.*** In this example we present Blasius' solution of the simplified boundary layer equation. Blasius' solution is for the velocity profile in a steady incompressible laminar boundary layer flow over a flat plate with zero pressure gradient. Therefore, the governing equations for this flow are

$$\frac{\partial u}{\partial x} + \frac{\partial v}{\partial y} = 0 \tag{A}$$

$$u\frac{\partial u}{\partial x} + v\frac{\partial u}{\partial y} = \nu\frac{\partial^2 u}{\partial y^2} \tag{B}$$

The boundary conditions for these equations are:
 (1) At the plate surface where $y = 0$, $u = 0$ and $v = 0$.
 (2) As $y \to \infty$, $u = U$.
 Equation (A) is satisfied if velocity components $u$ and $v$ are derived from a stream function $\psi(x, y)$, so that

$$u = \frac{\partial \psi}{\partial y} \qquad \text{and} \qquad v = -\frac{\partial \psi}{\partial x} \tag{C}$$

Substituting these partial differentiations of $\psi$ into Eq. (B) for $u$ and $v$, we obtain

$$\frac{\partial \psi}{\partial y}\frac{\partial^2 \psi}{\partial x\,\partial y} - \frac{\partial \psi}{\partial x}\frac{\partial^2 \psi}{\partial y^2} = \nu\frac{\partial^3 \psi}{\partial y^3} \tag{D}$$

This partial differential equation is to be reduced to an ordinary differential equation.
 The first step is to introduce a new dimensionless variable $\eta$ which is defined as

$$\eta(x, y) = \frac{y}{\sqrt{\nu x/U}} \tag{E}$$

and which is to be used in place of the $y$-coordinate. Then, a dimensionless stream function

$$f(\eta) = \frac{\psi}{\sqrt{\nu x U}} \tag{F}$$

will be used in place of the stream function $\psi$. Equation (F) can also be written in the following form:

$$\psi(x, \eta) = \sqrt{\nu x U}\, f(\eta) \tag{G}$$

Hence, by using Eqs. (E) and (G), we form the following partial derivatives which appear in Eq. (D):

$$\frac{\partial \psi}{\partial y} = \frac{\partial \psi}{\partial \eta}\frac{\partial \eta}{\partial y}$$

$$= \left(\sqrt{\nu x U}\,\frac{df}{d\eta}\right)\left(\frac{1}{\sqrt{\nu x/U}}\right) = U\frac{df}{d\eta} \tag{H}$$

$$\frac{\partial^2 \psi}{\partial y^2} = \left(\frac{\partial}{\partial \eta}\frac{\partial \psi}{\partial y}\right)\left(\frac{\partial \eta}{\partial y}\right) = \left(U\frac{d^2 f}{d\eta^2}\right)\left(\frac{1}{\sqrt{\nu x/U}}\right)$$

$$= \frac{U}{\sqrt{\nu x/U}}\frac{d^2 f}{d\eta^2} \tag{I}$$

$$\frac{\partial^3 \psi}{\partial y^3} = \left(\frac{\partial}{\partial \eta}\frac{\partial^2 \psi}{\partial y^2}\right)\left(\frac{\partial \eta}{\partial y}\right) = \left(\frac{U}{\sqrt{\nu x/U}}\frac{d^3 f}{d\eta^3}\right)\left(\frac{1}{\sqrt{\nu x/U}}\right)$$
$$= \frac{U}{\nu x/U}\frac{d^3 f}{d\eta^3} \tag{J}$$

$$\frac{\partial^2 \psi}{\partial x\,\partial y} = \left(\frac{\partial}{\partial \eta}\frac{\partial \psi}{\partial y}\right)\left(\frac{\partial \eta}{\partial x}\right)$$
$$= \left(U\frac{d^2 f}{d\eta^2}\right)\left(-\frac{y}{2}\frac{1}{\sqrt{\nu x/U}}\frac{1}{x}\right) \tag{K}$$
$$= -\frac{U\eta}{2x}\frac{d^2 f}{d\eta^2}$$

$$\frac{\partial \psi}{\partial x} = \left(\frac{\partial \psi}{\partial \eta}\right)_x \frac{\partial \eta}{\partial x} + \left(\frac{\partial \psi}{\partial x}\right)_\eta$$
$$= \left(\sqrt{\nu x U}\,\frac{df}{d\eta}\right)\left(-\frac{y}{2}\frac{1}{\sqrt{\nu x/U}}\frac{1}{x}\right) + \frac{f}{2}\sqrt{\frac{\nu U}{x}}$$
$$= -\frac{Uy}{2x}\frac{df}{d\eta} + \frac{f}{2}\sqrt{\frac{\nu U}{x}} \tag{L}$$
$$= -\frac{\eta}{2}\sqrt{\frac{\nu U}{x}}\left(\frac{df}{d\eta} - \frac{f}{\eta}\right)$$

Substituting these results into Eq. (D) and simplifying, we obtain the desired ordinary differential equation:

$$\frac{d^3 f}{d\eta^3} + \frac{1}{2}f\frac{d^2 f}{d\eta^2} = 0 \tag{M}$$

The boundary conditions for this equation are:
   (1) At $\eta = 0$; $f = 0$   and   $df/d\eta = 0$.
   (2) As $\eta \to \infty$; $df/d\eta = 1$.
Equation (M) is nonlinear, and so we cannot solve it for $f(\eta)$ in the closed form. Blasius obtained a series solution by expanding $f(\eta)$ into an infinite power series:

$$f(\eta) = A_0 + A_1\eta + A_2\frac{\eta^2}{2!} + A_3\frac{\eta^3}{3!} + \cdots \tag{N}$$

where $A_0$, $A_1$, $A_2$, etc. are constant coefficients to be determined from the boundary conditions and Eq. (M).

From the boundary conditions that $f = 0$ and $df/d\eta = 0$ at $\eta = 0$, coefficients $A_0$ and $A_1$ must be zero. Substituting the remaining series into Eq. (M) and collecting terms with like powers of $\eta$, we have

$$A_3 + A_4\eta + (A_2^2 + 2A_5)\frac{\eta^2}{2!} + (4A_2 A_3 + 2A_6)\frac{\eta^3}{3!} + \cdots = 0 \tag{O}$$

If the assumed series for $f(\eta)$ is to be a solution of Eq. (M), all coefficients of various powers of $\eta$ must vanish identically. Therefore, $A_3 = 0$, $A_4 = 0$, $2A_5 = -A_2^2$, $A_6 = 0$, etc. In fact, if we carry out computations beyond what we have shown above, we can easily establish that all $A$'s except $A_2$, $A_5$, $A_8$, ... are zero and that all the nonzero $A$'s can be expressed in terms of $A_2$. The series for $f(\eta)$ may be written in the following compact form:

$$f(\eta) = \sum_{n=0}^{\infty} \left(-\frac{1}{2}\right)^n \frac{A_2^{n+1} C_n}{(3n+2)!} \eta^{3n+2} \tag{P}$$

where the constant $C_n$ can be computed by comparison with the constants in Eq. (N). Blasius calculated the following values of $C_n$:

$$C_0 = 1; \qquad C_1 = 1; \qquad C_2 = 11$$
$$C_3 = 375; \qquad C_4 = 27,897; \qquad C_5 = 3,817,137$$

The only unknown quantity in Eq. (P) is $A_2$ which must be determined by the boundary condition that as $\eta \to \infty$, $df/d\eta = 1$. The result is $A_2 = 0.332$.

With these numerical values, the function $f(\eta)$ can be computed numerically and the ratio $u/U$ can be derived from Eq. (H). Thus,

$$\frac{u}{U} = \frac{df}{d\eta} \tag{Q}$$

Table 8–1 gives the velocity distribution as a function of $\eta$. Hence we can determine the velocity $u$ at any position $(x, y)$ by first determining $\eta$ from Eq. (E) and then using the data given in Table 8–1.

**TABLE 8–1†   Velocity Distribution for a Laminar Boundary Layer Flow**

| $\eta = \dfrac{y}{\sqrt{\nu x/U}}$ | $\dfrac{u}{U} = \dfrac{df}{d\eta}$ | $\eta = \dfrac{y}{\sqrt{\nu x/U}}$ | $\dfrac{u}{U} = \dfrac{df}{d\eta}$ |
|:---:|:---:|:---:|:---:|
| 0.0 | 0.0 | 2.4 | 0.729 |
| 0.2 | 0.066 | 2.8 | 0.812 |
| 0.4 | 0.133 | 3.2 | 0.876 |
| 0.6 | 0.199 | 3.6 | 0.923 |
| 0.8 | 0.265 | 4.0 | 0.956 |
| 1.0 | 0.330 | 4.4 | 0.976 |
| 1.2 | 0.394 | 4.8 | 0.988 |
| 1.4 | 0.456 | 5.2 | 0.994 |
| 1.6 | 0.517 | 5.6 | 0.997 |
| 1.8 | 0.575 | 6.0 | 0.999 |
| 2.0 | 0.630 | 6.4 | 1.000 |

†L. Howarth, "On the Solution of the Laminar Boundary Layer Equations," *Proc. Roy. Soc.*, (London), Vol. A164 (1938), 547.

*Illustrative Example 8-2.* Exact solutions for the boundary layer equations (Eqs. 8–6 and 8–7) are difficult to obtain. In this example we shall present the Kármán-Pohlhausen integral equation for the boundary layer flows.

Let us rewrite the steady boundary layer equations as follows:

$$\frac{\partial u}{\partial x} + \frac{\partial v}{\partial y} = 0 \tag{A}$$

$$u \frac{\partial u}{\partial x} + v \frac{\partial u}{\partial y} = -\frac{1}{\rho} \frac{dp}{dx} + \frac{\mu}{\rho} \frac{\partial^2 u}{\partial y^2} \tag{B}$$

Since the pressure inside of the boundary layer is the same as that in the local free-stream flow just outside of the boundary layer, and $p$ and $U$ outside of the boundary layer are related by Bernoulli's equation, it is possible to replace the pressure gradient term $-(1/\rho)\,dp/dx$ by $U\,dU/dx$ in Eq. (B). Integrating Eq. (B) with respect to $y$ between the limits zero and $\delta$ and replacing $\mu(\partial u/\partial y)_0$ by $-\tau_0$, we obtain

$$\int_0^\delta \left( u\frac{\partial u}{\partial x} + v\frac{\partial u}{\partial y} - U\frac{dU}{dx} \right) dy = -\frac{\tau_0}{\rho} \tag{C}$$

From Eq. (A),

$$v = \int_0^y \frac{\partial u}{\partial x}\, dy \tag{D}$$

which may be substituted into Eq. (C) to obtain

$$\int_0^\delta \left( u\frac{\partial u}{\partial x} - \frac{\partial u}{\partial y}\int_0^y \frac{\partial u}{\partial x}\, dy - U\frac{dU}{dx} \right) dy = -\frac{\tau_0}{\rho} \tag{E}$$

The second term can be integrated by parts as follows:

$$\int_0^\delta \frac{\partial u}{\partial y}\left( \int_0^y \frac{\partial u}{\partial x}\, dy \right) dy = U\int_0^\delta \frac{\partial u}{\partial x}\, dy - \int_0^\delta u\frac{\partial u}{\partial x}\, dy$$

and the result is substituted into Eq. (E) to yield

$$\int_0^\delta \left( 2u\frac{\partial u}{\partial x} - U\frac{\partial u}{\partial x} - U\frac{dU}{dx} \right) dy = -\frac{\tau_0}{\rho} \tag{F}$$

This equation can be rearranged as

$$\int_0^\delta \frac{\partial}{\partial x}[u(U-u)]\, dy + \frac{dU}{dx}\int_0^\delta (U-u)dy = \frac{\tau_0}{\rho} \tag{G}$$

since $dU/dx$ is the velocity gradient outside of the boundary layer and is independent of integration for the boundary layer. By recalling the definitions of $\delta^*$ and $\theta$ as given by Eqs. 8-1 and 8-2, respectively, and noting that differentiation with respect to $x$ is independent of the limits of integration with respect to $y$, we may also write the above equation as

$$\frac{d}{dx}(\theta U^2) + \frac{dU}{dx}\delta^*\, U = \frac{\tau_0}{\rho} \tag{H}$$

The partial differentiation of $\theta U^2$ with respect to $x$ has been changed to total differentiation because both $\theta$ and $U$ are functions of $x$ only. Equation (H) is frequently referred to as the *momentum equation for two-dimensional incompressible boundary layers*, both laminar and turbulent. In using this equation for solving any boundary layer flow problem, it is necessary to assume a reasonable velocity distribution equation for boundary layer flow which satisfies the boundary conditions at the wall and at the outer edge of the boundary layer. Pohlhausen† was able to obtain solutions to several flow problems of practical importance.

As a simple example, let us use Eq. (H) to calculate the wall shear stress $\tau_0$ for

---

†H. Schlichting, *Boundary Layer Theory*, 4th ed. (New York: McGraw-Hill Book Company, 1960) pp. 243–263.

the laminar boundary layer flow on a flat plate surface due to a uniform flow with velocity $U_0$ parallel to the length of the plate. For this flow, Eq. (H) becomes

$$U^2 \frac{d\theta}{dx} = \frac{\tau_0}{\rho} \tag{I}$$

since $U$ does not change with respect to $x$. If the velocity profile for the laminar boundary layer flow is assumed to be

$$\frac{u}{U} = F\left[\frac{y}{\theta(x)}\right] \tag{J}$$

the differentiation $du/dy$ can be evaluated in the following manner:

$$\frac{du}{dy} = U \frac{dF}{d(y/\theta)} \frac{d(y/\theta)}{dy} = \frac{U}{\theta} \frac{dF}{d(y/\theta)}$$

Then

$$\tau_0 = \mu \left(\frac{du}{dy}\right)_{y=0} = \frac{\mu U}{\theta} \left[\frac{dF}{d(y/\theta)}\right]_{y=0} \tag{K}$$

in which $[dF/d(y/\theta)]_{y=0}$ is a constant to be evaluated from an assumed velocity profile. Substitution of Eq. (K) into Eq. (I) yields

$$\theta \frac{d\theta}{dx} = \frac{\mu}{\rho U} \left[\frac{dF}{d(y/\theta)}\right]_{y=0}$$

which can be readily integrated to become

$$\theta = \sqrt{\frac{2\mu x}{\rho U} \left[\frac{dF}{d(y/\theta)}\right]_{y=0}} \tag{L}$$

Finally, by substituting this equation into Eq. (K), we obtain

$$\tau_0 = \rho U^2 \sqrt{\frac{\mu}{2Ux\rho} \left[\frac{dF}{d(y/\theta)}\right]_{y=0}} \tag{M}$$

In order to compare the result of this calculation with that to be obtained in Sec. 8-5, we shall use the following parabolic velocity distribution equation for the laminar boundary layer flow:

$$\frac{u}{U} = 2\frac{y}{\delta} - \left(\frac{y}{\delta}\right)^2 \tag{N}$$

The momentum thickness $\theta$ for this flow can be calculated by using Eq. 8–2:

$$\begin{aligned}
\theta &= \int_0^\infty \frac{u}{U}\left(1 - \frac{u}{U}\right) dy \\
&= \int_0^1 \delta\left[2\frac{y}{\delta} - \left(\frac{y}{\delta}\right)^2\right]\left[1 - 2\frac{y}{\delta} + \left(\frac{y}{\delta}\right)^2\right] d\left(\frac{y}{\delta}\right) \\
&= \tfrac{2}{15}\delta
\end{aligned} \tag{O}$$

With this value, Eq. (N) may also be written as

$$\frac{u}{U} = F\left(\frac{y}{\theta}\right) = \frac{4}{15}\frac{y}{\theta} - \frac{4}{225}\left(\frac{y}{\theta}\right)^2$$

Then

$$\left[\frac{dF}{d(y/\theta)}\right]_{y=0} = \frac{4}{15}$$

and the wall shear stress becomes

$$\tau_0 = 0.365 \rho U^2 \sqrt{\frac{\mu}{Ux\rho}} \tag{P}$$

which is in agreement with Eq. 8–17.

## 8-4  Von Kármán Integral-Momentum Equation

For the boundary layer flow on a flat plate surface, Theodore von Kármán proposed a momentum method[5] to calculate the growth of boundary layer thickness and the distribution of skin friction on the plate surface. Consider a control volume of boundary layer flow as shown in Fig. 8-5. This control volume is located at a distance $x$ downsteam from the leading edge of the plate of unit width. The rate of mass inflow into the indicated control volume through the left-hand vertical portion of the control surface is

$$\dot{m} = \int_0^\delta \rho u \, dy$$

and its $x$-component momentum influx is

$$P_x = \int_0^\delta \rho u^2 \, dy$$

At the same time, the rate of mass outflow and the $x$-component momentum efflux leaving the control volume through the right-hand vertical control surface are respectively

$$\dot{m} + \frac{\partial \dot{m}}{\partial x} dx = \int_0^\delta \rho u \, dy + \frac{\partial}{\partial x} \left( \int_0^\delta \rho u \, dy \right) dx$$

and

$$P_x + \frac{\partial P_x}{\partial x} dx = \int_0^\delta \rho u^2 \, dy + \frac{\partial}{\partial x} \left( \int_0^\delta \rho u^2 \, dy \right) dx$$

Clearly there is a net rate of mass outflow from the control volume through the two vertical portions of the control surface amounting to

$$\frac{\partial \dot{m}}{\partial x} dx = \frac{\partial}{\partial x} \left( \int_0^\delta \rho u \, dy \right) dx$$

By reason of the continuity equation, this rate of outflow must be balanced by the rate of inflow through the top control surface where the velocity is $U$. The inflow at the top control surface also brings into the control volume an $x$-component momentum influx of

$$(P_x)_{\text{top}} = U \frac{\partial}{\partial x} \left( \int_0^\delta \rho u \, dy \right) dx$$

---

[5]Th. von Kármán, *loc. cit.*

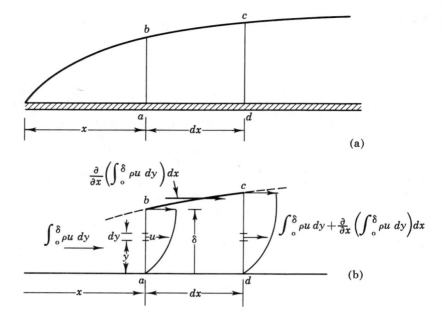

(a)

(b)

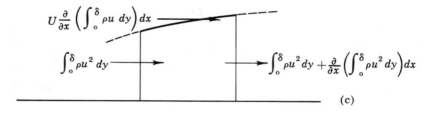

(c)

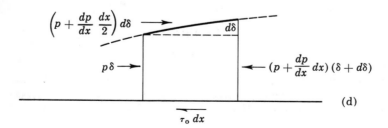

(d)

**Fig. 8-5.**  A short segment of boundary layer : (a) control  volume,  (b) mass rate of flow, (c) momentum flux, (d) surface forces.

Therefore, the total $x$-component momentum efflux for the control volume is

$$\Sigma P_x = \frac{\partial}{\partial x}\left( \int_0^\delta \rho u^2 \, dy \right) dx - U \frac{\partial}{\partial x}\left( \int_0^\delta \rho u \, dy \right) dx$$

which, according to the momentum equation, is equal to the $x$-component of the total force acting on the fluid inside of the control volume. From Fig. 8-5(d), the $x$-component of the total force can be written as

$$F_x = p\delta + \left( p + \frac{dp}{dx}\frac{dx}{2} \right) d\delta - \left( p + \frac{dp}{dx} dx \right)(\delta + d\delta) - \tau_0 \, dx$$

where $\tau_0$ is the wall shear stress. Expanding the above equation, canceling terms, and dropping second-order terms, we obtain

$$F_x = -\left( \delta \frac{dp}{dx} + \tau_0 \right) dx$$

Hence the $x$-component momentum equation for the indicated control volume becomes

$$-\left( \delta \frac{dp}{dx} + \tau_0 \right) dx = \frac{\partial}{\partial x}\left( \int_0^\delta \rho u^2 \, dy \right) dx - U \frac{\partial}{\partial x}\left( \int_0^\delta \rho u \, dy \right) dx$$

which can be simplified as

$$\delta\frac{dp}{dx} + \tau_0 = U\frac{\partial}{\partial x}\int_0^\delta \rho u \, dy - \frac{\partial}{\partial x}\int_0^\delta \rho u^2 \, dy \qquad \text{(8–9)}$$

This is von Kármán's integral-momentum equation for the boundary layer flow. This equation is applicable to both laminar and turbulent boundary layer flows. When $dp/dx = 0$, $U = U_0$ in the entire flow field, and von Kármán's integral-momentum equation can be reduced to the following more restricted form:

$$\tau_0 = \frac{\partial}{\partial x}\left[ \rho U_0^2 \delta \int_0^1 \left( 1 - \frac{u}{U_0} \right) \frac{u}{U_0} \, d\left( \frac{y}{\delta} \right) \right]$$
$$= \rho U_0^2 \frac{d\theta}{dx} \qquad \text{(8–10)}$$

where $\theta$ is the momentum thickness defined in Eq. 8-2. The partial differentiation of $\theta$ with respect to $x$ has been changed to total differentiation since $\theta$ varies with $x$ only.

For uniform flow over a flat plate surface with $dp/dx = 0$, the velocity profile for the boundary layer flow of a given mode is similar at all positions along the length of the plate and may be assumed to have the following general form:

$$u = U_0 f\left[ \frac{y}{\delta(x)} \right] \quad \text{or} \quad \frac{u}{U_0} = f\left[ \frac{y}{\delta(x)} \right] \qquad \text{(8–11)}$$

In the following two sections we shall use Eq. 8-10 in conjunction with assumed velocity profiles to analyze both the laminar and turbulent boundary layer flows. Any assumed velocity distribution equation must, however, satisfy the boundary conditions at the plate surface and at the outer edge of the boundary layer. These boundary conditions are:

(1) At the plate surface: $y = 0$, $u = 0$ and $du/dy$ = any finite value.

(2) At the outer edge of the boundary layer: $y = \delta$, $u = U_0$ and $du/dy = 0$.

## 8-5  Laminar Boundary Layer

For a laminar boundary layer flow on a flat plate with $dp/dx = 0$, several velocity distribution equations have been proposed for use in conjunction with von Kármán's integral-momentum equation. It turns out that the value of integral in Eq. 8-10 is rather insensitive to the exact functional relationship between $u/U_0$ and $y/\delta$. For example, a polynomial function or a sine function will yield satisfactory results. For this reason, let us assume that the velocity profile for the laminar boundary layer flow is a parabolic curve:

$$\frac{u}{U_0} = a + b\frac{y}{\delta} + c\left(\frac{y}{\delta}\right)^2 \qquad (8\text{–}12)$$

where the constants $a$, $b$, and $c$ are to be determined from the boundary conditions as follows:

(1) At the plate surface: $y/\delta = 0$ and $u/U_0 = 0$, hence $a = 0$.

(2) At the outer edge of the boundary layer: the conditions $y/\delta = 1$, $u/U_0 = 1$, and $d(u/U_0)/d(y/\delta) = 0$, with $a = 0$, will yield $b = 2$ and $c = -1$. Therefore, Eq. 8-12 becomes

$$\frac{u}{U_0} = 2\frac{y}{\delta} - \left(\frac{y}{\delta}\right)^2 \qquad (8\text{–}13)$$

Equation 8-13 may now be substituted into Eq. 8-10 to obtain

$$\tau_0 = \frac{d}{dx}\left\{\rho U_0^2 \delta \int_0^1\left[1 - 2\frac{y}{\delta} + \left(\frac{y}{\delta}\right)^2\right]\left[2\frac{y}{\delta} - \left(\frac{y}{\delta}\right)^2\right]d\left(\frac{y}{\delta}\right)\right\}$$

which, upon integrating, becomes

$$\tau_0 = \frac{2}{15}\rho U_0^2 \frac{d\delta}{dx} \qquad (8\text{–}14)$$

This equation contains the two unknowns $\tau_0$ and $\delta$ to be solved. Therefore, it is necessary for us to introduce an additional equation which also contains these two unknowns. For this purpose, we shall write Newton's law of viscosity at the wall in this flow:

$$\tau_0 = \mu \left(\frac{du}{dy}\right)_{y=0} = \mu \frac{U_0}{\delta} \left[\frac{d(u/U_0)}{d(y/\delta)}\right]_{y/\delta=0}$$

$$= \mu \frac{U_0}{\delta} \frac{d}{d(y/\delta)} \left[2 \frac{y}{\delta} - \left(\frac{y}{\delta}\right)^2\right]_{y/\delta=0} \qquad (8\text{-}15)$$

$$= 2\mu \frac{U_0}{\delta}$$

Combining this equation with Eq. 8-14, we obtain the following simple differential equation for $\delta(x)$:

$$\frac{2}{15} \rho U_0^2 \frac{d\delta}{dx} = 2\mu \frac{U_0}{\delta}$$

If $x$ is measured from the leading edge of the plate, the solution of the above differential equation gives the laminar boundary layer thickness $\delta$ as:

$$\delta = 5.48 \sqrt{\frac{\mu x}{\rho U_0}} = \frac{5.48x}{\sqrt{R_x}} \qquad (8\text{-}16)$$

in which $R_x$ ($= U_0 x \rho/\mu$) is called the *local Reynolds number* based on the distance $x$ from the leading edge of the plate as the characteristic linear dimension. The laminar boundary layer thickness is seen to increase as the square root of the distance $x$ from the leading edge.

The wall shear stress at any position along the plate can be obtained by substituting Eq. 8-16 into Eq. 8-15:

$$\tau_0 = \frac{2\mu U_0}{5.48\sqrt{\mu x/\rho U_0}} = \frac{0.365}{\sqrt{R_x}} \rho U_0^2 \qquad (8\text{-}17)$$

The total friction drag $F_{Df}$ on one side of the plate of length $L$ and unit width is then

$$F_{Df} = \int_0^L \tau_0 \, dx = \int_0^L \frac{2\mu U_0}{5.48\sqrt{\mu x/\rho U_0}} \, dx$$

$$= \frac{1.46}{\sqrt{R_L}} \frac{\rho U_0^2}{2} L \qquad (8\text{-}18)$$

The friction drag coefficient $C_{Df}$ is defined as $C_{Df} = F_{Df}/[L \, (\rho U_0^2/2)]$ and, by substitution of Eq. 8-18, $C_{Df}$ for laminar boundary layer flow on a flat plate is found to be

$$C_{Df} = \frac{1.46}{\sqrt{R_L}} \qquad (8\text{-}19)$$

It is interesting to note that the expressions for $\delta$, $\tau_0$, and $C_{Df}$ derived in this section have exactly the same form as those obtained from Blasius' mathematical solutions of the simplified partial differential equations for the laminar boundary layer flow except that the numerical coefficients are

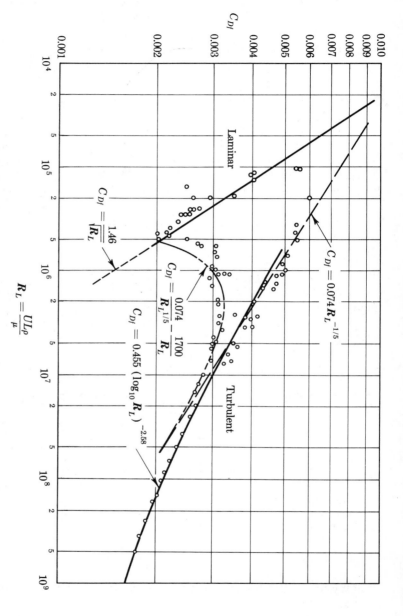

**Fig. 8-6.** Friction drag coefficients for a smooth plane surface as a function of Reynolds number.

slightly different. The numerical coefficients of Blasius' expressions for $\delta$, $\tau_0$, and $C_{Df}$ are, respectively, 4.91, 0.332, and 1.32.

Equation 8-19 is plotted in Fig. 8-6. The equation is in good agreement with experimental data for laminar boundary layer flow.

## 8-6   Turbulent Boundary Layer

In analyzing a turbulent boundary layer flow on a flat plate surface, we shall follow a procedure similar to that used for the laminar boundary layer flow of the preceding section. The first step is to assume a velocity profile for the turbulent boundary layer flow. As was shown in Sec. 7-5, the velocity profile for a turbulent parallel flow is a logarithmic function. However, when a logarithmic velocity distribution equation is used in conjunction with von Kámárn's integral-momentum equation, the calculations are rather complicated and lengthy.[6] In this calculation, we shall assume the plate surface to be smooth and use the one-seventh-power velocity distribution equation (Eq. 7-42) for simplicity:

$$\frac{\bar{u}}{\sqrt{\tau_0/\rho}} = 8.74 \left( \frac{\sqrt{\tau_0/\rho}\, y\rho}{\mu} \right)^{1/7} \tag{8–20}$$

In order to derive a velocity distribution equation in the form of Eq. 8-11, let us write the above equation for the conditions at the outer edge of the boundary layer where $y = \delta$ and $\bar{u} = U_0$:

$$\frac{U_0}{\sqrt{\tau_0/\rho}} = 8.74 \left( \frac{\sqrt{\tau_0/\rho}\, \delta\rho}{\mu} \right)^{1/7} \tag{8–21}$$

Division of Eq. 8-20 by Eq. 8-21 then yields the following desired velocity distribution equation for the turbulent boundary layer flow:

$$\frac{\bar{u}}{U_0} = \left( \frac{y}{\delta} \right)^{1/7} \tag{8–22}$$

One of the wall shear stress equations may be obtained by substituting Eq. 8-22 into Eq. 8-10 and then carrying out the indicated integration. The result is

$$\begin{aligned}
\tau_0 &= \frac{d}{dx} \left\{ \rho U_0^2 \delta \int_0^1 \left[ 1 - \left( \frac{y}{\delta} \right)^{1/7} \right] \left( \frac{y}{\delta} \right)^{1/7} d\left( \frac{y}{\delta} \right) \right\} \\
&= \frac{7}{72} \rho U_0^2 \frac{d\delta}{dx}
\end{aligned} \tag{8–23}$$

The other expression relating $\tau_0$ and $\delta$ is Eq. 8-21, which may be rearranged as

[6]H. Schlichting, *op. cit.*, pp. 539–543, 551–563.

$$\tau_0 = 0.0225\rho U_0^2 \left(\frac{\mu}{U_0\,\delta\rho}\right)^{1/4} \tag{8–24}$$

Combining this equation with Eq. 8-23, we obtain the following differential equation for the turbulent boundary layer thickness:

$$\frac{7}{72}\rho U_0^2 \frac{d\delta}{dx} = 0.0225\rho U_0^2 \left(\frac{\mu}{U_0\,\delta\rho}\right)^{1/4} \tag{8–25}$$

The solution of this differential equation can be obtained only when the boundary conditions are known. For the boundary layer flow under consideration, the flow is laminar on the leading-edge portion of the plate surface and becomes turbulent at some distance downstream from the leading edge. However, both the position of transition from laminar to turbulent flow and the initial thickness of the turbulent boundary layer are rather difficult to ascertain. We shall attempt to solve Eq. 8-25 by assuming the turbulent boundary layer to start at the leading edge of the plate. Thus, integration of Eq. 8-25, with the boundary condition $\delta = 0$ at $x = 0$, yields the following expression for the turbulent boundary layer thickness:

$$\delta = 0.37x \left(\frac{\mu}{U_0 x\rho}\right)^{1/5} = 0.37x \boldsymbol{R}_x^{-1/5} \tag{8–26}$$

The thickness of a turbulent boundary layer on a smooth plate increases with $x^{4/5}$; it grows at a more rapid rate than that of a laminar boundary layer.

Introducing Eq. 8-26 into Eq. 8-23, we obtain the following expression for $\tau_0(x)$:

$$\tau_0 = 0.0592 \frac{\rho U_0^2}{2} \left(\frac{\mu}{U_0 x\rho}\right)^{1/5} \tag{8–27}$$

The total friction drag $F_{Df}$ on one side of the smooth plate of length $L$ and unit width produced by turbulent boundary layer flow is then

$$\begin{aligned} F_{Df} &= \int_0^L \tau_0\,dx = \int_0^L 0.0592\,\frac{\rho U_0^2}{2}\left(\frac{\mu}{U_0 x\rho}\right)^{1/5} dx \\ &= 0.074\,\frac{\rho U_0^2}{2}L\left(\frac{\mu}{U_0 L\rho}\right)^{1/5} \end{aligned} \tag{8–28}$$

and the friction drag coefficient becomes

$$C_{Df} = \frac{F_{Df}}{L(\rho U_0^2/2)} = 0.074\boldsymbol{R}_L^{-1/5} \tag{8–29}$$

Equation 8-29 is plotted in Fig. 8-6 and is seen to be in good agreement with experimental data for the range of $5 \times 10^5 < \boldsymbol{R}_L < 10^7$.

For larger Reynolds numbers, Schlichting used a logarithmic velocity distrubution equation and derived the following friction drag coefficient for turbulent boundary layer flow on a smooth plate surface:

$$C_{Df} = 0.455 \,(\log_{10} \boldsymbol{R}_L)^{-2.58} \tag{8-30}$$

This equation is also plotted in Fig. 8-6, and it agrees well with experimental data up to $\boldsymbol{R}_L = 10^9$.

For turbulent boundary layer flow on a rough plate surface, the problem is further complicated by the variation of thickness of the laminar sublayer along the plate. As the wall shear stress decreases with $x$ (see Eq. 8-27), the thickness of the laminar sublayer increases with $x$ (see Eq. 7-40). Therefore, near the upstream region, where the thickness of laminar sublayer is small compared to the plate surface roughness, this portion of the plate behaves as a rough surface. With increasing thickness of the laminar sublayer along the plate, the downstream portion of the plate may become hydraulically smooth. Schlichting also used a logarithmic velocity distribution equation for turbulent flow on a rough surface and derived the following expression for friction drag coefficient:

$$C_{Df} = \left(1.89 + 1.62 \log_{10} \frac{L}{e}\right)^{-2.5} \tag{8-31}$$

in which $e$ is the average plate surface roughness.

*Illustrative Example 8-3.* Calculate the friction drag coefficient for the boundary layer flow on a smooth plate of unit width, as shown in the accompanying figure.

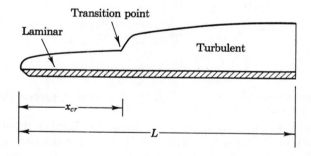

**Illustrative Example 8-3**

The flow is laminar over the upstream portion of length $x_{cr}$ of the plate and becomes turbulent for the rest of the plate. Assume that transition between laminar and turbulent boundary layer flow occurs at $U_0 x_{cr} \rho / \mu = 500,000$.

*Solution:* The friction drag due to the laminar boundary layer flow over the length $x_{cr}$ is given by Eq. 8-18, with the numerical coefficient changed to Blasius' value 1.32, to be

$$(F_{Df})_{\text{laminar}} = \frac{1.32}{\sqrt{U_0 x_{cr} \rho / \mu}} x_{cr} \frac{\rho U_0^2}{2} \tag{A}$$

The friction drag due to the indicated turbulent boundary layer flow can be calculated by first assuming the boundary layer flow to be turbulent over the entire length of the plate and then by subtracting the turbulent friction drag for the length $x_{cr}$ from that for the entire length of the plate. Therefore,

$$(F_{Df})_{\text{turb}} = \left[ \frac{0.074L}{(U_0 L\rho/\mu)^{1/5}} - \frac{0.074 x_{cr}}{(U_0 x_{cr}\rho/\mu)^{1/5}} \right] \frac{\rho U_0^2}{2} \qquad \text{(B)}$$

Adding Eqs. (A) and (B) gives the total friction drag for the entire plate

$$(F_{Df})_{\text{total}} = \left[ \frac{1.32 x_{cr}/L}{\sqrt{U_0 x_{cr}\rho/\mu}} + \frac{0.074}{(U_0 L\rho/\mu)^{1/5}} - \frac{0.074 x_{cr}/L}{(U_0 x_{cr}\rho/\mu)^{1/5}} \right] L \frac{\rho U_0^2}{2}$$

Hence

$$(C_{Df})_{\text{total}} = \frac{(F_{Df})_{\text{total}}}{L\rho U_0^2/2}$$

$$= \frac{1.32 x_{cr}/L}{\sqrt{U_0 x_{cr}\rho/\mu}} + \frac{0.074}{(U_0 L\rho/\mu)^{1/5}} - \frac{0.074 x_{cr}/L}{(U_0 x_{cr}\rho/\mu)^{1/5}} \qquad \text{(C)}$$

The ratio $x_{cr}/L$ may also be written as

$$\frac{x_{cr}}{L} = \frac{U_0 x_{cr}\rho/\mu}{U_0 L\rho/\mu}$$

which is substituted into Eq. (C) to obtain

$$(C_{Df})_{\text{total}} = \frac{0.074}{(U_0 L\rho/\mu)^{1/5}} - \frac{1}{U_0 L\rho/\mu} \left[ 0.074 \left( \frac{U_0 x_{cr}\rho}{\mu} \right)^{4/5} - 1.32 \left( \frac{U_0 x_{cr}\rho}{\mu} \right)^{1/2} \right] \qquad \text{(D)}$$

With $U_0 x_{cr}\rho/\mu = 500{,}000$, Eq. (D) becomes

$$(C_{Df})_{\text{total}} = \frac{0.074}{(U_0 L\rho/\mu)^{1/5}} - \frac{1700}{U_0 L\rho/\mu} \qquad \text{(E)}$$

This equation is plotted in Fig. 8-6.

## 8-7    Separation of Boundary Layer Flow and Pressure Drag

Although we have neglected the pressure gradient in the discussion of boundary layer flow in the preceding sections, the behavior of boundary layer flow along a flat plate surface depends largely on the pressure gradient in the direction of flow. When $dp/dx = 0$, the boundary layer grows indefinitely along the plate surface. If $dp/dx < 0$, the decreasing pressure along the plate tends to counteract partly the retarding action of the viscous frictional stresses near the plate surface and to reduce the thickness of the boundary layer in the downstream direction. With $dp/dx > 0$, the increasing pressure along the plate acting against the flow in the same direction as the viscous frictional stresses tends further to reduce the momentum of the boundary layer flow so that the boundary layer thickens rapidly. Near the plate surface the flow must overcome both the positive pressure gradient and the high wall shear stress, whereas away from the wall the viscous frictional stress is relatively small and the only resistance to flow is the positive pressure gradient. As a result, the flow near the plate surface is decelerated more rapidly and may eventually be forced to reverse its direction. The point where this reversal of flow occurs is called the *point of separation*. Positive pressure gradient is frequently referred to as *adverse pressure gradient*.

Figure 8-7 illustrates the development of boundary layer flow separation from a plate surface because of an adverse pressure gradient. This

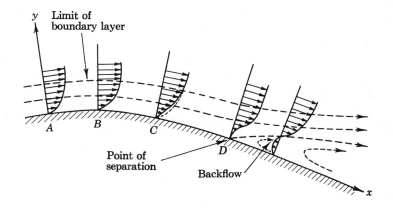

**Fig. 8-7.** Development of boundary layer flow separation from a solid surface because of adverse pressure gradients ($dp/dx > 0$).

plate surface is slightly curved. However, the radius of curvature of the curved surface is large in comparison with the boundary layer thickness. It has been shown by H. Schlichting[7] that the simplified boundary layer equations (Eqs. 8-6 and 8-7) for flat surfaces can be extended to such curved surfaces by considering $x$ as a curvilinear coordinate following the direction of the curved surface and $y$ as the normal distance away from the surface. For the curved surface in Fig. 8-7, the minimum pressure occurs at point $B$, and the pressure increases in the downstream direction starting at point $B$. The adverse pressure gradient tends to reduce the momentum of flow within the boundary layer. At point $C$, the velocity of flow close to the plate surface is reduced more than that near the outer edge of the boundary layer because the fluid near the plate surface is also subjected to a higher viscous frictional stress than that farther away from the surface. Farther downsteam at point $D$ more fluid near the plate sur-

---

[7]H. Schlichting, *op. cit.*, pp. 111–112.

face has been retarded, and the velocity gradient at the plate surface becomes zero; that is, $(\partial u/\partial y)_{y=0} = 0$. At this point the boundary layer flow starts to separate from the plate surface because further deceleration of flow near the surface is in the form of increasing negative velocity. Still farther downstream from point $D$ there is actually a backflow near the plate surface with the formation of large turbulent eddies in the zone of flow separation. These eddies will persist for some distance downstream until they are damped out by the viscous action of the fluid. Thus the kinetic energy of eddies is converted into internal energy.

Theoretically, we should be able to establish the position of the point of separation on a surface by locating the point at which $(\partial u/\partial y)_{y=0} = 0$. This could be done by first solving the steady irrotational flow past the surface and then by using pressures computed therefrom to analyze the boundary layer flow in order to locate the point at which $(\partial u/\partial y)_{y=0} = 0$. The calculations outlined are, however, very complicated. Furthermore, the results of calculations are generally not reliable because experiments show that the position of the point of separation depends not only on the geometrical curvature of the plate surface but also on the roughness of the plate surface and the Reynolds number of the free-stream flow.

We shall establish the fact that separation in steady flow occurs only when there is an adverse pressure gradient in the free-stream flow at the outer edge of the boundary layer. To do this, we shall make use of the simplified boundary layer equation (Eq. 8-8) and apply it at the surface where $y = 0$ and $u = v = 0$. Hence

$$\mu \left( \frac{\partial^2 u}{\partial y^2} \right)_{y=0} = \frac{dp}{dx} \qquad (8\text{–}32)$$

which shows that in the immediate neighborhood of a surface the curvature $(\partial^2 u/\partial y^2)$ of the velocity profile depends on the pressure gradient $dp/dx$ in the local free-stream flow, and $\partial^2 u/\partial y^2$ at the surface changes its sign with $dp/dx$. If $dp/dx < 0$, $\partial^2 u/\partial y^2$ is negative at the surface. Since, near the outer edge of the boundary layer, the velocity in the boundary layer flow approaches the local free-stream velocity asymptotically so that $\partial^2 u/\partial y^2$ is negative, we find that $\partial^2 u/\partial y^2$ is always negative over the entire thickness of the boundary layer. If $dp/dx > 0$, Eq. 8-32 specifies that $\partial^2 u/\partial y^2$ is positive near the surface. But, near the outer edge of the boundary layer, the velocity of boundary layer flow must still approach the local free-stream velocity asymtotically, and $\partial^2 u/\partial y^2$ is still negative. Hence there must exist a point of inflection in the velocity profile of the boundary layer flow whenever $dp/dx > 0$. At the point of flow separation, $\partial u/\partial y$ is zero at the surface and, in order for the velocity profile to increase in a continuous manner to become asymptotic to the velocity of the local free-stream flow, there must be a point of inflection in the velocity profile. Since a point of inflection occurs only when there is an adverse pressure gradient, it follows that reversal of flow and, consequently, flow separation can occur only in the region of an adverse pressure gradient.

Flow separation has serious consequences in the theoretical solution of fluid flow problems. Once flow separation occurs at the boundary of a submerged body, the resulting flow field departs greatly from that obtained by the theory of irrotational flow based on the boundary of the submerged body, because now the separating stream also forms a part of the new boundary. Compare Figs. 8-8 and 8-9. Figure 8-8(a) shows the

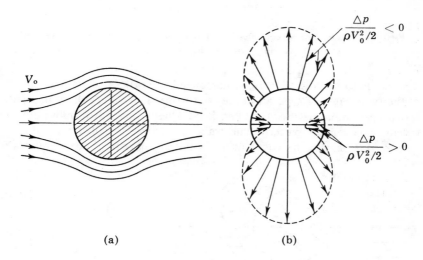

(a)                                              (b)

**Fig. 8-8.** Irrotational flow past a circular cylinder : (a) pattern of streamlines ; (b) pressure distribution on the cylinder surface.

irrotational flow pattern of a uniform flow past a circular cylinder. This flow pattern is possible only if the fluid is inviscid. For viscous fluid, the main flow will separate from the cylinder surface near the midsection where the pressure is at a minimum and where adverse pressure gradient along the cylinder surface starts, as shown in Fig. 8-9(a). Note the difference between the two streamline patterns in the region of separation.

The reversal of flow at the point of flow separation causes the formation of turbulent eddies and vortices in the region downstream from the point of separation. The disturbed downstream region is referred to as *turbulent wakes*. The main flow is diverted to the outside of the wakes.

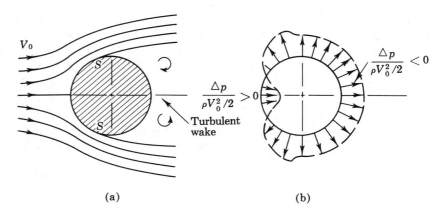

**Fig. 8-9.** Flow of viscous fluid past a circular cylinder: (a) pattern of streamlines; (b) pressure distribution on the cylinder surface.

For uniform flow past a circular cylinder, vortices which are formed at the two points of separation are seen to be shed off regularly in an alternating fashion, as shown in Fig. 8-10. These vortices will move downstream in a regular pattern. The train of vortices is called the *Kármán vortex trail* because of von Kármán's initial analysis of the stability of

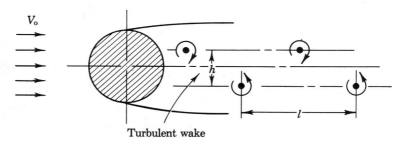

**Fig. 8-10.** Kármán vortex trail.

vortex trail behind a cylinder.[8] According to von Kármán's analysis, a stable vortex pattern must have a geometry such that

$$\frac{h}{l} = 0.281$$

where the linear dimensions $h$ and $l$ are shown in Fig. 8-10. The vortex

---

[8]Th. von Kármán and H. Rubach, "Über den Mechanismus des Flüssigkeit und Luftwiderstandes" (On the Mechanism of Fluid Resistance), *Physik. Z.*, p. 49, 1912.

trail moves downstream with a velocity $u_t$ which is smaller than the mainstream velocity. Von Kármán derived the following formula for calculating the drag per unit length of the cylinder:

$$F_D = \rho V_0^2 h \left[ 2.83 \frac{u_t}{V_0} - 1.12 \left( \frac{u_t}{V_0} \right)^2 \right] \tag{8-33}$$

in which $V_0$ is the uniform velocity of the approaching stream, and $h$ and $u_t$ are determined from experimental measurements.

The alternating shedding of vortices from the two points of separation on the surfaces of a circular cylinder produces transverse forces on the cylinder and causes the cylinder to oscillate. If the frequency of vortex shedding is in resonance with the natural frequency of the cylinder, the

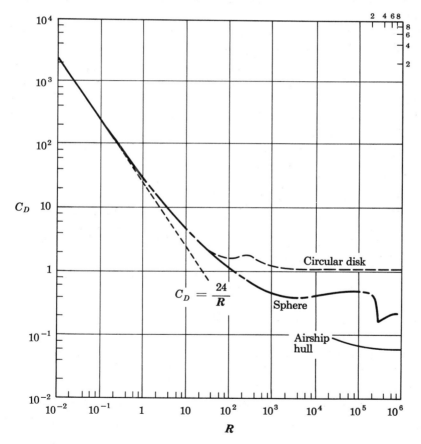

**Fig. 8-11.** Coefficients of drag versus Reynolds numbers for three-dimensional bodies of revolution.

cylinder will deflect excessively. This oscillating phenomenon is responsible for the vibration of transmission wires and the aerodynamic instability of suspension bridges and tall chimneys.

Since the point of separation on the surface of a submerged body is usually located in the region of low pressure and the pressure in the turbulent wakes is approximately the same as that at the point of separation, the pressure behind the body is lower than that at the front, as shown in Fig. 8-9(b). The pressure difference between the front and the rear of the submerged body produces an additional force in the direction of flow. This force is commonly known as the *pressure drag* or *form drag*. The sum of the pressure drag and the friction drag produced by the boundary layer flow upstream from the point of separation constitutes the total drag.

The magnitude of the total drag depends on the geometrical form of the object. If an object is properly streamlined so that the points of

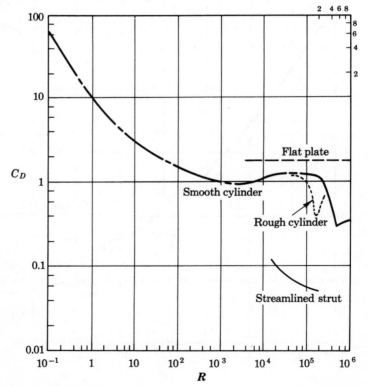

**Fig. 8-12.** Coefficients of drag versus Reynolds numbers for two-dimensional bodies.

separation occur at the extreme downstream end of the object, the wake region is small and the total drag is the friction drag, which can be calculated by using the boundary layer theory. On the other hand, for many objects with complex shape, flow separation occurs at an early section and is followed by a large wake region; the total drag is the sum of friction drag due to the boundary layer flow on the surface upstream from the point of separation and the pressure drag due to pressure differences caused by the flow separation. Under these latter circumstances, theoretical calculations become rather difficult, and the total drag on any given object is usually determined by experimental measurement. Experimental data for the total drag on several three-dimensional and two-dimensional bodies are shown in Figs. 8-11 and 8-12, respectively. In these figures, the total drag is expressed in terms of the coefficient of drag $C_D$, which is defined by the following formula:

$$F_D = C_D A \frac{\rho V^2}{2} \tag{8-34}$$

in which $A$ represents the characteristic area of the body and $V$ is the velocity of the approaching stream.

## PROBLEMS

**8-1.** Calculate the displacement thickness $\delta^*$, momentum thickness $\theta$, and energy thickness $\delta^{**}$ for the laminar boundary layer flow over a flat smooth plate with the following velocity distribution equations:

(a) $\quad u = U \frac{y}{\delta}$

(b) $\quad u = U \sin \frac{\pi}{2} \frac{y}{\delta}$

(c) $\quad u = U \left[ \frac{3}{2} \frac{y}{\delta} - \frac{1}{2} \left( \frac{y}{\delta} \right)^3 \right]$

**8-2.** Using the Kármán-Pohlhausen integral equation, find the expressions for $\tau_0$ for the laminar boundary layer flow over a flat smooth plate with the velocity distribution equations given in Prob. 8-1.

**8-3.** Using von Kármán's integral momentum equation, find the expressions for $\tau_0$, $\delta$, and $C_{Df}$ for the laminar boundary layer flow over a flat smooth plate with the velocity distribution equations given in Prob. 8-1.

**8-4.** Calculate the displacement thickness $\delta^*$, momentum thickness $\theta$, and energy thickness $\delta^{**}$ for the turbulent boundary layer flow over a flat smooth plate with the velocity distribution equation given by $\bar{u} = U(y/\delta)^{1/n}$.

**8–5.** Using von Kármán's integral momentum equation, find the expression for $\tau_0$, $\delta$, and $C_{Df}$ for the turbulent boundary layer flow over a flat smooth plate with the velocity distribution equation given by $\bar{u} = U(y/\delta)^{1/n}$.

**8–6.** Air at a temperature of 70°F and a pressure of 14.7 lbf/in.² abs. flows over a flat smooth plate with a velocity of 40 ft/sec. The length of the plate is 3 ft in the direction of flow. Calculate (a) the boundary layer thickness at 2 in. and 2 ft, respectively, from the leading edge of the plate, (b) the rates of growth of the boundary layer thickness at the same two points on the plate, and (c) the drag coefficient $C_{Df}$ for the plate surface.

**8–7.** Solve Prob. 8–6 if water at 80°F flows over the same plate surface with a velocity of 10 ft/sec.

**8–8.** Air at 70°F and 14.7 lbf/in.² abs. flows between two parallel flat smooth plates spaced 1 in. apart with a velocity of 0.5 ft/sec. At what distance from the entrance will the boundary layers on the two plates meet?

**8–9.** The flow in the entrance transition length of a round pipe may be regarded the same as the boundary layer flow on the inner surface of the pipe. At the section where the fully developed pipe flow first occurs, the edge of the boundary layer just reaches the pipe axis. Estimate the entrance transition length for an air flow which enters a 2-in. diameter smooth pipe at a uniform velocity of (a) 40 ft/sec, (b) 2 ft/sec, and (c) 0.02 ft/sec. Assume the air flow to be incompressible and to have a temperature of 70°F and a pressure of 14.7 lbf/in.² abs.

**8–10.** Transition between laminar and turbulent boundary layer flow on a flat smooth plate occurs at $U_0 x_{cr} \rho / \mu = 500{,}000$. What would be the corresponding value of $U_0 \delta_{cr} \rho / \mu$? Is this value comparable to the critical Reynolds number for flow in a round smooth pipe given in Chapter 7? Note that the radius of a pipe corresponds to the thickness $\delta$ of the boundary layer flow and the maximum velocity $u_{\max}$ at the pipe axis corresponds to the free-stream velocity $U_0$ at the outer edge of the boundary layer.

**8–11.** A sphere, 3 ft in diameter, is mounted on the top of a vertical cylindrical pole which is 30 ft tall and 6 in. in diameter. Calculate the bending moment at the base of the pole due to the drag force which is produced by a 50 miles/hour wind at 50°F and 14.7 lbf/in.² abs.

**8–12.** A 2-ft diameter sphere, weighing 720 lbf, is thrown into a deep lake. Calculate the terminal velocity of descent of the sphere in the lake when the water temperature is 40°F.

# 9

# Flow of
# Compressible Fluids

## 9-1  *Thermodynamic Considerations of Compressible Flow*

In the study of compressible flow, consideration must be given to the variation of fluid density as a result of variations in pressure and temperature in the flow. For any given fluid, its density is related to pressure and temperature by the so-called *equation of state*. Actually each fluid has its own unique equation of state which must be determined experimentally. However, under ordinary conditions, the behavior of most gases approximate those of a perfect gas. Therefore, the concept of a perfect gas is very useful in the study of compressible flow. In Sec. 1-8, we defined the equation of state for a perfect gas as

$$pv = RT \quad \text{or} \quad p = \rho RT \tag{9-1}$$

in which $p$ is the absolute pressure in the fluid, $T$ is the absolute temperature measured in degrees Rankine or Kelvin ($T°R = 459.6° + t°$ F and $T°$ K $= 273.2° + t°C$), and $R$ is the individual gas constant, depending only on the molecular weight of the gas. Table 9-1 gives approximate values of gas constants in the British engineering system of units.

Since the essence of the concept of a perfect gas is the complete absence of intermolecular attraction, Eq. 9-1 should not be applied to gases near

385

### TABLE 9–1.   Gas Properties at 60° F

| Gas | Engineering Individual Gas Constant R ft-lbf/lbm-°R | Specific Heat Btu/lbm-°R | | $k = \dfrac{c_p}{c_v}$ |
| --- | --- | --- | --- | --- |
| | | $c_p$ | $c_v$ | |
| Air | 53.3 | 0.240 | 0.171 | 1.40 |
| Water vapor, $H_2O$ | 85.6 | 0.451 | 0.339 | 1.33 |
| Oxygen, $O_2$ | 48.2 | 0.219 | 0.156 | 1.40 |
| Hydrogen, $H_2$ | 767 | 3.41 | 2.42 | 1.41 |
| Helium, He | 386 | 1.251 | 0.754 | 1.66 |
| Nitrogen, $N_2$ | 55.1 | 0.248 | 0.177 | 1.40 |
| Carbon dioxide, $CO_2$ | 34.9 | 0.195 | 0.150 | 1.30 |
| Carbon monoxide, CO | 55.1 | 0.248 | 0.177 | 1.40 |

condensation conditions because here they depart greatly from perfect gas behavior. In fact, studies of the behavior of different gases reveal that no real gas obeys exactly the equation of state of a perfect gas, although many gases under ordinary conditions approximate a perfect gas. The assumption of a perfect gas is essentially an abstraction like many other concepts in physics. A perfect gas is the simplest working fluid in thermodynamics; it is used extensively in fluid mechanics of compressible flow. There are, of course, equations of state for other than perfect gases, but these lack the simplicity and range of Eq. 9-1.

The differential equation of state for a perfect gas is obtained by taking the logarithmic differentiation of Eq. 9-1. Thus,

$$\ln p = \ln \rho + \ln R + \ln T$$

and, by differentiation,

$$\frac{dp}{p} = \frac{d\rho}{\rho} + \frac{dT}{T} \tag{9–2}$$

since $R$ is constant. We shall have occasion to use Eq. 9-2 in the development of compressible flow equations.

In compressible flows, quantities of heat or of thermal energy are usually involved in transition. The symbol $J$ is customarily used as a conversion factor between the thermal unit and its mechanical equivalent. Many careful experiments have been made to determine the numerical value of $J$. The experimental value, in the British engineering system of units, is

$$J = 778.16 \text{ ft-lbf/Btu} \quad \text{for water at } 60° \text{ F.}$$

If the mechanical energy is expressed in joules, the value of $J$ is

$$J = 4.1858 \text{ joules/calorie} \quad \text{for water at } 15° \text{ C.}$$

Since $J$ is a conversion factor, it is needed only in numercal calculations and hence it will not appear in the flow equations to be developed in this chapter.

The specific internal energy of a perfect gas behaves according to the relation

$$\left(\frac{\partial \hat{u}}{\partial v}\right)_T = 0 \tag{9-3}$$

where the subscript $T$ for the partial differentiation indicates an isothermal process. This relation means that the specific internal energy of a perfect gas depends only on the temperature; that is,

$$\hat{u} = \hat{u}(T) \tag{9-4}$$

A similar relation can be shown for the specific enthalpy for a perfect gas by first expressing the definition of specific enthalpy as

$$h = \hat{u} + pv \tag{9-5}$$

and then using Eq. 9-1 to replace $pv$ so that

$$h = \hat{u} + RT \tag{9-6}$$

The right-hand side is clearly a function of temperature only. Hence

$$h = h(T) \tag{9-7}$$

Specific heats $c_v$ and $c_p$ are defined as

$$c_v \equiv \left(\frac{\partial \hat{u}}{\partial T}\right)_v \tag{9-8}$$

$$c_p \equiv \left(\frac{\partial h}{\partial T}\right)_p \tag{9-9}$$

indicating that the specific heats are partial differentiations of thermodynamic properties. Consequently, the specific heats themselves are also thermodynamic properties. For a perfect gas, both $\hat{u}$ and $h$ are functions of temperature only, so that the partial derivatives of Eqs. 9-8 and 9-9 can be written as total derivatives. Thus, for a perfect gas,

$$c_v = \frac{d\hat{u}}{dT} \tag{9-8a}$$

$$c_p = \frac{dh}{dT} \tag{9-9a}$$

Furthermore, a simple relation between $c_v$ and $c_p$ for a perfect gas may be established by substituting $\hat{u} + RT$ for $h$ in Eq. 9-9a. Thus

$$c_p = \frac{d(\hat{u} + RT)}{dT} = c_v + R \tag{9-10}$$

By definition,

$$\frac{c_p}{c_v} = k \tag{9-11}$$

Simultaneous solution of Eqs. 9-10 and 9-11 yields

$$c_v = \frac{1}{k-1} R \tag{9-12}$$

$$c_p = \frac{k}{k-1} R \tag{9-13}$$

The specific heats of a perfect gas are not necessarily constant. Both the kinetic theory of gases and experiments have indicated that the specific heats of perfect gases depend on mainly the temperature, as was pointed out earlier. However, if the temperature range is not extreme, considerable simplification may be achieved by considering the specific heats of a perfect gas to be constant. Approximate values of specific heats for some common gases are also shown in Table 9-1.

In many compressible flow problems there is usually no heat transferred into or out of the flow system. Such a process is called the *adiabatic process*. An adiabatic reversible process with constant $c_v$ and $c_p$ may be represented by the following simple relationship:

$$pv^k = C \quad \text{or} \quad p\rho^{-k} = C \tag{9-14}$$

The derivation of this equation can be found in any modern thermodynamics textbook.

## 9-2  *The Speed of Propagation of Sound Waves*

In the study of compressible flow, we shall consider variation in density throughout the flow field. In many cases these density variations are caused principally by pressure changes from one point to another in the compressible flow field. Consequently, the rate of change of density with respect to pressure is an important parameter in the analysis of compressible flow, and, as was shown in Sec. 1-8, it is intimately related to the speed of propagation of sound waves. The speed of sound $a$ is actually the speed at which pressure disturbances are propagated in the form of small pressure waves through a compressible medium. In an incompressible flow, pressure disturbances propagate at infinite speed and so in the usual sense there are no pressure waves to be considered.

We shall derive an expression for the speed of propagation of small pressure waves by using an idealized model, as shown in Fig. 9-1(a). The long rigid tube has a uniform cross-sectional area $A$ and is fitted with a piston at the left end. The compressible fluid inside the tube is initially at rest. If we push the piston impulsively, a small pressure wave front propagates steadily to the right with a velocity $a$. The conditions of fluid are different on the two sides of the wave front. On the left side, through which

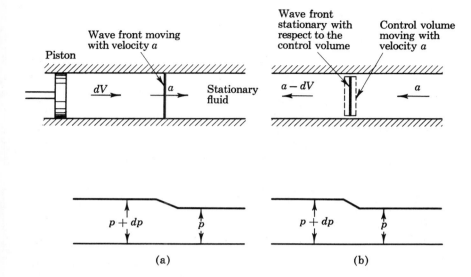

**Fig. 9-1.** One-dimensional propagation of a pressure wave front.

the wave front has just passed, the fluid is moving to the right with a velocity $dV$, and its pressure and density are, respectively, $p + dp$ and $\rho + d\rho$. On the right side, into which the wave front is moving, the fluid is stationary, and its pressure and density are, respectively, $p$ and $\rho$.

In order to simplify the analysis, we shall attach a coordinate system to the wave front and a moving control volume enclosing the wave front, as shown in Fig. 9-1(b). Therefore, relative to this coordinate system, the control volume and the enclosed wave front appear to be stationary, whereas the fluid to the right of the wave front moves toward the left with a velocity $a$ and the fluid to the left of the wave front moves with a velocity $a - dV$.

The continuity equation for this control volume is

$$a\rho A = (a - dV)(\rho + d\rho)A$$
$$= (a\rho + a\,d\rho - \rho\,dV - dV\,d\rho)A$$

which, after canceling of the common factor $A$ from both sides of the equation and dropping of the second-order differential term $dV\,d\rho$, becomes

$$a\,d\rho = \rho\,dV \qquad\qquad \textbf{(9–15)}$$

To write the momentum equation for the control volume, we will note that the shear force on this control volume is negligibly small. Hence the momentum equation can be written as

$$(p + dp)A - pA = \rho aA\,[-(a - dV)] - \rho aA(-a)$$

which is readily simplified to the following form:

$$dp = \rho a\,dV \qquad (9\text{--}16)$$

Eliminating $dV$ from Eqs. 9-15 and 9-16 yields

$$a^2 = \frac{dp}{d\rho} \quad \text{or} \quad a = \sqrt{\frac{dp}{d\rho}} = \sqrt{\left(\frac{\partial p}{\partial \rho}\right)_s} \qquad (9\text{--}17)$$

We have expressed the ratio $dp/d\rho$ in the above equation as a partial derivative at constant entropy because the changes in density, pressure, and temperature in the pressure wave propagation are all infinitesimally small, and so the process is nearly reversible. Furthermore, the rapidity of the pressure wave propagation and the accompanying infinitesimal changes in temperature make the process almost adiabatic. As a result, the process involved in an infinitesimal pressure wave is very close being to isentropic.

If the compressible fluid is a perfect gas, the logarithmic differentiation of the isentropic pressure-density relationship: $p = C\rho^k$ and the equation of state for a perfect gas: $p = \rho RT$ yield the following expression for $(\partial p/\partial \rho)_s$:

$$\left(\frac{\partial p}{\partial \rho}\right)_s = \frac{dp}{d\rho} = \frac{kp}{\rho} = \frac{k\rho RT}{\rho} = kRT$$

The sonic speed of an isentropic flow of a perfect gas then becomes

$$a = \sqrt{kRT} \qquad (9\text{--}18)$$

which indicates that $a$ is a function of absolute temperature of the perfect gas only.

The pressure waves which have been considered in this section involve infinitesimal pressure variations; in Sec. 9-10 we shall consider shock waves in which comparatively large pressure variations take place over a very narrow shock front. Shock waves are not isentropic, and their speeds are considerably larger than sonic speed discussed in this section. In fact, sonic waves may be regarded as limiting cases of shock waves in which the variation in pressure across the wave becomes infinitesimally small.

## 9-3  Mach Number and Mach Cone

At any point in a compressible flow, the ratio of the local stream velocity $V$ and the sonic speed $a$ is called the Mach number $M$. Thus,

$$M = \frac{V}{a} \qquad (9\text{--}19)$$

in which $a$ is computed from the local thermodynamic conditions of the stream.

For a perfect gas, the Mach number may be written as

$$M = \frac{V}{\sqrt{kRT}} \tag{9-20}$$

which, after logarithmic differentiation, becomes

$$\frac{dM}{M} = \frac{dV}{V} - \frac{1}{2}\frac{dT}{T} \tag{9-21}$$

since both $k$ and $R$ are constant for a perfect gas.

The magnitude of Mach number is used for the classification of various regimes of compressible flow.

(1) Subsonic flow.  $M < 1$.

(2) Transonic flow.  The Mach number is in the neighborhood of unity.

(3) Supersonic flow.  $1 < M < 3$.

(4) Hypersonic flow.  $M > 3$.

Since the Mach number is the ratio of the local stream velocity to the velocity of propagation of small pressure waves in a compressible flow, its numerical value can be used to describe the pattern of pressure wave fronts in the compressible flow. Let us consider a stationary source emitting small pressure waves as a fluid moves over it with different velocities, as shown in Fig. 9-2.

Figure 9-2(a) shows the pattern of pressure wave fronts at succeeding time intervals in a fluid which moves very slowly (i.e., $M \approx 0$). In this case the pressure wave fronts spread spherically with the sonic speed, as evaluated in the preceding section.

The pressure wave pattern in Fig. 9-2(b) is formed by the wave fronts which are emitted in a fluid moving from the left to the right at subsonic speed (i.e., $M < 1$). Here the pressure wave fronts are felt in all directions, but the intensity is not symmetrical.

When the fluid velocity is the same as the sonic speed (i.e., $M = 1$), as shown in Fig. 9-2(c), the fluid is moving to the right at exactly the same speed as the pressure wave fronts move through the fluid. As a result, infinitesimal pressure waves can never move upstream against the fluid stream.

In Fig. 9-2(d), the fluid is moving at a supersonic velocity (i.e., $M > 1$). All the pressure wave fronts are limited to a cone which has its apex at the stationary source of pressure wave fronts. The pressure wave fronts cannot be detected upstream from the apex. This cone is called the *Mach cone*.

The phenomena in a supersonic flow are entirely different from those in

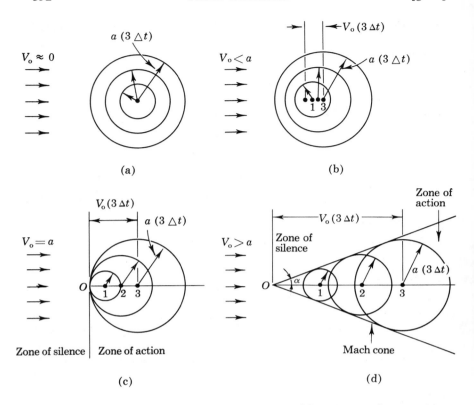

**Fig. 9-2.** Patterns of pressure wave fronts: (a) subsonic velocity with $M \approx 0$, (b) subsonic velocity with $M < 1$, (c) sonic velocity with $M = 1$, (d) supersonic volocity with $M > 1$.

a subsonic flow. Using the Mach cone in Fig. 9-2(d), von Kármán[1] postulated the following three rules for supersonic flow:

(1) *The rule of forbidden signals.* Small pressure wave fronts produced by a stationary source in a moving fluid cannot reach points upstream from the source if the fluid is moving at a supersonic velocity. Similarly, the small pressure wave fronts produced by a body moving at a supersonic speed through a fluid cannot reach points ahead of the body.

(2) *The rule of the zone of action and the zone of silence.* Small pressure wave fronts emitting from a stationary source in a supersonic fluid stream can have effects only on points that lie on or inside of the Mach cone extending downstream from the source. Similarly, conditions at an arbi-

---

[1]Th. von Kármán, "Supersonic Aerodynamics—Principles and Applications," *J. Aero. Sci.*, Vol. XIV, No. 7, 1947.

trary point can be influenced only by disturbances acting at points that lie on or inside of a cone extending upstream from the chosen arbitrary point and having the same vertex angle as the Mach cone.

(3) *The rule of concentrated action.* The distance between the circles (or spheres, in three dimensions) which represent pressure wave fronts in Fig. 9-2 is a measure of the intensity of pressure disturbance at each point in the flow field. The intensity of pressure disturbance is inversely proportional to the distance between the circles; the closer the circles are, the stronger the intensity of pressure disturbance in that region. For a stationary source in a stationary fluid, the intensity of pressure disturbance is symmetrical about the source. For a source moving at a subsonic speed, the intensity is unsymmetrical about the source; and for a source moving at a supersonic speed, the pressure disturbance is largely concentrated in the neighborhood of the Mach cone which forms the outer boundary of the zone of action.

These rules apply exactly for small disturbances but are only qualitatively applicable for large disturbances.

The half-angle of the Mach cone is called the *Mach angle,* which is designated as $\alpha$ in Fig. 9-2(d). Clearly

$$\alpha = \arcsin \frac{a}{V_0} = \arcsin \frac{1}{M} \qquad (9\text{–}22)$$

Note that the Mach angle cannot exist for subsonic flow since, in Eq. 9-22, $\alpha$ becomes imaginary for $M < 1$. The concept of Mach angle is extremely valuable in analyzing two-dimensional supersonic flow, as will be shown in Sec. 9-18.

In a two-dimensional supersonic flow the disturbances will propagate

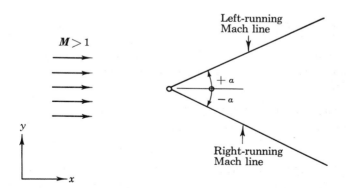

**Fig. 9-3.**   Left-running and right-running Mach lines in a two-dimensional supersonic flow.

along a *Mach wedge* instead of a Mach cone. The traces of the Mach wedge are called the *Mach lines* or *Mach waves*. Thus, there are two Mach lines emanating from any point in a two-dimensional supersonic flow field, as shown in Fig. 9-3. The angle $\alpha$ for such lines is measured in a counterclockwise direction from an axis which is parallel to the direction of the free stream. If we look in the direction of flow, it appears that one line runs to the left and the other to the right. They are, therefore, referred to as a *left-running Mach line* and a *right-running Mach line*, respectively, as indicated in Fig. 9-3. We shall discuss the left-running and right-running Mach lines again in Sec. 9-18.

## PART I. ONE-DIMENSIONAL COMPRESSIBLE FLOW

### 9-4  Basic Equations of One-dimensional Compressible Flow

In Sec. 2-3, we defined a one-dimensional flow as a flow in which all fluid properties and flow characteristics are expressible as functions of position along some flow passage and time. Thus, when flows in nozzles, diffusers, or ducts are assumed to be one-dimensional, we mean that all fluid properties and flow characteristics are uniform over any cross section of a flow passage. Although, in reality, this uniformity may not be fully attained, the rate of change of fluid properties and flow characteristics across the flow section is, in general, negligibly small compared with the rate of change in the direction of flow. An idealization of one-dimensional flow then yields average values of fluid properties and flow characteristics along a flow passage. Such information is often of great interest for a variety of practical engineering problems.

The basic equations of one-dimensional flow represent formulations of the principles of conservation of mass flow, momentum, and energy based on a one-dimensional flow model. In this section, we shall first state these basic relations in terms of the local velocity and then in terms of the Mach number corresponding to local thermodynamic conditions for a perfect gas. The use of Mach number will enable us to reduce the number of variables and to facilitate the necessary integration.

**Continuity equations.** The continuity equation expressing the steady rate of mass flow through a flow channel is simply

$$\dot{m} = \rho V A = \text{constant} \qquad (9\text{--}23)$$

in which the density $\rho$, velocity $V$, and cross-sectional area $A$ may all vary along the channel. Logarithmic differentiation of the above equation yields the following differential equation of continuity for one-dimensional compressible flow:

$$\frac{d\rho}{\rho} + \frac{dV}{V} + \frac{dA}{A} = 0 \qquad (9\text{-}24)$$

For a perfect gas, Eq. 9-23 may be transformed to be expressed in terms of the Mach number by the following algebraic manipulations which make use of the equation of state (Eq. 9-1) and the equation of the Mach number (Eq. 9-20) for a perfect gas:

$$\dot{m} = \rho V A \frac{\sqrt{kRT}}{\sqrt{kRT}} = \rho RT \frac{V}{\sqrt{kRT}} \frac{\sqrt{k}}{\sqrt{RT}} A$$

$$= pM \frac{\sqrt{k}}{\sqrt{RT}} A \qquad (9\text{-}25)$$

Taking the logarithmic differentiation of Eq. 9-25 and noting that $k$ and $R$ are both constant for a perfect gas, we obtain the following differential equation of continuity for the one-dimensional flow of a perfect gas:

$$\frac{dp}{p} + \frac{dM}{M} - \frac{1}{2}\frac{dT}{T} + \frac{dA}{A} = 0 \qquad (9\text{-}26)$$

**Momentum equation.** The momentum equation of fluid motion through an inertia control volume was derived in Sec. 2-6. In high-speed compressible flows, the effect of gravity on the flow is usually negligible. Therefore, the momentum equation for the indicated control volume in Fig. 9-4 in the direction of flow may be written as

$$pA + \left(p + \frac{dp}{2}\right)dA - (p + dp)(A + dA) - dF_R$$

$$= \rho VA(V + dV) - \rho VAV$$

where $F_R$ is the frictional force from the channel wall on the flow. Upon canceling terms, dropping second-order differential terms, and rearranging

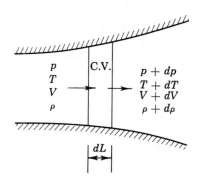

**Fig. 9-4.** Variation in the state of fluid in a compressible flow through a variable-area passage.

the remaining terms, we see that the above equation takes the following simple form:

$$V\,dV + \frac{dp}{\rho} + \frac{dF_R}{A\rho} = 0 \qquad (9\text{-}27)$$

in which the velocity $V$, pressure $p$, fluid density $\rho$, and area $A$ may all vary along the channel. Equation 9-27 is the momentum equation for one-dimensional compressible flow.

When the fluid is a perfect gas, we may restate the momentum equation in terms of the Mach number by first dividing Eq. 9-27 by $V^2$ and substituting $\rho$ in the second term by $p/RT$:

$$\frac{dV}{V} + \frac{RT}{V^2}\frac{dp}{p} + \frac{dF_R}{A\rho V^2} = 0$$

we then use Eqs. 9-20 and 9-21 to replace $V$ in the first two terms by $M$. The resulting expression

$$\frac{dM}{M} + \frac{dT}{2T} + \frac{1}{kM^2}\frac{dp}{p} + \frac{dF_R}{A\rho V^2} = 0 \qquad (9\text{-}28)$$

is the differential momentum equation for the one-dimensional flow of a perfect gas.

**Energy equation.** The energy equation for one-dimensional steady flow, which was derived in Sec. 2-12, is readily applicable to the flow of compressible fluid through the control volume shown in Fig. 9-5. By using the

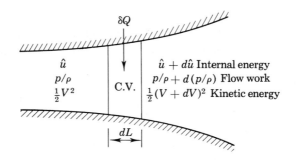

**Fig. 9-5.** Variations in energies in a compressible flow.

notations in Fig. 9-5 and neglecting gravitational effects, we see that the energy equation for the flow through this control volume becomes

$$\frac{dQ/dt}{\dot{m}} - \frac{dW_{\text{shaft}}/dt}{\dot{m}} = \frac{1}{2}(V + dV)^2 + (h + dh) - \frac{V^2}{2} - h$$

Each term in this equation has the dimensions of energy per unit mass of the fluid flowing through the control volume. Expanding the right-hand side of the equation and neglecting the second-order differential term $(dV)^2/2$, we immediately obtain the following energy equation for one-dimensional compressible flow:

$$\frac{dQ/dt}{\dot m} - \frac{dW_{\text{shaft}}/dt}{\dot m} = V\,dV + dh \qquad (9\text{--}29)$$

When the compressible fluid is a perfect gas, Eq. 9-9(a) gives

$$dh = c_p\,dT \qquad (9\text{--}30)$$

so that Eq. 9-29 may also be written as

$$\frac{dQ/dt}{\dot m} - \frac{dW_{\text{shaft}}/dt}{\dot m} = V\,dV + c_p\,dT \qquad (9\text{--}31)$$

In order to express the energy equation in terms of the Mach number, the first step is to divide Eq. 9-31 by $c_p\,T$ and to rearrange the resulting equation in the following form:

$$\frac{dQ/dt}{\dot m c_p T} - \frac{dW_{\text{shaft}}/dt}{\dot m c_p T} = \frac{V^2}{c_p T}\frac{dV}{V} + \frac{dT}{T}$$

Utilizing Eqs. 9-13, 9-20, and 9-21, we may transform the above equation to obtain

$$\frac{dQ/dt}{\dot m c_p T} - \frac{dW_{\text{shaft}}/dt}{\dot m c_p T} = (k-1)M\,dM + \left(1 + \frac{k-1}{2}M^2\right)\frac{dT}{T} \qquad (9\text{--}32)$$

This is the differential energy equation for the one-dimensional flow of perfect gases.

## 9-5    One-dimensional Reversible Adiabatic Flow of a Perfect Gas

In solving fluid flow problems, we are interested in obtaining equations relating variables at different positions in a flow field. In this section we shall derive equations, each of which relates one variable at any given flow section to that at another, in terms of the Mach numbers at these two sections, in a one-dimensional reversible adiabatic flow of a perfect gas. These equations can be used to study high-velocity flows of gases in nozzles and diffusers in which losses are small.

In a reversible adiabatic flow, all dissipative effects vanish. Therefore, with $dF_R = 0$, the momentum equation (Eq. 9-28) becomes

$$\frac{dM}{M} + \frac{dT}{2T} + \frac{1}{kM^2}\frac{dp}{p} = 0 \qquad (9\text{--}33)$$

and, with $dQ/dt$ and $dW_{\text{shaft}}/dt$ equal to zero, the energy equation (Eq.

9-32) is reduced to

$$(k-1)M\,dM + \left(1 + \frac{k-1}{2}M^2\right)\frac{dT}{T} = 0 \qquad (9\text{–}34)$$

The temperature variation $dT/T$ can be obtained immediately from Eq. 9-34. Thus,

$$\frac{dT}{T} = -\frac{(k-1)M\,dM}{1 + [(k-1)/2]M^2} = -\frac{2M\,dM}{[2/(k-1)] + M^2} \qquad (9\text{–}35)$$

which may now be substituted into Eq. 9-33 to obtain

$$\frac{dp}{p} = kM^2\left(\frac{M\,dM}{[2/(k-1)] + M^2} - \frac{dM}{M}\right)$$

$$= -\frac{k}{k-1}\frac{2M\,dM}{[2/(k-1)] + M^2} \qquad (9\text{–}36)$$

The velocity variation $dV/V$ is obtained by substituting Eq. 9-35 into Eq. 9-21:

$$\frac{dV}{V} = \frac{dM}{M} + \frac{dT}{2T} = \left(1 - \frac{M^2}{[2/(k-1)] + M^2}\right)\frac{dM}{M} \qquad (9\text{–}37)$$

Finally, the area variation $dA/A$ is found by substituting for $dT/T$ and $dp/p$ in Eq. 9-26 by Eqs. 9-35 and 9-36, respectively,

$$\frac{dA}{A} = \frac{dT}{2T} - \frac{dp}{p} - \frac{dM}{M}$$

$$= \left(\frac{k+1}{k-1}\frac{M^2}{[2/(k-1)] + M^2} - 1\right)\frac{dM}{M} \qquad (9\text{–}38)$$

Equations 9-35 through 9-38 can be readily integrated between any two sections, say 1 and 2, in a flow channel, because all integrals in these equations are of the following two simple forms:

$$\int_{x_1}^{x_2}\frac{dx}{x} = \ln\frac{x_2}{x_1}$$

and

$$\int_{x_1}^{x_2}\frac{x\,dx}{C+x^2} = \frac{1}{2}\ln\frac{C+x_2^2}{C+x_1^2}$$

Therefore,

Temperature ratio:

$$\frac{T_2}{T_1} = \frac{1 + [(k-1)/2]M_1^2}{1 + [(k-1)/2]M_2^2} \qquad (9\text{–}39)$$

Pressure ratio:

$$\frac{p_2}{p_1} = \left(\frac{1 + [(k-1)/2]M_1^2}{1 + [(k-1)/2]M_2^2}\right)^{k/(k-1)} \qquad (9\text{–}40)$$

Velocity ratio:

$$\frac{V_2}{V_1} = \frac{M_2}{M_1}\left(\frac{1 + [(k-1)/2]M_1^2}{1 + [(k-1)/2]M_2^2}\right)^{1/2} \tag{9-41}$$

Area ratio:

$$\frac{A_2}{A_1} = \frac{M_1}{M_2}\left(\frac{1 + [(k-1)/2]M_2^2}{1 + [(k-1)/2]M_1^2}\right)^{(k+1)/2(k-1)} \tag{9-42}$$

From the reversible adiabatic pressure-density relationship: $p_2/p_1 = (\rho_2/\rho_1)^k$ and Eq. 9-40, the density ratio is

$$\frac{\rho_2}{\rho_1} = \left(\frac{p_2}{p_1}\right)^{1/k} = \left(\frac{1 + [(k-1)/2]M_1^2}{1 + [(k-1)/2]M_2^2}\right)^{1/(k-1)} \tag{9-43}$$

With these equations, variables at all sections in a one-dimensional reversible adiabatic flow of a perfect gas can be readily calculated once the flow conditions at any given section are known. However, these equations are seldom used in their present form in engineering calculations because, as we shall show in the next section, they can be further simplified by referring the flow conditions to a reference state.

## 9-6   Reference States

When Eqs. 9-39 through 9-43 are used to solve practical flow problems, the solution is greatly simplified if variables are related to those at a reference state. There are two reference states most frequently used in the study of compressible flow. They are the stagnation state and the state with $M = 1$.

The stagnation state is characterized by the condition that the velocity is zero. The stagnation state corresponds to a large storage reservoir (real or imaginary) connected to a flow passage, as shown in Fig. 9-6. In a re-

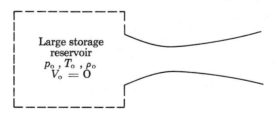

**Fig. 9-6.**   The stagnation state of a gas in a large storage reservoir.

versible adiabatic flow, all possible states lie on a line of constant entropy as illustrated in the *h-s* diagram in Fig. 9-7. The stagnation state is reached

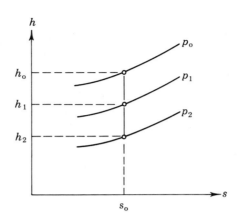

**Fig. 9-7.** An h-s diagram.

from any other state by proceeding from the state point to the stagnation enthalpy along a line of constant entropy. Thus, in order to obtain the stagnation properties from those at a given point, it is necessary only to bring the velocity at the given point to zero by an isentropic process. Once the stagnation state has been established, it immediately fixes all stagnation properties, such as stagnation temperature $T_0$, stagnation pressure $p_0$, etc. Stagnation properties are denoted by a subscript 0.

Equations relating properties at the stagnation state and those at any section in a one-dimensional reversible adiabatic flow of a perfect gas may be obtained by taking the fluid state at section 2 to be at the stagnation state and section 1 as any other state. Therefore, we may set $M_2 = 0$, replace the subscripts 2 by 0, and drop the subscripts 1 in all the equations derived in Sec. 9-5 to obtain:

Temperature ratio:

$$\frac{T_0}{T} = 1 + \frac{k-1}{2} M^2 \tag{9-44}$$

Pressure ratio:

$$\frac{p_0}{p} = \left(1 + \frac{k-1}{2} M^2\right)^{k/(k-1)} \tag{9-45}$$

Density ratio:

$$\frac{\rho_0}{\rho} = \left(1 + \frac{k-1}{2} M^2\right)^{1/(k-1)} \tag{9-46}$$

The state with $M = 1$ is reached by bringing the velocity of flow isentropically to the sonic velocity. The state with $M = 1$ is indicated by the use of an asterisk, such as $T^*$, $p^*$, $\rho^*$, etc. The dimensionless ratio $T/T^*$, for example, is obtained from Eq. 9-39 by letting $M_1 = 1$, $T_1 = T^*$,

$M_2 = M$, and $T_2 = T$. That is,

$$\frac{T}{T^*} = \frac{1 + [(k-1)/2]}{1 + [(k-1)/2]M^2} = \frac{k+1}{2 + (k-1)M^2} \tag{9-47}$$

Other ratios, such as $p/p^*$, $V/V^*$, etc., can be obtained in a similar manner.

The temperature, pressure, and density ratios between the two reference states are of particular interest. These ratios and their numerical values for $k = 1.4$ are

$$\frac{T^*}{T_0} = \frac{2}{k+1} = 0.833 \tag{9-48}$$

$$\frac{p^*}{p_0} = \left(\frac{2}{k+1}\right)^{k/(k-1)} = 0.528 \tag{9-49}$$

$$\frac{\rho^*}{\rho_0} = \left(\frac{2}{k+1}\right)^{1/(k-1)} = 0.634 \tag{9-50}$$

Hence, in an isentropic flow of a perfect gas, the temperature at the state with $M = 1$ is about 83 per cent of the stagnation temperature, whereas the pressure at the state with $M = 1$ is merely a little over half of the stagnation pressure.

## 9-7   Distinction Between a Subsonic and a Supersonic One-dimensional Flow

Important differences in behavior between a subsonic and a supersonic one-dimensional flow may be observed from an area-velocity relationship which is obtained by combining the continuity equation and the momentum equation for a steady reversible adiabatic flow through a channel of varying cross-sectional area. As derived in Sec. 9-4, the continuity and the momentum equations for such a flow are respectively

$$\frac{d\rho}{\rho} + \frac{dV}{V} + \frac{dA}{A} = 0 \tag{9-51}$$

and

$$V\, dV = -\frac{dp}{\rho} = -\frac{dp}{\rho}\frac{d\rho}{d\rho} = -a^2\frac{d\rho}{\rho} \tag{9-52}$$

since a reversible adiabatic flow is isentropic and $dp/d\rho = (\partial p/\partial \rho)_s = a^2$. Introducing the Mach number into Eq. 9-52, we have

$$\frac{d\rho}{\rho} = -M^2\frac{dV}{V} \tag{9-53}$$

which may be substituted into Eq. 9-51 to yield an area-velocity relationship:

$$\frac{dV}{V} = \frac{dA/A}{M^2 - 1} \qquad (9\text{--}54)$$

Equation 9-54 gives the following information concerning the differences between a subsonic and a supersonic one-dimensional flow:

(1) For a subsonic flow, $M < 1$, and the two sides of Eq. 9-54 have opposite signs. Thus, an increase in area will cause a decrease in velocity, and vice versa. The area-velocity relation for a subsonic comperssible flow is qualitatively the same as that for an incompressible flow.

(2) For a supersonic flow, $M > 1$, and both sides of Eq. 9-54 have the same sign. We have the rather surprising phenomenon that an increase in area will cause an increase in velocity. This behavior of a supersonic flow is contrary to our familiar experience with incompressible flow. The reason may be seen from Eq. 9-53 that when $M > 1$, the decrease in density is greater than the increase in velocity and so the area must increase in order to maintain a steady rate of mass flow in the channel.

(3) For flow at sonic velocity, $M = 1$, and Eq. 9-54 indicates that $dA/A$ must be zero. Hence, in a variable-area channel, the sonic velocity can only occur at the section with minimum area no matter whether the flow in the channel is initially subsonic or supersonic. However, the reverse is not necessarily true; the velocity at the section with minimum area does not always have to be sonic. It is important to note that in order for a compressible flow in a channel to change isentropically from an initially subsonic to a supersonic state, or vice versa, the channel must contain a convergent section, a throat, and a divergent section, as will be discussed in Sec. 9-8.

The area-velocity relationship is just one of the many differences in behavior between subsonic and supersonic flow. They are summarized in Table 9-2.

**TABLE 9–2. Differences in Behavior between Subsonic and Supersonic One-dimensional Reversible Adiabatic Flow**

| | Subsonic | | Supersonic | |
|---|---|---|---|---|
| | convergent | divergent | convergent | divergent |
| Area variation | − | + | − | + |
| Velocity variation | + | − | − | + |
| Mach number variation | + | − | − | + |
| Pressure variation | − | + | + | − |
| Temperature variation | − | + | + | − |
| Density variation | − | + | + | − |

## 9-8   Compressible Flow in Nozzles

**Convergent nozzle.** Let us consider the compressible flow in a convergent nozzle, as shown in Fig. 9-8. The flow is supplied from a reservoir

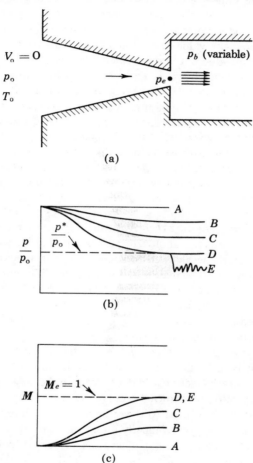

**Fig. 9-8.**   Compressible flow in a convergent nozzle.

in which the pressure $p_0$ and temperature $T_0$ will be kept at constant values. The flow passes through the nozzle and discharges into a chamber in which the pressure $p_b$ may be varied. We shall denote $p_e$ as the pressure at the exit of the nozzle.

Curves in Fig. 9-8(b) and (c) illustrate the different flow conditions in the nozzle as the back pressure $p_b$ is varied. If $p_b/p_0$ equals unity, the pressure is constant throughout the nozzle and there is no flow, as indicated by curve $A$. As $p_b$ is reduced gradually, the pressure disturbances moving upstream within the nozzle cause the flow to accelerate subsonically in the nozzle. The flow conditions indicated by curves $B$ and $C$ are qualitatively the same. Of course, smaller values of $p_b/p_0$ yield larger rates of mass flow. With subsonic flow at the exit, the exit pressure $p_e$ is substantially the same as the back pressure $p_b$. Curve $D$ represents the limiting condition that the value of $p_b/p_0$ has been reduced to a critical value $(p_b/p_0)_{cr}$, which produces a sonic velocity at the exit. Further reduction in $p_b/p_0$ to a value below $(p_b/p_0)_{cr}$ cannot cause any further change in flow conditions within the nozzle and the pressure at the exit, since the sonic velocity at the exit is the maximum velocity for a compressible flow in a convergent nozzle. Therefore, for $p_b/p_0 < (p_b/p_0)_{cr}$ (curve $E$), the flow conditions within the nozzle, the pressure $p_e^*$ at the exit, and the rate of mass flow remain the same as those at the critical condition. This phenomenon is called the *choked flow*. With $p_b/p_0 < p_e^*/p_0$, the flow at the exit expands rapidly into the chamber and rather complex pressure adjustment occurs in the chamber.

**Convergent-divergent nozzle.** By attaching a divergent section to the throat of the convergent nozzle, as shown in Fig. 9-9(a), the compressible flow can be accelerated to supersonic velocities in the divergent section. Curves in Fig. 9-9(b) and (c) illustrate the different flow conditions in the convergent-divergent nozzle. If $p_b = p_0$, there is no flow through the nozzle, as indicated by curve $A$ in Fig. 9-9. As the back pressure $p_b$ is gradually reduced, there are four possible conditions of flow in the nozzle, depending on the value of $p_b/p_0$.

(1) As long as $p_b/p_0 > p_t^*/p_0$, $p_t^*$ being the critical pressure at the throat, the flow is subsonic throughout the entire nozzle. The flow accelerates in the convergent section and decelerates in the subsequent divergent section isentropically, as shown by curve $B$.

(2) When $p_b/p_0$ is reduced to the value corresponding to curve $C$, the value of $p/p_0$ decreases isentropically along the convergent section to the critical value $p_t^*/p_0$ at the throat where the velocity just becomes sonic, and then the value of $p/p_0$ increases isentropically along the divergent section to the value of $p_b/p_0$ at the exit of the nozzle.

(3) When the value of the back pressure $p_b/p_0$ is further reduced, the flow conditions in the convergent section, the value of $p_t^*/p_0$ at the throat, and the rate of mass flow will remain the same as those in (2), although new flow conditions occur in the divergent section. When the value of $p_b/p_0$ corresponds to curve $G$, the flow accelerates isentropically throughout the entire nozzle, and is supersonic in the divergent section.

(4) When the value of $p_b/p_0$ is between those of curves $C$ and $G$, no flow pattern can be found to satisfy the isentropic conditions throughout

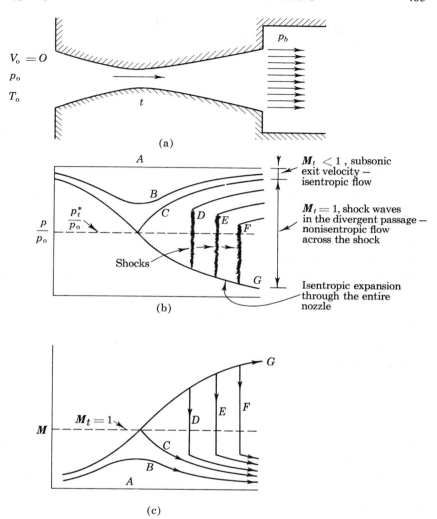

**Fig. 9-9.** Compressible flow in a convergent-divergent nozzle.

the divergent section. One possible solution is to introduce the occurrence of irreversible discontinuities within the divergent section. These discontinuities are called *shock fronts*, which will be discussed in Sec. 9-10.

## 9-9  The Fanno Line and Rayleigh Line

Before discussing nonisentropic flow through a shock front, we shall investigate the Fanno and Rayleigh lines for the steady compressible flow through a duct of constant cross section $A$, as shown in Fig. 9-10. The Fanno and Rayleigh lines are extremely useful in gaining a physical understanding of nonisentropic flows.

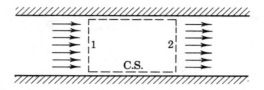

**Fig. 9-10.** A steady compressible flow through a duct of constant cross section.

**The Fanno line.** Let us consider the flow in Fig. 9-10 to be adiabatic and the nonisentropic effect of fluid friction to be present. We may readily write the following equations to account for the flow conditions through the indicated control volume.

Continuity equation:

$$\frac{\dot{m}}{A} = \rho_1 V_1 = \rho_2 V_2 = \text{constant} \tag{9-55}$$

Momentum equation:

$$p_1 - p_2 - \frac{F_R}{A} = \frac{\dot{m}}{A}(V_2 - V_1) \tag{9-56}$$

Energy equation:

$$h_1 + \frac{V_1^2}{2} = h_2 + \frac{V_2^2}{2} = h_0 \tag{9-57}$$

Equations of state:

$$h = h(s, \rho) \tag{9-58}$$

$$s = s(p, \rho) \tag{9-59}$$

In a given flow, if flow conditions at section 1 are competely known, we can identify the thermodynamic state at this section as point 1 on an $h$-$s$ diagram, as shown in Fig. 9-11. We wish to ascertain the corresponding flow conditions at section 2 for the given conditions at section 1 and for various values of $F_R$ in Eq. 9-56. Equations 9-55, 9-57, 9-58, and 9-59 together define a locus of states passing through point 1 on the $h$-$s$ diagram of Fig. 9-11. This locus is called the *Fanno line*.

The construction of the Fanno line is as follows. Suppose we choose some velocity $V_2$, then we may ascertain the corresponding density $\rho_2$ from Eq. 9-55 and specific enthalpy $h_2$ from Eq. 9-57. Using Eqs. 9-58 and 9-59, we can find $s_2$ and $p_2$, and thus locate a point on the $h$-$s$ diagram

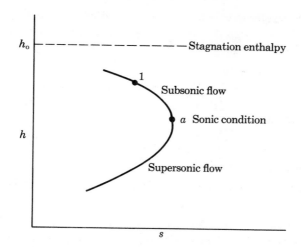

**Fig. 9-11.** The Fanno line.

corresponding to the chosen values of $V_2$. We may then determine $F_R$ from Eq. 9-56 for this particular point. By repeating this calculation for various values of $V_2$, the Fanno line is readily constructed. This Fanno line represents the locus of states reached at section 2 for the flow starting with the known conditions at section 1 by simply changing the amount of fluid friction (represented by $F_R$) in an adiabatic flow.

The Fanno line has the following three characteristics. (1) Point $a$ in the Fanno line in Fig. 9-11 is the point of maximum entropy. This point corresponds to sonic conditions $M = 1$. (2) The part of the Fanno line above point $a$ is asymptotic to the stagnation enthalpy as shown in Fig. 9-11; this part of the Fanno line represents subsonic flow. (3) The lower part of the Fanno line represents supersonic flow.

For an adiabatic flow, the second law of thermodynamics stipulates that the entropy of the flow must increase. This means that, starting with either subsonic or supersonic flow, the Mach number reaches the limiting value of unity for the condition of maximum entropy. Therefore, for adiabatic constant-area conditions, a subsonic flow can never become supersonic and, in the absence of a discontinuity, a supersonic flow cannot become subsonic.

**The Rayleigh line.** The Rayleigh line is the locus of points representing states for flow through a constant-area duct in which heat transfer occurs but in which the boundary-layer friction is considered negligible. Under such conditions, we may write the following equations to relate the flow conditions through the control volume of Fig. 9-10.

Continuity equation:

$$\frac{\dot{m}}{A} = \rho_1 V_1 = \rho_2 V_2 = \text{constant} \qquad (9\text{--}60)$$

Momentum equation:

$$p_1 - p_2 = \frac{\dot{m}}{A}(V_2 - V_1) \qquad (9\text{--}61)$$

Energy equation:

$$h_1 + \frac{V_1^2}{2} + \frac{dQ/dt}{\dot{m}} = h_2 + \frac{V_2^2}{2} \qquad (9\text{--}62)$$

Equations of state:

$$h = h(s, \rho) \qquad (9\text{--}63)$$

$$s = s(p, \rho) \qquad (9\text{--}64)$$

Again, flow conditions at section 1 are assumed to be completely known. The thermodynamic state at this point is plotted as point 1 on an $h$-$s$ diagram in Fig. 9-12. The procedure this time is again to choose a velo-

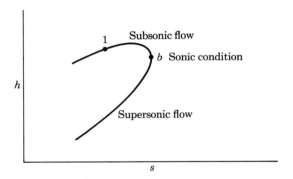

**Fig. 9-12.** The Rayleigh line.

city $V_2$ for which $\rho_2$ is determined by Eq. 9-60, $p_2$ by Eq. 9-61, and $h_2$ and $s_2$ by Eqs. 9-63 and 9-64, respectively. By repeating these calculations for various values of $V_2$, a locus of $(h_2, s_2)$-points may be plotted on the $h$-$s$ diagram. This locus is called the *Rayleigh line*. Using Eq. 9-62, we can ascertain the value of $(dQ/dt)/\dot{m}$ for each state point. Thus, the Rayleigh line represents the locus of states which can be reached at section 2 for the flow starting with the known conditions at section 1 corresponding to various quantities of heat transfer in a flow with negligible boundary-layer friction.

The point of maximum entropy, indicated by point $b$ in Fig. 9-12, is a sonic point for the Rayleigh line. The upper branch of the Rayleigh line describes the changes of state in subsonic flow, whereas the lower branch represents states in supersonic flow. Since boundary-layer friction is assumed to be absent, the entropy change in the flow is positive for heating and negative for cooling processes for both subsonic and supersonic flows.

## 9-10   One-dimensional Normal Shock

Figure 9-13 shows a one-dimensional normal shock, which is essentially a plane surface of discontinuity normal to the direction of flow.

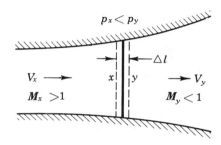

**Fig. 9-13.** A one-dimensional stationary normal shock front.

Although the thickness of the normal shock is usually very small, rather complex irreversible dissipative phenomena occur in the interior of the shock. It is, however, very difficult to obtain data on these dissipative phenomena which occur in the interior of the shock. Fortunately, for practically all engineering calculations we can ignore the interior of the shock, since we are primarily interested in the net changes in fluid properties across the shock. Therefore, the shock is treated as a discontinuity across which finite changes take place in flow conditions. The flow can be considered as passing through a constant-area control volume which includes the discontinuity. Both heat transfer and boundary-layer friction can be disregarded for the control volume.

Flow conditions on the upstream and downstream sides of the normal shock are denoted respectively by subscripts $x$ and $y$, as shown in Fig. 9-13. When conditions at section $x$ are known, the conditions at section $y$ can be calculated from those at section $x$ by means of the continuity, momentum, energy, and state equations. However, before we formulate these equations, it is informative to point out that points representing states at sections $x$ and $y$ on the two sides of the shock discontinuity must lie at the intersections of the Fanno and Rayleigh lines drawn on an $h$-$s$ diagram, as shown in Fig. 9-14. Both lines are constructed to

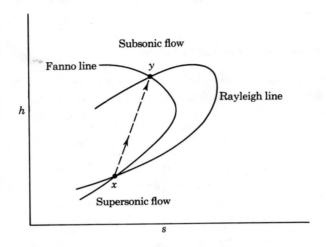

**Fig. 9-14.** The Fanno and Rayleigh lines for a flow past a normal shock.

pass through point $x$, which represents the known fluid state at section $x$. Points on the Fanno line represent various possible fluid states in an adiabatic flow which starts with the fluid state corresponding to section $x$, whereas points on the Rayleigh line represent various fluid states in a flow with no boundary-layer friction which starts with the same fluid state. Since the flow passing through the shock is both adiabatic and without boundary-layer friction, the fluid state at $y$ must be at the second intersection of the Fanno and Rayleigh lines, which is indicated as point $y$ in Fig. 9-14.

In all compressible flows thus tested, if $x$ lies on the supersonic branch, $y$ appears on the subsonic branch. Furthermore, it has been found that point $y$ is always to the right of point $x$. Therefore, we may use Fig. 9-14 to make the following generalizations. (1) From the second law of thermodynamics, the flow passing a normal shock must always proceed from point $x$ to point $y$ and not the other way, since the entropy of an irreversible, dissipative system always increases. (2) A normal shock can occur only in supersonic flow; the supersonic flow approaching a shock is converted into a subsonic flow immediately downstream of the shock.

Assuming that a perfect gas flows steadily through the control volume of Fig. 9-13, we may formulate the following basic equations for this control volume:

Continuity equation:

$$\frac{\dot{m}}{A} = \rho_x V_x = \rho_y V_y \qquad (9\text{--}65)$$

Momentum equation:

$$p_x - p_y = \rho_y V_y^2 - \rho_x V_x^2 \qquad (9\text{--}66)$$

Energy equation:

$$\frac{V_x^2}{2} + \frac{k}{k-1}\frac{p_x}{\rho_x} = \frac{V_y^2}{2} + \frac{k}{k-1}\frac{p_y}{\rho_y} \qquad (9\text{--}67)$$

Elimination of $V_x$, $V_y$, and $\dot{m}/A$ from the above three equations results in the following relationship between the pressure ratio and density ratio for the two sides of the normal shock:

$$\frac{p_y}{p_x} = \frac{[(k+1)/(k-1)](\rho_y/\rho_x) - 1}{[(k+1)/(k-1)] - (\rho_y/\rho_x)} \qquad (9\text{--}68)$$

This is one form of the Rankine-Hugoniot equation[2] for relating the state ratios across the shock. Other ratios such as $V_y/V_x$, $T_y/T_x$, and $\rho_y/\rho_x$ may be readily determined by the algebraic manipulation of the equation of state for a perfect gas, the continuity equation, and the Rankine-Hugoniot equation. However, we shall derive equations relating the variables across a normal shock in terms of the initial Mach number $M_x$, which is usually known for any given flow.

Introducing the Mach number $M = V/\sqrt{kp/\rho}$, we may transform the momentum equation (Eq. 9-66) and the energy equation (Eq. 9-67) for the flow across a normal shock to be written in terms of the Mach numbers as follows.

Momentum equation:

$$p_x \frac{k\rho_x}{\rho_x} + \rho_x V_x^2 \frac{k\rho_x}{\rho_x} = p_y \frac{k\rho_y}{\rho_y} + \rho_y V_y^2 \frac{k\rho_y}{\rho_y}$$

$$\rho_x V_x^2 \left(\frac{1}{M_x^2} + k\right) = \rho_y V_y^2 \left(\frac{1}{M_y^2} + k\right)$$

$$\frac{V_x}{V_y}\left(\frac{1}{M_x^2} + k\right) = \frac{1}{M_y^2} + k \qquad (9\text{--}69)$$

since, by the continuity equation, $\rho_x V_x = \rho_y V_y$.

[2]W. J. W. Rankine, "On the Thermodynamic Theory of Finite Longitudinal Disturbances," *Phil. Trans. Roy. Soc.* (London), Vol. CLX (1870), 277–288.

H. Hugoniot, "Memoire sur la propagation du mouvement dans les corps et spécialement dans les gases perfaits" (Memoir on the Propagation of Motion in Bodies and Particularly in Perfect Gases), *J. école polytech.* (Paris), Cahier LVII (1887), 3–97, and Cahier LVIII (1888), 1–126.

Energy equation:

$$\frac{V_x^2}{2}\left[(k-1)+2\frac{kp_x/\rho_x}{V_x^2}\right]=\frac{V_y^2}{2}\left[(k-1)+2\frac{kp_y/\rho_y}{V_y^2}\right]$$

$$\frac{V_x^2}{V_y^2}\left[(k-1)+\frac{2}{M_x^2}\right]=(k-1)+\frac{2}{M_y^2} \tag{9-70}$$

Multiplying Eq. 9-69 by 2 and subtracting the resulting equation from Eq. 9-70 to eliminate $M_y$, we obtain, after some algebraic manipulation,

$$\left(\frac{V_x}{V_y}-1\right)\left\{\frac{V_x}{V_y}\left[(k-1)+\frac{2}{M_x^2}\right]-(k+1)\right\}=0$$

This is a quadratic equation with two parts, one of which $V_x/V_y-1=0$ leads to a trivial solution. The remaining part is easily solved for the velocity ratio $V_y/V_x$:

$$\frac{V_y}{V_x}=\frac{(k-1)M_x^2+2}{(k+1)M_x^2} \tag{9-71}$$

Then, the density ratio $\rho_y/\rho_x$ may be obtained from the continuity equation (Eq. 9-65) as

$$\frac{\rho_y}{\rho_x}=\frac{V_x}{V_y}=\frac{(k+1)M_x^2}{(k-1)M_x^2+2} \tag{9-72}$$

the pressure ratio $p_y/p_x$ from the Rankine-Hugoniot equation (Eq. 9-68):

$$\frac{p_y}{p_x}=\frac{2kM_x^2-(k-1)}{k+1} \tag{9-73}$$

and the temperature ratio from the equation of state for a perfect gas:

$$\frac{T_y}{T_x}=\frac{p_y}{p_x}\frac{\rho_x}{\rho_y}=\frac{2kM_x^2-(k-1)}{k+1}\frac{(k-1)M_x^2+2}{(k+1)M_x^2} \tag{9-74}$$

Finally, when Eqs. 9-69 and 9-71 are combined by eliminating the velocity ratio $V_y/V_x$, and then the resulting expression is solved for $M_y^2$, we obtain

$$M_y^2=\frac{(k-1)M_x^2+2}{2kM_x^2-(k-1)} \tag{9-75}$$

To evaluate the entropy change across a normal shock, we employ the following thermodynamic formula for a perfect gas:

$$s_y-s_x=\frac{1}{k-1}R\ln\frac{p_y}{p_x}+\frac{k}{k-1}R\ln\frac{\rho_x}{\rho_y} \tag{9-76}$$

which, after substitutions from Eq. 9-72 for $\rho_x/\rho_y$ and Eq. 9-73 for $p_y/p_x$, becomes

$$s_y-s_x=\frac{1}{k-1}R\ln\left[\frac{2kM_x^2-(k-1)}{k+1}\right]+\frac{k}{k-1}R\ln\left[\frac{(k-1)M_x^2+2}{(k+1)M_x^2}\right] \tag{9-77}$$

The entropy difference $s_y - s_x$ is positive if $M_x$ is greater than unity, again indicating that a normal shock can occur only in a supersonic flow.

## 9-11  Oblique Shocks

An oblique shock is formed when a supersonic flow approaches a shock at an angle $\beta$, as shown in Fig. 9-15. The total velocity of flow

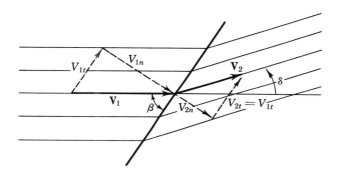

**Fig. 9-15.**  An oblique shock.

before the shock is shown as $\mathbf{V}_1$, which has been decomposed into a component $V_{1n}$ normal to the shock and a component $V_{1t}$ parallel to the shock. As the flow passes through an oblique shock, the tangential component of the velocity remains unchanged, whereas the normal component $V_{1n}$ will change to $V_{2n}$ in accordance with the shock theory derived in the preceding section. Clearly $V_{1n}$ must be greater than $a_1$, since a shock can occur only in a supersonic flow. After the shock, $V_{2n}$ becomes less than $a_2$. The flow characteristics, such as densities, pressures, temperatures, etc., on both sides of an oblique shock are related by the normal shock equations derived in the preceding section by using $V_{1n}$ and $V_{2n}$ in place of $V_x$ and $V_y$, respectively.

Since the magnitude of $V_t$ is not affected by the shock and $V_{2n}$ is less than $V_{1n}$, the final velocity $\mathbf{V}_2$ must turn through an angle $\delta$ toward the shock, as shown in Fig. 9-15. Furthermore, $\mathbf{V}_2$ may be either supersonic or subsonic, depending on the magnitude of $V_t$. If $V_t$ is large, the angle $\beta$ is relatively small, and the flow, after passing the shock, may remain supersonic. On the other hand, a small $V_t$ indicates that the angle $\beta$ is almost 90° and the flow after the shock is most likely to be subsonic.

The phenomena of oblique shocks are useful in studying supersonic flows at corners. Supersonic flows at concave corners are illustrated in Fig. 9-16. Here oblique shocks are formed as flow turns through the deflection angle $\delta$. From the shock relations, we know that the shock

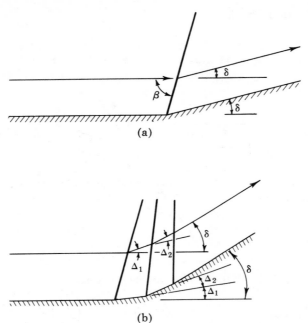

(a)

(b)

**Fig. 9-16.** Supersonic flows at concave corners.

will increase the density, pressure, and temperature of the fluid. The fluid is compressed nonisentropically as it proceeds along the curve. When the concave corner is a smooth and continuous curve, the individual shocks may approach Mach lines as limits, and then the fluid is compressed isentropically.

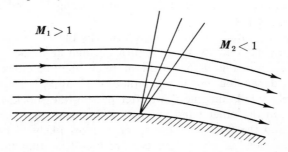

**Fig. 9-17.** Expansion waves in a supersonic flow at a convex corner.

When a supersonic flow occurs at a convex corner, as shown in Fig. 9-17, the fluid expands along its curved path, and no oblique shock can be formed in an expanding supersonic flow. Figure 9-17 illustrates that rapid expansions in supersonic flows take place over a series of Mach lines which emanate from the corner. These oblique expansion waves are referred to as *Prandtl-Meyer expansions*.

## PART II.   INTRODUCTION TO MULTIDIMENSIONAL COMPRESSIBLE FLOW

### 9-12   Derivation of the Basic Equation for Three-dimensional Compressible Flow

The theory of one-dimensional compressible flow can yield only the average conditions of flow over various sections along a flow passage. In order to study the details of the flow patterns, it is necessary to treat the flow field as either three-dimensional or two-dimensional. However, the general theory of three-dimensional flow of a compressible fluid with a complicated equation of state, including friction, heat transfer, and shocks, is a highly complex subject. This complexity lies in mathematical difficulties. Indeed, the mathematics involved in the general theory of three-dimensional compressible flow is so complicated that it is almost a hopeless task to obtain solutions without considerable simplification of the flow model. Therefore, in this derivation, we shall incorporate the following simplifications:

(1) The flow is steady.

(2) The free-stream flow outside the boundary layer is inviscid and nonheat-conducting so that the effect of viscosity and heat transfer need be considered only in a boundary layer or within a shock. The free-stream flow is, therefore, both irrotational and isentropic.

(3) The body forces are negligibly small as compared to other forces.

(4) The fluid is a perfect gas with constant specific heats.

As was discussed in Chapter 3, the condition of irrotationality is automatically satisfied through the introduction of the velocity potential $\phi$ such that the velocity field is expressible as the gradient of $\phi$. That is,

$$\mathbf{V} = \nabla\phi = \frac{\partial\phi}{\partial x}\mathbf{i} + \frac{\partial\phi}{\partial y}\mathbf{j} + \frac{\partial\phi}{\partial z}\mathbf{k} \qquad (9\text{–}78)$$

With this expression, the continuity equation for a steady compressible flow may be written in terms of the velocity potential as

$$\nabla \cdot (\rho\mathbf{V}) = \nabla \cdot (\rho\nabla\phi) = \rho\nabla^2\phi + \nabla\phi \cdot \nabla\rho = 0 \qquad (9\text{–}79)$$

or, in scalar form,

$$\rho\left(\frac{\partial^2\phi}{\partial x^2} + \frac{\partial^2\phi}{\partial y^2} + \frac{\partial^2\phi}{\partial z^2}\right) + \frac{\partial\phi}{\partial x}\frac{\partial\rho}{\partial x} + \frac{\partial\phi}{\partial y}\frac{\partial\rho}{\partial y} + \frac{\partial\phi}{\partial z}\frac{\partial\rho}{\partial z} = 0 \quad (9\text{–}80)$$

Newton's second law of motion for the flow with the above-stated restrictions takes the form of the modified Euler equation:

$$dp = -\rho d\left(\frac{V^2}{2}\right) = -\frac{\rho}{2}\,d(\boldsymbol{\nabla}\phi \cdot \boldsymbol{\nabla}\phi)$$

$$= -\frac{\rho}{2}\,d\left[\left(\frac{\partial\phi}{\partial x}\right)^2 + \left(\frac{\partial\phi}{\partial y}\right)^2 + \left(\frac{\partial\phi}{\partial z}\right)^2\right] \quad (9\text{–}81)$$

We will recall from Chapter 3 that this equation is written along an arbitrary displacement $d\mathbf{s}$ in the flow field.

The sonic velocity in a fluid is given by $a^2 = (\partial p/\partial\rho)_s$, where the subscript $s$ denotes the partial differentiation to be taken at constant entropy. Therefore, in an isentropic flow, the sonic velocity may be written in terms of the actual differential changes of the pressure and density, respectively, of any moving fluid element. That is, $a^2 = dp/d\rho$ and

$$d\rho = \frac{dp}{a^2}$$

Substituting the right-hand side of Eq. 9-81 for $dp$ in this equation, we have

$$d\rho = -\frac{\rho}{2a^2}\,d\left[\left(\frac{\partial\phi}{\partial x}\right)^2 + \left(\frac{\partial\phi}{\partial y}\right)^2 + \left(\frac{\partial\phi}{\partial z}\right)^2\right]$$

from which the partial derivatives of $\rho$ with respect to $x$, $y$, and $z$, respectively, are

$$\frac{\partial\rho}{\partial x} = -\frac{\rho}{a^2}\left[\frac{\partial\phi}{\partial x}\frac{\partial^2\phi}{\partial x^2} + \frac{\partial\phi}{\partial y}\frac{\partial^2\phi}{\partial y\,\partial x} + \frac{\partial\phi}{\partial z}\frac{\partial^2\phi}{\partial z\,\partial x}\right]$$

$$\frac{\partial\rho}{\partial y} = -\frac{\rho}{a^2}\left[\frac{\partial\phi}{\partial x}\frac{\partial^2\phi}{\partial x\,\partial y} + \frac{\partial\phi}{\partial y}\frac{\partial^2\phi}{\partial y^2} + \frac{\partial\phi}{\partial z}\frac{\partial^2\phi}{\partial z\,\partial y}\right]$$

$$\frac{\partial\rho}{\partial z} = -\frac{\rho}{a^2}\left[\frac{\partial\phi}{\partial x}\frac{\partial^2\phi}{\partial x\,\partial z} + \frac{\partial\phi}{\partial y}\frac{\partial^2\phi}{\partial y\,\partial z} + \frac{\partial\phi}{\partial z}\frac{\partial^2\phi}{\partial z^2}\right]$$

We then substitute these expressions into Eq. 9-80 and rearrange the resulting equation in the following form:

$$\left[1 - \frac{1}{a^2}\left(\frac{\partial\phi}{\partial x}\right)^2\right]\frac{\partial^2\phi}{\partial x^2} + \left[1 - \frac{1}{a^2}\left(\frac{\partial\phi}{\partial y}\right)^2\right]\frac{\partial^2\phi}{\partial y^2} + \left[1 - \frac{1}{a^2}\left(\frac{\partial\phi}{\partial z}\right)^2\right]\frac{\partial^2\phi}{\partial z^2}$$

$$-\frac{2}{a^2}\left(\frac{\partial\phi}{\partial x}\frac{\partial\phi}{\partial y}\frac{\partial^2\phi}{\partial x\,\partial y} + \frac{\partial\phi}{\partial y}\frac{\partial\phi}{\partial z}\frac{\partial^2\phi}{\partial y\,\partial z} + \frac{\partial\phi}{\partial z}\frac{\partial\phi}{\partial x}\frac{\partial^2\phi}{\partial z\,\partial x}\right) = 0 \quad (9\text{–}82)$$

This partial differential equation for the velocity potential $\phi$ combines the continuity and momentum equations for the isentropic and irrotational flow of a compressible fluid. Note that when $a$ approaches infinity, as in an incompressible flow, the equation degenerates to $\nabla^2\phi = 0$, which is indeed the combination of the continuity and momentum equations for an irrotational flow of an incompressible fluid.

We can show the local sonic velocity $a$ in Eq. 9-82 to be related to $\phi$ by first writing the energy equation between the stagnation point and any point in the flow field as

$$\frac{k}{k-1}\frac{p_0}{\rho_0} = \frac{k}{k-1}\frac{p}{\rho} + \frac{V^2}{2}$$

For isentropic flow of a perfect gas, $a^2 = kp/\rho$ and $a_0^2 = kp_0/\rho_0$. The energy equation then becomes

$$a^2 = a_0^2 - \frac{k-1}{2}V^2 = a_0^2 - \frac{k-1}{2}(\nabla\phi \cdot \nabla\phi)$$

$$= a_0^2 - \frac{k-1}{2}\left[\left(\frac{\partial\phi}{\partial x}\right)^2 + \left(\frac{\partial\phi}{\partial y}\right)^2 + \left(\frac{\partial\phi}{\partial z}\right)^2\right] \tag{9-83}$$

Substitution of Eq. 9-83 into Eq. 9-82 would yield a partial differential equation for $\phi$ in terms of $x$, $y$, and $z$, an equation which represents the steady, irrotational, isentropic flow of a perfect gas. The resulting equation satisfies simultaneously the laws of conservation of mass flow, momentum and energy.

Because Eq. 9-82 is a nonlinear partial differential equation for which the solution is extremely difficult, it is necessary to linearize the equation by imposing further restrictions and thus to simplify the equation to a more tractable form. There are several methods by which the equation may be linearized.[3] In the next section we shall present the *small-perturbation theory* of linearizing the potential equation for two-dimensional compressible flow. Then the linear equation will be applied to some problems of two-dimensional compressible flow in subsequent sections.

## 9-13    Small Perturbation Theory of Linearizing the Potential Equation for Two-dimensional Compressible Flow

For steady, two-dimensional, irrotational, isentropic motion of a compressible flow in the $xy$ plane, Eq. 9-82 and 9-83 are simplified to give

$$\left[1 - \frac{1}{a^2}\left(\frac{\partial\phi}{\partial x}\right)^2\right]\frac{\partial^2\phi}{\partial x^2} + \left[1 - \frac{1}{a^2}\left(\frac{\partial\phi}{\partial y}\right)^2\right]\frac{\partial^2\phi}{\partial y^2} - \frac{2}{a^2}\left(\frac{\partial\phi}{\partial x}\frac{\partial\phi}{\partial y}\frac{\partial^2\phi}{\partial x\,\partial y}\right) = 0 \tag{9-84}$$

---

[3]See, for example, A. H. Shapiro, *The Dynamics and Thermodynamics of Compressible Fluid Flow*. New York: The Ronald Press Company, 1953.

$$a^2 = a_0^2 - \frac{k-1}{2}\left[\left(\frac{\partial\phi}{\partial x}\right)^2 + \left(\frac{\partial\phi}{\partial y}\right)^2\right] \qquad (9\text{--}85)$$

We now consider a steady, two-dimensional, uniform flow, as shown in Fig. 9-18(a). The coordinate system has been chosen so that the uniform velocity $V_\infty$ is parallel to the $x$-axis. We shall use the subscript $\infty$ to indicate all properties of the uniform stream, such as $p_\infty$, $T_\infty$, $\rho_\infty$, etc. The corresponding sonic velocity is $a_\infty$ and the Mach number is $M_\infty$, which equals $V_\infty/a_\infty$.

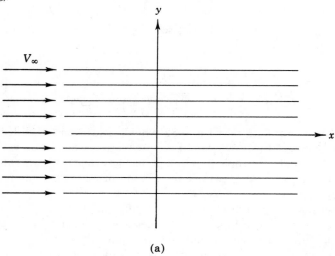

(a)

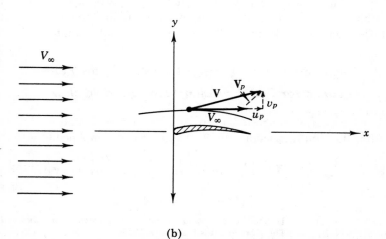

(b)

**Fig. 9-18.** Perturbation motion in a two-dimensional compressible flow.

If a thin solid body, such as an airfoil, is placed in the uniform stream as shown in Fig. 9-18(b), the body will disturb the uniform motion. The velocity at any point in the new flow field, in the presence of the body, is then given by the vector sum of the uniform velocity $V_\infty \mathbf{i}$ and the perturbed velocity $\mathbf{V}_p = u_p \mathbf{i} + v_p \mathbf{j}$. The perturbation velocity components $u_p$ and $v_p$ are small compared with the velocity $V_\infty$. The subscript $p$ has been used to denote perturbation conditions.

We shall employ $\phi$ to represent the potential of the total velocity field and $\phi_p$ to represent the potential of the perturbation velocity field. Thus, we have for this flow

$$\frac{\partial \phi}{\partial x} = u = V_\infty + u_p = V_\infty + \frac{\partial \phi_p}{\partial x}$$

$$\frac{\partial \phi}{\partial y} = v = v_p = \frac{\partial \phi_p}{\partial y}$$

With these relations we rewrite Eq. 9-84 in terms of the uniform and perturbation velocities. Therefore, upon multiplying through by $a^2$ and rearranging terms, we may write Eq. 9-84 as

$$a^2 \left( \frac{\partial^2 \phi}{\partial x^2} + \frac{\partial^2 \phi}{\partial y^2} \right) = (V_\infty + u_p)^2 \frac{\partial^2 \phi}{\partial x^2} + v_p^2 \frac{\partial^2 \phi}{\partial y^2} + 2(V_\infty + u_p) v_p \frac{\partial^2 \phi}{\partial x \, \partial y}$$

$$(9\text{--}86)$$

The sonic velocity $a$ in the above equation is a variable quantity in the flow field. We shall find an expression for $a^2$ in terms of the uniform and perturbation velocities so that we may use it to replace $a^2$ in the above equation. To do this, we formulate the energy equation between the uniform stream and any point in the flow field and then follow calculations similar to those used in obtaining Eq. 9-85. Hence

$$a^2 = a_\infty^2 - \frac{k-1}{2}(V^2 - V_\infty^2)$$

$$= a_\infty^2 - \frac{k-1}{2}[(V_\infty + u_p)^2 + v_p^2 - V_\infty^2]$$

$$(9\text{--}87)$$

Substituting this into Eq. 9-86, dividing the resulting equation through by $a_\infty^2$, and rearranging terms, we obtain

$$(1 - M_\infty)^2 \frac{\partial^2 \phi}{\partial x^2} + \frac{\partial^2 \phi}{\partial y^2} = M_\infty^2 \left[ (k+1) \frac{u_p}{V_\infty} + \frac{k+1}{2} \left( \frac{u_p}{V_\infty} \right)^2 \right.$$

$$\left. + \frac{k-1}{2} \left( \frac{v_p}{V_\infty} \right)^2 \right] \frac{\partial^2 \phi}{\partial x^2} + M_\infty^2 \left[ (k-1) \frac{u_p}{V_\infty} + \frac{k+1}{2} \left( \frac{v_p}{V_\infty} \right)^2 \right. \quad (9\text{--}88)$$

$$\left. + \frac{k-1}{2} \left( \frac{u_p}{V_\infty} \right)^2 \right] \frac{\partial^2 \phi}{\partial y^2} + 2 M_\infty^2 \left( 1 + \frac{u_p}{V_\infty} \right) \frac{v_p}{V_\infty} \frac{\partial^2 \phi}{\partial x \, \partial y}$$

This is the two-dimensional potential equation in terms of the uniform and perturbation velocities.

Since the perturbation velocity components are small compared with $V_\infty$, it becomes possible to state that

$$M_\infty^2 \left(\frac{u_p}{V_\infty}\right)^2 \ll 1, \qquad M_\infty^2 \left(\frac{v_p}{V_\infty}\right)^2 \ll 1, \qquad M_\infty^2 \left(\frac{u_p v_p}{V_\infty^2}\right) \ll 1$$

and to omit these terms from Eq. 9-88. Thus, we obtain the simpler potential equation

$$\begin{aligned}
(1 - M_\infty^2)\frac{\partial^2 \phi}{\partial x^2} + \frac{\partial^2 \phi}{\partial y^2} &= M_\infty^2 (k + 1)\frac{u_p}{V_\infty}\frac{\partial^2 \phi}{\partial x^2} \\
&+ M_\infty^2 (k - 1)\frac{u_p}{V_\infty}\frac{\partial^2 \phi}{\partial y^2} + 2M_\infty^2 \frac{v_p}{V_\infty}\frac{\partial^2 \phi}{\partial x\,\partial y}
\end{aligned} \qquad (9\text{–}89)$$

Unfortunately, this equation is still nonlinear despite the numerous assumptions already made. Further simplification of the equation would require considerable care.

Let us consider the flow in which $M_\infty$ neither is excessively large nor has a numerical value close to unity. For very thin bodies, $u_p/V_\infty \ll 1$ and $v_p/V_\infty \ll 1$ so that we may drop the terms on the right-hand side of Eq. 9-89. Thus, we obtain the following linear partial differential equation:

$$(1 - M_\infty^2)\frac{\partial^2 \phi}{\partial x^2} + \frac{\partial^2 \phi}{\partial y^2} = 0 \qquad (9\text{–}90)$$

which is valid for steady, two-dimensional, irrotational flow of a perfect gas around thin bodies. The equation is applicable to both subsonic and supersonic flows outside the hypersonic and transonic ranges.

For transonic flow where $M_\infty \to 1$, the coefficient of $\partial^2 \phi/\partial x^2$ on the left-hand side of Eq. 9-89 becomes very small, and it is then necessary to retain the first term on the right-hand side. Thus, the following equation

$$(1 - M_\infty^2)\frac{\partial^2 \phi}{\partial x^2} + \frac{\partial^2 \phi}{\partial y^2} = M_\infty^2 (k + 1)\frac{u_p}{V_\infty}\frac{\partial^2 \phi}{\partial x^2} \qquad (9\text{–}91)$$

is valid for subsonic, transonic, and supersonic flows with small perturbation. Note that this equation is also nonlinear because of the quadratic term on the right-hand side.

In this chapter we shall deal with only Eq. 9-90, which is linear. We will note that in Eq. 9-90 the coefficient $(1 - M_\infty^2)$ changes sign when the flow changes from subsonic to supersonic. From a mathematical point of view, this change in sign is important because the very nature of the partial differential equation depends on whether the coefficient is positive or negative. For subsonic flow ($M_\infty < 1$), the coefficient is positive and the resulting partial differential equation is of elliptic type. An elliptic-type equation may be readily transformed to the Laplace equation, which, we will recall, is the basic equation for incompressible flow. Therefore, the physical characteristics of subsonic compressible flow are somewhat similar to those of incompressible flow. For supersonic flow ($M_\infty > 1$), the coefficient becomes negative and the resulting equation belongs to the hyperbolic-type partial differential equation. A hyperbolic-type equation may be transformed to the classical wave equation. Hence, linearized supersonic flows have features similar to those of wave phenomena, such as vibrating strings, air columns, elastic beams, etc.

As was shown in Chapters 3, 4, and 5, the solution of an irrotational incompressible flow is given by a velocity potential which simultaneously satisfies the Laplace equation and the given boundary conditions. Therefore the solution of an irrotational compressible flow constitutes the determination of a velocity potential which will satisfy simultaneously Eq. 9-90 and the given boundary conditions. Since the first derivatives of the velocity potentials for the total flow field and the perturbation flow field differ only by the constant $V_\infty$, it is clear that both velocity potentials will satisfy Eq. 9-90 since only second-order derivatives appear in this equation. We shall discuss boundary conditions for irrotational compressible flows in Sec. 9-15.

## 9-14   Small Perturbation Theory of Linearizing the Pressure Coefficient

The pressure distribution in a given flow pattern is of great parctical significance. If the pressure distribution is completely known, it is possible to calculate the forces and moments produced by the flow field on submerged solid boundaries. Furthermore, a knowledge of pressure gradient at a solid boundary is necessary for predicting the development and behavior of the boundary layer.

We shall use a nondimensional pressure coefficient to describe the pressure distribution. The pressure coefficient $C_p$ is defined as

$$C_p = \frac{p - p_\infty}{\frac{1}{2}\rho_\infty V_\infty^2} = \frac{(p - p_\infty)(p_\infty/p_\infty)}{\frac{1}{2}\rho_\infty V_\infty^2(kp_\infty/kp_\infty)} = \frac{(p/p_\infty) - 1}{\frac{1}{2}kM_\infty^2} \qquad (9\text{-}92)$$

To express $C_p$ in terms of the perturbation velocity components, we first write the energy equation for the isentropic flow of a perfect gas as

$$c_p T_\infty + \frac{V_\infty^2}{2} = c_p T + \frac{V^2}{2}$$

from which

$$T_\infty - T = \frac{V^2 - V_\infty^2}{2c_p} = \frac{(V_\infty + u_p)^2 + v_p^2 - V_\infty^2}{2c_p}$$

$$= \frac{2V_\infty u_p + u_p^2 + v_p^2}{2c_p}$$

Dividing this equation through by $T_\infty$, replacing $c_p$ by $kR/(k-1)$, and rearranging terms, we obtain

$$\frac{T}{T_\infty} = 1 - \frac{k-1}{2} \frac{2V_\infty u_p + u_p^2 + v_p^2}{kRT_\infty}$$

or, after employing the relations: $a_\infty^2 = kRT_\infty$ and $M_\infty = V_\infty/a_\infty$,

$$\frac{T}{T_\infty} = 1 - \frac{k-1}{2} M_\infty^2 \left(2\frac{u_p}{V_\infty} + \frac{u_p^2 + v_p^2}{V_\infty^2}\right)$$

Then the isentropic relation enables us to write

$$\frac{p}{p_\infty} = \left(\frac{T}{T_\infty}\right)^{k/(k-1)} = \left[1 - \frac{k-1}{2} M_\infty^2 \left(2\frac{u_p}{V_\infty} + \frac{u_p^2 + v_p^2}{V_\infty^2}\right)\right]^{k/(k-1)}$$

which is substituted into Equation 9-92 to yield

$$C_p = \frac{2}{kM_\infty^2} \left\{\left[1 - \frac{k-1}{2} M_\infty^2 \left(2\frac{u_p}{V_\infty} + \frac{u_p^2 + v_p^2}{V_\infty^2}\right)\right]^{k/(k-1)} - 1\right\}$$

In small perturbation flow, the second term inside the square brackets is less than unity and so the bracketed terms may be expanded into a binomial series. By retaining the first few terms of the series and simplifying the resulting expression, we obtain

$$C_p = -\left[\frac{2u_p}{V_\infty} + (1 - M_\infty^2)\frac{u_p^2}{V_\infty^2} + \frac{v_p^2}{V_\infty^2}\right] \qquad (9\text{--}93)$$

The final expression for $C_p$ of the linearized theory is simply

$$C_p = -\frac{2u_p}{V_\infty} \qquad (9\text{--}94)$$

From the foregiong development, it is obvious that Eq. 9-94 should not be applied to flows within the hypersonic and transonic ranges.

### 9-15  Boundary Conditions

For a flow past a submerged body, one of the boundary conditions can be formulated at the surface of the submerged body. Since the compressible flow is irrotational, the boundary of a submerged body forms one of the streamlines in the flow field. Hence, at the surface of a submerged body, the direction of the flow must be tangential to the solid surface. That is,

$$\left(\frac{dy}{dx}\right)_b = \frac{v}{u} = \frac{v_p}{V_\infty + u_p} \qquad (9\text{--}95)$$

where $(dy/dx)_b$ is the slope of the boundary surface, and $v_p/(V_\infty + u_p)$ is the slope of the streamline at the boundary. We have used the subscript $b$ to denote conditions at the boundary. In a small perturbation flow field,

$u_p \ll V_\infty$, and Eq. 9-95 can be simplified to become

$$v_p = V_\infty \left(\frac{dy}{dx}\right)_b \qquad (9\text{-}96)$$

Therefore, in solving any compressible flow problem, we shall determine a velocity field such that, when the coordinates $(x_b, y_b)$ of a point on the surface of the submerged body are substituted into $v_p(x, y)$, the resulting $v_p$ should be equal to the product of $V_\infty$ and the slope of the surface at the same point $(x_b, y_b)$.

We can further simplify Eq. 9-96 by noting that the assumptions of small perturbation flow require the submerged body to be thin. Now, if the body lies on the x-axis, the coordinate $y_b$ must be very small and, at any point $(x_b, y_b)$ on the boundary, $v_p$ may be expressed as a Taylor series in powers of $y_b$. That is,

$$v_p(x, y) = v_p(x, 0) + \left(\frac{\partial v_p}{\partial y}\right)_{(x, 0)} y_b + \cdots$$

Clearly, we may neglect all terms involving $y_b$ because $y_b$ is small. Thus, for thin profiles, $v_p(x, y) = v_p(x, 0)$, and the boundary condition at the surface then becomes

$$v_p(x, 0) = V_\infty \left(\frac{dy}{dx}\right)_b \qquad (9\text{-}97)$$

The other boundary condition is to be found at infinity. Depending on the nature of the particular problem involved, we may specify the perturbation velocities at infinity to be either finite or zero.

We shall use these boundary conditions in subsequent calculations for two-dimensional compressible flow past a wave-shaped wall.

## 9-16 Two-dimensional Flow With a Wave-shaped Wall

We now demonstrate the application of the linearized small-perturbation theory to a simple example involving a two-dimensional flow past a wave-shaped wall. In subsequent sections, we shall solve this boundary-value problem for a subsonic and a supersonic flow, respectively. The solutions will be worked out in detail in order to show the significant differences between characteristics of subsonic and supersonic two-dimensional flows.

Figure 9-19 shows a wave-shaped wall in a uniform stream with $V_\infty$. The equation for this boundary is given by the following sinusoidal function:

$$y_b = \epsilon \sin \frac{2\pi}{\lambda} x \qquad (9\text{-}98)$$

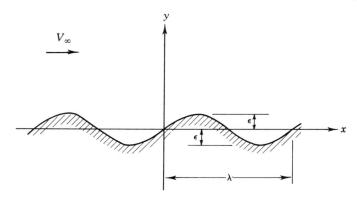

**Fig. 9-19.** A wave-shaped wall in a uniform stream.

where $\epsilon$ is the amplitude of the wavy boundary and $\lambda$ is the wavelength. Note that the use of the linearized small-perturbation theory requires that $\epsilon/\lambda \ll 1$.

For both subsonic and supersonic flows, the perturbation flow field is determined by solving for $\phi_p$ from the linear partial differential equation

$$(1 - M_\infty^2)\frac{\partial^2 \phi_p}{\partial x^2} + \frac{\partial^2 \phi_p}{\partial y^2} = 0 \tag{9–99}$$

subject to the following two boundary conditions:

1. At the wall:

$$v_p(x, 0) = \left(\frac{\partial \phi_p}{\partial y}\right)_{(x,0)} = V_\infty \left(\frac{dy}{dx}\right)_b = V_\infty \epsilon \frac{2\pi}{\lambda} \cos \frac{2\pi}{\lambda} x \tag{9–100}$$

2. At infinity:

$$u_p = \frac{\partial \phi_p}{\partial x} = \text{some finite value or zero}$$

$$v_p = \frac{\partial \phi_p}{\partial y} = \text{some finite value or zero}$$

Subsonic and supersonic flows will be treated separately in the following two sections.

### 9-17   Two-dimensional Subsonic Flow With a Wave-shaped Wall

For subsonic flow, $M_\infty < 1$ and $1 - M_\infty^2$ is positive. If we let $1 - M_\infty^2 = \beta^2$, we may write Eq. 9-99 as

$$\frac{\partial^2 \phi_p}{\partial x^2} + \frac{1}{\beta^2}\frac{\partial^2 \phi_p}{\partial y^2} = 0 \tag{9–101}$$

which is an elliptic-type partial differential equation. We now employ the method of separation of variables to solve for $\phi_p$ in this equation. In this method, $\phi_p$ is considered to be the product of functions of independent variables. That is,

$$\phi_p(x, y) = [X(x)][Y(y)] \qquad (9\text{–}102)$$

where $X$ and $Y$ are functions of $x$ and $y$, respectively. Substituting this value of $\phi_p$ into Eq. 9-101, dividing the resulting expression by $XY$, and rearranging terms, we obtain

$$\frac{1}{X}\frac{\partial^2 X}{\partial x^2} = -\frac{1}{\beta^2}\frac{1}{Y}\frac{\partial^2 Y}{\partial y^2} \qquad (9\text{–}103)$$

Here the left-hand side is a function of $x$ only and the right-hand side of $y$ only. If the equality of the two sides is to be maintained for all values of $x$ and $y$, each side must be equal to a common constant, say $-k^2$. We choose $-k^2$ as the constant so that we may replace Eq. 9-103 with the following two ordinary differential equations:

$$\frac{d^2 X}{dx^2} + k^2 X = 0 \qquad (9\text{–}104)$$

$$\frac{d^2 Y}{dy^2} - \beta^2 k^2 Y = 0 \qquad (9\text{–}105)$$

Equations similar to these are frequently encountered in the formulation of mechanical and electrical problems, and their solutions are well known. The solutions for these two equations are

$$X = A_1 \cos kx + A_2 \sin kx \qquad (9\text{–}106)$$

and

$$Y = B_1 e^{\beta ky} + B_2 e^{-\beta ky} \qquad (9\text{–}107)$$

where the constants of integration $A_1$, $A_2$, $B_1$, and $B_2$ are to be determined from the boundary conditions of the problem. Therefore,

$$\phi_p = (A_1 \cos kx + A_2 \sin kx)(B_1 e^{\beta ky} + B_2 e^{-\beta ky}) \qquad (9\text{–}108)$$

is the general solution of Eq. 9-101.

We now consider the boundary conditions in order to determine the constants. The boundary condition that the first derivatives of $\phi_p$ must be finite at infinity requires that $B_1 = 0$. The boundary condition at the wall is, from Eq. 9-100,

$$\left(\frac{\partial \phi_p}{\partial y}\right)_{(x,0)} = (A_1 \cos kx + A_2 \sin kx)B_2(-\beta k)$$

$$= V_\infty \epsilon \frac{2\pi}{\lambda} \cos \frac{2\pi}{\lambda} x \qquad (9\text{–}109)$$

By comparing the terms on both sides of the equation, we see that

$$A_2 = 0$$

$$-A_1 B_2 \beta k = V_\infty \epsilon \frac{2\pi}{\lambda}$$

$$k = \frac{2\pi}{\lambda}$$

Combining the last two expressions and remembering that $\beta^2 = 1 - M_\infty^2$, we may write

$$A_1 B_2 = -\frac{V_\infty \epsilon}{\sqrt{1 - M_\infty^2}}$$

Hence Eq. 9-108 becomes

$$\phi_p = -\frac{V_\infty \epsilon}{\sqrt{1 - M_\infty^2}} e^{-2\pi\sqrt{1-M_\infty^2}\,y/\lambda} \cos \frac{2\pi}{\lambda} x \qquad (9\text{–}110)$$

This is the perturbation velocity potential for this flow. By difinition, the perturbation velocity field is given by $\nabla\phi_p$, and so the total velocity field is then

$$\mathbf{V} = V_\infty \mathbf{i} + \nabla\left(-\frac{V_\infty \epsilon}{\sqrt{1 - M_\infty^2}} e^{-2\pi\sqrt{1-M_\infty^2}\,y/\lambda} \cos \frac{2\pi}{\lambda} x\right) \qquad (9\text{–}111)$$

or

$$\mathbf{V} = \left(V_\infty + \frac{2\pi V_\infty \epsilon}{\lambda\sqrt{1 - M_\infty^2}} e^{-2\pi\sqrt{1-M_\infty^2}\,y/\lambda} \sin \frac{2\pi}{\lambda} x\right)\mathbf{i}$$
$$+ \frac{2\pi V_\infty \epsilon}{\lambda} e^{-2\pi\sqrt{1-M_\infty^2}\,y/\lambda} \cos \frac{2\pi}{\lambda} x\mathbf{j} \qquad (9\text{–}112)$$

The streamlines for this flow are shown in Fig. 9-20(a).

The pressure distribution in the flow field can be determined by Eqs. 9-94 and 9-110. Thus

$$C_p = -\frac{2u_p}{V_\infty} = -2\frac{\partial\phi_p/\partial x}{V_\infty}$$
$$= -\frac{4\pi\epsilon}{\lambda\sqrt{1 - M_\infty^2}} e^{-2\pi\sqrt{1-M_\infty^2}\,y/\lambda} \sin \frac{2\pi}{\lambda} x \qquad (9\text{–}113)$$

At the wall, $y_b$ is approximately equal to zero, and the pressure coefficient becomes

$$C_{pb} = -\frac{4\pi\epsilon}{\lambda\sqrt{1 - M_\infty^2}} \sin \frac{2\pi}{\lambda} x_b \qquad (9\text{–}114)$$

indicating that on the wave-shaped wall the pressure is a minimum at the highest points of the crests and is a maximum at the lowest points of the troughs. The pressure variation along the wall, as shown in Fig. 9-20(b), is one-half wave length out of phase with the wave shape of the wall.

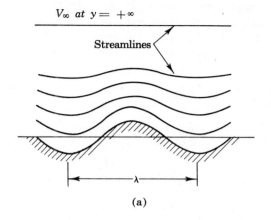

$V_\infty$ at $y = +\infty$

Streamlines

λ

(a)

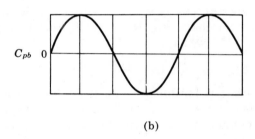

$C_{pb}$    0

(b)

**Fig. 9-20.** Uniform subsonic flow past a wave-shaped wall. (a) Streamlines; (b) pressure variation along the wall.

## 9-18  Two-dimensional Supersonic Flow With a Wave-shaped Wall

For supersonic flow, $M_\infty > 0$ and $1 - M_\infty^2$ becomes negative. Equation 9-99 is then written as

$$\frac{\partial^2 \phi_p}{\partial x^2} - \frac{1}{M_\infty^2 - 1} \frac{\partial^2 \phi_p}{\partial y^2} = 0 \qquad (9\text{–}115)$$

which is a hyperbolic-type partial differential equation. This equation is in the form of a simple wave equation. Hence the general solution to this equation is given by

$$\phi_p(x, y) = \phi_1(x - \sqrt{M_\infty^2 - 1}\,y) + \phi_2(x + \sqrt{M_\infty^2 - 1}\,y) \qquad (9\text{–}116)$$

where $\phi_1$ is an arbitrary function of the argument $(x - \sqrt{M_\infty^2 - 1}\,y)$

and $\phi_2$ is an arbitrary function of the argument $(x + \sqrt{M_\infty^2 - 1}\,y)$.

To demonstrate that the above value of $\phi_p$ is indeed the solution to Eq. 9-115, we need to prove by direct substitution that the particular solutions $\phi_1$ and $\phi_2$ satisfy Eq. 9-115. Let us consider the particular solution $\phi_1$. The derivatives[4] of $\phi_1(x - \sqrt{M_\infty^2 - 1}\,y)$ are

$$\frac{\partial \phi_1}{\partial x} = \frac{\partial \phi_1}{\partial(x - \sqrt{M_\infty^2 - 1}\,y)} \frac{\partial(x - \sqrt{M_\infty^2 - 1}\,y)}{\partial x} = \phi_1' \quad \textbf{(9–117)}$$

$$\frac{\partial^2 \phi_1}{\partial x^2} = \frac{\partial \phi_1'}{\partial(x - \sqrt{M_\infty^2 - 1}\,y)} \frac{\partial(x - \sqrt{M_\infty^2 - 1}\,y)}{\partial x} = \phi_1'' \quad \textbf{(9–118)}$$

$$\frac{\partial \phi_1}{\partial y} = \frac{\partial \phi_1}{\partial(x - \sqrt{M_\infty^2 - 1}\,y)} \frac{\partial(x - \sqrt{M_\infty^2 - 1}\,y)}{\partial y} = -\sqrt{M_\infty^2 - 1}\,\phi_1'$$

$$\textbf{(9–119)}$$

$$\frac{\partial^2 \phi_1}{\partial y^2} = \frac{\partial(-\sqrt{M_\infty^2 - 1}\,\phi_1')}{\partial(x - \sqrt{M_\infty^2 - 1}\,y)} \frac{\partial(x - \sqrt{M_\infty^2 - 1}\,y)}{\partial y} = (-\sqrt{M_\infty^2 - 1})^2 \phi_1''$$

$$\textbf{(9–120)}$$

where $\phi_1'$ and $\phi_1''$ are respectively the first and second derivatives of $\phi_1$ with respect to its argument $(x - \sqrt{M_\infty^2 - 1}\,y)$. By substituting Eqs. 9-118 and 9-120 into Eq. 9-115, we have

$$\phi_1'' - \frac{1}{M_\infty^2 - 1}(-\sqrt{M_\infty^2 - 1})^2 \phi_1'' = 0$$

showing that the arbitrary function $\phi_1$ satisfies Eq. 9-115. Therefore, $\phi_1$ is a particular solution. In a similar manner, we may demonstrate that $\phi_2$ is also a particular solution. Hence the sum of $\phi_1$ and $\phi_2$ becomes the general solution to Eq. 9-115.

The next step is to find the particular forms of $\phi_1$ and $\phi_2$ from the boundary conditions of the given problem. However, before we do so, we shall investigate the physical characteristics of a supersonic flow with small perturbations in which either $\phi_1$ or $\phi_2$ is constant throughout the flow field. The results of such an investigation will be useful in finding solutions for problems involving given boundary conditions.

Let us consider, for example, the flow field in which $\phi_1 = $ constant. The $\phi_1$-lines in such a flow are represented by the equation

$$x - \sqrt{M_\infty^2 - 1}\,y = \text{constant}$$

---

[4] We will recall from calculus that if $\phi = \phi(F)$ and, in turn, $F = F(x, y)$, we may write

$$d\phi = \frac{\partial \phi}{\partial F} dF = \frac{\partial \phi}{\partial F}\left(\frac{\partial F}{\partial x} dx + \frac{\partial F}{\partial y} dy\right)$$

so that

$$\frac{\partial \phi}{\partial x} = \frac{\partial \phi}{\partial F}\frac{\partial F}{\partial x} = \phi'\frac{\partial F}{\partial x}$$

where $\phi'$ is the derivative of $\phi$ with respect to its argument $F$.

for if the argument of $\phi_1$ is constant, $\phi_1$ must also be constant. Clearly
the $\phi_1$-lines are a family of parallel lines with a slope

$$\frac{dy}{dx} = \frac{1}{\sqrt{M_\infty^2 - 1}}$$

as shown in Fig. 9-21. The angle $\alpha$ which the $\phi_1$-lines make with respect

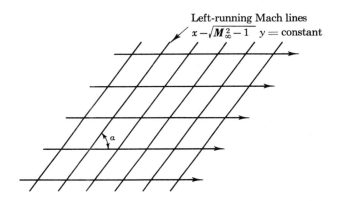

**Fig. 9-21.** Supersonic flow with only left-running Mach lines present.

to the undisturbed flow corresponds to the Mach angle in a two-dimensional supersonic flow (Sec. 9-3), since from the definition of Mach angle
(Eq. 9-22)

$$\sin \alpha = \frac{1}{M} \quad \text{and} \quad \tan \alpha = \frac{1}{\sqrt{M^2 - 1}}$$

Thus, the $\phi_1$-lines are identified with the left-running Mach lines in a

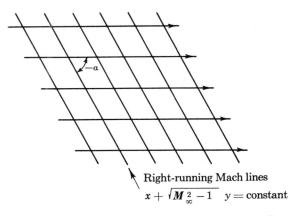

**Fig. 9-22.** Supersonic flow with only right-running Mach lines present.

supersonic flow. In a similar manner, we may establish that, in a super-sonic flow with $\phi_2 =$ constant, $\phi_2$-lines can be identified with the right-running Mach lines, as shown in Fig. 9-22. The existence of these $\phi$-lines is independent of the specific boundary conditions since they are already contained in the general solution in Eq. 9-116. It can be shown[5] that along a Mach line all streamlines have the same slope, as illustrated in the case of a supersonic flow moving over a surface with a small bump in Fig. 9-23.

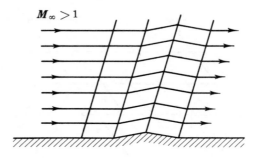

$M_\infty > 1$

**Fig. 9-23.** A supersonic flow moving over a surface with a small bump.

Now, if a thin body interacts with a supersonic flow, we may imagine each segment of the boundary as disturbing the flow adjacent to it. Mach lines can be considered to originate from the boundary. As was pointed out in Sec. 9-3, a disturbance in a supersonic flow is propagated along a Mach line inclined at an angle $\alpha$ with respect to the direction of motion. Since the vertex angle of the Mach wedge must be less than $\pi$, the Mach lines above a boundary are left-running and those below are right-running as shown in Fig. 9-24.

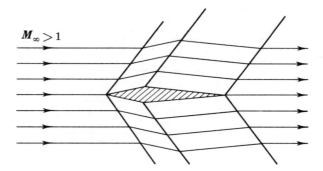

$M_\infty > 1$

**Fig. 9-24.** A supersonic flow past a thin body.

---

[5]A. H. Shapiro, *op. cit.*, pp. 429–434.

We now return to our problem in which the supersonic flow occurs above a wave-shaped wall. For the reasons stated above, we have only the left-running Mach lines in this flow. Therefore, in considering the solution for this problem, the function $\phi_2$ may be set equal to zero, and the form of the function $\phi_1$ can then be determined from the boundary conditions of the problem.

The boundary condition at the wall is given by Eq. 9-100. Thus,

$$\left(\frac{\partial \phi_p}{\partial y}\right)_{(x,0)} = -\sqrt{M_\infty^2 - 1}\,(\phi_1')_{y=0} = V_\infty \left(\frac{dy}{dx}\right)_b$$
$$= V_\infty \epsilon \frac{2\pi}{\lambda} \cos \frac{2\pi}{\lambda} x \tag{9-121}$$

where $(\phi_1')_{y=0}$ denotes the derivative of $\phi_1$ with respect to its argument, the derivative being evaluated at $(x,0)$. Hence the value of $\phi_1'$ at any point $(x,y)$ in the flow field must be

$$\phi_1' = \frac{-2\pi V_\infty \epsilon}{\lambda\sqrt{M_\infty^2 - 1}} \cos\left[\frac{2\pi}{\lambda}(x - \sqrt{M_\infty^2 - 1}\,y)\right]$$

Integration of this equation then yields

$$\phi_1 = \phi_p = -\frac{V_\infty \epsilon}{\sqrt{M_\infty^2 - 1}} \sin\left[\frac{2\pi}{\lambda}(x - \sqrt{M_\infty^2 - 1}\,y)\right] \tag{9-122}$$

in which the constant of integration has been omitted. Note that the first derivatives of $\phi_p$ with respect to $x$ and $y$ are finite at infinity. Thus, all boundary conditions of the problem are satisfied by Eq. 9-122.

The total velocity field for this flow is then

$$\mathbf{V} = V_\infty \mathbf{i} + \nabla \phi_p$$
$$= V_\infty \mathbf{i} + \nabla\left\{-\frac{V_\infty \epsilon}{\sqrt{M_\infty^2 - 1}} \sin\left[\frac{2\pi}{\lambda}(x - \sqrt{M_\infty^2 - 1}\,y)\right]\right\} \tag{9-123}$$

Here the perturbation velocity does not have an exponential attenuation factor like that for the subsonic flow, and hence the perturbation velocity in a supersonic flow does not diminish with respect to the distance from the wall. Figure 9-25(a) shows the streamlines for this flow.

The pressure distribution in the flow field is given by Eqs. 9-94 and 9-122. Thus,

$$C_p = -\frac{2u_p}{V_\infty} = -2\frac{\partial \phi_p/\partial x}{V_\infty}$$
$$= \frac{4\pi\epsilon}{\lambda\sqrt{M_\infty^2 - 1}} \cos\left[\frac{2\pi}{\lambda}(x - \sqrt{M_\infty^2 - 1}\,y)\right] \tag{9-124}$$

At the wall, $y_b$ is approximately equal to zero, and the pressure coefficient becomes

$$C_{pb} = \frac{4\pi\epsilon}{\lambda\sqrt{M_\infty^2 - 1}} \cos \frac{2\pi}{\lambda} x_b \tag{9-125}$$

which indicates that the points of the maximum and minimum pressures

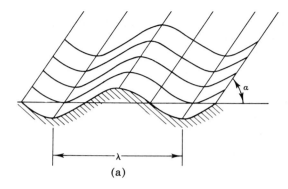

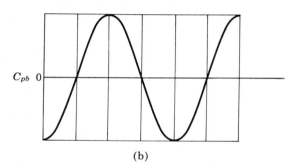

**Fig. 9-25.** Uniform supersonic flow past a wave-shaped wall. (a) Stream-lines; (b) pressure variation along the wall.

at the wall are now shifted by the phase $\pi/2$ from the highest points of the crests and the lowest points of the troughs of the wave-shaped surface, as shown in Fig. 9-25(b).

A careful comparison of the subsonic and supersonic flows will reveal the vast differences in the characteristics of the two flows. Indeed the experience which we have gained in dealing with subsonic flow problems does not help in the understanding of supersonic flow. It is only through careful analytical study of some supersonic flow problems that we are now able to explain strange and unexpected phenomena which are encountered in supersonic flows.

## PROBLEMS

**9–1.** Derive the isentropic equation $pv^k = C$ for a perfect gas.

**9–2.** Starting with $pv^k = C$, derive the isentropic equations relating (a) $p$ and $T$, and (b) $T$ and $\rho$.

**9–3.** In a perfect gas undergoing isothermal changes, show that the speed of sound becomes

$$a_{\text{isothermal}} = \sqrt{RT}$$

**9–4.** In a liquid with a bulk modulus $E$ and a density $\rho$, show that the speed of sound is

$$a_{\text{liquid}} = \sqrt{E/\rho}$$

**9–5.** A jet airplane is flying at a speed corresponding to $M = 0.8$ at an altitude of 30,000 ft in standard atmosphere. What would be its ground speed if the air is stationary with respect to the ground?

**9–6.** A source of acoustic wave moving in the atmosphere forms a Mach angle of 30 degrees. What is the velocity of the source, in ft/sec? Assume standard atmosphere at the sea level.

**9–7.** The compressed air in a large reservoir is kept at a constant pressure of 120 lbf/in.² abs. and a constant temperature of 60°F. This reservoir is connected to a tank through a convergent-divergent nozzle with a throat area of 4 in.² and an exit area of 16 in.². The pressure in the receiving tank can be adjusted to any value. Assuming isentropic flow, calculate (a) the maximum rate of mass flow of air, in lbm/sec, through the nozzle, (b) the two values of pressure in the receiving tank for which this maximum rate of mass flow occurs, and (c) the values of the Mach number of flow at the nozzle exit corresponding to these two values of pressure.

**9–8.** Air is drawn from the atmosphere ($p = 14.7$ lbf/in.² abs. and $T = 70°F$) into a large vacuum tank through a variable-area duct. At a section of the duct where the cross sectional area is 3 ft², the static pressure is 3.0 lbf/in.² abs. Assuming isentropic flow of a perfect gas, calculate (a) the Mach number at this section, and (b) the rate of mass flow of air, in lbm/sec, through the duct.

**9–9.** A rocket engine is designed to develop a thrust of 50,000 lbf at the sea level ($p = 14.7$ lbf/in.² abs. and $T = 75°F$). The flow of the combustion gases through the exhaust nozzle can be regarded as an isentropic flow of a perfect gas with $k = 1.2$. If the combustion chamber pressure and temperature are respectively 500 lbf/in.² abs. and 6000°R, calculate (a) the Mach number of flow at the nozzle exit and (b) the cross sectional areas of the nozzle exit and the nozzle throat.

**9–10.** Air enters a 60-degree pipe bend at a pressure of 30 lbf/in.² abs., a temperature of 70°F, and a velocity of 300 ft/sec. The area at the entrance is 5.0 ft². The air leaves the pipe bend at the atmospheric pressure of 14.7 lbf/in.² abs. through an exit with an area of 4.0 ft². Assuming isentropic flow, calculate the resultant force on the pipe bend.

**9–11.** A subsonic air flow with a pressure $p$, density $\rho$, velocity $V$, and Mach number $M$ is brought to a stagnation state isentropically. Show that the stagnation pressure $p_s$ is given approximately by

$$p_s = p + \tfrac{1}{2}\rho V^2(1 + \tfrac{1}{4}M^2)$$

**9–12.** The speed of sound at $M = 1$ is denoted by $a^*$ and is called the critical speed of sound. Show that $a^*$ is related to the stagnation temperature $T_0$ by the following equation:

$$a^{*2} = \frac{2}{k+1} kRT_0$$

**9–13.** If $T_0$ is the temperature of a perfect gas in a reservoir, show that the maximum velocity $V_{max}$ that can be attained in the flow of perfect gas from this reservoir is given by the following equation:

$$V^2_{max} = \frac{2}{k-1} kRT_0$$

**9–14.** Show that the sonic conditions exist at the point of maximum entropy on the Fanno line.

**9–15.** Show that the sonic conditions exist at the point of maximum entropy on the Rayleigh line.

**9–16.** Air initially at rest at a pressure of 14.7 lbf/in.² abs. and a temperature of 70°F is accelerated isentropically to a Mach number of 3.0. It then passes through a stationary normal shock. Downstream from the shock, the air flow is decelerated isentropically to a stagnation state. Find (a) the conditions immediately downstream from the shock and (b) the final stagnation pressure and stagnation temperature. Explain why the final stagnation pressure and stagnation temperature are different from the initial values.

**9–17.** A supersonic air flow with a velocity of 3500 ft/sec and a temperature of 32°F passes through a stationary normal shock. Downstream from the shock, the air flow is accelerated isentropically to a final state at which the pressure is exactly the same as that immediately upstream from the shock. Calculate the velocity and temperature of the air flow at the final state. Explain why the final values of the velocity and temperature are different from the initial values.

**9–18.** A pitot tube is placed in a supersonic stream as shown in Fig. 9–26.

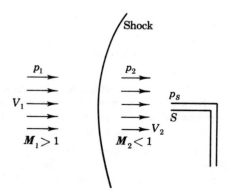

**Fig. 9-26.**

Assuming isentropic flow of a perfect gas, show that the stagnation pressure at the tip of the Pitot tube is

$$p_s = p_1 \left[ \frac{\left(\frac{k+1}{2} M_1^2\right)^k}{\frac{2kM_1^2 - (k-1)}{k+1}} \right]^{1/(k-1)}$$

**9-19.** A supersonic air flow at $M = 3.0$ approaches an oblique shock at an angle $\beta = 60°$ (see Figure 9-15). Calculate the final Mach number of flow immediately downstream from the shock when the temperature upstream from the shock is 30°F.

**9-20.** Show that, in the flow of a perfect gas through an oblique shock with an angle $\beta$ (see Figure 9-15), the ratio of the pressure after the shock to the pressure before the shock is

$$\frac{p_2}{p_1} = \frac{2k}{k+1} M_1^2 \sin^2 \beta - \frac{k-1}{k+1}$$

**9-21.** The Mach numbers of an air flow before and after an oblique shock are respectively 3.5 and 1.5. The initial temperature is 20°F. Calculate the angle $\beta$ between the approaching stream and the shock. (See Figure 9-15).

**9-22.** A supersonic air stream flows along a horizontal wall at a Mach number of 3.0 and a pressure of 5 lbf/in.² abs. and encounters a concave corner as shown in Fig. 9-27. Calculate (a) the Mach number and the pressure of the air stream after the corner and (b) the angle $\theta$ of the oblique shock.

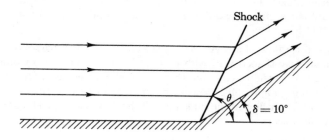

Shock

$\theta$

$\delta = 10°$

**Fig. 9-27.**

**9-23.** For a compressible flow of a perfect gas in a constant-area duct with boundary-layer friction but with no heat transfer, show that the following equation accounts for the friction loss along the duct between section 1 and section 2:

$$\frac{fL}{8R_h} = \frac{1}{2k} \left(\frac{1}{M_1^2} - \frac{1}{M_2^2}\right) + \frac{k+1}{4k} \ln \frac{M_2^2 \left(1 + \frac{k-1}{2} M_1^2\right)}{M_1^2 \left(1 + \frac{k-1}{2} M_2^2\right)}$$

where $f$ is the average friction factor for the flow in the duct;
$R_h$ is the hydraulic radius of the duct;

$M_1$ is the Mach number of flow at section 1;

$M_2$ is the Mach number of flow at section 2.

Section 2 is at a distance $L$ downstream from section 1.

9–24. For a compressible flow of a perfect gas in a constant-area duct with heat transfer but with no boundary-layer friction, show that the ratio of pressures at sections 1 and 2 along the duct is

$$\frac{p_2}{p_1} = \frac{1 + kM_1^2}{1 + kM_2^2}$$

where $M_1$ is the Mach number of flow at section 1;

$M_2$ is the Mach number of flow at section 2.

Section 2 is at a distance $L$ downstream from section 1.

9–25. For an isothermal compressible flow of a perfect gas in a constant-area duct with boundary-layer friction and heat transfer, show that the following equation accounts for the friction loss along the duct between section 1 and section 2:

$$\frac{fL}{8R_h} = \ln\frac{M_1}{M_2} + \frac{1}{2kM_1^2}\left[1 - \left(\frac{M_1}{M_2}\right)^2\right]$$

where $f$ is the average friction factor for the flow in the duct;

$R_h$ is the hydraulic radius of the duct;

$M_1$ is the Mach number of flow at section 1;

$M_2$ is the Mach number of flow at section 2.

Section 2 is at a distance $L$ downstream from section 1.

9–26. Derive a partial differential equation for the velocity potential $\phi$, in polar coordinates, for a two-dimensional, isentropic, irrotational flow of a compressible fluid.

9–27. A uniform flow of air with $M_\infty = 0.5$ and $T_\infty = 70°F$ passes over a sinusoidal wave-shaped wall with $\epsilon = 0.2$ ft and $\lambda = 4$ ft. (a) Compute the velocity of air flow at a point which is 2 ft above the crest of the boundary, assuming compressible flow with small perturbation. (b) Compute the velocity of air flow at the same point if the flow is assumed incompressible and nonviscous.

9–28. Work Problem 9–27 for $M_\infty = 0.8$.

9–29. Work Part (a) of Problem 9–27 for $M_\infty = 2.5$.

# 10     Magnetofluidmechanics

## 10-1   Introduction

Magnetofluidmechanics is the study of the flow of an electrically conducting fluid in the presence of an electromagnetic field. An electrically conducting fluid may be a liquid, such as mercury, or an ionized gas. Ionized gases are often called *plasmas*. Thus, physicists commonly use the name *plasma physics* for the study of plasma phenomena. In this book we shall adopt the more general name *magnetofluidmechanics*. The names *magnetohydrodynamics* and *magnetogasdynamics* then refer to flows of incompressible and compressible electrically conducting fluids, respectively.

Although the mathematical formulation of magnetofluidmechanics is based on the equations of classical fluid mechanics and electromagnetism, no serious studies in this field were made by engineers unitl relatively recent times. This is because the strength of the coupling between the electromagnetic field and the fluid flow field is extremely small for ordinary flow phenomena involving fluids of small electrical conductivity, such as air at ordinary temperatures. However, studies of the phenomena encountered in magnetofluidmechanics have been made for many years in connection with astrophysical and geophysical problems, such as the origin of the magnetic fields of celestial bodies, heating of the solar corona, theory of magnetic storms, sun-spot theory, etc. Only recently the phenomena of the flow of electrically conducting fluids in electromagnetic fields have found numerous possibilities of application in engineering devices and processes. Some of the most important applications are listed as follows.

1. *Harnessing fusion energy*. The control of thermonuclear reaction is a central problem in the design of a nuclear-fusion device for power generation. Fusion reaction takes place only at extremely high temperatures. The ignition temperature is in the order of several hundred million degrees Kelvin, at which the gas is in the plasma state. In fusion research, electromagnetic field is employed to heat the cold plasmas to the temperature above the ignition temperature. The hot plasmas are then magnetically pinched by the current in the plasmas, as shown in Fig. 10-1.

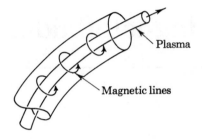

**Fig. 10-1.** A magnetically confined plasma.

The induced magnetic field encircles the current and exerts an inward force on plasma particles to keep them from touching the material container. Thus the encircling magnetic field serves as a magnetic container for the hot plasmas. Unfortunately, a pinched column of plasmas has been shown to be unstable.[1] The stability of the flow of plasmas in a magnetic field is important for successful fusion reaction.

2. *Power generation*. In a magnetogasdynamic power generator, electricity is generated by a linearly accelerated stream of plasmas, as shown in Fig. 10-2. Because there is no rotating armature in such a generator and because of the high temperature involved in the plasmas, the efficiency of a magnetogasdynamic generator is superior to other conventional types of power generating devices.

3. *Plasma propulsion*. Plasma propulsion unit has been suggested for vehicles traveling in space. In a plasma propulsion device (Fig. 10-3), electrical energy is used to generate hot plasmas which are then acceler-

───────────

[1]M. Kruskal and M. Schwarzschild, "Some Instabilities of a Completely Ionized Plasma," *Proc. Roy. Soc.* (London), Vol. A223 (1954), 348.

ated in a suitable nozzle with externally applied magnetic field to produce additional thrust.

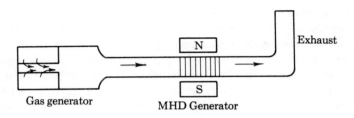

**Fig. 10-2.**  Schematic diagram of a magnetogasdynamic power generator.

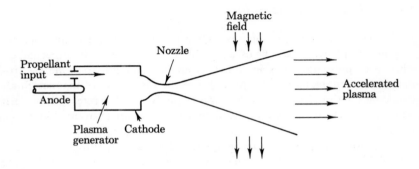

**Fig. 10-3.**  Schematic diagram of a plasma propulsion device.

4. *Reentry problems of missiles and space ships.* Many problems are associated with the high speed of reentry of hypersonic vehicles into the atmosphere. For example, the effects of electromagnetic fields on the flow of ionized gases in boundary layers are very important. Magnetic field can be applied to modify the velocity and temperature gradients in the boundary layer flows of conducting gases. Furthermore, the high speed of reentry produces a plasma sheath in front of a homebound space ship. This plasma sheath causes considerable difficulty in transmitting signals for communication and guidance between the ground and the pilot.

5. *Flow control.* Special techniques are required to pump, control, and measure the flow of liquid metals. Because of the conducting properties of liquid metals, magnetohydrodynamic devices have been widely employed for such purposes. In biological research, magnetohydrodynamic flow meters may be used to measure the rate of flow of blood or other saline solutions in circulatory systems.

It should be pointed out here that most engineering applications of magnetofluidmechanics are still in their experimental stage. Their continual development and improvement will require extensive research efforts in this newly established science.

In addition to engineering applications, magnetofluidmechanics also offers us the opportunity of pursuing interdisciplinary studies in two branches of physical sciences—fluid mechanics and electromagnetism. Both of these disciplines share similar types of mathematical formalism. Individually they are well developed and cover great varieties of physical phenomena. Thus, the combination of these two disciplines will undoubtedly yield many new phenomena which are far beyond our imaginations today.

## 10-2   Electromagnetic Fields

We shall now present some pertinent information concerning electromagnetic fields which will be useful in the study of magnetofluidmechanics. This brief presentation is intended as an introduction to some electromagnetic phenomena which are useful in the discussion of magnetofluidmechanics in this chapter. The reader is strongly urged to refer to a modern textbook on electromagnetic field theory for a complete discussion of the subject.

We adopt the MKS or Giorgi system of units for writing electromagnetic field equations. In this system the meter is used as the unit of length; the kilogram, as the unit of mass; the second, as the unit of time. We shall adopt the coulomb as the basic unit for electromagnetic quantities.[2]

## 10-3   Electrostatic Field

**Coulomb's law.** Consider two point charges $Q_1$ and $Q_2$ separated by a distance $r$, as shown in Fig. 10-4. Coulomb's law states that the force $\mathbf{F}_{12}$ exerted by $Q_1$ on $Q_2$ is proportional to the product $Q_1Q_2$ and inversely proportional to the square of the distance $r$ separating $Q_1$ and $Q_2$, the force $\mathbf{F}_{12}$ being along the line joining $Q_1$ and $Q_2$. The mathematical expression of Coulomb's law is written as

$$\mathbf{F}_{12} = \frac{Q_1 Q_2}{4\pi\epsilon_0 r^2}\,\mathbf{r}_{12} = -\frac{Q_1 Q_2}{4\pi\epsilon_0}\,\nabla\left(\frac{1}{r}\right) \tag{10-1}$$

where $\mathbf{r}_{12}$ is a unit vector pointing in the direction from $Q_1$ to $Q_2$. In this

---

[2]The charge of an electron has been measured as $1.602 \times 10^{-19}$ coulomb and the mass as $9.107 \times 10^{-31}$ kg.

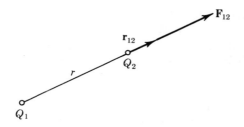

**Fig. 10-4.** Electrostatic force between two point charges.

equation $\mathbf{F}_{12}$ is measured in newtons; $Q_1$ and $Q_2$, in coulombs; and $r$, in meters. The constant $\epsilon_0$ is called the *permittivity of free space* and its numerical value is found to be $8.854 \times 10^{-12}$ farad/meter. A farad is equivalent to coulomb$^2$/(newton)(meter). Coulomb's law applies both to like charges and to unlike charges. The force is attractive if $Q_1$ and $Q_2$ are of different signs, and is repulsive if they are of the same sign.

**The electrostatic field intensity.** If we consider $Q_1$ fixed in position and move $Q_2$ slowly around, we will note that a force $\mathbf{F}_2$ is exerted on $Q_2$ at whatever position it may occupy. The ratio of $\mathbf{F}_2$ to $Q_2$ is called the *electric field intensity* $\mathbf{E}$. Thus,

$$\mathbf{E} = \frac{\mathbf{F}_2}{Q_2} = \frac{Q_1}{4\pi\epsilon_0 r^2} \mathbf{r}_{12} \qquad (10\text{--}2)$$

The electric field intensity is measured in volts/meter (or newtons/coulomb).

**The electrostatic potential.** It can be shown that the work done in transporting a unit charge between any two points in an electric field is independent of the path. An electrostatic field is therefore a conservative field. Thus the vector $\mathbf{E}$ can be obtained from a suitable electrostatic scalar potential $V_e$ such that

$$V_e = \frac{Q}{4\pi\epsilon_0 r} \qquad (10\text{--}3)$$

Then

$$\mathbf{E} = -\nabla V_e \qquad (10\text{--}4)$$

Taking the curl on both sides of this equation, we obtain

$$\nabla \times \mathbf{E} = \nabla \times (-\nabla V_e) = 0 \qquad (10\text{--}5)$$

since, from vector analysis, $\nabla \times \nabla V_e = 0$.

**The electric displacement vector D.** As a result of his experimental work, Faraday introduced the concept of electric displacement flux **D** in dielectric media. At some point in an isotropic dielectric medium, the electric displacement flux **D** is related to the electric field intensity **E** through the permittivity or dielectric constant $\epsilon$ of the medium. Thus,

$$\mathbf{D} = \epsilon\mathbf{E} \tag{10-6}$$

The electric displacement flux is measured in coulomb/meter². In an isotropic medium, $\epsilon$ is a scalar quantity and the vectors **D** and **E** are in the same direction. For an anisotropic medium, $\epsilon$ becomes a dyadic tensor quantity and the vectors **D** and **E** no longer parallel.

**Relation between $\epsilon$ and $\epsilon_0$.** Whenever an electric field is set up in a material medium, it is important to know whether the medium is a conductor or a dielectric. If a conductor is placed in an electric field, the outer electrons detach from the atoms and wander readily. On the other hand, when a dielectric is under the influence of an electric field, the electrons remain bound to the atoms although they are displaced with respect to their nuclei so that the atoms behave as atomic dipoles. Thus, the dielectric is said to be *polarized*. The polarization vector **P** of a dielectric is related to the other two electric field vectors in the following manner:

$$\mathbf{D} = \epsilon_0\mathbf{E} + \mathbf{P} \tag{10-7}$$

This equation, upon dividing by **E**, becomes

$$\epsilon = \epsilon_0 + \frac{\mathbf{P}}{\mathbf{E}} \tag{10-8}$$

since, by recalling Eq. 10-6, $\mathbf{D}/\mathbf{E} = \epsilon$.

**Gauss' law.** Gauss' law relates the flux of the electric field intensity vector **E** through a closed surface to the net charge $Q$ enclosed within that surface as follows:

$$\oiint_A \mathbf{E} \cdot d\mathbf{A} = \frac{Q}{\epsilon_0} \tag{10-9}$$

For dielectrics, $Q$ must include both free and polarization charges:

$$Q = \iiint_V (\rho_e + \rho_e')\, d V$$

where $\rho_e$ and $\rho_e'$ are respectively free and polarization charge densities which are measured in coulombs/meter³. Therefore, Eq. 10-9 becomes

$$\oiint_A \mathbf{E} \cdot d\mathbf{A} = \iiint_V \frac{\rho_e + \rho_e'}{\epsilon_0}\, d V \tag{10-9a}$$

Note that this equation is similar to the continuity equation for a fluid flow through an arbitrary control volume. Upon employing the divergence theorem to change the surface integral to a volume integral, we may rewrite Eq. 10-9a as

$$\iiint_V \nabla \cdot \mathbf{E} \, d V = \iiint_V \frac{\rho_e + \rho_e'}{\epsilon_0} \, d V \qquad (10\text{–}9b)$$

Since the volume is chosen arbitrarily, the integrands must equal to each other. That is,

$$\nabla \cdot \mathbf{E} = \frac{\rho_e + \rho_e'}{\epsilon_0} \qquad (10\text{–}10)$$

The polarization charge density $\rho_e'$ is related to the polarization vector $\mathbf{P}$ as

$$\rho_e' = -\nabla \cdot \mathbf{P} \qquad (10\text{–}11)$$

and so Eq. 10-10 may be written as

$$\nabla \cdot (\epsilon_0 \mathbf{E} + \mathbf{P}) = \rho_e \qquad (10\text{–}12)$$

This equation, upon substituting from Eq. 10-7, becomes

$$\nabla \cdot \mathbf{D} = \rho_e \qquad (10\text{–}13)$$

This is the differential form Gauss' law. It is applicable to any dielectric medium as well as to a vacuum. This equation is also the first of Maxwell's four fundamental equations of electromagnetism.

From a physical point of view, Eq. 10-13 states that the lines of force of $\mathbf{D}$ begin or end only on free charges, whereas Eq. 10-10 indicates that the lines of $\mathbf{E}$ begin or end on either free or polarized charges. Thus, the charges distributed with a density $\rho_e$ constitute the sources of the vector $\mathbf{D}$.

## 10-4   Magnetic Fields of Steady Current

**Magnetic forces.** It is common laboratory experience that two circuits carrying electric currents attract or repel each other. Consider two circuits carrying currents $I_1$ and $I_2$ as shown in Fig. 10-5. The force $\mathbf{F}_{12}$ exerted on $I_1$ by $I_2$ can be calculated by the magnetic force law:

$$\mathbf{F}_{12} = \frac{\mu_{e0}}{4\pi} I_1 I_2 \oint_1 \oint_2 \frac{d\mathbf{l}_1 \times (d\mathbf{l}_2 \times \mathbf{r}_{21})}{r^2} \qquad (10\text{–}14)$$

The line-element vectors $d\mathbf{l}_1$ and $d\mathbf{l}_2$ point in the directions of positive current flow; $r$ is the distance betweeen $d\mathbf{l}_1$ and $d\mathbf{l}_2$; and the unit vector $\mathbf{r}_{21}$ points from $d\mathbf{l}_2$ to $d\mathbf{l}_1$. The constant $\mu_{e0}$ is called the *magnetic permeability of free space* and has the defined value of $4\pi \times 10^{-7}$ henry/meter (or newton/ampere²).

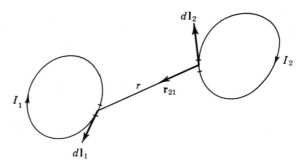

**Fig. 10-5.**  Two circuits carrying electric currents in the vicinity of each other.

**Biot-Savart law.** We may rewrite Eq. 10-14 as

$$\mathbf{F}_{12} = I_1 \oint_1 d\mathbf{l}_1 \times \left( \frac{\mu_{e0}}{4\pi} I_2 \oint_2 \frac{d\mathbf{l}_2 \times \mathbf{r}_{21}}{r^2} \right) \tag{10–14a}$$

to separate the interaction between the two circuits into a field produced by circuit 2 and a force on circuit 1, since

$$\frac{\mu_{e0}}{4\pi} I_1 \oint_2 \frac{d\mathbf{l}_2 \times \mathbf{r}_{21}}{r^2} = \mathbf{B}_2 \tag{10–15}$$

represents the magnetic field of induction of circuit 2 at $d\mathbf{l}_1$ of circuit 1. The vector $\mathbf{B}_2$ is called the *magnetic flux density*, which is measured in webers/meter$^2$, the weber being a volt-second. Equation 10-15 is called the *Biot-Savart law*.

**The Lorentz force.** If the current $I$ is distributed in space with a current density $\mathbf{J}$ amperes/meter$^2$, then $I$ becomes $\mathbf{J} \cdot d\mathbf{a}$, where $d\mathbf{a}$ is a differential area of the conducting medium. The quantity $(\mathbf{J} \cdot d\mathbf{a}) \, d\mathbf{l}$ may be written as $\mathbf{J} \, d\mathcal{V}$, where $d\mathcal{V}$ is a differential volume of the conducting medium. Therefore, in the general case, the magnetic flux density $\mathbf{B}$ at a point in space is given by

$$\mathbf{B} = \frac{\mu_{e0}}{4\pi} \int \int \int_{\mathcal{V}} \frac{\mathbf{J} \times \mathbf{r}}{r^2} \, d\mathcal{V} \tag{10–16}$$

and, by referring to Eq. 10-14a, we see that the force $d\mathbf{F}$ on a current element $I \, d\mathbf{l}$ (or $\mathbf{J} \, d\mathcal{V}$) becomes

$$d\mathbf{F} = I \, d\mathbf{l} \times \mathbf{B} = \mathbf{J} \, d\mathcal{V} \times \mathbf{B} \tag{10–17}$$

We now let

$$\mathbf{J} = nQ\mathbf{V} \tag{10–18}$$

where $n$ is the number of charge carriers per unit volume, $Q$ is the charge on each carrier, and $\mathbf{V}$ is the velocity of each carrier. Then Eq. 10-17 may be written as

$$\mathbf{f}_m = \frac{d\mathbf{F}}{n\,d\mathcal{V}} = Q(\mathbf{V} \times \mathbf{B}) \qquad (10\text{–}19)$$

Clearly the term $n\,d\mathcal{V}$ represents the total number of charge carriers in the volume $d\mathcal{V}$, and so $d\mathbf{F}/(n\,d\mathcal{V})$ is the magnetic force on each charge carrier. This force is known as the *Lorentz force;* for which we have used the symbol $\mathbf{f}_m$.

In an electromagnetic field, the presence of an electric field $\mathbf{E}$ also gives rise to an electric force on a moving charge. Thus, the total electromagnetic force $\mathbf{f}_{em}$ on a charge $Q$ moving with a velocity $\mathbf{V}$ in both an electric field and a magnetic field is

$$\mathbf{f}_{em} = Q[\mathbf{E} + (\mathbf{V} \times \mathbf{B})] \qquad (10\text{–}20)$$

**The divergence of magnetic flux density** $\mathbf{B}$. The proof that $\nabla \cdot \mathbf{B} = 0$ can be established from the Biot-Savart law (Eq. 10-15),

$$\mathbf{B} = \frac{\mu_{eo}}{4\pi} I \oint \frac{d\mathbf{l} \times \mathbf{r}}{r^2} \qquad (10\text{–}21)$$

where $\mathbf{B}$ is the magnetic flux density at a field point $P(x, y, z,)$ induced by an element of conductor $d\mathbf{l}$ carrying the current $I$, as shown in Fig. 10-6. We take the divergence of Eq. 10-21 and obtain

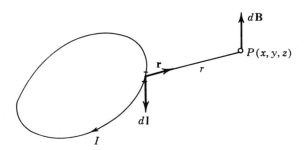

**Fig. 10-6.** The induction of magnetic flux density $d\mathbf{B}$ at a field point $P$ due to an element $d\mathbf{l}$ of a circuit which carries an electric current $I$.

$$\nabla \cdot \mathbf{B} = \nabla \cdot \left(\frac{\mu_{eo}}{4\pi} I \oint \frac{d\mathbf{l} \times \mathbf{r}}{r^2}\right)$$
$$= \frac{\mu_{eo}}{4\pi} I \oint \nabla \cdot \frac{d\mathbf{l} \times \mathbf{r}}{r^2} \qquad (10\text{–}22)$$

since the differentiation and integration operations are interchangeable. From the vector identity, we have

$$\nabla \cdot \frac{d\mathbf{l} \times \mathbf{r}}{r^2} = \frac{\mathbf{r}}{r^2} \cdot (\nabla \times d\mathbf{l}) - d\mathbf{l} \cdot \left(\nabla \times \frac{\mathbf{r}}{r^2}\right) \qquad (10\text{–}23)$$

The first term on the right-hand side is zero because $d\mathbf{l}$ is not a function of the position $(x, y, z)$ of the field point $P$ for which $\nabla \cdot \mathbf{B}$ is to be evaluated. The second term may be written as

$$d\mathbf{l} \cdot \left(\nabla \times \frac{\mathbf{r}}{r^2}\right) = d\mathbf{l} \cdot \left[\nabla \times \nabla\left(-\frac{1}{r}\right)\right] = 0$$

and is also equal to zero, since the curl of the gradient is zero. Therefore Eq. 10-22 becomes

$$\nabla \cdot \mathbf{B} = 0 \qquad (10\text{–}24)$$

This is the second of the four Maxwell equations. This equation tells us that there are no sources of magnetic induction at which the divergence of $\mathbf{B}$ would be different from zero and that, from Gauss' law, there are no free magnetic charges corresponding to the free electrical charges in an electrostatic field. Therefore, the source of an electromagnetic field is a distribution of electric charge and current.

**The conservation of charge.** There is no experimental evidence to indicate that under ordinary conditions charge may be either created or destroyed in macroscopic quantities. For any region of volume $V$ enclosed by a closed surface of area $A$, the mathematical expression for the principle of conservation of charge can be written as

$$\oiint_A \mathbf{J} \cdot d\mathbf{A} = -\int\int\int_V \frac{\partial \rho_e}{\partial t} dV \qquad (10\text{–}25)$$

Total efflux of     Rate of loss of<br>J across the       charge within the<br>entire surface     enclosed volume

This is the integral form of the principle of conservation of charge. To obtain the differential form, we need to change the surface integral on the left-hand side to a volume integral by the divergence theorem. Therefore,

$$\int\int\int_V \nabla \cdot \mathbf{J} \, dV = -\int\int\int_V \frac{\partial \rho_e}{\partial t} dV \qquad (10\text{–}26)$$

This equation is valid for any volume and so the integrands must be equal to each other. Hence the differential equation

$$\nabla \cdot \mathbf{J} = -\frac{\partial \rho_e}{\partial t} \qquad (10\text{–}27)$$

expresses the conservation of charge in the neighorhood of a point.

In the case that at every point in the region the charge density is constant (i.e., $\partial \rho_e / \partial t = 0$), then $\nabla \cdot \mathbf{J} = 0$ and the current is said to be *stationary* or *steady*.

**The charge density in a conducting medium.** Equation 10-27 enables us to determine the charge density $\rho_e$ at any point in a conducting medium. The current density $\mathbf{J}$ in a conducting medium is given by

$$\mathbf{J} = \sigma \mathbf{E} \qquad (10\text{--}28)$$

where $\sigma$ is the conductivity of the medium. This is Ohm's law in its general form.

Now, from Eq. 10-27,

$$\nabla \cdot \mathbf{J} + \frac{\partial \rho_e}{\partial t} = \nabla \cdot \sigma \mathbf{E} + \frac{\partial \rho_e}{\partial t} = 0$$

Replacing $\mathbf{E}$ by $\mathbf{D}/\epsilon$ (Eq. 10-6) and then $\nabla \cdot \mathbf{D}$ by $\rho_e$, we obtain the following differential equation for $\rho_e$:

$$\frac{\partial \rho_e}{\partial t} + \frac{\sigma}{\epsilon} \rho_e = 0 \qquad (10\text{--}29)$$

The solution of this equation yields the charge density $\rho_e$ at any instant as

$$\rho_e = \rho_{e0} \, e^{-(\sigma/\epsilon)t} \qquad (10\text{--}30)$$

where the constant of integration $\rho_{e0}$ is the charge density at $t = 0$. Equation 10-30 shows that at any point the initial charge density decays exponentially with a time constant of $\epsilon/\sigma$. This time constant $\epsilon/\sigma$ is called the *relaxation time;* which is the time required for the charge to decay to $1/e$ of its original value. In all but the poorest conductors, $\epsilon/\sigma$ is extremely small. Thus, in sea water, for example, the relaxation time is $2 \times 10^{-10}$ sec; that is, in $2 \times 10^{-10}$ sec, any charge we place in the interior of a body of sea water has dropped to about 37 per cent of its initial value.

Physically, for electrostatics, no charge and no electric current may reside within a conducting medium. By the law of conservation of charge, interior charge will appear almost instantaneously on the surface as surface charge.

**The magnetic field intensity $\mathbf{H}$.** In magnetism as in electricity two vectors are defined. One of them is $\mathbf{B}$, and the other one is the magnetic field intensity $\mathbf{H}$. These two vectors are related through the magnetic permeability $\mu_e$ of the medium in the following manner:

$$\mathbf{B} = \mu_e \mathbf{H} \qquad (10\text{--}31)$$

Hence $\mathbf{H}$ is measured in amperes/meter.

When a magnetic material is placed in a magnetic field, the situation is quite similar to that of a dielectric in an electric field. Since magnetic effects arise from moving electric charges, the latter produce magnetic fields which add to those produced by the conduction currents. Thus the magnetization vector **M** of a magnetic material contributes to the magnetic induction **B** at any field point, and so

$$\mathbf{B} = \mu_{e0}(\mathbf{H} + \mathbf{M}) \tag{10-32}$$

Here **M** has the same units as **H**. Diving this equation through by **H** and recalling Eq. 10-31, we obtain

$$\mu_e = \mu_{e0}\left(1 + \frac{\mathbf{M}}{\mathbf{H}}\right) \tag{10-33}$$

**Ampere's circuital law.** Ampere's circuital law states that the line integral of **H** around a closed path is equal to the current crossing any surface bounded by the same line integral path. Thus,

$$\oint_l \mathbf{H} \cdot d\mathbf{l} = I = \iint_A \mathbf{J} \cdot d\mathbf{A} \tag{10-34}$$

is the integral form of Ampere's circuital law. It can be used to compute **H** for cases in which **H** is constant along some chosen integration path. Thus, Ampere's law is somewhat similar to Gauss' law, which is used to compute the electrostatic field intensity **E** when **E** is constant over a closed surface.

We may employ Stokes' theorem in vector analysis to transform the line integral to a surface integral in Eq. 10-34. Hence

$$\iint_A (\nabla \times \mathbf{H}) \cdot d\mathbf{A} = \iint_A \mathbf{J} \cdot d\mathbf{A}$$

and, since the integrations hold for any area,

$$\nabla \times \mathbf{H} = \mathbf{J} \tag{10-35}$$

This is the differential form of Ampere's circuital law.

Both Eqs. 10-34 and 10-35 are limited to steady currents and to non-magnetic materials.

## 10-5   The Faraday Induction Law

Faraday succeeded in demonstrating the induction phenomena. A time-varying magnetic field produces an electromotive force which may establish a current in a suitable closed circuit. Faraday's induction law is frequently stated in the following mathematical form:

$$\oint_l \mathbf{E} \cdot d\mathbf{l} = -\frac{d}{dt} \iint_A \mathbf{B} \cdot d\mathbf{A} \tag{10-36}$$

The line integral on the left-hand side is defined as the electromotive force around a specific closed path, whereas the term on the right-hand side represents the time rate of change of magnetic flux which passes through any surface enclosed by the same closed path. The negative sign indicates that, if the directions of the line integral and of the enclosed area are related according to the right-hand screw rule, a flux density $\mathbf{B}$ in the direction of $d\mathbf{A}$ and increasing with time will produce an electric field intensity $\mathbf{E}$ which is in the negative direction of the line integral. However, Eq. 10-36 itself says nothing about the induced electric field intensity.

If the chosen path is fixed in space, we may rewrite Eq. 10-36 as

$$\oint_l \mathbf{E} \cdot d\mathbf{l} = -\int\int_A \frac{\partial \mathbf{B}}{\partial t} \cdot d\mathbf{A} \tag{10–37}$$

since $\mathbf{B}$ is the only time-varying quantity on the right-hand side. We then apply Stokes' theorem to the left-hand side to obtain

$$\int\int_A (\nabla \times \mathbf{E}) \cdot d\mathbf{A} = -\int\int_A \frac{\partial \mathbf{B}}{\partial t} \cdot d\mathbf{A}$$

This equation is valid for all surfaces and so the integrands must be equal at every point. That is,

$$\nabla \times \mathbf{E} = -\frac{\partial \mathbf{B}}{\partial t} \tag{10–38}$$

This is the differential form of Faraday's induction law relating the space derivative of $\mathbf{E}$ at any point to the time rate of change of $\mathbf{B}$ at the same point. This equation is also the third of the four Maxwell equations.

## 10-6  Maxwell's Electromagnetic Field Equations

So far we have derived three of the four Maxwell electromagnetic field equations. They are

$$\nabla \cdot \mathbf{D} = \rho_e \tag{10–13}$$

$$\nabla \cdot \mathbf{B} = 0 \tag{10–24}$$

$$\nabla \times \mathbf{E} = -\frac{\partial \mathbf{B}}{\partial t} \tag{10–38}$$

The fourth Maxwell field equation is

$$\nabla \times \mathbf{H} = \mathbf{J} + \frac{\partial \mathbf{D}}{\partial t} \tag{10–39}$$

We will recall that for steady currents the differential form of Ampere's circuital law was derived in the form of Eq. 10-35:

$$\nabla \times \mathbf{H} = \mathbf{J} \tag{10–35}$$

If we take the divergence of this equation, we have

$$\nabla \cdot \nabla \times \mathbf{H} = \nabla \cdot \mathbf{J} = 0$$

since the divergence of curl is zero. However, the law of conservation of charge, $\nabla \cdot \mathbf{J} = -\partial \rho_e / \partial t$, indicates that $\nabla \cdot \mathbf{J} = 0$ only when $\partial \rho_e / \partial t = 0$. This is true for the special case of steady current. For fields with unsteady currents, $\partial \rho_e / \partial t$ is no longer equal to zero and Eq. 10-35 must be modified. We may do so by adding an unknown vector field $\mathbf{Y}$ to Eq. 10-35 to obtain

$$\nabla \times \mathbf{H} = \mathbf{J} + \mathbf{Y} \qquad (10\text{--}40)$$

Then taking the divergence, we have

$$\nabla \cdot \nabla \times \mathbf{H} = \nabla \cdot \mathbf{J} + \nabla \cdot \mathbf{Y} = 0$$

By combining this equation with the law of conservation of charge, we see that

$$\nabla \cdot \mathbf{Y} = \frac{\partial \rho_e}{\partial t} = \frac{\partial}{\partial t} \nabla \cdot \mathbf{D}$$

where the last step is made by reason of Eq. 10-13. For a continuous vector field with continuous derivatives, the order of differentiations is immaterial. Therefore,

$$\mathbf{Y} = \frac{\partial \mathbf{D}}{\partial t}$$

and Eq. 10-39 becomes the fourth Maxwell field equation. From a physical point of view, Eq. 10-39 is Ampere's circuital law for fields with unsteady currents.

The four Maxwell field equations form the basis of all electromagnetic theory. They are linear partial differential equations relating electromagnetic fields. We shall use them in the study of magnetofluidmechanics.

## 10-7   The Poynting Theorem

We now introduce the Poynting theorem for determining the flow of electromagnetic energy through a closed surface located in an electromagnetic field. We form the dot product of $\mathbf{E}$ and Eq. 10-39:

$$\mathbf{E} \cdot (\nabla \times \mathbf{H}) = \mathbf{E} \cdot \mathbf{J} + \mathbf{E} \cdot \frac{\partial \mathbf{D}}{\partial t} \qquad (10\text{--}41)$$

in which the left-hand term is given by the following vector identity:

$$\mathbf{E} \cdot (\nabla \times \mathbf{H}) = \mathbf{H} \cdot (\nabla \times \mathbf{E}) - \nabla \cdot (\mathbf{E} \times \mathbf{H})$$

Hence Eq. 10-41 may be written as

$$\mathbf{H} \cdot (\nabla \times \mathbf{E}) - \nabla \cdot (\mathbf{E} \times \mathbf{H}) = \mathbf{E} \cdot \mathbf{J} + \mathbf{E} \cdot \frac{\partial \mathbf{D}}{\partial t}$$

Substituting $-\partial\mathbf{B}/\partial t$ for $\nabla \times \mathbf{E}$, $\epsilon\mathbf{E}$ for $\mathbf{D}$, and $\mu_e\mathbf{H}$ for $\mathbf{B}$ into the above equation and rearranging terms, we have

$$-\nabla \cdot (\mathbf{E} \times \mathbf{H}) = \mathbf{E} \cdot \mathbf{J} + \mathbf{E} \cdot \frac{\partial \epsilon\mathbf{E}}{\partial t} + \mathbf{H} \cdot \frac{\partial \mu_e\mathbf{H}}{\partial t}$$

or

$$-\nabla \cdot (\mathbf{E} \times \mathbf{H}) = \mathbf{E} \cdot \mathbf{J} + \frac{\partial}{\partial t} \left( \frac{1}{2} \epsilon E^2 + \frac{1}{2} \mu_e H^2 \right) \qquad (10\text{–}42)$$

since

$$\mathbf{E} \cdot \frac{\partial \epsilon\mathbf{E}}{\partial t} = E \frac{\partial \epsilon E}{\partial t} = \frac{\partial}{\partial t} \left( \frac{1}{2} \epsilon E^2 \right)$$

and

$$\mathbf{H} \cdot \frac{\partial \mu_e\mathbf{H}}{\partial t} = H \frac{\partial \mu_e H}{\partial t} = \frac{\partial}{\partial t} \left( \frac{1}{2} \mu_e H^2 \right)$$

We then integrate Eq. 10-42 over a chosen volume and apply the divergence theorem to convert the left-hand volume integral to a surface integral. The result is the desired expression for the Poynting theorem:

$$- \oiint_A (\mathbf{E} \times \mathbf{H}) \cdot d\mathbf{A} = \iiint_V (\mathbf{E} \cdot \mathbf{J}) \, dV + \frac{\partial}{\partial t} \iiint_V \left( \frac{1}{2} \epsilon E^2 + \frac{1}{2} \mu_e H^2 \right) dV$$

| Total power flowing out of the volume through the entire surface | Total ohmic power dissipated within the volume | Time rate of increase of electromagnetic energy stored in the volume |
|---|---|---|

$$(10\text{–}43)$$

The cross product $\mathbf{E} \times \mathbf{H}$ is called the *Poynting vector*, which represents the amount of power crossing a unit surface area. The Poynting vector is measured in watts/meter$^2$.

## 10-8   *Fundamental Equations of Magnetofluidmechanics*

Since magnetofluidmechanics is the study of flow of an electrically conducting fluid in the presence of an electromagnetic field, the fundamental equations of magnetofluidmechanics are a combination of electromagnetic field equations and fluid flow equations, modified to include the effect of the interaction between the fluid motion and the electromagnetic field. We shall again treat fluid medium as a continuum and employ the macroscopic approach[3] to derive the fundamental equations of magnetofluidmechanics.

The usual assumption in magnetofluidmechanics is that the induced current in the fluid will interact with the electromagnetic field in accordance

---

[3]We may adopt the microscopic or gas kinetic approach by combining Boltzmann's equation with electromagnetic terms to obtain the fundamental equations of magnetofluidmechanics.

with the classical laws governing electromagnetic interactions. Maxwell's field equations are therefore a part of the fundamental equations of magnetofluidmechanics. However, when Maxwell's equations are applied to magnetofluidmechanic problems, considerable simplifications are possible because the flow velocity is considerably smaller than the high speed of electron motion. If the fluid medium is a good electrical conductor, any local excess or deficiency of electrons compared with the positive-charge carriers will be removed almost simultaneously[4] by the electric field which results from this charge unbalance. Therefore, we may neglect the accumulation of excess charge and the displacement current $\partial \mathbf{D}/\partial t$, since the displacement current is important only when currents can pile up electric charges. Hence, in magnetofluidmechanics Maxwell's field equations are reduced to the following forms:

$$\nabla \cdot \mathbf{D} = \rho_e = 0 \tag{10-44}$$

$$\nabla \cdot \mathbf{B} = 0 \tag{10-45}$$

$$\nabla \times \mathbf{E} = -\frac{\partial \mathbf{B}}{\partial t} \tag{10-46}$$

$$\nabla \times \mathbf{H} = \mathbf{J} \tag{10-47}$$

For a moving medium, the total electric field intensity is the sum of the applied electric field intensity $\mathbf{E}$ and the induced electric field intensity $\mathbf{V} \times \mathbf{B}$, where $\mathbf{V}$ is the local velocity of flow. Hence by Ohm's law,

$$\mathbf{J} = \sigma(\mathbf{E} + \mathbf{V} \times \mathbf{B}) \tag{10-48}$$

Note that we have again neglected the excess charges in the above equation. By combining Eqs. 10-46, 10-47, and 10-48, after $\mathbf{H}$ is replaced by $\mathbf{B}/\mu_e$, we obtain the following induction equation:

$$\frac{\partial \mathbf{B}}{\partial t} = \nabla \times (\mathbf{V} \times \mathbf{B}) + \frac{1}{\sigma \mu_e} \nabla^2 \mathbf{B} \tag{10-49}$$

which can be used to determine $\mathbf{B}$ for given values of $\mathbf{V}$. Then the current density $\mathbf{J}$ can be found by means of Eq. 10-47. Knowing $\mathbf{B}$ and $\mathbf{J}$, we can further obtain $\mathbf{E}$ from Eq. 10-48.

In magnetofluidmechanics, as in other fluid mechanic problems, fluid motion is governed by the laws of conservation of mass, momentum, and energy. The equation of continuity remains unchanged. The momentum and energy equations must be modified by incorporating into them appropriate momentum and energy terms obtained from Maxwell's field equations and Ohm's law, since fluid particles are now electrically conduct-

---

[4]For example, in the ionosphere the time required for the charge equalization is approximately $5 \times 10^{-8}$ sec.

ing and they will interact with the applied and induced electromagnetic fields.

In the momentum equation, we have to include the electromagnetic forces as a part of the body forces. For a charged particle moving with a velocity $\mathbf{V}$ in an electromagnetic field with an electric field intensity $\mathbf{E}$ and a magnetic flux density $\mathbf{B}$, the electric force on this particle is $\rho_e \mathbf{E}$ and the magnetic force is $\mathbf{J} \times \mathbf{B}$. Hence the electromagnetic force $\mathbf{f}_{em}$ is

$$\mathbf{f}_{em} = \rho_e \mathbf{E} + \mathbf{J} \times \mathbf{B} \tag{10-50}$$

per unit volume. However, in magnetofluidmechanic problems, the charge density $\rho_e$ is zero and the electromagnetic force reduces to

$$\mathbf{f}_{em} = \mathbf{J} \times \mathbf{B} \tag{10-51}$$

It is only necessary to add this force to the different forms of differential momentum equations which were derived in Sec. 6-2 to obtain magneto-fluidmechanic momentum equations. For example, if the fluid medium is an electrically conducting Newtonian fluid with constant density and viscosity, we add $\mathbf{f}_{em}$ to the Navier-Stokes equation (Eq. 6-16) to obtain the following magnetohydrodynamic momentum equation:

$$\rho \frac{D\mathbf{V}}{Dt} = \rho \mathbf{g} - \nabla p + \mu \nabla^2 \mathbf{V} + \mathbf{J} \times \mathbf{B} \tag{10-52}$$

The energy equation for the flow of viscous compressible fluids was derived in Sec. 6-5. To derive a mangetofluidmechanic energy equation, we need to add to the energy equation for fluid flow the following terms in their proper forms:

1. Rate of heat radiation $dQ_r/dt$ from a control volume.
2. Rate of electromagnetic energy $dE_{em}/dt$ which crosses the control volume surface.
3. Rate of change of the electromagnetic energy $D\hat{u}_{em}/Dt$ in the fluid.

The rate of heat radiation $dQ_r/dt$ from a control volume can be written as

$$\frac{dQ_r}{dt} = \oiint_A \mathbf{q}_r \cdot d\mathbf{A} = \iiint_{\mathcal{V}} \nabla \cdot \mathbf{q}_r \, d\mathcal{V}$$

where the vector $\mathbf{q}_r$ is the radiation heat flux which crosses the control volume surface. Therefore, the rate of heat radiation from a fluid element of unit volume is simply $\nabla \cdot \mathbf{q}_r$.

It was shown in Sec. 10-7 that the surface integral of the Poynting vector defines the amount of electromagnetic power which crosses the control volume surface. Hence

$$\frac{dE_{em}}{dt} = \oiint_A (\mathbf{E} \times \mathbf{H}) \cdot d\mathbf{A} = \iiint_{\mathcal{V}} \nabla \cdot (\mathbf{E} \times \mathbf{H}) \, d\mathcal{V}$$

and the amount of electromagnetic power which crosses a unit volume of fluid is $\nabla \cdot (\mathbf{E} \times \mathbf{H})$.

For a body moving within an electromagnetic field, the scalar product of the electromagnetic force and the velocity of the body is the rate at which mechanical work is done by the body. Thus, the rate of change of electromagnetic energy $D\hat{u}_{em}/Dt$ in the fluid is

$$\frac{D\hat{u}_{em}}{Dt} = \mathbf{f}_{em} \cdot \mathbf{V} = \mathbf{J} \times \mathbf{B} \cdot \mathbf{V}$$

per unit volume. By Ohm's law,

$$\mathbf{J} \cdot \mathbf{E} = \mathbf{J} \cdot \left(-\mathbf{V} \times \mathbf{B} + \frac{\mathbf{J}}{\sigma}\right) = \mathbf{V} \cdot \mathbf{J} \times \mathbf{B} + \frac{J^2}{\sigma}$$

from which

$$\frac{D\hat{u}_{em}}{Dt} = \mathbf{V} \cdot \mathbf{J} \times \mathbf{B} = \mathbf{J} \cdot \mathbf{E} - \frac{J^2}{\sigma}$$

where $J^2/\sigma$ is the rate of Ohmic heating of the fluid.

Adding these terms, with proper signs, to the energy equation (Eq. 6-27) for a compressible Newtonian fluid, we obtain the following magnetogasdynamic energy equation:

$$\nabla \cdot k\nabla T - \nabla \cdot \mathbf{q}_r - \nabla \cdot \mathbf{E} \times \mathbf{H} = \rho \frac{D\hat{u}}{Dt} + p\nabla \cdot \mathbf{V} - \mu\Phi_v + \mathbf{J} \cdot \mathbf{E} - \frac{J^2}{\sigma}$$

$$(10\text{--}53)$$

However, Eq. 10-43 indicates that

$$-\nabla \cdot \mathbf{E} \times \mathbf{H} = \mathbf{E} \cdot \mathbf{J} + \tfrac{1}{2}\epsilon E^2 + \tfrac{1}{2}\mu_e H^2$$

so that the magnetogasdynamic energy equation for an electrically conducting compressible Newtonian fluid may also be written as

$$\nabla \cdot k\nabla T - \nabla \cdot \mathbf{q}_r + \frac{1}{2}\epsilon E^2 + \frac{1}{2}\mu_e H^2 = \rho \frac{D\hat{u}}{Dt} + p\nabla \cdot \mathbf{V} - \mu\Phi_v - \frac{J^2}{\sigma}$$

$$(10\text{--}54)$$

We will note that the fundamental equations of magnetofluidmechanics just derived are nonlinear. There is no general solution for these nonlinear equations. Each magnetofluidmechanic problem must be solved individually.

## 10-9  Electromagnetic Waves and Alfvén Waves

Two waves are of particular interest in magnetofluidmechanics: electromagnetic waves and Alfvén waves.

**Electromagnetic waves.** Electromagnetic waves are important in the study of magnetofluidmechanics in that electromagnetic measurements in magnetofluidmechanic phenomena depend on signals which travel at the velocity of propagation of electromagnetic waves.

For the sake of simplicity, we shall restrict our discussion of the phenomena to electromagnetic waves in a vacuum. In this case, Maxwell's equations reduce to

$$\nabla \cdot \mathbf{D} = 0 \tag{10-55}$$

$$\nabla \cdot \mathbf{B} = 0 \tag{10-56}$$

$$\nabla \times \mathbf{E} = -\frac{\partial \mathbf{B}}{\partial t} \tag{10-57}$$

$$\nabla \times \mathbf{H} = \frac{\partial \mathbf{D}}{\partial t} \tag{10-58}$$

where

$$\mathbf{D} = \epsilon_0 \mathbf{E} \tag{10-59}$$

$$\mathbf{B} = \mu_{e0} \mathbf{H} \tag{10-60}$$

To derive electromagnetic waves equations, we first take the curl of Eq. 10-57 to obtain

$$\nabla \times (\nabla \times \mathbf{E}) = -\frac{\partial}{\partial t} (\nabla \times \mathbf{B}) \tag{10-61}$$

Then we employ the triple vector identity for $\mathbf{E}$ to rewrite Eq. 10-61 as

$$\nabla(\nabla \cdot \mathbf{E}) - \nabla^2 \mathbf{E} = -\frac{\partial}{\partial t} (\nabla \times \mathbf{B}) \tag{10-62}$$

which, upon substitution from Eqs. 10-55, 10-58, and 10-59, becomes

$$\nabla^2 \mathbf{E} = \epsilon_0 \mu_{e0} \frac{\partial^2 \mathbf{E}}{\partial t^2} \tag{10-63}$$

This is the vector wave equation for $\mathbf{E}$.

In a similar manner, starting with Eq. 10-58, we can derive an identical vector wave equation for $\mathbf{H}$:

$$\nabla^2 \mathbf{H} = \epsilon_0 \mu_{e0} \frac{\partial^2 \mathbf{H}}{\partial t^2} \tag{10-64}$$

Clearly we can also obtain identical vector wave equations for $\mathbf{D}$ and $\mathbf{B}$ simply by multiplying Eq. 10-63 by $\epsilon_0$ and Eq. 10-64 by $\mu_{e0}$. Thus, the four field vectors $\mathbf{E}$, $\mathbf{H}$, $\mathbf{D}$, and $\mathbf{B}$, all satisfy the same vector wave equation.

Each of the four vector wave equations can be written in their respective component forms. For example, the Cartesian component forms of Eq. 10-63 are simply

$$\left(\frac{\partial^2}{\partial x^2} + \frac{\partial^2}{\partial y^2} + \frac{\partial^2}{\partial z^2}\right) E_x = \epsilon_0 \mu_{e0} \frac{\partial^2 E_x}{\partial t^2} \tag{10-65a}$$

$$\left(\frac{\partial^2}{\partial x^2} + \frac{\partial^2}{\partial y^2} + \frac{\partial^2}{\partial z^2}\right) E_y = \epsilon_0 \mu_{e0} \frac{\partial^2 E_y}{\partial t^2} \tag{10-65b}$$

$$\left(\frac{\partial^2}{\partial x^2} + \frac{\partial^2}{\partial y^2} + \frac{\partial^2}{\partial z^2}\right) E_z = \epsilon_0 \mu_{e0} \frac{\partial^2 E_z}{\partial t^2} \tag{10-65c}$$

Similar expressions may be written for the other three field vectors **H**, **D**, and **B**,

These partial differential equations are for an unattenuated wave traveling at a velocity $V \doteq \pm 1/\sqrt{\epsilon_0 \mu_{e0}}$ which has a numerical value of $2.9979 \times 10^8$ meters/sec. We will recall that $V$ equals the speed of light $c$ in vacuo, which is a fundamental constant of nature. Thus, for an electrically conducting fluid medium, in which $\rho_e$ and **J** are equal to zero, the electromagnetic waves are seen to travel with the speed of light.

**Alfvén waves.** Alfvén waves are hydromagnetic waves which result from the interaction of electromagnetic wave phenomena with hydrodynamic phenomena. Alfvén waves are transverse waves occurring in incompressible media. In this discussion, we shall assume that Alfvén waves are associated with small electromagnetic disturbances and that the occurrence of Alfvén waves is an isentropic process. Therefore, Alfvén waves can be considered as idealized waves similar to Mach waves in perfect gases.

The derivation of the expression for the Alfvén wave is based on an idealized magnetofluidmechanic flow model, in which a homogeneous, inviscid, and perfectly conducting fluid is subject to a uniform magnetic field having a field intensity **H₀**. The fluid is initially in equilibrium. Then a small disturbance is introduced into the flow to produce a small perturbation motion with velocity **V'**. This perturbation motion of the conducting fluid induces electric fields **E'** which, in turn, produce small magnetic effects **H'**. The current density associated with **E'** is denoted by **J'**. Therefore, the resulting fields for this small perturbation motion are

$$\mathbf{V} = \mathbf{V'}; \qquad \mathbf{H} = \mathbf{H}_0 + \mathbf{H'}; \qquad \mathbf{E} = \mathbf{E'}; \qquad \mathbf{J} = \mathbf{J'}$$

Note that the primed quantities represent small changes caused by the small disturbance in the fluid medium.

It seems reasonable to assume that the small perturbation motion is nondissipative and adiabatic. Furthermore, for a perfectly conducting medium, the displacement currents in the flow are negligibly small compared with the conduction currents. Under these conditions the complete set of equations, in the absence of gravitational forces, for this flow reduces to the following:

Maxwell's equations:

$$\nabla \cdot (\mathbf{H}_0 + \mathbf{H'}) = 0 \tag{10-66}$$

$$\nabla \times \mathbf{E'} = -\mu_e \frac{\partial \mathbf{H'}}{\partial t} \tag{10-67}$$

$$\nabla \times \mathbf{H'} = \mathbf{J'} \tag{10-68}$$

Ohm's law:

$$\mathbf{E'} = \frac{\mathbf{J'}}{\sigma} - \mathbf{V'} \times \mu_e(\mathbf{H_0} + \mathbf{H'}) \qquad (10\text{-}69)$$

Continuity equation:

$$\nabla \cdot \mathbf{V'} = 0 \qquad (10\text{-}70)$$

Momentum equation:

$$\rho \frac{\partial \mathbf{V'}}{\partial t} = \mathbf{J'} \times \mu_e(\mathbf{H_0} + \mathbf{H'}) \qquad (10\text{-}71)$$

In order to arrive at a wave equation, we assume that $\mathbf{V'}$ is along the $y$-axis and the magnetic field $\mathbf{H_0}$ is directed along the $z$-axis of a Cartesian coordinate system, as shown in Fig. 10-7. Furthermore, for a first ap-

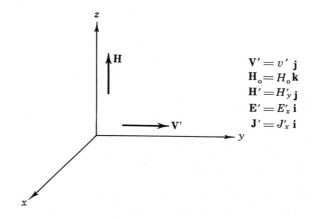

$$\mathbf{V'} = v' \,\mathbf{j}$$
$$\mathbf{H_0} = H_0 \,\mathbf{k}$$
$$\mathbf{H'} = H'_y \,\mathbf{j}$$
$$\mathbf{E'} = E'_x \,\mathbf{i}$$
$$\mathbf{J'} = J'_x \,\mathbf{i}$$

**Fig. 10-7.** Coordinates used for deriving Alfvén wave equation.

proximation, we shall neglect terms involving squares and products of primed quantities. Hence, for this special case, Eqs. 10-66 through 10-71 may be rewritten as:

Maxwell's equations:

$$\frac{\partial H'_y}{\partial y} + \frac{\partial H_0}{\partial z} = 0 \qquad (10\text{-}66a)$$

$$\frac{\partial E'_x}{\partial z} = -\mu_e \frac{\partial H'_y}{\partial t} \qquad (10\text{-}67a)$$

$$\frac{\partial H'_y}{\partial z} = J'_x \qquad (10\text{-}68a)$$

Ohm's law:

$$E'_x = \frac{J'_x}{\sigma} - \mu_e v' H_0 \qquad (10\text{-}69a)$$

Continuity equation:

$$\frac{\partial v'}{\partial y} = 0 \tag{10–70a}$$

Momentum equation:

$$\rho \frac{\partial v'}{\partial t} = J'_x \mu_e H_0 \tag{10–71a}$$

Combining Eqs. 10-67a, 10-68a, 10-69a, and 10-71a to eliminate all the field variables except $H$, we finally obtain the following Alfvén wave equation for $H$:

$$\frac{\partial^2 H'_y}{\partial t^2} = \frac{\mu_e H_0^2}{\rho} \frac{\partial^2 H'_y}{\partial z^2} \tag{10–72}$$

This wave equation represents a magnetic wave which propagates along the $z$-axis (i.e., along the direction of the applied magnetic field $\mathbf{H}_0$) with the velocity

$$V_A = \pm H_0 \sqrt{\frac{\mu_e}{\rho}} = \pm \frac{B_0}{\sqrt{\mu_e \rho}} \tag{10–73}$$

We call $V_A$ the *Alfvén wave velocity*. The existence of this transverse magnetic wave in magnetohydrodynamic flow, in the direction of the applied magnetic field, was predicted analytically by H. Alfvén[5] in 1942, and the wave phenomena have been observed repeatedly in experiments using different conducting fluid media.[6]

In the foregoing derivations for electromagnetic and Alfvén waves, we have used an idealized flow model. Both waves are damped by dissipative effects and finite electrical conductivity of the medium. Because the velocity and magnetic waves are damped differently, the resulting damped wave motions are therefore three-dimensional in nature. We shall not consider these effects in this book.

## 10-10  Magnetohydrodynamic Diffusion Equation

In this investigation, we shall consider an incompressible electrically conducting fluid moving adiabatically in a magnetic field $\mathbf{B}$. The interac-

---

[5]H. Alfvén, "Existence of Electromagnetic-Hydrodynamic Waves," *Nature*, Vol. CL, No. 3805 (1942), 405.

[6]For example, S. Lundquist, "Experimental Investigations of Magnetohydrodynamic Waves," *Phys. Rev.*, Vol. LXXVI (1949), 1805.

B. Lehnert, "Magneto-hydrodynamic Waves in Liquid Sodium," *Phys. Rev.*, Vol. XCIV, No. 4 (1954), 815.

T. K. Allen, W. R. Baker, R. V. Pyle, and J. M. Wilcox, "Experimental Generation of Plasma Alfvén Waves," *Phys. Rev. Letters*, Vol. II, No. 9 (1959), 383.

D. F. Jephcott, "Alfvén Waves in a Gas Discharge," *Nature*, Vol. CLXXXIII, No. 4676 (1959), 1652.

tion between the magnetic field and the fluid flow field is manifested in the induction equation (Eq. 10-49):

$$\frac{\partial \mathbf{B}}{\partial t} = \nabla \times (\mathbf{V} \times \mathbf{B}) + \frac{1}{\sigma \mu_e} \nabla^2 \mathbf{B} \qquad (10\text{--}74)$$

The constant $1/\sigma \mu_e$ is defined as the magnetic kinematic viscosity or magnetic diffusivity $\nu_m$ so that the above equation is frequently written as

$$\frac{\partial \mathbf{B}}{\partial t} = \nabla \times (\mathbf{V} \times \mathbf{B}) + \nu_m \nabla^2 \mathbf{B} \qquad (10\text{--}75)$$

and is referred to as the *magnetohydrodynamic diffusion equation*. This equation gives the changes in the magnetic field caused by the velocity field of the conducting fluid.

There are two limiting conditions for this equation. First, the conducting fluid is moving with a velocity $\mathbf{V}$ but has negligible electrical resistance so that $\sigma \rightarrow \infty$ and $\nu_m$ may be assumed equal to zero. Hence Eq. 10-75 reduces to

$$\frac{\partial \mathbf{B}}{\partial t} = \nabla \times (\mathbf{V} \times \mathbf{B}) \qquad (10\text{--}76)$$

This equation for $\mathbf{B}$ is identical with that satisfied by the vorticity of an ideal fluid, with the vector $\mathbf{B}$ playing the same role as the vorticity vector. It is implied in the vorticity theorem that vortex lines move with the fluid. Hence Eq. 10-76 also implies that the magnetic lines are locked into the conducting fluid medium while they move with the medium. For this reason, we frequently say that the magnetic lines are "frozen" into the medium.

The other limiting condition occurs when the conducting fluid medium is at rest; that is, $\mathbf{V} = 0$. Then Eq. 10-75 becomes simply

$$\frac{\partial \mathbf{B}}{\partial t} = \nu_m \nabla^2 \mathbf{B} \qquad (10\text{--}77)$$

This equation has the form of a diffusion equation. The equation describes magnetic field leakage through a stationary fluid medium from point to point.

Now, if both terms on the right-hand side of Eq. 10-75 are of the same order of magnitude, then the magnetic lines tend to be "frozen" in the moving fluid and, at the same time, they leak through it.

To determine the relative significance of the two terms on the right-hand side of Eq. 10-75, we shall introduce a dimensionless parameter in the following manner. Let us choose a length $L$ which is comparable with the dimensions of the region containing the magnetic field $\mathbf{B}$, and a velocity $V$ which is comparable with the fluid flow velocity $\mathbf{V}$. The magnetic transport term $\nabla \times (\mathbf{V} \times \mathbf{B})$ is dimensionally proportional to $VB/L$ and the diffusion term $\nu_m \nabla^2 \mathbf{B}$ is dimensionally proportional to $\nu_m B/L^2$. Therefore, if $VB/L \gg \nu_m B/L^2$, the transport term predominates in Eq. 10-75. Hence, by analogy to the Reynolds number $\mathbf{R} = VL/\nu$ in viscous flow, we define the magnetic Reynolds number $\mathbf{R}_m$ by the equation

$$\mathbf{R}_m = \frac{VB/L}{\nu_m B/L^2} = \frac{VL}{\nu_m} \tag{10–78}$$

The magnetic Reynolds number $\mathbf{R}_m$ is a measure of the motion-induced field relative to the applied magnetic field. When $\mathbf{R}_m \gg 1$, the motion-induced field predominates and Eq. 10-76 shows that the induced electromagnetic field is coupled rigidly with the hydrodynamic field. When $\mathbf{R}_m \ll 1$, the applied magnetic field predominates and Eq. 10-77 shows that the applied magnetic field diffuses through the hydrodynamic field.

## 10-11   Magnetohydrodynamic Parallel Flow

Figure 10-8 illustrates a steady, laminar flow of an incompressible, electrically conducting fluid between two parallel, insulating plates at rest. The flow is in the $y$-direction under a constant pressure gradient

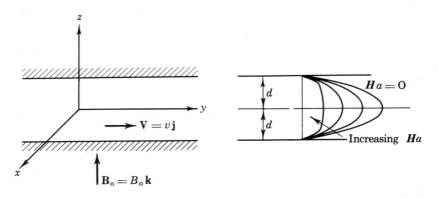

**Fig. 10-8.** Magnetohydrodynamic parallel flow.

$-\partial p/\partial y$. The velocity field of the flow is given by $\mathbf{V} = v\mathbf{j}$, where $v = v(z)$. A uniform magnetic field $\mathbf{B}_0$ is applied in the $z$-direction and so $\mathbf{B}_0 = B_0\mathbf{k}$. Because the velocity $v$ is nonuniform across the flow channel, the fast-moving layers tend to pull out the lines of force in the direction of flow. Therefore, the field also acquires a magnetic field component $B_y$ in the direction of flow; $B_y$ is a function of $z$ alone. By assuming that the $xy$ plane is a horizontal plane, we may neglect the gravitational force and write the magnetohydrodynamic momentum equation for this steady flow in the direction of flow in the following form:

$$-\frac{\partial p}{\partial y} + \mu \frac{\partial^2 v}{\partial z^2} + |\mathbf{J} \times \mathbf{B}|_y = 0 \tag{10-79}$$

in which the last term means the $y$-component of the $(\mathbf{J} \times \mathbf{B})$-vector.

It is necessary to determine $\mathbf{J}$ in this hydromagnetic flow field in order to evaluate the magnetic term in the above equation. We will recall from Maxwell's equations that, in the absence of the displacement current,

$$\mathbf{J} = \nabla \times \mathbf{H} = \nabla \times \mu_e \mathbf{B}$$

Knowing that $\mathbf{B} = B_y \mathbf{j} + B_0 \mathbf{k}$, we can expand this vector equation in Cartesian coordinate form and find that $J_y = J_z = 0$ and $J_x$ is the only nonzero component. Hence Eq. 10-79 reduces to

$$-\frac{\partial p}{\partial y} + \mu \frac{\partial^2 v}{\partial z^2} - J_x B_0 = 0 \tag{10-80}$$

in which $J_x$ can be evaluated by Ohm's law as

$$J_x = \sigma(E_x + vB_0) \tag{10-81}$$

Since the applied magnetic field in this flow is constant, $\nabla \times \mathbf{E} = 0$ and so the component $E_x$ of the induced electric field is also constant. Substituting Eq. 10-81 into Eq. 10-80, we finally have

$$\mu \frac{\partial^2 v}{\partial z^2} - \sigma v B_0^2 = \frac{\partial p}{\partial y} + \sigma E_x B_0 \tag{10-82}$$

This is the differential equation for magnetohydrodynamic parallel flow. The boundary conditions for this flow are: (1) $v = 0$ at the two plates (i.e., at $z = \pm d$), and (2) $dv/dz = 0$ at the median plane of the channel (i.e., at $z = 0$).

The solution to Eq. 10-82 is

$$v = -\frac{\partial p/\partial y + \sigma E_x B_0}{\sigma B_0^2} \left[ 1 - \frac{\cosh (B_0 \sqrt{\sigma/\mu}\, z)}{\cosh (B_0 \sqrt{\sigma/\mu}\, d)} \right] \tag{10-83}$$

However, this equation becomes more meaningful if we introduce a dimensionless parameter called the *Hartmann number* **Ha**, which is the square root of the ratio of electromagnetic force to viscous force. The electromagnetic force per unit volume $f_{em}$ is defined dimensionally as $f_{em} = \sigma V B^2$ and the viscous force per unit volume $f_v$ is dimensionally equal to $\mu V/L^2$. Thus,

$$Ha = \sqrt{\frac{\sigma V B^2}{\mu V/L^2}} = \sqrt{\frac{\sigma}{\mu}}\, BL \tag{10-84}$$

The magnitude of the Hartmann number is an indication of the relative effects of magnetic and viscous drags for the flow of an electrically conducting viscous fluid across magnetic lines. A high value of Hartmann number would indicate a large magnetic drag in the flow. Therefore, we may rewrite Eq. 10-83 as

$$v = -\frac{\partial p/\partial y + \sigma E_x B_0}{\sigma B_0^2}\left[1 - \frac{\cosh{(Ha\,z/d)}}{\cosh Ha}\right] \qquad (10\text{–}85)$$

in which we have set

$$Ha = \sqrt{\frac{\sigma}{\mu}}\,B_0 d \qquad (10\text{–}86)$$

The velocity profiles corresponding to different values of $Ha$ are shown on the right-hand side of Fig. 10-8. If $Ha$ is small, the viscosity effect is more important than the magnetic effect, and the velocity profile is nearly parabolic, just as would be expected in a laminar flow. On the other hand, as $Ha$ becomes increasingly large, the parabolic velocity profile of viscous flow is flattened by the increasing magnetic drag.

## 10-12  Magnetofluidmechanic Deceleration of Flow

From discussions in the foregoing section, it is clear that a suitably applied magnetic field can be employed to cause deceleration of flow, as illustrated in the vector diagram of Fig. 10-9. We will recall from the

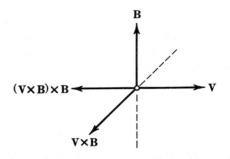

**Fig. 10-9.**  Vector diagram illustrating magnetofluidmechanic deceleration of flow.

magnetofluidmechanic momentum equation that the electromagnetic body force is given by the vector $\mathbf{J} \times \mathbf{B}$. By Ohm's law,

$$\mathbf{J} \times \mathbf{B} = \sigma(\mathbf{E} + \mathbf{V} \times \mathbf{B}) \times \mathbf{B}$$
$$= \sigma(\mathbf{E} \times \mathbf{B}) + \sigma(\mathbf{V} \times \mathbf{B}) \times \mathbf{B} \qquad (10\text{–}87)$$

If the term $\sigma(\mathbf{E} \times \mathbf{B})$ is small compared to $\sigma(\mathbf{V} \times \mathbf{B}) \times \mathbf{B}$, the latter vector is seen to oppose the fluid motion, as indicated in Figure 10-9, and so it tends to decelerate the flow.

A possible application of this effect is in missile reentry, during which an increased drag on the missile is highly desirable. Figure 10-10 illus-

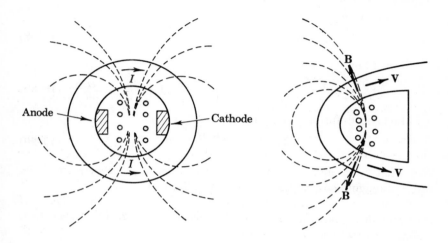

**Fig. 10-10.**  Schematic diagrams illustrating the production of magnetic drag on a missile nose.

trates a scheme which could be used to produce magnetic drag on a missile nose. The missile nose is shown enveloped by a shroud of hot, ionized air. A magnetic field **B** is provided as shown. The current thus generated is made to flow through electrodes. Therefore, the resulting net electromagnetic force would act as a drag on the missile.

## 10-13   Magnetofluidmechanic Boundary Layer Flow

By applying a properly placed magnetic field, we may modify both the velocity and temperature profiles in boundary layer flow near a solid boundary. Indications are that magnetofluidmechanic effects can be employed to increase the drag and decrease the heat transfer. The magnetic drag tends to raise the critical Reynolds number and thereby may serve to delay the breakdown of a laminar boundary layer flow to a turbulent boundary layer flow.

Boundary-layer flow for nonconducting viscous fluid was discussed in Chapter 8. Since differential equations for the laminar boundary layer in planar flow were derived in Sec. 8-3, we shall investigate the same flow model except that the fluid is electrically conducting and that the flow occurs in a magnetic field. The fundamental equations for a steady, two-dimensional, magnetohydrodynamic laminar boundary layer can be written as follows:

Continuity equation:

$$\frac{\partial u}{\partial x} + \frac{\partial v}{\partial y} = 0 \tag{10-88}$$

Momentum equation:

$$u\frac{\partial u}{\partial x} + v\frac{\partial u}{\partial y} = -\frac{1}{\rho}\frac{\partial p}{\partial x} + \nu\frac{\partial^2 u}{\partial y^2} + \frac{\mu_e}{\rho}H_y\left(\frac{\partial H_y}{\partial x} - \frac{\partial H_x}{\partial y}\right) \tag{10-89}$$

Magnetic diffusion equation:

$$H_y\frac{\partial u}{\partial y} + \nu_m\frac{\partial^2 H_x}{\partial y^2} = 0 \tag{10-90}$$

Note that these equations are formulated after we have performed the order-of-magnitude analysis as outlined in Sec. 8-3.

We now consider the case in which the pressure gradient $\partial p/\partial x$ is zero and the applied magnetic field $\mathbf{B}_0$ is in the $y$-direction. Then Eqs. 10-89 and 10-90 become respectively

$$u\frac{\partial u}{\partial x} + v\frac{\partial u}{\partial y} = \nu\frac{\partial^2 u}{\partial y^2} + \frac{\mu_e}{\rho}H_0\frac{\partial H_x}{\partial y} \tag{10-91}$$

and

$$H_0\frac{\partial u}{\partial y} + \nu_m\frac{\partial^2 H_x}{\partial y^2} = 0 \tag{10-92}$$

Equation 10-92, when integrated, yields

$$H_0 u + \nu_m\frac{\partial H_x}{\partial y} = 0 \tag{10-93}$$

which is then substituted into Eq. 10-91 to obtain

$$u\frac{\partial u}{\partial x} + v\frac{\partial u}{\partial y} = \nu\frac{\partial^2 u}{\partial y^2} - \frac{\mu_e}{\rho\nu_m}H_0^2 u \tag{10-94}$$

This is the desired differential equation for a steady, two-dimensional, incompressible, boundary layer flow in the presence of a transverse magnetic field. The boundary conditions for this equation are:

(1) At $y = 0$, $u = v = 0$

(2) As $y \to \infty$, $u = U$ ($U$ being the velocity in the free-stream flow), $v = 0$, $\partial u/\partial y = 0$, and $\partial u/\partial x = -\mu_e H_0^2/\rho\nu_m$.

Equation 10-94 can be solved by using the well-known Blasius method of solution of ordinary boundary layer equations. The solution has been worked out by V. J. Rossow[7], who gave the following formula for the local friction drag coefficient $c_{Df}$ at any position $x$ along a flat plate:

$$c_{Df} = \frac{0.664 - 1.789\,mx + 0.706\,m^2 x^2 - \cdots}{R_x} \quad (10\text{–}95)$$

where $m = \mu_e H_0^2/\rho \nu_m U$ and $R_x = Ux/\nu$. This equation shows that the applied transverse magnetic field tends to cause a decrease in friction drag. If $m = 0$, Eq. 10-95 reduces to the formula for ordinary boundary layer flow. Rossow also showed that the decelerating effect of the magnetic field increases with fluid velocity, causing a flattening of the velocity profile for the boundary layer flow.

## PROBLEMS

10–1. Three point charges of $2 \times 10^{-5}$ coulomb, $4 \times 10^{-5}$ coulomb, and $8 \times 10^{-5}$ coulomb are located at points (1, 2, 3), (−4, 3, 1), and (5, −1, −2), respectively, in a medium having a permittivity $\epsilon = 85.0 \times 10^{-12}$ farad/meter. The coordinates are measured in meters. Find the force on the $2 \times 10^{-5}$ coulomb charge.

10–2. The surface of a copper sphere of radius $r_0$ has a uniform charge density $\rho_s$ coulombs/meter$^2$. At points inside the copper sphere the net charge is zero. Show that the electric flux density $\mathbf{D}$ at any point outside of the sphere at a distance $r$ from the center of the sphere is

$$\mathbf{D} = \rho_s \frac{r_0^2}{r^2}\mathbf{r} \quad r > r_0$$

where $\mathbf{r}$ is a unit vector directed radially outward.

10–3. A small test charge is used in an experiment to determine the static electric and magnetic field at a given point in space. The experiment consists of varying the velocity of the test charge and, simultaneously, measuring the resulting force on the charge. When the charge moves in the $y$-direction, the force acting on the charge equals $2000\mathbf{i} - 1000\mathbf{j} - 2400\mathbf{k}$ newtons/coulomb and this force is found to be independent of the magnitude of $\mathbf{V}$. When the charge moves in the $x$-direction with a velocity $\mathbf{V} = 12,000\mathbf{i}$ meter/second, the force on the charge becomes $2000\mathbf{i} - 1000\mathbf{j} + 1200\mathbf{k}$ newtons/coulomb. Determine the electric field $\mathbf{E}$ and the magnetic field $\mathbf{B}$.

10–4. Verify the induction equation as given in Equation 10–49.

10–5. An electrically conducting liquid flows steadily down an inclined flat insulated plate surface with a uniform externally applied magnetic field

---

[7]V. J. Rossow, "On Flow of Electrically Conducting Fluids over a Flat Plate in the Presence of a Transverse Magnetic Field," NACA TN 3971, May 1957.

$\mathbf{B}_0 = B_0\mathbf{j}$ as shown in Fig. 10–11. Write the governing equations for this magnetohydrodynamic flow. What are the appropriate boundary conditions for the solution of this flow problem?

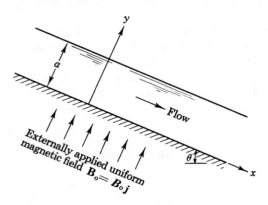

**Fig. 10-11.**

**10–6.** Consider a one-dimensional steady flow of an electrically neutral and inviscid plasma which is subjected to an externally applied magnetic field **H**. Assuming that there is no applied electric field, show that, in the absence of gravitational forces, the momentum equation for the flow can be derived as

$$dp + \rho V \, dV + \mu_e H \, dH = 0$$

**10–7.** Set up the governing equations for the two-dimensional magnetohydrodynamic free vortex flow of an inviscid, incompressible fluid.

**10–8.** Set up the governing equations for the magnetohydrodynamic flow of an electrically conducting, viscous, incompressible fluid near a suddenly accelerated flat plate. List the initial and boundary conditions for the solution of this flow problem.

# Selected
# References

Aris, Rutherford, *Vectors, Tensors, and the Basic Equations of Fluid Mechanics.* Englewood Cliffs, N.J.: Prentice-Hall, Inc., 1962.

Artley, John, *Fields and Configurations.* New York: Holt, Rinehart, & Winston, Inc., 1965.

Bakhmeteff, B. A., *The Mechanics of Turbulent Flow.* Princeton, N.J.: Princeton University Press, 1936.

Batchelor, G. K., *The Theory of Homogeneous Turbulence.* London: Cambridge University Press, 1956.

Bershader, D., ed., *The Magnetodynamics of Conducting Fluids.* Stanford, Calif.: Stanford University Press, 1959.

Binder, R. G., *Advanced Fluid Mechanics* (2 vols.). Englewood Cliffs, N.J.: Prentice-Hall, Inc., 1958.

Birkhoff, G., *Hydrodynamics.* Princeton, N.J.: Princeton University Press, 1953.

Birkhoff, G., and E. H. Zarantonello, *Jets, Wakes, and Cavities.* New York: Academic Press, Inc., 1957.

Bird, R. B., W. E. Stewart, and E. N. Lightfoot, *Transport Phenomena.* New York: John Wiley & Sons, Inc., 1960.

Brillouin, Léon, *Tensors in Mechanics and Elasticity*. New York: Academic Press, Inc., 1964.

Borg, S. F., *Matrix-Tensor Methods in Continuum Mechanics*. Princeton, N.J.: D. Van Nostrand Co., Inc., 1963.

Cambel, A. B., *Plasma Physics and Magnetofluidmechanics*. New York: McGraw-Hill Book Company, 1963.

Cambel, A. B. and B. H. Jennings, *Gas Dynamics*. New York: McGraw-Hill Book Company, 1958.

Carafoli, H., *High-Speed Aerodynamics*. London: Pergamon Press, Ltd., 1956.

Chandrasekhar, S., *Plasma Physics*. Chicago, Ill.: The University of Chicago Press, 1960.

Chang, T. S., *Intermediate Fluid Mechanics*. Ann Arbor, Mich.: J. W. Edwards, Publisher, Inc., 1962.

Chernyi, G. G., *Introduction to Hypersonic Flow*. New York: Academic Press, Inc., 1961.

Chow, V. T., *Open-Channel Hydraulics*. New York: McGraw-Hill Book Company, 1961.

Cole, G. H. A., *Fluid Dynamics*. New York: John Wiley & Sons, Inc., 1962.

Collar, A. R. and J. Tinkler, eds., *Hypersonic Flow*. New York: Academic Press, Inc., 1960.

Corcoran, W. H., J. B. Opfell, and B. H. Sage, *Momentum Transfer in Fluids*. New York: Academic Press, Inc., 1956.

Corson, D. R. and P. Lorrain, *Introduction to Electromagnetic Fields and Waves*. San Francisco, Calif.: W. H. Freeman & Co., Publishers, 1962.

Courant, R. and K. O. Friedrichs, *Supersonic Flow and Shock Waves*. New York: Interscience Publishers, Inc., 1948.

Cowling, T. G., *Magnetohydrodynamics*. New York: Interscience Publishers, Inc., 1957.

Curle, N., *The Laminar Boundary Layer Equations*. London: Oxford University Press, 1962.

Dorrance, W. H., *Viscous Hypersonic Flow*. New York: McGraw-Hill Book Company, 1962.

Drummond, J. E., *Plasma Physics*. New York: McGraw-Hill Book Company, 1961.

Dryden, H. L., F. P. Murnaghan, and H. Bateman, *Hydrodynamics*. New York: Dover Publications, Inc., 1956.

Duncan, W. J., A. S. Thom, and A. D. Young, *An Elementary Treatise on the Mechanics of Fluids*. London: Edward Arnold (Publishers), Ltd., 1960.

Durand, W. F., ed.-in-chief, *Aerodynamic Theory* (6 vols.). New York: Dover Publications, Inc., 1963.

Dwinnell, J. H., *Principles of Aerodynamics*. New York: McGraw-Hill Book Company, 1949.

Emmons, H. W., ed., *High Speed Aerodynamics and Jet Propulsion*, Vol. III, *Fundamentals of Gas Dynamics*. Princeton, N.J.: Princeton University Press, 1958.

Eringen, A. C., *Nonlinear Theory of Continuous Media*. New York: McGraw-Hill Book Company, 1962.

Fano, R. M., L. J. Chu, and R. B. Adler, *Electromagnetic Fields, Energy, and Forces*. New York: John Wiley & Sons, Inc., 1960.

Fermi, E., *Thermodynamics*. New York: Dover Publications, Inc., 1956.

Frederick, Daniel and T. S. Chang, *Continuum Mechanics*. Boston, Mass.: Allyn and Bacon, Inc., 1965.

Fredrickson, Arnold G., *Principles and Applications of Rheology*. Englewood Cliffs, N.J.: Prentice-Hall, Inc., 1964.

Flügge, W., ed.-in-chief, *Handbook of Engineering Mechanics*, Part VII, *Fluid Mechanics*. New York: McGraw-Hill Book Company, 1962.

Foa, J. V., *Elements of Flight Propulsion*. New York: John Wiley & Sons, Inc., 1960.

Friedlander, S. K. and L. Topper, eds., *Turbulence*. New York: Interscience Publishers, Inc., 1961.

Ginzburg, I. P., *Applied Fluid Dynamics*. Published for the National Science Foundation, Washington, D.C. by the Israel Program for Scientific Translations, Jerusalem, 1963.

Glauert, H., *The Elements of Aerofoil and Airscrew Theory*, (2nd ed.). London: Cambridge University Press, 1959.

Goldstein, S., *Lectures on Fluid Mechanics*. New York: Interscience Publishers, Inc., 1960.

Goldstein, S., ed., *Modern Developments in Fluid Dynamics* (2 vols.). London: Oxford University Press, 1938.

Hall, N. A., *Thermodynamics of Fluid Flow*. Englewood Cliffs, N.J.: Prentice-Hall, Inc., 1951.

Hansen, Arthur G., *Similarity Analyses of Boundary Value Problems in Engineering*. Englewood Cliffs, N.J.: Prentice-Hall, Inc., 1964.

Happel, John and Howard Brenner, *Low Reynolds Number Hydrodynamics*. Englewood Cliffs, N.J.: Prentice-Hall, Inc., 1965.

Harris, L. P., *Hydromagnetic Channel Flow*. New York: John Wiley & Sons, Inc., 1960.

Hayes, W. D. and R. F. Probstein, *Hypersonic Flow Theory*. New York: Academic Press, Inc., 1959.

Hayt, W. H., *Engineering Electromagnetics*. New York: McGraw-Hill Book Company, 1958.

Henshaw, J. T., ed., *Supersonic Engineering*. New York: John Wiley & Sons, Inc., 1963.

Hinze, J. O., *Turbulence*. New York: McGraw-Hill Book Company, 1959.

Howarth, L., ed., *Modern Developments in Fluid Dynamics; High Speed Flow* (2 vols.). London: Oxford University Press, 1953.

Hughes, W. F. and E. W. Gaylord, *Basic Equations of Engineering Sciences*. New York: Schaum Publishing Co., 1964.

Hunt, J. N., *Incompressible Fluid Dynamics*. New York: John Wiley & Sons, Inc., 1964.

Jaeger, Charles, *Engineering Fluid Mechanics*. London: Blackie & Sons, Limited, 1956.

Katys, G. P., *Continuous Measurement of Unsteady Flow*. London: Pergamon Press, Ltd., 1964.

Kaufmann, W., *Fluid Mechanics*. New York: McGraw-Hill Book Company, 1963.

Keenan, J. H., *Thermodynamics*. New York: John Wiley & Sons, Inc., 1941.

Kline, Stephen J., *Similitude and Approximation Theory*. New York: McGraw-Hill Book Company, 1965.

Knudsen, J. G. and D. L. Katz, *Fluid Dynamics and Heat Transfer*. New York: McGraw-Hill Book Company, 1958.

Kochin, N. E., I. A. Kibel, and N. V. Roze, *Theoretical Hydromechanics*. New York: Interscience Publishers, Inc., 1964.

Kuethe, A. M. and J. D. Schetzer, *Foundations of Aerodynamics* (2nd ed.). New York: John Wiley & Sons, Inc., 1959.

Lamb, H., *Hydrodynamics* (6th ed.). New York: Dover Publications, Inc., 1945.

Landau, L. D. and E. M. Lifshitz, *Fluid Mechanics*. Reading, Mass.: Addison-Wesley Publishing Company, Inc., 1959.

Landshoff, R. K. M., ed., *Magnetohydrodynamics*. Stanford, Calif.: Stanford University Press, 1957.

Landshoff, R. K. M., ed., *The Plasma in a Magnetic Field*. Stanford, Calif.: Stanford University Press, 1958.

Langhaar, H. L., *Dimensional Analysis and Theory of Models*. New York: John Wiley & Sons, Inc., 1951.

Langlois, W. E., *Slow Viscous Flow*. New York: The Macmillan Company, 1964.

Lee, J. F. and F. W. Sears, *Thermodynamics* (2nd ed.). Reading, Mass.: Addison-Wesley Publishing Company, Inc., 1963.

Levich, Veniamin, *Physicochemical Hydrodynamics*. Englewood Cliffs, N.J.: Prentice-Hall, Inc., 1962.

Liepmann, H. W. and A. Roshko, *Elements of Gasdynamics*. New York: John Wiley & Sons, Inc., 1957.

Lin, C. C., *The Theory of Hydrodynamic Stability*. London: Cambridge University Press, 1955.

Lin, C. C., ed., *High Speed Aerodynamics and Jet Propulsion*, Vol. V, *Turbulent Flows and Heat Transfer*. Princeton, N.J.: Princeton University Press, 1959.

Loeb, Leonard B., *The Kinetic Theory of Gases* (3rd ed.). New York: Dover Publications, Inc., 1961.

Long, R. R., *Mechanics of Solids and Fluids*. Englewood Cliffs, N.J.: Prentice-Hall, Inc., 1961.

Longmire, C. L., *Elementary Plasma Physics*, New York: Interscience Publishers, Inc., 1963.

McLeod, E. B., Jr., *Introduction to Fluid Dynamics*. New York: The Macmillan Company, 1963.

Miles, E. R. C., *Supersonic Aerodynamics*. New York: Dover Publications, Inc., 1950.

Milne-Thomson, L. M., *Theoretical Hydrodynamics* (4th ed.). New York: The Macmillan Company, 1960.

Mkhitaryan, A. M., *Hydraulics and Fundamentals of Gas Dynamics*. Published for the National Science Foundation, Washington, D.C. by the Israel Program for Scientific Translations, Jerusalem, 1964.

Moore, F. K., ed., *High Speed Aerodynamics and Jet Propulsion*, Vol. IV, *Theory of Laminar Flows*. Princeton, N.J.: Princeton University Press, 1964.

Nielsen, J. N., *Missile Aerodynamics*. New York: McGraw-Hill Book Company, 1960.

Oswatitsch, K. *Gas Dynamics*. New York: Academic Press, Inc., 1956.

Pai, S. I., *Fluid Dynamics of Jets*. Princeton, N.J.: D. Van Nostrand Co., Inc., 1954.

Pai, S. I., *Introduction to the Theory of Compressible Flow*. Princeton, N.J.: D. Van Nostrand Co., Inc., 1959.

Pai, S. I., *Magnetogasdynamics and Plasma Dynamics*. Englewood Cliffs, N.J.: Prentice-Hall, Inc., 1962.

Pai, S. I., *Viscous Flow Theory* (2 vols.). Princeton, N. J.: D. Van Nostrand Co., Inc., 1957.

Pao, Richard H. F., *Fluid Mechanics*. New York: John Wiley & Sons, Inc., 1961.

Patterson, G. N., *Molecular Flow of Gases.* New York: John Wiley & Sons, Inc., 1956.

Planck, M., *The Mechanics of Deformable Bodies.* New York: The Macmillan Company, 1949.

Prager, W., *Introduction to Mechanics of Continua.* Boston, Mass.: Ginn & Company, 1961.

Prandtl, L., *Applied Hydro- and Aeromechanics.* New York: McGraw-Hill Book Company, 1934.

Prandtl, L., *Fundamentals of Hydro- and Aeromechanics.* New York: McGraw-Hill Book Company, 1934.

Prandtl, L., *The Essentials of Fluid Dynamics.* London: Blackie & Son, Limited, 1953.

Present, R. D., *Kinetic Theory of Gases.* New York: McGraw-Hill Book Company, 1958.

Purday, F. F. P., *Streamline Flow.* London: Constable & Co., Ltd., 1949.

Rauscher, M., *Introduction to Aeronautical Dynamics.* New York: John Wiley & Sons, Inc., 1953.

Richardson, E. G., *Dynamics of Real Fluids.* London: Edward Arnold (Publishers), Ltd., 1950.

Robertson, James M., *Hydrodynamics in Theory and Application.* Englewood Cliffs, N.J.: Prentice-Hall, Inc., 1965.

Rohsenow, W. M. and H. Y. Choi, *Heat, Mass, and Momentum Transfer.* Englewood Cliffs, N.J.: Prentice-Hall, Inc., 1961.

Rosenhead, L., ed., *Laminar Boundary Layers.* London: Oxford University Press, 1963.

Rotty, R. M., *Introduction to Gas Dynamics.* New York: John Wiley & Sons, Inc., 1962.

Rouse, H., ed., *Advanced Mechanics of Fluids.* New York: John Wiley & Sons, Inc., 1959.

Rouse, H., ed., *Engineering Hydraulics.* New York: John Wiley & Sons, Inc., 1950.

Rouse H., *Fluid Mechanics for Hydraulic Engineers.* New York: McGraw-Hill Book Company, 1938.

Rouse, H. and S. Ince, *History of Hydraulics.* Iowa City: Iowa Institute of Hydraulic Research, State University of Iowa, 1957.

Rutherford, D. E., *Fluid Dynamics.* Edinburgh and London: Oliver and Boyd, 1959.

Sauer, R., *Introduction to Theoretical Gas Dynamics.* Ann Arbor, Mich.: J. W. Edwards, Publisher, Inc., 1947.

Scheidegger, A. E., *The Physics of Flow through Porous Media*. New York: The Macmillan Company, 1960.

Schlichting, H., *Boundary Layer Theory* (4th ed.). New York: McGraw-Hill Book Company, 1960.

Scorer, R. S., *Natural Aerodynamics*. London: Pergamon Press, Ltd., 1958.

Sears, W. R., ed., *High Speed Aerodynamics and Jet Propulsion*, Vol. VI, *General Theory of High Speed Aerodynamics*. Princeton, N.J.: Princeton University Press, 1954.

Sedov, L., *Two-Dimensional Problems in Hydrodynamics and Aerodynamics*. New York: John Wiley & Sons, Inc., 1965.

Seifert, H., ed., *Space Technology*. New York: John Wiley & Sons, Inc., 1959.

Shapiro, A. H., *The Dynamics and Thermodynamics of Compressible Fluid Flow* (2 vols.). New York: The Ronald Press Company, 1954.

Sibert, H. W., *High-Speed Aerodynamics*. Englewood Cliffs, N.J.: Prentice-Hall, Inc., 1948.

Sommerfeld, A., *Mechanics of Deformable Bodies*. New York: Academic Press, Inc., 1950.

Spitzer, L., *Physics of Fully Ionized Gases*. New York: Interscience Publishers, Inc., 1956.

Stanyukovich, K. P., *Unsteady Motion of Continuous Media*. London: Pergamon Press, Ltd., 1960.

Stewartson, K., *The Theory of Laminar Boundary Layers in Compressible Fluids*. London: Oxford University Press, 1964.

Stoker, J. J., *Water Waves*. New York: Interscience Publishers, Inc., 1957.

Streeter, V. L., *Fluid Dynamics*. New York: McGraw-Hill Book Company, 1948.

Streeter, V. L., ed.-in-chief, *Handbook of Fluid Dynamics*. New York: McGraw-Hill Book Company, 1961.

Temple, G., *An Introduction to Fluid Dynamics*. London: Oxford University Press, 1958.

Thwaites, B., ed., *Incompressible Aerodynamics*. London: Oxford University Press, 1960.

Townsend, A. A., *The Structure of Turbulent Shear Flow*. London: Cambridge University Press, 1956.

Truitt, R. W., *Hypersonic Aerodynamics*. New York: The Ronald Press Company, 1959.

Vallentine, H. R., *Applied Hydrodynamics*. London: Butterworth Scientific Publications, 1959.

Van Dyke, Milton, *Perturbation Methods in Fluid Mechanics*. New York: Academic Press, Inc., 1964.

Vavra, M. H., *Aero-Thermodynamics and Flow in Turbomachines*. New York: John Wiley & Sons, Inc., 1960.

Von Kármán, Th., *Aerothermodynamics*. Notes on twelve lectures given in the department of physics, Columbia University, 1947.

Von Kármán, Th., *Aerodynamics*. Ithaca, N.Y.: Cornell University Press, 1954.

Von Kármán, Th., *Collected Works of Theodore von Kármán* (4 vols.). London: Butterworth Scientific Publications, 1956.

Von Kármán, Th., *From Low Speed Aerodynamics to Astronautics*. London: Pergamon Press, Ltd., 1963.

Von Mises, R., *Mathematical Theory of Compressible Fluid Flow*. New York: Academic Press, Inc., 1958.

Von Mises, R., *Theory of Flight*. New York: Dover Publications, Inc., 1959.

Ward, G. N., *Linearized Theory of Steady High-Speed Flow*. London: Cambridge University Press, 1955.

Wilkinson, W. L., *Non-Newtonian Fluids*. London: Pergamon Press, Ltd., 1960.

Wilson, D. H., *Hydrodynamics*. London: Edward Arnold (Publishers), Ltd., 1959.

Woods, L. C., *The Theory of Subsonic Plane Flow*. London: Cambridge University Press, 1961.

Zucrow, M. J., *Aircraft and Missile Propulsion* (2 vols.). New York: John Wiley & Sons, Inc., 1958.

# Appendix

## A–1. Approximate Physical Properties of Liquids at 60°F and Standard Atmospheric Pressure

| Liquid | Density $\rho$ slugs/ft$^3$ | Specific Weight $\gamma$ lbf/ft$^3$ | Bulk Modulus $E \times 10^{-3}$ lbf/in.$^2$ | Vapor Pressure $p_v$ lbf/in.$^2$ |
|---|---|---|---|---|
| Benzene | 1.71 | 54.9 | 150 | 1.45 |
| Castor oil | 1.86 | 59.9 | 210 | |
| Carbon tetrachloride | 3.09 | 99.5 | 160 | 1.74 |
| Ethyl alcohol | 1.53 | 49.3 | 175 | 0.85 |
| Gasoline | 1.30 | 42.0 | | |
| Glycerine | 2.45 | 78.8 | 630 | $2 \times 10^{-6}$ |
| Kerosene | 1.58 | 50.0 | | |
| Mercury | 26.3 | 847.0 | 3800 | $2.5 \times 10^{-5}$ |
| Oil | | | | |
|   lubricating | 1.68 | 54.1 | | |
|   crude | 1.73 | 55.7 | | |
|   fuel | 1.85 | 59.6 | | |
| Water | | | | |
|   fresh | 1.94 | 62.4 | 312 | 0.34 |
|   salt | 1.99 | 64.0 | | |

## A–2. Physical Properties of Water at Standard Atmospheric Pressure

| Temperature $T$ °F | Density $\rho$ slugs/ft$^3$ | Specific Weight $\gamma$ lbf/ft$^3$ | Dynamic Viscosity $\mu \times 10^5$ lbf-sec/ft$^2$ | Kinematic Viscosity $\nu \times 10^5$ ft$^2$/sec | Bulk Modulus $E \times 10^{-3}$ lbf/in.$^2$ | Vapor Pressure $p_v$ lbf/in.$^2$ |
|---|---|---|---|---|---|---|
| 32 | 1.94 | 62.4 | 3.75 | 1.93 | 289 | 0.08 |
| 40 | 1.94 | 62.4 | 3.24 | 1.67 | 296 | 0.11 |
| 50 | 1.94 | 62.4 | 2.74 | 1.41 | 305 | 0.17 |
| 60 | 1.94 | 62.4 | 2.34 | 1.21 | 312 | 0.26 |
| 70 | 1.94 | 62.3 | 2.04 | 1.05 | 319 | 0.36 |
| 80 | 1.93 | 62.2 | 1.80 | 0.930 | 325 | 0.51 |
| 90 | 1.93 | 62.1 | 1.59 | 0.823 | 329 | 0.70 |
| 100 | 1.93 | 62.0 | 1.42 | 0.736 | 330 | 0.96 |
| 120 | 1.92 | 61.7 | 1.17 | 0.610 | 333 | 1.7 |
| 140 | 1.91 | 61.4 | 0.981 | 0.514 | 330 | 2.9 |
| 160 | 1.90 | 61.0 | 0.838 | 0.442 | 326 | 4.7 |
| 180 | 1.88 | 60.6 | 0.726 | 0.385 | 318 | 7.5 |
| 200 | 1.87 | 60.1 | 0.637 | 0.341 | 308 | 11.5 |
| 212 | 1.86 | 59.8 | 0.593 | 0.319 | 300 | 14.7 |

## A–3. Physical Properties of Air at Standard Atmospheric Pressure

| Temperature $T$ °F | Density $\rho \times 10^3$ slugs/ft$^3$ | Specific Weight $\gamma \times 10^2$ lbf/ft$^3$ | Dynamic Viscosity $\mu \times 10^7$ lbf-sec/ft$^2$ | Kinematic Viscosity $\nu \times 10^4$ ft$^2$/sec |
|---|---|---|---|---|
| 0 | 2.68 | 8.62 | 3.28 | 1.26 |
| 10 | 2.63 | 8.46 | 3.45 | 1.31 |
| 20 | 2.57 | 8.27 | 3.50 | 1.36 |
| 30 | 2.52 | 8.11 | 3.58 | 1.42 |
| 40 | 2.47 | 7.94 | 3.62 | 1.46 |
| 50 | 2.42 | 7.79 | 3.68 | 1.52 |
| 60 | 2.37 | 7.63 | 3.74 | 1.58 |
| 70 | 2.33 | 7.50 | 3.82 | 1.64 |
| 80 | 2.28 | 7.35 | 3.85 | 1.69 |
| 90 | 2.24 | 7.23 | 3.90 | 1.74 |
| 100 | 2.20 | 7.09 | 3.96 | 1.80 |
| 120 | 2.15 | 6.84 | 4.07 | 1.89 |
| 140 | 2.06 | 6.63 | 4.14 | 2.01 |
| 160 | 1.99 | 6.41 | 4.22 | 2.12 |
| 180 | 1.93 | 6.21 | 4.34 | 2.25 |
| 200 | 1.87 | 6.02 | 4.49 | 2.40 |
| 250 | 1.74 | 5.60 | 4.87 | 2.80 |

## A–4. Properties of the ICAO Standard Atmosphere†

| Altitude ft | Absolute Temperature °R | Absolute Pressure lbf/ft² | Density $\rho \times 10^3$ slugs/ft³ | Specific Weight $\gamma \times 10^2$ lbf/ft³ | Dynamic Viscosity $\mu \times 10^7$ lbf-sec/ft² |
|---|---|---|---|---|---|
| 0 | 518.7 | 2,116 | 2.38 | 7.65 | 3.75 |
| 5,000 | 500.9 | 1,761 | 2.05 | 6.59 | 3.64 |
| 10,000 | 483.0 | 1,455 | 1.76 | 5.65 | 3.54 |
| 15,000 | 465.2 | 1,194 | 1.50 | 4.81 | 3.43 |
| 20,000 | 447.4 | 972.5 | 1.27 | 4.08 | 3.32 |
| 25,000 | 429.5 | 785.3 | 1.07 | 3.43 | 3.21 |
| 30,000 | 411.7 | 628.4 | 0.889 | 2.86 | 3.10 |
| 35,000 | 393.9 | 498.0 | 0.737 | 2.37 | 2.99 |
| 36,089 | 389.9 | 472.7 | 0.706 | 2.27 | 2.96 |
| 40,000 | 389.9 | 391.7 | 0.585 | 1.88 | 2.96 |
| 45,000 | 389.9 | 308.0 | 0.460 | 1.48 | 2.96 |
| 50,000 | 389.9 | 242.2 | 0.362 | 1.16 | 2.96 |
| 60,000 | 389.9 | 149.8 | 0.224 | 0.720 | 2.96 |
| 70,000 | 389.9 | 94.53 | 0.140 | 0.449 | 2.96 |
| 80,000 | 389.9 | 58.83 | 0.0873 | 0.279 | 2.96 |
| 90,000 | 389.9 | 36.61 | 0.0544 | 0.173 | 2.96 |
| 100,000 | 389.9 | 22.81 | 0.0339 | 0.108 | 2.96 |

†Adapted from NACA Report 1235.

## A–5. Conversion of Units*

| | |
|---|---|
| *Length:* | 1 ft $\equiv$ 30.48 cm |
| | 1 mile $\equiv$ 5280 ft |
| *Volume:* | 1 ft³ $\equiv$ 7.48 gal |
| *Velocity:* | 1 mile/hr $\equiv$ 1.467 ft/sec |
| | 1 knot $\equiv$ 1.69 ft/sec |
| *Discharge:* | 1 ft³/sec $\equiv$ 449 gal/min |
| *Mass:* | 1 slug $\equiv$ 32.174 lbm |
| | 1 lbm $\equiv$ 454 grams |
| *Force:* | 1 lbf $\equiv$ 32.174 poundals $\equiv$ 4.45 $\times$ 10⁵ dynes $\equiv$ 0.454 kg |
| *Energy:* | 1 Btu $\equiv$ 778.16 ft-lbf |
| | 1 kwhr $\equiv$ 2.66 $\times$ 10⁶ ft-lbf |
| *Power:* | 1 hp $\equiv$ 550 ft-lbf/sec $\equiv$ 0.746 kw |
| *Viscosity:* | 1 lbf-sec/ft² $\equiv$ 478 poises |
| | 1 ft²/sec $\equiv$ 929 stokes |

*The symbol $\equiv$ denotes "is equivalent to."

# Name Index

# Subject Index